Course	General Bacteriology Vol. 1
Course Number	**MCRO 20**
	San Jose State University
	BIOLOGY

http://create.mheducation.com

ISBN-10: 1308120516 ISBN-13: 9781308120515

Contents

Credits

CHAPTER **1** The Main Themes of Microbiology

A plankton sample from the Atlantic Ocean yields up its jewels. The larger gold, white, and blue cells are a type of algae called diatoms, and the tiny white and blue cells are unknown prokaryotes.

A view of the North Atlantic Ocean, a fitting place to mine for marine microbes.

 CASE STUDY **Part 1** The Search for Biological Dark Matter

From 2002 to 2010, a 100-foot sailboat called the *Sorcerer II* was engaged in a groundbreaking fishing expedition in the oceans of the world. What was highly unusual about this voyage was that it did not involve hooking or netting fish. Instead, the ship was hauling in billions of the tiniest **microorganisms** that float in the upper levels of the marine environment. What researchers aimed to do with their catch was to harness a powerful and very different way to examine the living world.

"Microbes rule the earth."

This project was the brainchild of Dr. Craig Venter, a prominent genetics researcher,* whose goal was to survey the microbial **diversity** of ocean water in more detail than ever before. Scientists aboard the vessel randomly collected surface water about every 200 miles with very fine nets that extracted the **microscopic plankton,** primarily **bacteria,** and sent samples back to Venter's laboratory. Instead of painstakingly isolating and identifying the individual microbes in the sample, as might have been done in the past, they extracted the **genetic material (DNA)** from the samples and analyzed the DNA using state-of-the-art molecular techniques and computers.** When results from the studies were published, even seasoned **microbiologists** were stunned at the variety and numbers of marine microbes they had discovered.

Microbiologists had previously described around 6,000 different types of bacteria, but the evidence from these new studies showed that this number represented only the tiniest "drop in the ocean." Some data revealed more than 20,000 different kinds of microorganisms in just a single liter of seawater, most of them

unidentified. Considering how the ocean's vast realm supports an impressive variety of **habitats,** specialists estimate that the ocean environment could easily harbor 10 million to 20 million different microscopic creatures, each of them having unique **characteristics** and **niches.** And even more intriguing was the discovery that up to 20% of the analyzed genetic material could not be matched to any known sort of microorganism. Because there is so much still to be learned about all earthly habitats, biologists have dubbed this sort of shadow life that functions behind the scenes without yet being identified as "biological dark matter."

Dr. David Thomassen, Chief Scientist, Department of Energy, aptly expressed the outcome of these studies: "Microbes rule the earth. Scientists estimate that there are more microbes on earth than there are stars in the universe—an estimated nonillion (one followed by 30 zeros). Microbes and their communities make up the foundation of the biosphere and sustain all life on earth."

▶ *In addition to bacteria, which other groups of microorganisms would likely be found in the plankton?*

▶ *What fields of microbiology would be involved in the further study of these planktonic microbes?*

To continue the Case Study, go to page 24.

*Dr. Venter was one of the main individuals behind the mapping of the human genome.

**To read more about this technique, called metagenomic analysis, look ahead to chapter 10.

1.1 The Scope of Microbiology

 Expected Learning Outcomes

1. Define *microbiology* and *microorganisms,* and identify the major organisms included in the science of microbiology.
2. Name and define the primary areas included in microbiological studies.

As we observe the natural world, teeming with life, we cannot help but be struck by its beauty and complexity. But for every feature that is visible to the naked eye, there are millions of other features that are concealed beyond our sight because of their small size. This alternate microscopic universe is populated by a vast microbial menagerie that is equally beautiful and complex. To sum up the presence of microbes in one word, they are **ubiquitous.*** They are found in all natural habitats and most of those that have been created by humans. As scientists continue to explore remote and unusual environments, the one entity they always find is microbes. They exist deep beneath the polar ice caps, in the ocean to a depth of 7 miles, in hot springs and thermal vents, in toxic waste dumps, and even in the clouds.

Microbiology is a specialized area of biology that deals with tiny life forms that are not readily observed without magnification, which is to say they are **microscopic.*** These microscopic organisms are collectively referred to as **microorganisms, microbes,*** or several other terms, depending upon the purpose. Some people call them "germs" or "bugs" in reference to their role in infection and disease, but those terms have other biological meanings and perhaps place undue emphasis on the disagreeable reputation of microorganisms. The major groups of microorganisms included in this study are **bacteria, viruses, fungi, protozoa, algae,** and **helminths** (parasitic worms). As we will see in subsequent chapters, each group exhibits a distinct collection of biological characteristics. The nature of microorganisms makes them both easy and difficult to study. Easy, because they reproduce so rapidly and can usually be grown in large numbers in the laboratory. Difficult, because we can't observe or analyze them without special techniques, especially the use of microscopes (see chapter 3).

Microbiology is one of the largest and most complex of the biological sciences because it integrates subject matter from many diverse disciplines. Microbiologists study every aspect of microbes—their genetics, their physiology, characteristics that may be harmful or beneficial, the ways they interact with the environment, the ways they interact with other organisms, and their uses in industry and agriculture.

See **table 1.1** for an overview of some fields and occupations that involve basic study or applications in microbiology. Each major discipline in microbiology contains numerous subdivisions or specialties that deal with a specific subject area or field (table 1.1). In fact, many areas of this science have become so specialized that it is not uncommon for a microbiologist to spend an entire career concentrating on a single group or type of microbe, biochemical process, or disease.

Among the specialty professions of microbiology are:

- geomicrobiologists, who focus on the roles of microbes in the development of earth's crust (table 1.1B);
- marine microbiologists, who study the oceans and its smallest inhabitants;
- medical technologists, who do the tests that help diagnose pathogenic microbes and their diseases;
- nurse epidemiologists, who analyze the occurrence of infectious diseases in hospitals; and
- astrobiologists, who study the possibilities of organisms in space (see Case Study, page 29).

Studies in microbiology have led to greater understanding of many general biological principles. For example, the study of microorganisms established universal concepts concerning the chemistry of life (see chapters 2 and 8), systems of inheritance (see chapter 9), and the global cycles of nutrients, minerals, and gases (see chapter 26).

1.2 General Characteristics of Microorganisms and Their Roles in the Earth's Environments

 Expected Learning Outcomes

3. Describe the basic characteristics of prokaryotic cells and eukaryotic cells and their evolutionary origins.
4. State several ways that microbes are involved in the earth's ecosystems.
5. Describe the cellular makeup of microorganisms and their size range, and indicate how viruses differ from cellular microbes.

The Origins and Dominance of Microorganisms

For billions of years, microbes have extensively shaped the development of the earth's habitats and influenced the evolution of other life forms. It is understandable that scientists searching for life on other planets first look for signs of microorganisms.

The fossil record uncovered in ancient rocks and sediments points to bacteria-like cells having existed on earth for at least 3.5 billion years (**figure 1.1**). Early microorganisms of this type dominated the earth's life forms for the first 2 billion years. These ancient cells were small, simple, and lacked specialized internal structures to carry out their functions. It is apparent that genetic material of these cells was not bound into a separate compartment called a nucleus or "karyon." The term assigned to cells and microbes of this type is **prokaryotic,*** meaning "before the nucleus." About 1.8 billion years ago, there appeared in the fossil record a more complex cell, which had developed a nucleus and various specialized internal structures called **organelles.*** These types of cells and organisms are defined as **eukaryotic*** in reference to their

* *ubiquitous* (yoo-bik'-wih-tis) L. *ubique,* everywhere and *ous,* having. Being, or seeming to be, everywhere at the same time.
* *microscopic* (my"-kroh-skaw'-pik) Gr. *mikros,* small, and *scopein,* to see.
* *microbe* (my'-krohb) Gr. *mikros,* small, and *bios,* life.

* *prokaryotic* (proh"-kar-ee-ah'-tik) Gr. *pro,* before, and *karyon,* nucleus. Sometimes spelled procaryotic and eucaryotic.
* *organelles* (or-gan'-elz) Gr. *organa,* tool, and *ella,* little.
* *eukaryotic* (yoo"-kar-ee-ah'-tik) Gr. *eu,* true or good, and *karyon,* nucleus.

TABLE 1.1 A Sampling of Fields and Occupations in Microbiology

A. Public Health Microbiology and Epidemiology

These branches monitor and control the spread of diseases in communities. Some of the institutions charged with this task are the U.S. Public Health Service (USPHS) and the Centers for Disease Control and Prevention (CDC). The CDC collects information and statistics on diseases from around the United States and publishes it in a newsletter, *The Morbidity and Mortality Weekly Report* (see chapter 13).

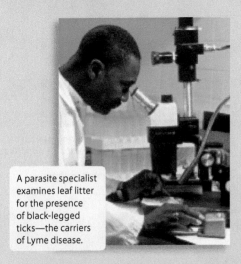

A parasite specialist examines leaf litter for the presence of black-legged ticks—the carriers of Lyme disease.

C. Biotechnology

This branch is defined by any process that harnesses the actions of living things to derive a desired product, ranging from beer to stem cells. It includes industrial microbiology, which uses microbes to produce and harvest large quantities of such substances as vaccines, vitamins, drugs, and enzymes (see chapters 10 and 27).

A technician tests the effectiveness of microorganisms in the production of new sources of energy.

B. Environmental Microbiology

This field encompasses the study of microorganisms and their ecological relationships in such natural habitats as soil and water.

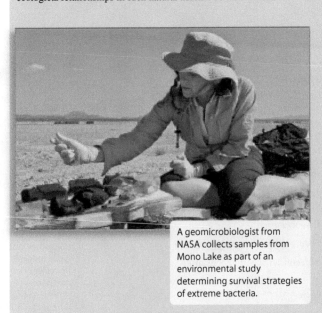

A geomicrobiologist from NASA collects samples from Mono Lake as part of an environmental study determining survival strategies of extreme bacteria.

D. Immunology

This branch studies the complex web of protective substances and reactions caused by invading microbes and other harmful entities. It includes such diverse areas as blood testing, vaccination, and allergy (see chapters 15, 16, and 17).

A CDC virologist examines cultures of influenza virus that are used in producing vaccines. This work requires high-level biohazard containment.

TABLE 1.1 (*continued*)

E. Genetic Engineering and Recombinant DNA Technology

These interrelated fields involve deliberate alterations of the genetic makeup of organisms to create novel microbes, plants, and animals with unique behavior and physiology. This is a rapidly expanding field that often complements biotechnology (see chapter 10).

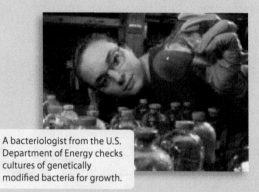

A bacteriologist from the U.S. Department of Energy checks cultures of genetically modified bacteria for growth.

F. Agricultural Microbiology

This branch is concerned with the relationships between microbes and domesticated plants and animals. Plant specialists focus on plant diseases, soil fertility, and nutritional interactions. Animal specialists work with infectious diseases and other interactions between animals and microorganisms.

Microbiologists from the U.S. Food and Drug Administration collect soil samples to detect animal pathogens.

G. Food Microbiologists

These scientists are concerned with the impact of microbes on the food supply, including such areas as food spoilage, food-borne diseases, and production.

A U.S. Department of Agriculture technician observes tests for the presence of *Escherichia coli* in foods.

H. Branches of Microbiology

Branch	Chapter	Involved in the Study of:
Bacteriology	4	The bacteria—small single-celled prokaryotic organisms
Mycology	5, 22	The fungi, a group of eukaryotes that includes both microscopic eukaryotes (molds and yeasts) and larger organisms (mushrooms, puffballs)
Protozoology	5, 23	The protozoa—animal-like and mostly single-celled eukaryotes
Virology	6, 24, 25	Viruses—minute, noncellular particles that parasitize cells
Parasitology	5, 23	Parasitism and parasitic organisms—traditionally including pathogenic protozoa, helminth worms, and certain insects
Phycology or Algology	5	Simple photosynthetic eukaryotes, the algae, ranging from single-celled forms to large seaweeds
Morphology	4, 5, 6	The detailed structure of microorganisms
Physiology	7, 8	Microbial function (metabolism) at the cellular and molecular levels
Taxonomy	1, 4, 5, 17	Classification, naming, and identification of microorganisms
Microbial Genetics, Molecular Biology	9, 10	The function of genetic material and biochemical reactions that make up a cell's metabolism
Microbial Ecology	7, 26	Interrelationships between microbes and the environment; the roles of microorganisms in the nutrient cycles and natural ecosystems

A medical microbiologist tests specimens for evidence of antibodies to the human immunodeficiency virus (HIV).

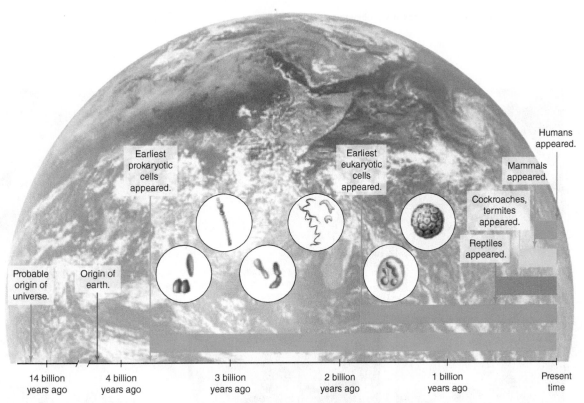

Figure 1.1 Evolutionary time line. The first simple prokaryotes appeared approximately 3.5 billion years ago, and the first eukaryotes arose about 2 billion years ago. Although these appearances seem abrupt, hundreds of millions of years of earth's history passed while they were evolving to these stages. The fossil record for these periods are incomplete because most of the tiny microbes were too delicate to fossilize.

"true" nucleus. **Figure 1.2** compares the two cell types and includes some examples of viruses, for comparison. In chapter 5, we will learn more about the origins of eukaryotic cells—they didn't arise suddenly out of nowhere—they evolved over millennia from prokaryotic cells through an intriguing process called endosymbiosis. The early eukaryotes, probably similar to algae and protozoa, started lines of evolution that eventually gave rise to fungi, plants, and multicellular animals such as worms and insects. You can see from figure 1.1 how long that took! The bacteria preceded even the earliest animals by about 3 billion years. This is a good indication that humans are not likely to, nor should we try to, eliminate microorganisms from our environment. They are the ultimate survivors.

The Cellular Organization of Microorganisms

As a general rule, prokaryotic cells are smaller than eukaryotic cells, and in addition to lacking a nucleus, as previously mentioned, they lack organelles, which are structures in cells bound by one or more membranes. Examples of organelles include the mitochondria and Golgi complexes, and several others, which perform specific

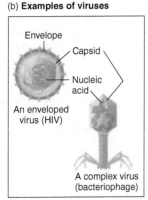

Figure 1.2 Basic structure of cells and viruses. (a) Comparison of a prokaryotic cell and a eukaryotic cell. **(b)** Two examples of viruses. These cell types and viruses are discussed in more detail in chapters 4, 5, and 6.

Reproductive spores

Bacteria: *Mycobacterium tuberculosis*, a rod-shaped cell (15,500x).

Fungi: *Histoplasma capsulatum*, with lollipop-like reproductive structures (750x). This agent is the cause of Ohio Valley fever.

Algae: desmids, *Spirogyra* filament, and diatoms (golden cells) (500x).

A single virus particle

Virus: *Herpes simplex*, the cause of cold sores (100,000x).

Protozoa: A protozoan, *Oxytricha trifallax* bearing tufts of cilia that function like tiny legs (3,500x).

Helminths: Roundworms of *Trichinella spiralis* coiled in the muscle of a host (250x). This worm causes trichinellosis.

Figure 1.3 The six basic types of microorganisms. Organisms are not shown at the same magnifications; approximate magnification is provided. To see these microorganisms arrayed more accurately to scale, look for them in figure 1.4.

functions such as transport, feeding, energy release and use, and synthesis. Prokaryotes perform similar functions, but they lack dedicated organelles to carry them out (figure 1.2).

The body plan of most microorganisms consists of a single cell or clusters of cells (**figure 1.3**). All prokaryotes are microorganisms and include the bacteria and archaea (see figure 1.14). Only some of the eukaryotes are microorganisms: primarily algae, protozoa, molds and yeasts (types of fungi), and certain animals such as worms and arthropods. These last two groups are not all microscopic, but certain members are still included in the study because worms can be involved in infections and may require a microscope to identify them. Some arthropods such as fleas and ticks may also be carriers of infectious diseases. Additional coverage on cell types and microorganisms appears in chapters 4 and 5.

Where Do the Viruses Fit?

Viruses are considered one type of microbe because they are microscopic and can cause infections and disease, but they are not cells.

They are small particles that exist at a level of complexity somewhere between large molecules and cells (see figure 1.4). Viruses are much simpler than cells; they are composed essentially of a small amount of hereditary material wrapped up in a protein covering. Some biologists refer to viruses as parasitic particles; others consider them to be very primitive organisms. Despite this slight disagreement, the impact of viruses is undeniable. Not only are they the most common microbes on earth, but they invade their hosts' cells and inflict serious damage and death.

An adenovirus

Microbial Dimensions: How Small Is Small?

When we say that microbes are too small to be seen with the unaided eye, what sorts of dimensions are we talking about? This concept is best visualized by comparing microbial groups with some organisms of the macroscopic world and also with the molecules and atoms of the molecular world (**figure 1.4**). The dimensions

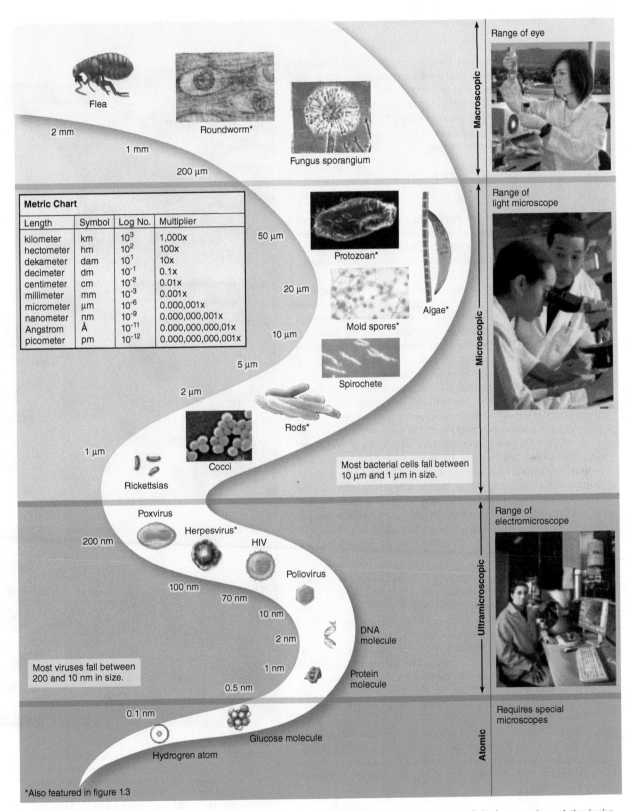

Metric Chart

Length	Symbol	Log No.	Multiplier
kilometer	km	10^3	1,000x
hectometer	hm	10^2	100x
dekameter	dam	10^1	10x
decimeter	dm	10^{-1}	0.1x
centimeter	cm	10^{-2}	0.01x
millimeter	mm	10^{-3}	0.001x
micrometer	μm	10^{-6}	0.000,001x
nanometer	nm	10^{-9}	0.000,000,001x
Angstrom	Å	10^{-11}	0.000,000,000,01x
picometer	pm	10^{-12}	0.000,000,000,001x

Range of eye

Macroscopic

Flea

2 mm

1 mm

Roundworm*

200 μm

Fungus sporangium

Range of
light microscope

50 μm

Protozoan*

20 μm

Algae*

Mold spores*

10 μm

Microscopic

5 μm

Spirochete

2 μm

Rods*

1 μm

Cocci

Most bacterial cells fall between
10 μm and 1 μm in size.

Rickettsias

Poxvirus

Range of
electromicroscope

Herpesvirus*

200 nm

HIV

Poliovirus

100 nm

70 nm

10 nm

DNA
molecule

2 nm

Ultramicroscopic

Most viruses fall between
200 and 10 nm in size.

1 nm

Protein
molecule

0.5 nm

0.1 nm

Requires special
microscopes

Glucose molecule

Atomic

Hydrogren atom

*Also featured in figure 1.3

Figure 1.4 The sizes of the smallest organisms and objects. Even though they are all very small, they still display extensive variation in size. This illustration organizes the common measurements used in microbiology along with examples of organisms or items that fall into these measurement ranges. The scale includes macroscopic, microscopic, ultramicroscopic, and atomic dimensions. Most microbes we study measure somewhere between 100 micrometers (μm) and 10 nanometers (nm) overall. The examples are more or less to scale within a size zone but not between size zones.

of macroscopic organisms are usually given in centimeters (cm) and meters (m), whereas those of most microorganisms fall within the range of micrometers (μm) and, sometimes, nanometers (nm) and millimeters (mm). The size range of most microbes extends from the smallest viruses, measuring around 10 nm and actually not much bigger than a large molecule, to protozoans measuring 3 to 4 mm and visible with the naked eye.

Microbial Involvement in Energy and Nutrient Flow

The microbes in all natural environments have lived and evolved there for billions of years. We do not yet know everything they do, but it is likely they are vital components of the structure and function of these ecosystems and critical to the operations of the earth.

Microbes are deeply involved in the flow of energy and food through the earth's ecosystems.[1] Most people are aware that plants carry out **photosynthesis,** which is the light-fueled conversion of carbon dioxide to organic material, accompanied by the formation of oxygen. But microorganisms were photosynthesizing long before the first plants appeared. In fact, they were responsible for changing the atmosphere of the earth from one without oxygen to one with oxygen. Today photosynthetic microorganisms (including algae) account for more than 50% of the earth's photosynthesis, contributing the majority of the oxygen to the atmosphere (**figure 1.5a**).

Another process that helps keep the earth in balance is the process of biological **decomposition** and nutrient recycling. Decomposition involves the breakdown of dead matter and wastes into simple compounds that can be directed back into the natural cycles of living things (**figure 1.5b**). If it were not for multitudes of bacteria and fungi, many chemical elements would become locked up and unavailable to organisms. In the long-term scheme of things, microorganisms are the main forces that drive the structure and content of the soil, water, and atmosphere. For example:

- Earth's temperature is regulated by "greenhouse gases," such as carbon dioxide and methane, that create an insulation layer in the atmosphere and help retain heat. A significant proportion of these gases is produced by microbes living in the environment and the digestive tracts of animals.
- Recent estimates propose that, based on weight and numbers, up to 50% of all organisms exist within and beneath the earth's crust in soil, rocks, and even the frozen Antarctic (**figure 1.5c**). It is increasingly evident that this enormous underground community of microbes is a major force in weathering, mineral extraction, and soil formation.
- Bacteria and fungi live in complex associations with plants. They assist the plants in obtaining nutrients and water and may protect them against disease. Microbes form similar interrelationships with animals, notably as residents of numerous bodily sites.

1. Ecosystems are communities of living organisms and their surrounding environment.

(a)

(b)

(c)

Figure 1.5 A microscopic wonderland. (a) A summer pond is heavily laden with surface scum that reveals several different types of green algae called desmids (600×). **(b)** A rotting tomato being invaded by a fuzzy forest of mold. The fungus is *Botrytis*, a common decomposer of tomatoes and grapes (250×). **(c)** Even a dry lake in Antarctica, one of the coldest places on earth (−35°C), can harbor microbes under its icy sheet. Here we see a red cyanobacterium, *Nostoc* (3,000×), that has probably been frozen in suspended animation there for 3,000 years. This is one kind of habitat on earth that may well be a model for conditions on Mars.

Check Your Progress SECTIONS 1.1–1.2

1. Define what is meant by the term "microorganism" and outline the important contributions microorganisms make to the earth's ecosystems.
2. Describe five different ways in which humans exploit microorganisms for our benefit.
3. Identify the groups of microorganisms included in the scope of microbiology, and explain the criteria for including these groups in the field.
4. Observe figure 1.3 and place the microbes pictured in a size ranking, going from smallest to largest. Use the magnification as your gauge.
5. Construct a table that displays all microbial groups based on what kind of cells they have or do not have.
6. Explain this statement: Microorganisms—we need to live with them because we can't live without them.

(a)

1.3 Human Use of Microorganisms

Expected Learning Outcome

6. Discuss the ways microorganisms can be used to create solutions for environmental problems and industrial products.

The incredible diversity and versatility seen in microbes make them excellent candidates for solving human problems. By accident or choice, humans have been using microorganisms for thousands of years to improve life and even to further human progress. Yeasts, a type of microscopic fungi, cause bread to rise and ferment sugar to make alcoholic beverages. Historical records show that households in ancient Egypt kept moldy loaves of bread to apply directly to wounds and lesions, which was probably the first use of penicillin! The manipulation of microorganisms to make products in an industrial setting is called **biotechnology.** One newer application of this process uses farmed algae to extract a form of oil (biodiesel) to be used in place of petroleum products (**figure 1.6a**).

Genetic engineering is a newer area of biotechnology that manipulates the genetics of microbes, plants, and animals for the purpose of creating new products and genetically modified organisms. One powerful technique for designing new organisms is termed **recombinant DNA.** This technology makes it possible to deliberately alter DNA[2] and to switch genetic material from one organism to another. Bacteria and fungi were some of the first organisms to be genetically engineered, because their relatively simple genetic material is readily manipulated in the laboratory. Recombinant DNA technology has unlimited potential in terms of medical, industrial, and agricultural uses. Microbes can be engineered to synthesize desirable proteins such as drugs, hormones, and enzymes (see table 1.1*C*).

Among the genetically unique organisms that have been designed by bioengineers are bacteria that contain a natural pesticide,

(b)

Figure 1.6 Microbes at work. (a) A scientist from the National Oceanic and Atmospheric Agency (NOAA) demonstrates a series of biodiesel reactors that culture single-celled algae (inset 750×) as a source of oil. This new "green" renewable energy source looks very promising. **(b)** Biotechnology meets bioremediation. Scientists at Pacific Northwest National Laboratories (PNNL) test the capacity of two newly discovered bacteria—*Shewanella* (green) and *Synechococcus* (yellow) (1,000×)—to reduce and detoxify radioactive waste. The process, carried out in large bioreactors, could speed the clean up of hazardous nuclear waste deposits.

yeasts that produce human hormones, pigs that produce hemoglobin, and plants that are resistant to disease (see table 1.1*E*). The techniques have also paved the way for characterizing human genetic material and diseases.

Another way of tapping into the unlimited potential of microorganisms is the relatively new science of **bioremediation.** This

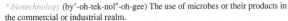

* *biotechnology* (by'-oh-tek-nol"-oh-gee) The use of microbes or their products in the commercial or industrial realm.

2. DNA, or deoxyribonucleic acid, the chemical substance that comprises the genetic material of organisms.

* *bioremediation* (by'-oh-ree-mee-dee-ay"-shun) *bios*, life; *re*, again; *mederi*, to heal. The use of biological agents to remedy environmental problems.

process introduces microbes into the environment to restore stability or to clean up toxic pollutants. Bioremediation is required to control the massive levels of pollution that result from human activities. Microbes have a surprising capacity to break down chemicals that would be harmful to other organisms. Agencies and companies have developed microbes to handle oil spills and detoxify sites contaminated with heavy metals, pesticides, and even radioactive wastes (**figure 1.6b**). The solid waste disposal industry is focusing on methods for degrading the tons of garbage in landfills, especially plastics and paper products. One form of bioremediation that has been in use for some time is the treatment of water and sewage. With dwindling clean freshwater supplies worldwide, it will become even more important to find ways to reclaim polluted water.

1.4 Microbial Roles in Infectious Diseases

 Expected Learning Outcomes

7. Review the roles of microorganisms as parasites and pathogens that cause infection and disease.

8. Define what is meant by emerging and reemerging diseases.

It is important to remind you that the large majority of microorganisms are relatively harmless and highly beneficial and essential. They live a free existence in the array of habitats on earth and are able to derive their requirements for life from the nonliving environment. Much of the time, they form cohesive communities with other organisms, sharing habitat and nutrients. Examples include the natural partnerships that are found in symbiosis and biofilms.[3]

Some microbes have adapted to a non-free-living lifestyle called parasitism. A **parasite** lives in or on the body of a larger organism called the **host** and derives most of its sustenance from that host. A parasite's actions generally damage the host through infection and disease. Another term that can be used to specify this type of microbe is **pathogen.***

Humanity is plagued by nearly 2,000 different pathogens that can cause various types of disease. Infectious diseases still devastate human populations worldwide, despite significant strides in understanding and treating them. The most recent estimates from the World Health Organization (WHO) point to around 10 billion infections of all types across the world every year. There are more infections than people because many people acquire more than one infection. Infectious diseases are also among the most common causes of death in much of humanity, and they still kill a significant percentage of the U.S. population. The worldwide death toll from infections is about 13 million people per year, and 90% of the deaths are caused by six infectious agents. **Table 1.2** arrays the most predominant infectious diseases on earth and their estimated yearly case numbers. **Figure 1.7** compares the death rate among four groups that differ significantly in socioeconomic levels from around the world. It is quite evident which world inhabitants suffer

TABLE 1.2	The Most Common Infections and Infectious Agents
Infections/Diseases Caused by Multiple Pathogens	**Estimated No. per Year, Worldwide***
Parasitic Worm Infections	663,000,000
Schistosomiasis, ascariasis, hookworm, tapeworm, trichuriasis, oncocercosis	
Parasitic Protozoan Infections	523,000,000
Leishmaniasis, trypanosomiasis, malaria, amebic dysentery	
Sexually Transmitted Infections	448,000,000
HIV, genital warts, chlamydia, gonorrhea, syphilis, trichomoniasis	
Diarrheal Infections	112,000,000
Typhoid fever, *Shigella* dysentery, cholera	
Respiratory Tract Infections	14,100,000
Pneumonia, influenza	

Infections Caused by Single Pathogens	**No. of Cases***
Tuberculosis**	1–2 billion
Malaria (protozoan)	500 million
Viral hepatitis (A, B, C)	216 million
Rotavirus	125 million
Shigellosis (dysentery)	90 million
Dengue fever (virus)	50 million
HIV/AIDS	34 million
Measles (virus)	30 million
Typhoid fever	12 million
Influenza (virus)	3–5 million

*Estimates from most recent CDC and World Health Organization statistics.

**This wide range recognizes the presence of people who may be long-term carriers of the tuberculosis (TB) bacterium.

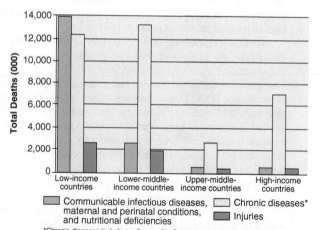

Figure 1.7 Chart comparing the major causes of death among world socioeconomic levels. The relationship between income and rate of death from infectious diseases is most evident in this comparison. What other correlation can we make from these data?

3. A biofilm is a complex network of microbes and their secretions that form in most natural environments, discussed further in chapter 4.

* *pathogen* (path′-oh-jen) Gr. *pathos*, disease, and *gennan*, to produce. Disease-causing agents.

the most from infectious diseases. Note that many of these infections are treatable with drugs or preventable with vaccines.

Those hardest hit are residents in countries where access to adequate medical care is lacking. One-third of the earth's inhabitants live on less than $1 per day, are malnourished, and are not fully immunized, and one-third of 7 billion humans have no access to drugs. Take the case of malaria, caused by a microorganism transmitted by mosquitoes, which kills 1 to 2 million people every year worldwide. Currently the most effective way for citizens of developing countries to avoid infection is to sleep under a bed net, because the mosquitoes are most active in the evening. Yet even this inexpensive solution is beyond the reach of people in many developing countries who cannot afford the $3 to $5 for nets to protect their family. Fortunately for many countries in the malaria zone, several international organizations have collaborated to provide special insecticide-treated nets that can help lower the rate of infections.

Emerging and Reemerging Diseases Among the more significant factors in the overall picture of infectious diseases are emerging and reemerging diseases (**1.1 Making Connections**). **Emerging diseases** are newly identified conditions that are being reported in increasing numbers. Since 1969, at least 26 novel infectious agents have arisen within the human population. Some of them have been associated with a specific location (Ebola fever virus), whereas others have become pandemics, meaning they spread across continents (human immunodeficiency virus—HIV). A number of them cause **zoonoses,*** which are infectious diseases native to animals that can be transmitted to humans. One recent example is the West Nile virus spread by mosquitoes to birds and humans and other mammals. This virus first traveled from Africa to the eastern United States in 1999, and is now established throughout the American continent and even the Hawaiian Islands. In 2012, the infection resurged to the highest numbers since 2003, probably because of conditions favorable to the life cycle of mosquitoes.

Reemerging diseases are older, well-known diseases that are increasing in occurrence for reasons outlined in 1.1 Making Connections. Among the most common reemerging infectious diseases are tuberculosis (TB), influenza, malaria, cholera, and hepatitis B. Tuberculosis, which has been known since ancient times, still causes 8 million new infections and kills 1 million to 2 million people every year. As you will see, numerous factors play a part in the tenaciousness of infectious diseases, but fundamental to all of them is the formidable capacity of microbes to adapt to alterations in the individual, community, and environment.

 CLINICAL CONNECTIONS

Are Microbes a Hidden Cause of Diseases?

One of the most eye-opening discoveries has been that many diseases once considered noninfectious probably do involve microbial infection. Most scientists expect that, in time, a majority of chronic conditions will be be linked to microbial agents. The most famous of these is gastric

ulcers, now known to be caused by a bacterium called *Helicobacter* (see chapter 21). But there are more. A connection has been established, between diabetes and the coxsackievirus, and between obesity and a common adenovirus. Diseases as disparate as multiple sclerosis, obsessive compulsive disorder, and coronary artery disease have been linked to chronic infections with microorganisms. It seems that the golden age of microbiological discovery, during which all of the "obvious" diseases were characterized and cures or preventions were devised for them, should more accurately be referred to as the *first* golden age. We're now discovering the roles of microorganisms in hidden but slowly destructive diseases. These include female infertility caused by *Chlamydia* infection and malignancies such as liver cancer (hepatitis viruses) and cervical cancer (human papillomavirus). In fact, epidemiologists analyzing statistics on world cancer have estimated that one in six cancers can be associated with an infectious agent.

Another important development in infectious disease trends is the increasing number of patients with weakened defenses who are kept alive for extended periods. We are becoming more susceptible to infectious disease precisely because of advances in medicine. People are living longer. Sicker people are staying alive much longer than in the past. Older and sicker people have heightened susceptibility to what we might call "garden-variety" microbes.

Why would chronic infections be more likely to be associated with diseases like cancer? *Answer available at http://www.mhhe.com/talaro9*

 Check Your Progress SECTIONS 1.3–1.4

7. Describe several ways that the beneficial qualities of microbes greatly outweigh their roles as infectious agents.

8. Look up some of the diseases shown in table 1.2 in the index and determine which ones could be prevented by vaccines or cured with drugs. Are there other ways (besides vaccines) to prevent any of these?

9. Distinguish between emerging and reemerging infectious diseases and explain what factors contribute to their development.

1.5 The Historical Foundations of Microbiology

Expected Learning Outcomes

9. Outline the major events in the history of microbiology, including the major contributors to the early development of microscopy, medical advances, aseptic techniques, and the germ theory of disease.

10. Explain the main features of the scientific method, and differentiate between inductive and deductive reasoning and between hypothesis and theory.

If not for the extensive interest, curiosity, and devotion of thousands of microbiologists over the last 300 years, we would know little about the microscopic realm that surrounds us. Many of the discoveries in this science have resulted from the prior work of men and women who toiled long hours in dimly lit laboratories with the

* *zoonoses* (zoh″-uh-noh′-seez) Gr. *zoion*, animal and *nosos*, disease. Any disease indigenous to animals transmissible to humans.

1.1 MAKING CONNECTIONS

The Changing Spectacle of Infectious Diseases

The middle of the last century was a time of great confidence in science and medicine. The introduction of antibiotics in the 1940s and a lengthening list of vaccines for preventing numerous diseases caused many medical experts to declare a victory. For a short time, there was a sense that infectious diseases were going to be completely manageable. But this optimistic viewpoint was on a collision course with a vast army of very tiny invaders that are everywhere—namely, microorganisms. Because humans are constantly interacting with microbes, we serve as a handy incubator for infectious diseases, both those newly recognized and older ones previously identified.

All together, government agencies are keeping track of a total of 75 emerging and reemerging infectious diseases (see examples in figure).* The newer or emerging diseases usually erupt suddenly with no warning (SARS respiratory syndrome). Older or reemerging diseases demonstrate just how difficult it is to eradicate microbes and the diseases they cause, even though we are very aware of them and often have drugs and vaccines to combat them. Only smallpox has been completely eliminated, although we are very close to eradicating polio. In fact, we continue to experience epidemics of childhood diseases that are usually preventable with vaccines. Starting in 2010, pertussis (whooping cough) cases began to increase dramatically over the next 2 years. Some communities recorded the highest rates of pertussis in decades, even though children were being vaccinated. It now appears that the vaccine's effectiveness wears off and may require additional inoculations to create adequate protection.

What are some of the reasons that account for this dilemma with our microbial coinhabitants? A major contributing factor is our increased mobility and travel, especially by air. An infected person can travel around the world before showing any symptoms of infection. He can carry the infectious agent to many far-flung locations, exposing populations along the way, who in turn can infect their contacts. An outbreak of H1N1 influenza (swine flu) provides a dramatic example. After being first diagnosed in Mexico in March 2009, it spread around the world in 6 short weeks! Within 6 months, it had caused millions of cases and thousands of deaths and had been reported in at least 200 countries.

Other significant effects involve our expanding population and global food-growing practices. As we continue to encroach into new territory and wild habitats, there is potential for contact with emerging pathogens, as we saw with Ebola fever, Lyme disease, and hantavirus pulmonary syndrome. Our agricultural practices can unearth microbes that were lying dormant or hidden. A bacterium carried in the intestine of domestic cattle, *Escherichia coli* O157:H7, the agent of a serious kidney disease, has been associated with hundreds of thousands of infections from food and water contaminated with cattle feces. Much mass-produced fresh food can also travel around the world, infecting people along the way. Several large outbreaks of salmonellosis, shigellosis, and listeriosis have been traced to contaminated dairy and poultry products, and vegetables. In some areas of the world, farmers knowingly or unknowingly use fecally contaminated water and fertilizer on fresh produce that will be on your table the next week.

Then there is the matter of the incredible resistance of microbes. You know about their capacity to live where no other living things could— volcanoes, salt lakes, radioactive waste pits—so it has not been a surprise to discover how readily they can adapt to drugs we use to treat them. The emergence of drug-resistant "superbugs" has become a massive problem in medicine. Some forms of *Staphylococcus aureus* (MRSA) and *Mycobacterium tuberculosis* are resistant to so many drugs that there are few, and sometimes no, choices left.

As hard as we may try to manage microbes, we keep coming up against a potent reality, a sentiment summed up by the renowned microbiologist Louis Pasteur over 130 years ago when he declared: "Microbes will have the last word."

Why do you think it is unlikely that infectious diseases can ever be completely eradicated? *Answer available at http://www.mhhe.com/talaro9*

*http://www3.niaid.nih.gov/topics/emerging/list.htm

crudest of tools. Each additional insight, whether large or small, has added to our current knowledge of life forms and processes. This section summarizes the prominent discoveries made in the past 300 years: microscopy, the rise of the scientific method, and the development of medical microbiology, including the germ theory and the origins of modern microbiological techniques. The Significant Events in Microbiology Table found at http://www.mhhe.com/talaro9 summarizes some of the pivotal events in microbiology from its earliest beginnings to the present.

The Development of the Microscope: "Seeing Is Believing"

It is likely that from the very earliest history, humans noticed that when certain foods spoiled, they became inedible or caused illness and yet other "spoiled" foods did no harm and even had enhanced flavor. Even several centuries ago, there was already a sense that diseases such as the black plague and smallpox were caused by some sort of transmissible matter. But the causes of such phenomena were vague and obscure because the technology to study them was lacking. Consequently, they remained cloaked in mystery and regarded with superstition—a trend that led even well-educated scientists to believe in spontaneous generation (**1.2 Making Connections**).

True awareness of the widespread distribution of microorganisms and some of their characteristics was finally made possible by the development of the first microscopes. These devices revealed microbes as discrete entities sharing many of the characteristics of larger, visible plants and animals. Several early scientists fashioned magnifying lenses and microscopes, but these lacked the optical clarity needed for examining bacteria and other small, single-celled organisms. The most careful and exacting observations awaited the simple single-lens

EMERGING AND REEMERGING INFECTIOUS DISEASES: 1996-2009

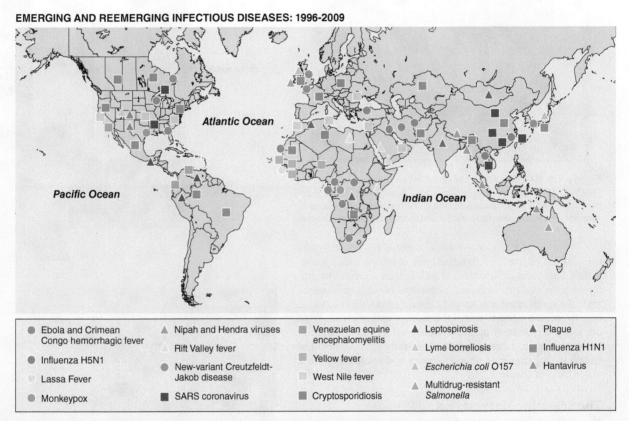

● Ebola and Crimean Congo hemorrhagic fever	▲ Nipah and Hendra viruses	■ Venezuelan equine encephalomyelitis	▲ Leptospirosis	▲ Plague
● Influenza H5N1	△ Rift Valley fever	■ Yellow fever	△ Lyme borreliosis	■ Influenza H1N1
● Lassa Fever	● New-variant Creutzfeldt-Jakob disease	■ West Nile fever	△ *Escherichia coli* O157	▲ Hantavirus
● Monkeypox	■ SARS coronavirus	■ Cryptosporidiosis	△ Multidrug-resistant *Salmonella*	

This figure is based on data from the WHO that traces the worldwide appearance of emerging and reemerging diseases.

microscope hand-fashioned by **Antonie van Leeuwenhoek,** a Dutch linen merchant and self-made microbiologist **(figure 1.8).**

During the late 1600s in Holland, Leeuwenhoek used his early lenses to examine the thread patterns of the draperies and upholstery he sold in his shop. Between customers, he retired to the workbench in the back of his shop, grinding glass lenses to ever-finer specifications. He could see with increasing clarity, but after a few years he became interested in things other than thread counts. He took rainwater from a clay pot, smeared it on his specimen holder, and peered at it through his finest lens. He found "animals appearing to me ten thousand times more than those which may be perceived in the water with the naked eye."

Quick Search
To find out more about van Leeuwenhoek, search the internet and view sites such as MicrobiologyBytes on YouTube.

He didn't stop there. He scraped plaque from his teeth, and from the teeth of volunteers who had never cleaned their teeth in their lives, and took a close look at that. He recorded: "In the said matter there were many very little living animalcules, very prettily a-moving. . . . Moreover, the other animalcules were in such enormous numbers, that all the water . . . seemed to be alive." Leeuwenhoek started sending his observations to the Royal Society of London, and eventually he was recognized as a scientist of great merit.

Leeuwenhoek constructed more than 250 small, powerful microscopes that could magnify up to 300 times **(figure 1.9).** Considering that he had no formal training in science and that he was the first person ever to faithfully record this strange new world, his descriptions of bacteria and protozoa (which he called "animalcules") were astute and precise. Because of Leeuwenhoek's extraordinary contributions to microbiology, he is sometimes considered the father of bacteriology and protozoology.

Figure 1.8 An oil painting of Antonie van Leeuwenhoek (1632–1723) sitting in his laboratory. How astonishing to realize that this curious and original man was the first human being on earth ever to glimpse the "cavorting wee beasties" (his description) of the microbial world!

From the time of Leeuwenhoek, microscopes became more complex and improved, with the addition of refined lenses, a condenser, finer focusing devices, and built-in light sources. The prototype of the modern compound microscope, in use from about the mid-1800s, was capable of magnifications of 1,000 times or more, largely because it had two sets of lenses for magnification. Even our modern laboratory microscopes are not greatly different in basic structure and function from those early microscopes. The technical characteristics of microscopes and microscopy are a major focus of chapter 3.

The Scientific Method and the Search for Knowledge

The research that led to acceptance of biogenesis provides us one example of the early development of science-based thought. Over the next few sections, we will glimpse other important milestones in the development of the scientific method such as vaccination, germ theory, asepsis, and Koch's postulates. The impact of science is so pervasive that you may not realize how much of our everyday life is built upon applications of the scientific method. Vaccines, antibiotics, space travel, computers, medical diagnosis, and DNA testing exist primarily because of the work of thousands of scientists doing objective observations and collecting evidence that is measurable, can be expressed quantitatively, and is subject to critical analysis.

The information obtained through the scientific method is explanatory and predictive. It aims to explain how and why phenomena occur and to predict what is expected to happen under known conditions. Two very recent events dramatically contrast the differences between scientific versus non-scientific reasoning. In 2012, NASA sent the *Curiosity* spacecraft on a 225 million-mile journey to Mars and landed it at a very precise time and place—an incredible achievement that brought to bear vast knowledge of physics, engineering, and mathematics. That same year, rumors

Lens

Specimen holder

Focus screw

Handle

(a)

(b)

Figure 1.9 Leeuwenhoek's microscope. (a) A brass replica of a Leeuwenhoek microscope and how it is held. **(b)** Examples of bacteria drawn by Leeuwenhoek.

started about doomsday predictions supposedly found in interpretations of an ancient Mayan calendar. A surprisingly large number of people all over the world were convinced that the world would come to an end on December 21, 2012. The fact that you are reading this textbook absolutely verifies which of these approaches is more reliable and predictive.

How do scientists apply the scientific method? In the **deductive reasoning** approach, a scientist uses general observations of some phenomenon to develop a set of facts to explain that phenomenon—that is, they *deduce* the facts that can account for what they have observed. This early explanation is considered a **hypothesis,** and however tentative it may start out, it is still based

1.2 MAKING CONNECTIONS

The Fall of Superstition and the Rise of Microbiology

For thousands of years, people believed that certain living things arose from vital forces present in nonliving or decomposing matter. This ancient idea, known as **spontaneous generation,** was continually reinforced as people observed that meat left out in the open soon "produced" maggots, that mushrooms appeared on rotting wood, that rats and mice emerged from piles of litter, and that other magical phenomena occurred. Though some of these early ideas seem quaint and ridiculous in light of modern knowledge, we must remember that, at the time, mysteries in life were accepted and the scientific method was not widely practiced.

Even after single-celled organisms were discovered during the mid-1600s, the idea of spontaneous generation continued to exist. Some scientists assumed that microscopic beings were an early stage in the development of more complex ones.

Over the subsequent 200 years, scientists waged an experimental battle over the two hypotheses that could explain the origin of simple life forms. Some tenaciously clung to the idea of **abiogenesis*** which embraced spontaneous generation. On the other side were advocates of **biogenesis,*** saying that living things arise only from others of their same kind. There were serious proponents on both sides, and each side put forth what appeared on the surface to be plausible explanations of why their evidence was more correct. Gradually, the abiogenesis hypothesis was abandoned, as convincing evidence for biogenesis continued to mount. The following series of experiments were among the most important in finally tipping the balance.

Among the important variables to be considered in testing the hypotheses were the effects of nutrients, air, and heat, and the presence of preexisting life forms in the environment. One of the first people to test the spontaneous generation theory was **Francesco Redi** of Italy. He conducted a simple experiment in which he placed meat in a jar and covered it with fine gauze. Flies gathering at the jar were blocked from entering and thus laid their eggs on the outside of the gauze. The maggots subsequently developed without access to the meat, indicating that maggots were the offspring of flies and did not arise from some "vital force" in the meat. This and related experiments laid to rest the idea that more complex animals such as insects and mice developed through abiogenesis, but it did not convince many scientists of the day that simpler organisms could not arise in that way.

The Frenchman **Louis Jablot** reasoned that even microscopic organisms must have parents, and his experiments with infusions (dried hay steeped in water) supported that hypothesis. He divided an infusion that had been boiled to destroy any living things into two containers: a heated container that was closed to the air and a heated container that was freely open to the air. Only the open vessel developed microorganisms, which he presumed had entered in air laden with dust. Regrettably, the validation of biogenesis was temporarily set back by **John Needham,** an Englishman who did similar experiments using mutton gravy. His results were in conflict with Jablot's because both his heated and unheated test containers teemed with microbes. Unfortunately, his experiments were done before the realization that heat-resistant microbes

are not usually killed by mere boiling. Apparently Jablot had been lucky; his infusions were sterile.

Then, in the mid-1800s, the acclaimed microbiologist **Louis Pasteur** entered the arena. He had recently been studying the roles of microorganisms in the fermentation of beer and wine, and it was clear to him that these processes were brought about by the activities of microbes introduced into the beverage from air, fruits, and grains. The methods he used to discount abiogenesis were simple yet brilliant.

Pasteur's Experiment

Microbes being destroyed

Vigorous heat is applied.

Two flasks start out free of live cells (sterile)

One flask is snapped off at the top; growth appears in broth.

Neck of second flask remains intact; no growth occurs.

To further clarify that air and dust were the source of microbes, Pasteur filled flasks with broth and fashioned their openings into elongate, swan-neck-shaped tubes. The flasks' openings were freely open to the air but were curved so that gravity would cause any airborne dust particles to deposit in the lower part of the necks. He heated the flasks to sterilize the broth and then incubated them. As long as the flask remained intact, the broth remained sterile, but if the neck was broken off so that dust fell directly down into the container, microbial growth immediately commenced.

Pasteur summed up his findings, "For I have kept from them, and am still keeping from them, that one thing which is above the power of man to make; I have kept from them the germs that float in the air, I have kept from them life."

What type of microorganisms were likely responsible for the misleading results of John Needham's experiment and were absent in Jablot's and Pasteur's experiments? *Answer available at http://www.mhhe.com/talaro9*

* *abiogenesis* (ah-bee″-oh-jen′-uh-sis) L. *a,* without, *bios,* life, and *genesis,* beginning.
* *biogenesis* (by-oh-gen′-uh-sis) to begin with life.

Observations/ information gathering	**Formation of Jenner's hypothesis**	**Testing the hypothesis, experiment I**	**Testing the hypothesis, experiment II**
1. Dr. Jenner observed that cows had a form of pox similar to smallpox. Jenner also noted that milkmaids acquired cowpox only on the hands, and they appeared to be immune to smallpox.	2. Jenner deduced that the cowpox was closely related to smallpox and could possibly be used on patients to provide protection similar to that of the milkmaids he had seen.	3. Jenner took scrapings from cowpox blisters on the hand of a milkmaid and inoculated them into a boy who had not had smallpox. He developed minor symptoms but remained healthy.	4. After a few weeks, the child was exposed twice to the pus from an active smallpox lesion. He did not acquire smallpox and appeared to have immune protection.

Figure 1.10 Edward Jenner and the saga of the smallpox vaccine. Jenner's work documents the first scientific method–based attempt to control an infectious disease—smallpox. This disease was characterized by raised skin blisters called pox, and it often caused severe damage to organs. Throughout its long history, this deadly disease decimated many populations worldwide until 1977, when the last case was reported.

on scientific thought rather than subjective beliefs that come from superstition or myth. A valid hypothesis will allow for experimentation and testing and can be shown to be false. An example of a workable hypothesis based on deduction might speculate that a disease such as hemophilia is an inheritable condition. This would pave the way for specific experiments that test for the influence of genetics. A nonworkable hypothesis would be that hemophilia is caused by a curse placed on the royal family of England. Because supernatural beliefs offer no basis for experimentation and must be taken on faith, they can never be subjected to the rigors of the scientific method.

With **inductive reasoning,** one applies specific observations to develop a general explanation. This method is often used in the early phases of evaluation and can formulate a generalization to be tested deductively. In the previous example, induction might begin with the observation of a family in which several people have hemophilia, and this may lead to the general idea that it is inheritable.

A lengthy process of experimentation, analysis, and testing eventually leads to conclusions that either support or refute the hypothesis. If experiments do not uphold the hypothesis—that is, if it is found to be flawed—the hypothesis or some part of it is reconsidered. This does not mean the results are invalid; it means the hypothesis may require reworking or additional tests. Eventually, it is either discarded or modified to fit the results of the experiment. If the hypothesis is supported by the experiment, it is not (or should not be) immediately accepted as fact. It then must be tested and retested. Indeed, this is an important guideline in the acceptance of a hypothesis. The results of the experiment must be published and repeated by other investigators.

In time, as each hypothesis is supported by a growing body of data and survives rigorous scrutiny, it moves to the next level of acceptance—the **theory.** A theory is a collection of statements, propositions, or concepts that explains or accounts for a natural event. A theory is not the result of a single experiment repeated over and over again but is an entire body of ideas that expresses or explains many aspects of a phenomenon. When an unsupported idea is dismissed as being "just a theory," this is an incorrect use of the term as far as science is concerned. A theory is far from a weak notion or wild guess. It is a viable explanation that has stood the test of time and has yet to be disproved by serious scientific inquiries. Often, theories develop and progress through decades of research and are added to and modified by new findings. At some point, evidence of the accuracy and predictability of a theory is so compelling that the next level of confidence is reached, and the theory becomes a **law,** or principle. For example, the **germ theory of disease** has been so thoroughly tested that it has clearly passed into the realm of law.

Science and its hypotheses and theories must progress along with technology. As advances in instrumentation allow new, more detailed views of living phenomena, old theories may be reexamined and altered and new ones proposed. Scientific knowledge is accumulative, and it must have built-in flexibility to accommodate new findings. It is for these reasons that scientists do not take a stance that theories or even laws are absolutely proved.

Figure 1.10 provides a summary of the scientific method in action using Edward Jenner's monumental discovery of vaccines. What is remarkable about Jenner's work is that he was the first to use scientific thought to construct a rigorous experimental model to inoculate people against disease, and he carried it through to its completion. It is also remarkable that he did this knowing nothing about viruses or even microbes. He worked out the concept of safely conferring artificial immunity long before there was any understanding of the immune system (look ahead to 15.2 Making Connections).

Countries reporting smallpox (1950-1980)

1965: Vaccine campaign

1979: Smallpox eradicated

Reproducibility of results

5. Jenner went on to inoculate 23 other test subjects with cowpox. For the first time, he used lesions from one child to inoculate another. All subjects remained protected from smallpox.

Publishing of results; other medical testing

6. Jenner wrote a paper detailing his experiment. He called his technique *vaccination*, from the Latin *vacca* for cow. Other local English physicians began to vaccinate patients with some success.

Vaccination theory becomes widespread.

7. Over the next 100 years vaccination was brought to the rest of the world through local programs. Scientists used Jenner's methods to develop vaccines for other pathogens. The theory of artificial immunity became well established.

Smallpox is eradicated from the world.

8. A massive vaccination campaign aimed to reduce cases and to stamp out the disease completely. Billions of doses given over a decade reduced smallpox to zero. The last cases occurred in 1977, and in 1979 the disease was declared eradicated.

The Development of Medical Microbiology

Early experiments on the sources of microorganisms led to the profound realization that microbes are everywhere: Not only are air and dust full of them, but the entire surface of the earth, its waters, and all objects are inhabited by them. This discovery led to immediate applications in medicine. Thus the seeds of medical microbiology were sown in the middle to latter half of the nineteenth century with the introduction of the first practical vaccine, the germ theory of disease, and the resulting use of sterile, aseptic, and pure culture techniques.

Jenner and the Introduction of Vaccination

We saw in figure 1.10 how the English physician and scientist **Edward Jenner** modeled the scientific method. His experiments ultimately gave rise to the first viable method to control smallpox by inoculating patients with a closely related disease agent. His contributions to medical science so changed the practice of medicine that he is considered the "Father of Immunology." It is often said of Jenner that his discovery saved more lives than any other in history. His work marked the beginning of an era of great scientific achievement—one that produced some of the most far-reaching developments in microbiology and medicine.

The Discovery of Spores and Sterilization

Following Pasteur's inventive work with infusions (1.2 Making Connections), it was not long before English physicist **John Tyndall** provided the initial evidence that some of the microbes in dust and air have very high heat resistance and that particularly vigorous treatment is required to destroy them. Later, the discovery and detailed description of heat-resistant bacterial endospores by **Ferdinand Cohn,** a German botanist, clarified the reason that heat would sometimes fail to completely eliminate all microorganisms. The modern sense of the word **sterile,** meaning completely free of all life forms including spores and viruses, had its beginnings here (see chapter 11). The capacity to sterilize objects and materials is an absolutely essential part of microbiology, medicine, dentistry, and some industries.

The Development of Aseptic Techniques

From earliest history, humans experienced a vague sense that "unseen forces" or "poisonous vapors" emanating from decomposing matter could cause disease. As the study of microbiology became more scientific and the invisible was made visible, the fear of such mysterious vapors was replaced by the knowledge and sometimes even the fear of "germs." About 130 years ago, the first studies by **Robert Koch** clearly linked a microscopic organism with a specific disease. Since that time, microbiologists have conducted a continuous search for disease-causing agents.

At the same time that abiogenesis was being hotly debated, a few budding microbiologists began to suspect that microorganisms could cause not only spoilage and decay but also infectious diseases. It occurred to these rugged individualists that even the human body itself was a source of infection. **Dr. Oliver Wendell Holmes,** an American physician, observed that mothers who gave birth at home experienced fewer infections than did mothers who gave birth in the hospital, and the Hungarian **Dr. Ignaz Semmelweis** showed quite clearly that women became infected in the maternity ward after examinations by physicians coming directly from the autopsy room.

The English surgeon **Joseph Lister** took notice of these observations and was the first to introduce **aseptic* techniques** aimed at reducing microbes in a medical setting and preventing wound infections. Lister's concept of asepsis was much more limited than our modern precautions. It mainly involved disinfecting the hands and

* *aseptic* (ay-sep′-tik) Gr. *a,* no, and *sepsis,* decay or infection. These techniques are aimed at reducing pathogens and do not necessarily sterilize.

the air with strong antiseptic chemicals, such as phenol, prior to surgery. It is hard for us to believe, but as recently as the late 1800s, surgeons wore street clothes in the operating room and had little idea that hand washing was important. Lister's techniques and the application of heat for sterilization became the bases for microbial control by physical and chemical methods, which are still in use today.

The Discovery of Pathogens and the Germ Theory of Disease

Two ingenious founders of microbiology, **Louis Pasteur** of France (**figure 1.11**) and **Robert Koch** of Germany (**figure 1.12**), introduced techniques that are still used today. Pasteur made enormous contributions to our understanding of the roles of microorganisms

Figure 1.11 Photograph of Louis Pasteur (1822–1895), the father of microbiology. Few microbiologists can match the scope and impact of his contributions to the science of microbiology.

Figure 1.12 Photograph of Robert Koch looking through a microscope with colleague Richard Pfeiffer looking on. Robert Koch won the Nobel Prize for Physiology or Medicine in 1905 for his work on *Mycobacterium tuberculosis*. Richard Pfeiffer discovered *Haemophilus influenzae* and was a pioneer in typhoid vaccination.

in many aspects of medicine and industry. He developed two vaccines (rabies and anthrax) and clarified the actions of microbes in wine and beer fermentation. He invented pasteurization and completed some of the first studies showing that human diseases could arise from infection. These studies, supported by the work of other scientists, became known as the **germ theory of disease.** Pasteur's contemporary, Koch, established *Koch's postulates,* a series of proofs that verified the germ theory and could establish whether an organism was pathogenic and which disease it caused (see chapter 13). About 1875, Koch used this experimental system to show that anthrax was caused by a bacterium called *Bacillus anthracis.* So useful were his postulates that the causative agents of 20 other diseases were discovered between 1875 and 1900, and even today, they serve as a basic premise for establishing a pathogen-disease link.

Numerous exciting technologies emerged from Koch's prolific and probing laboratory work. During this golden age of microbiology, he realized that study of the microbial world would require separating microbes from each other and growing them in culture. It is not an overstatement to say that he and his colleagues invented many of the techniques that are described in chapter 3: inoculation, isolation, media, maintenance of pure cultures, and preparation of specimens for microscopic examination. Other highlights in this era of discovery are presented in later chapters on microbial control (see chapter 11) and vaccination (see chapter 15).

 Check Your Progress SECTION 1.5

10. Outline the most significant discoveries and events in microscopy, culture techniques, and other methods of handling or controlling microbes.

11. Differentiate between a hypothesis and a theory. If someone says a scientific explanation is "only a theory," what do they really mean?

12. Is the germ theory of disease really a law, and why?

13. Why was the abandonment of the spontaneous generation theory so significant?

1.6 Taxonomy: Organizing, Classifying, and Naming Microorganisms

 Expected Learning Outcomes

11. Define taxonomy and its supporting terms classification, nomenclature, and identification.

12. Explain how the levels of a taxonomic scheme relate to each other. Give the names of the levels, and place them in a hierarchy.

13. Describe the goals of nomenclature and how the binomial system is structured. Know how to correctly write a scientific name.

Students just beginning their microbiology studies are often dismayed by the seemingly endless array of new, unusual, and sometimes confusing names for microorganisms. Learning microbial **nomenclature***

* *nomenclature* (noh'-men-klay"-chur) L. *nomen,* name, and *clare,* to call. A system of naming.

is very much like learning a new language, and occasionally its demands may be a bit overwhelming. But paying attention to proper microbial names is just like following a baseball game or a theater production: You cannot tell the players apart without a program! Your understanding and appreciation of microorganisms will be greatly improved by learning a few general rules about how they are named.

The formal system for organizing, classifying, and naming living things is **taxonomy.*** This science originated more than 250 years ago when **Carl von Linné** (also known as Linnaeus; 1701–1778), a Swedish botanist, laid down the basic rules for taxonomic categories, or **taxa.** Von Linné realized early on that a system for recognizing and defining the properties of living things would prevent chaos in scientific studies by providing each organism with a unique name and an exact "slot" in which to catalog it. This classification would then serve as a means for future identification of that same organism and permit workers in many biological fields to know if they were indeed discussing the same organism. The von Linné system has served well in categorizing the 2 million or more different types of organisms that have been discovered since that time.

The primary concerns of taxonomy are classification, nomenclature, and identification. These three areas are interrelated and play a vital role in keeping a dynamic inventory of the extensive array of living things. **Classification** is an orderly arrangement of organisms into groups that indicate evolutionary relationships and history. **Nomenclature** is the system of assigning names to the various taxonomic rankings of each microbial species. **Identification** is the process of determining and recording the traits of organisms in order to trace their exact identity and placement in taxonomy. A survey of some general methods of identification appears in chapter 3.

The Levels of Classification

The main taxa, or groups, in a classification scheme are organized into several descending ranks called a **hierarchy.** It begins with **domain,** which is a giant, all-inclusive category based on a unique cell type, and ends with **species,*** the smallest and most specific taxon. All the members of a domain share only one or few general characteristics, whereas members of a species are essentially the same kind of organism—that is, they share the majority of their characteristics. The order of taxa between the top and bottom levels is, in descending order: **domain, kingdom, phylum*** or **division,**[4] **class, order, family, genus,*** and **species.** Thus, each domain may be subdivided into a series of kingdoms, each kingdom is made up of several phyla, each phylum contains several classes, and so on. Because taxonomic schemes are to some extent artificial, certain groups of organisms cannot be arranged in an exact eight-part taxonomic scheme. In that case, additional levels can be imposed immediately above (super) or below (sub) a taxon, giving us such categories as superphylum and subclass.

To illustrate how this hierarchy works, we compare the taxonomic breakdowns of a human and a common pond protozoan (**figure 1.13**). Humans and protozoa belong to the same domain (Eukarya) but are placed in different kingdoms. To emphasize just how broad the category kingdom is, ponder the fact that humans belong to the same kingdom as jellyfish. Of the several phyla within this kingdom, humans are in the Phylum Chordata, but even a phylum is rather all-inclusive, considering that humans share it with other vertebrates as well as with creatures called sea squirts. The next level, Class Mammalia, narrows the field considerably by grouping only those vertebrates that have hair and suckle their young. Humans belong to the Order Primates, a group that also includes apes, monkeys, and lemurs. Next comes the Family Hominoidea, containing only humans and apes. The final levels are our genus, *Homo* (all races of modern and ancient humans), and our species, *sapiens* (meaning wise). Notice that for both the human and the protozoan, the categories become less inclusive and the individual members more closely related and similar in overall appearance. Other examples of classification schemes are provided in sections of chapters 4 and 5 and in several later chapters. A superior source for the taxonomic breakdown of microbes is Wikipedia. Go there to search the scientific name of any species, and its taxonomy will be shown in a box on the upper right portion of the first page.

We need to remember that all taxonomic hierarchies are based on the judgment of scientists with certain expertise in a particular group of organisms and that not all other experts may agree with the system being used. Consequently, no taxa are permanent to any degree; they are constantly being revised and refined as new information becomes available or new viewpoints become prevalent. Our primary aim in introducing taxonomy is to present an organizational tool that helps you keep track of the various microbial groups and recognize their major categories. For the most part, our emphasis will remain on the higher-level taxa (phylum, class) and genus and species.

Assigning Scientific Names

Many larger organisms are known by a common name suggested by certain dominant features. For example, a bird species may be called a yellow-bellied sapsucker, or a flowering plant, a sunflower. Some species of microorganisms (especially pathogens) are also sometimes designated by informal names, such as the gonococcus (*Neisseria gonorrhoeae*) or the TB bacillus (*Mycobacterium tuberculosis*), but this is not the usual practice. If we were to adopt common names such as the "little yellow coccus" (for *Micrococcus luteus**) or the "club-shaped diphtheria bacterium" (for *Corynebacterium diphtheriae**), the terminology would become even more cumbersome and challenging than scientific names. Even worse, common names are notorious for varying from region to region, even within the same country. A decided advantage of standardized nomenclature is that it provides a universal language that enables scientists from all countries on the earth to freely exchange information.

* *taxonomy* (tacks-on″-uh-mee) Gr. *taxis*, arrangement, and *nomos*, name.

* *species* (spee′-sheez) L. *specere*, kind. In biology, this term is always in the plural form.

* *phylum* (fy′-lum) pl. phyla (fye′-luh) Gr. *phylon*, race.

4. The term *phylum* is used for protozoa, animals, bacteria, and fungi. Division is for algae and plants.

* *genus* (jee′-nus) pl. genera (jen′-er-uh) L. birth, kind.

* *Micrococcus luteus* (my″-kroh-kok′-us loo′-tee-us) Gr. *micros*, small, and *kokkus*, berry; L. *luteus*, yellow.

* *Corynebacterium diphtheriae* (kor-eye″-nee-bak-ter′-ee-yum dif′-theer-ee-eye) Gr. *coryne*, club, *bacterion*, little rod, and *diphtheriae*, the causative agent of the disease diphtheria.

Domain: Eukarya (All eukaryotic organisms)

Kingdom: Animalia

Sea squirt Lemur Sea star

Phylum: Chordata

Class: Mammalia

Order: Primates

Family: Hominoidea

Genus: *Homo*

Species: *sapiens*
Scientific name: *Homo sapiens*

(a)

Domain: Eukarya (All eukaryotic organisms)

Kingdom: Protista
Includes
protozoa
and algae

Phylum: Ciliophora
Protozoa with cilia
Covered by flexible
pellicle
Contain two types
of nuclei

Class: Oligohymenophora
Single, rapidly
swimming cells
Regular rows of cilia
Distinct ciliated oral
groove

Order: Peniculida
Uniform dense cilia
dispersed over cell
Oral cilia are peniculae
Trichocysts in outer
membrane

Family: Parameciidae
Cells round to elongate
Rotate while swimming
Deep oral grooves

Genus: *Paramecium*
Ovoid, cigar- and foot-shaped cells

Species: *caudatum*
Cells elongate, cylindrical
Blunt at one end and tapered to a
point at the other
Scientific name: *Paramecium caudatum*

(b)

Figure 1.13 **Sample taxonomy.** Two organisms belonging to Domain Eukarya, traced through their taxonomic series. **(a)** Modern humans, *Homo sapiens*. **(b)** A common protozoan, *Paramecium caudatum*.

The **scientific name,** also known as the **specific epithet,** is assigned by using a **binomial** (two-name) **system** of nomenclature. The scientific name is always a combination of the generic (genus) name followed by the species name. The generic part of the scientific name is capitalized, and the species part begins with a lowercase letter. Both should be italicized (or underlined if italics are not available), as follows:

Histoplasma capsulatum or <u>*Histoplasma capsulatum*</u>

Because other taxonomic levels are not italicized and consist of only one word, one can always recognize a scientific name. An organism's scientific name is sometimes abbreviated to save space, as in

H. capsulatum, but only if the genus name has already been stated. The source for nomenclature is usually Latin or Greek. If other languages such as English or French are used, the endings of these words are revised to have Latin endings. In general, the name first applied to a species will be the one that takes precedence over all others.

An international group oversees the naming of every new organism discovered, making sure that standard procedures have been followed and that there is not already an earlier name for the organism or another organism with that same name. The inspiration for names is extremely varied and often rather imaginative. Some species have been named in honor of a microbiologist who originally discovered the microbe or who has made outstanding

contributions to the field. Other names may designate a characteristic of the microbe (shape, color), a location where it was found, or a disease or symptom that it causes. Some examples of scientific names, pronunciations, and origins are:

- ***Histoplasma capsulatum*** (hiss″-toh-plaz′-mah cap″-soo-lay′-tum) Gr. *histo,* tissue, *plasm,* to form, and L. *capsula,* small sheath. A fungus that causes Ohio Valley fever.
- ***Trichinella spiralis*** (trik′-ih-nel′-uh spy-ral′-iss) Gr. *trichos,* hair, *ella,* little, and L. *spira,* coiled. The nematode worm that causes the food-borne infection, trichinellosis.
- ***Shewanella oneidensis*** (shee″-wan-el′-uh oh-ny″-den′-siss). Named for British bacteriologist J. M. Shewan and Lake Oneida, New York, where it was discovered. This is a remarkable species that can bioremediate radioactive metals in contaminated waste sites.
- ***Bordetella pertussis*** (bor″-duh-tel′-uh pur-tuss′-iss) After Jules Bordet, a Belgian microbiologist who discovered this bacterium, and L. *per,* severe, and *tussis,* cough. This is the cause of pertussis, or whooping cough.

When you encounter the name of a microorganism in the chapters ahead, it is helpful to take the time to sound it out one syllable at a time and repeat until it seems familiar. You are much more likely to remember the names that way—and they will become part of the new language you will be learning.

> **Quick Search**
> Go to the "Pathogen Pronunciation Stations" for help in correctly pronouncing some common names.

 Check Your Progress SECTION 1.6

14. Differentiate between taxonomy, classification, and nomenclature.
15. What is the basis for a phylogenetic system of classification?
16. Explain the binomial system of nomenclature and give the correct order of taxa, going from most general to most specific.
17. Give some reasons to explain the benefits of using scientific names for organisms.

1.7 The Origin and Evolution of Microorganisms

 Expected Learning Outcomes

14. Discuss the fundamentals of evolution, evidence used to verify evolutionary trends, and its use in studying organisms.
15. Explain the concepts behind the organization of the two main trees of life, and indicate where the major groups of microorganisms fall on these trees.

16. Explain the bases for classification, taxonomy, and nomenclature.
17. Recall the order of taxa and the system of notation used in creating scientific names.

All Life Is Related and Connected Through Evolution

As we indicated earlier, *taxonomy,* the classification of biological species, is a system used to organize all of the forms of life. In biology today, there are different methods for deciding on taxonomic categories, but they all rely on the history and relatedness of organisms. The natural relatedness between groups of living things is called their **phylogeny.** Biologists can apply their knowledge of phylogenetic relationships to develop a system of taxonomy.

To understand how organisms originate, we must understand some fundamentals of **evolution.** You have no doubt heard comments that dismiss evolution as "only a theory" as though there remain significant problems with its acceptance. But you have also learned that a scientific theory is a highly-documented and well-established concept. The process of evolution has accumulated such a significant body of knowledge over hundreds of years that scientists from all disciplines consider it to be a fact. It is an important theme that underlies all of biology, including microbiology. Put simply, evolution states that living things change gradually through billions of years and that these evolvements result in various types of structural and functional adaptations through many generations. The process of evolution is selective: Those changes that most favor the survival of a particular organism or group of organisms tend to be retained, and those that are less beneficial to survival tend to be lost. The great naturalist Charles Darwin labeled this process natural selection. Space does not permit a detailed analysis of evolutionary theories, but the occurrence of evolution is supported by a tremendous amount of evidence from the fossil record and from the study of **morphology** (structure), **physiology** (function), and **genetics** (inheritance). Evolution accounts for the millions of different species on the earth and their adaptation to its many and diverse habitats.

Evolution is founded on two premises: (1) that all new species originate from preexisting species through inheritance of traits, and (2) that closely related organisms have similar features because they evolved from common ancestral forms. Usually, evolution progresses toward greater complexity, and evolutionary stages range from simple, less evolved forms that are close to an ancestral organism to more complex, evolved forms that have advanced beyond the ancestral forms. Regardless of their evolutionary history, all species presently residing on the earth are modern, but some have arisen more recently in evolutionary history than others.

Traditionally we present the history of life, or phylogeny, in the form of branching trees that are designed to show the origins of various life forms (**figures 1.14** and **1.15**). At the base are the oldest ancestral forms (somewhat like roots), and the trunk indicates the progression of major lines that emerge through selection. Branches split off the main trunk as further selection and modification occurs. With this arrangement, more closely related organisms appear nearer each other on the tree. As more genetic information is discovered, many biologists think that the actual pattern should be more of a bush or web to show greater complexity and interrelatedness.

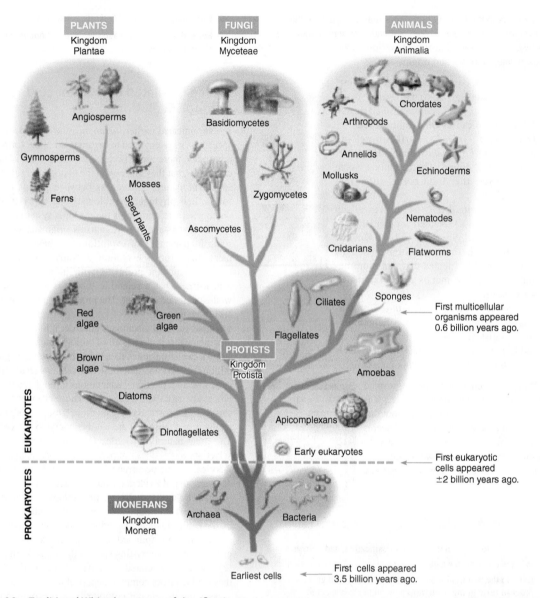

Figure 1.14 Traditional Whittaker system of classification. In this system, kingdoms are based on cell structure and type, the nature of body organization, and nutritional type. Bacteria and Archaea (monerans) have prokaryotic cells and are unicellular. Protists have eukaryotic cells and are mostly unicellular. They can be photosynthetic (algae), or they can feed on other organisms (protozoa). Fungi are eukaryotic cells and are unicellular or multicellular; they have cell walls and are not photosynthetic. Plants have eukaryotic cells, are multicellular, have cell walls, and are photosynthetic. Animals have eukaryotic cells, are multicellular, do not have cell walls, and derive nutrients from other organisms.

Although all trees are artificial and tend to simplify relationships, they still can provide a basic picture of phylogeny that we need to organize our study.

Systems for Presenting a Universal Tree of Life

The first trees of life were constructed on the basis of just two kingdoms (plants and animals). In time, it became clear that certain organisms did not truly fit either of those categories, so a third kingdom for simpler organisms that lacked tissue differentiation (protists) was recognized. Eventually, when significant differences became evident even among the protists, a fourth kingdom was proposed for the bacteria. Robert Whittaker built on this work and during the period of 1959 through 1969 added a fifth kingdom for fungi. Whittaker's five-kingdom system served as the standard for a simple working model for a number of years.

A detailed example of a phylogenetic tree of life based on the five kingdoms is shown in figure 1.14. The relationships considered in constructing the tree were based on structural similarities and differences, such as cellular organization and the way the organisms

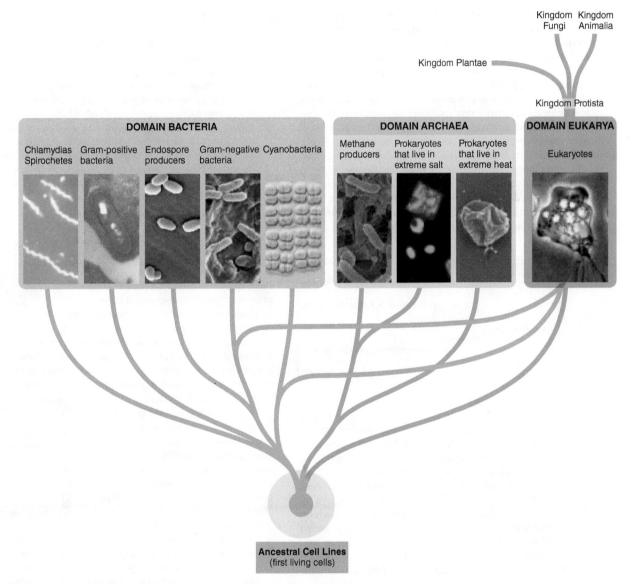

Figure 1.15 **Woese-Fox system.** A system for representing the origins of cell lines and major taxonomic groups as proposed by Carl Woese and colleagues. They propose three distinct cell lines placed in superkingdoms called domains. We know little about the earliest cells, called progenotes, except that they were prokaryotic. Lines of these early primitive cells gave rise to the Domains Bacteria and Archaea. Molecular evidence indicates that the Archaea started the branch that would eventually become the Domain Eukarya. Notice that two early bacterial lines contributed to the evolution of the Eukarya. Selected representatives of the Domains are included. The traditional eukaryotic kingdoms are still present with this system (see figure 1.14). Further details of classification systems are covered in chapters 4 and 5.

*also known as Kingdom Myceteae

acquire nutrition. These methods produced a system with five major kingdoms: the monera, fungi, protists, plants, and animals. Because these kingdoms easily accommodate the prokaryotic and eukaryotic cell types, this plan of classification has proved useful (figure on left).

Applying newer methods for determining phylogeny has led to the development of a differently shaped tree—with important implications for our understanding of evolutionary relatedness. The new techniques come from *molecular biology* and include a study of genes—both their structure and function—at the molecular level. Molecular biological methods have demonstrated that certain types

of molecules in cells, called small ribosomal ribonucleic acid (rRNA), provide a "living record" of the evolutionary history of an organism. Analysis of this molecule in prokaryotic and eukaryotic cells indicates that certain unusual cells called **archaea*** (originally archae-bacteria) are so different from the other two groups that they should be included in a separate superkingdom. Many archaea are characterized by their ability to live in extreme environments, such as hot springs or highly salty environments. Under the microscope they resemble bacteria, but molecular biology has revealed that the cells of archaea, though prokaryotic in nature, are actually more closely related to eukaryotic cells than to bacterial cells (see figure 4.27).

To reflect these relationships, Carl Woese and George Fox have proposed a system that assigns all organisms to one of three domains, each described by a different type of cell (see box below and figure 1.15). The prokaryotic cell types are placed in the Domains **Archaea** and **Bacteria.** Eukaryotes are all placed in the Domain **Eukarya.**

It is believed that the first two domains emerged from very simple prokaryotic cells that developed in the conditions of the hot early earth. We do not know at this time if there was a common ancestor or several different ones. In time the Archaea line branched off and gave rise to the Eukarya. As these evolutionary periods progressed, the members of the three domains evolved separately into major life trees of their own with many offshoots. Notice that two early bacterial lines contributed to the evolution of the eukaryotic cell and Eukarya by becoming the mitochondria and the chloroplasts. We will touch on this relationship in chapter 5. This revised system can be represented as a six-kingdom system with Bacteria and Archaea serving as both Domain and Kingdom. It is still undergoing analysis, and it somewhat complicates the presentation of some organisms by disposing of some traditional groups, although three of the five original kingdoms (animals, plants, fungi) still work within this framework. The original Kingdom Protista may also be represented as a collection of protozoa and algae in several separate taxons discussed in chapter 5.

Which scheme you use does not greatly affect the presentation of most microbes, because we discuss them mostly at the genus or species level. But be aware that biological taxonomy—and more important, our understanding of the early evolution of organisms—is in a period of transition. It is essential that any methods of classification reflect our current understanding and can be altered as new information is uncovered.

Please note that viruses are *not* included in any of the classification or evolutionary schemes, because they are not cells and their position cannot be given with any confidence. Their special taxonomy is discussed in chapter 6.

* *archaea* (ar'-kee-uh) sing. archaeon. Gr *archaeo,* ancient, and *an,* one.

Check Your Progress SECTION 1.7

18. Define what is meant by the term evolution.

19. Evolution accounts for the millions of different species on the earth and their adaptation to its many and diverse habitats. Explain how this happens and cite examples in your answer.

20. Looking at the tree of life (figure 1.14), determine which kingdom or kingdoms humans are most closely related to.

21. Archaea are often found living in extreme conditions of heat, salt, and acidity, which are similar to those found in early earth. Speculate on the origin of life, especially as it relates to the archaea.

22. Compare the domain system with the five-kingdom system. Does the newer system change the basic idea of prokaryotes and eukaryotes? What is the third cell type?

CASE STUDY Part 2

Eventually, the studies in the marine environments of the earth led to the discovery of 20 million previously unknown genes and thousands of new species. Much of the information gathered will help us understand the ecology of communities, how the members interact, what kinds of nutrients they use or waste products they produce. Discoveries may lead to applications for tapping energy sources, bioremediation, climate change, soil fertility, and even new medicines and industrial products.

The technology featured in this Case Study is also focused on "mining" the microbial diversity of habitats such as soil, icebergs, hot springs, deep-ocean sediments, and even the human body. As information begins pouring in from many of these environments, it is clear that after 300 years of observing the microbial world, we have really just scratched the surface.

> **Quick Search**
> Go to "Exploring an Icy Invisible Realm in Antarctica" on YouTube.

For quite some time, microbiologists have known that the human body harbors nine bacterial cells for every one of our own cells. But now we are developing greater insight into the identity and function of these resident microbes. So far, genomic studies of various body habitats have revealed thousands of new kinds of microbes, most of them inhabiting the mouth and intestinal tract. The reason that these microbes had never been previously sampled or identified arises from our inability to grow them in the laboratory. The research now suggests that these microbes cannot be cultivated because they are so closely associated with humans that they have come to depend on us for survival. But these microbes are not passive passengers—they contribute to human health, immunity, development, and nutrition in significant ways.

■ Some microbiologists analyzing the results of these studies have proposed that we are likely to uncover totally new domains of organisms. Discuss this possibility based on the known domains and their evolutionary history.

These topics are further explored in chapters 7 and 13.

To conclude this Case Study, go to Perspectives on the Connect website.

 Chapter Summary with Key Terms

1.1 The Scope of Microbiology

A. **Microbiology** is the study of **bacteria, viruses, fungi, protozoa,** and **algae,** which are collectively called **microorganisms,** or microbes. In general, microorganisms are **microscopic** and, unlike **macroscopic** organisms, which are readily visible, they require magnification to be adequately observed or studied.

B. The science of microbiology is diverse and has branched out into many subsciences and applications. Important subsciences include **immunology, epidemiology,** and public health, food, dairy, aquatic, and industrial microbiology.

1.2 General Characteristics of Microorganisms and Their Roles in the Earth's Environments

Microbes live in most of the world's habitats and are indispensable for normal, balanced life on earth. They play many roles in the functioning of the earth's ecosystems.

A. Microbes are **ubiquitous.**

B. There are many kinds of relationships between microorganisms and humans; most are beneficial, but a few are harmful.

C. Microbes are involved in nutrient production and energy flow. Algae and certain bacteria trap the sun's energy to produce food through **photosynthesis.**

D. Other microbes are responsible for the breakdown and recycling of nutrients through **decomposition.** Microbes are essential to the maintenance of the air, soil, and water.

E. Microbial cells are either the small, relatively simple, nonnucleated **prokaryotic** variety or the larger, more complex **eukaryotic** type that contain a **nucleus** and **organelles.**

F. **Viruses** are microbes but not cells. They are smaller in size and infect their prokaryotic or eukaryotic hosts in order to reproduce themselves.

G. **Parasites** and **pathogens** are microorganisms that invade the bodies of **hosts,** often causing damage through infection and disease.

1.3 Human Use of Microorganisms

Microbes have been called upon to solve environmental, agricultural, and medical problems.

A. **Biotechnology** applies the power of microbes toward the manufacture of industrial products, foods, and drugs.

B. Microbes form the basis of **genetic engineering** and **recombinant DNA** technology, which alter genetic material to produce new products and modified life forms.

C. In **bioremediation,** microbes are used to clean up pollutants and wastes in natural environments.

1.4 Microbial Roles in Infectious Diseases

A. Nearly 2,000 microbes are **pathogens** that cause infectious diseases that result in high levels of mortality and morbidity (illness). Many infections are **emerging,** meaning that they are newly identified pathogens gaining greater prominence. Many older diseases are also reemerging.

B. Some diseases previously thought to be noninfectious may involve microbial infections (e.g., *Helicobacter,* causing gastric ulcers, and coxsackieviruses, causing diabetes).

C. An increasing number of individuals have weak immune systems, which makes them more susceptible to infectious diseases.

1.5 The Historical Foundations of Microbiology

A. Microbiology as a science is about 300 years old. Hundreds of contributors have provided discoveries and knowledge to enrich our understanding.

B. With his simple microscope, van Leeuwenhoek discovered organisms he called animalcules. As a consequence of his findings and the rise of the **scientific method,** the notion of **spontaneous generation,** or **abiogenesis,** was eventually abandoned for **biogenesis.** The scientific method develops rational **hypotheses** and **theories** that can be tested. Theories that withstand repeated scrutiny become **laws** in time.

C. Early microbiology blossomed with the conceptual developments of **sterilization, aseptic techniques,** and the **germ theory of disease.** Prominent scientists from this period include Robert Koch, Louis Pasteur, and Joseph Lister.

1.6 Taxonomy: Organizing, Classifying, and Naming Microorganisms

A. **Taxonomy** is a hierarchical scheme for the **classification, identification,** and **nomenclature** of organisms, which are grouped in categories called **taxa,** based on features ranging from general to specific.

B. Starting with the broadest category, the taxa are **domain, kingdom, phylum** (or **division**), **class, order, family, genus,** and **species.** Organisms are assigned **binomial scientific names** consisting of their genus and species names.

1.7 The Origin and Evolution of Microorganisms

A. All life on earth **evolved** from simple cells appearing in ancient oceans about 3.5 billion years ago.

B. Evolutionary change occurs when the environment places pressure on organisms that selects for survival of those with more adaptive inheritable traits.

C. All new species are the products of preexisting species, and their ancestry may be traced by examining fossils, morphology, physiology, genetics, and other scientific forms of investigation.

D. The records of **phylogeny** are displayed in the form of a tree of life that shows organisms' relatedness.

E. One classification scheme is based on a five-kingdom organization developed by Whittaker that includes:
 1. Kingdom Prokaryotae (Monera), containing eubacteria and archaea;
 2. Kingdom Protista, containing primitive unicellular microbes such as algae and protozoa;
 3. Kingdom Myceteae, containing the fungi;
 4. Kingdom Animalia, containing animals; and
 5. Kingdom Plantae, containing plants.

F. A newer classification scheme for living things is based on the genetic structure of their ribosomes. This Woese-Fox system recognizes three **Domains: Archaea,** simple prokaryotes that often live in extreme environments; **Bacteria,** typical prokaryotes; and **Eukarya,** all types of eukaryotic organisms.

Level I. Knowledge and Comprehension

These questions require a working knowledge of the concepts in the chapter and the ability to recall and understand the information you have studied.

? Multiple-Choice Questions

Select the correct answer from the answers provided. For questions with blanks, choose the combination of answers that most accurately completes the statement.

1. Which of the following is not considered a microorganism?
 a. archaeon
 b. bacterium
 c. protozoan
 d. mushroom

2. An area of microbiology that is concerned with the occurrence of disease in human populations is
 a. immunology
 b. parasitology
 c. epidemiology
 d. bioremediation

3. Which process involves the deliberate alteration of an organism's genetic material?
 a. bioremediation
 b. biotechnology
 c. decomposition
 d. recombinant DNA

4. A prominent difference between prokaryotic and eukaryotic cells is the
 a. larger size of prokaryotes
 b. lack of pigmentation in eukaryotes
 c. presence of a nucleus in eukaryotes
 d. presence of a cell wall in prokaryotes

5. Which of the following parts was absent from Leeuwenhoek's microscopes?
 a. focusing screw c. specimen holder
 b. lens d. condenser

6. Abiogenesis refers to the
 a. spontaneous generation of organisms from nonliving matter
 b. development of life forms from preexisting life forms
 c. development of aseptic technique
 d. germ theory of disease

7. A hypothesis can be defined as
 a. a belief based on knowledge
 b. knowledge based on belief
 c. a scientific explanation that is subject to testing
 d. a theory that has been thoroughly tested

8. Which early microbiologist was most responsible for developing standard microbiology laboratory techniques?
 a. Louis Pasteur c. Carl von Linné
 b. Robert Koch d. John Tyndall

9. Which scientist is most responsible for finally laying the theory of spontaneous generation to rest?
 a. Joseph Lister c. Francesco Redi
 b. Robert Koch d. Louis Pasteur

10. When a hypothesis has been thoroughly supported by long-term study and data, it is considered
 a. a law
 b. a speculation
 c. a theory
 d. proved

11. Which is the correct order of the taxonomic categories, going from most specific to most general?
 a. domain, kingdom, phylum, class, order, family, genus, species
 b. division, domain, kingdom, class, family, genus, species
 c. species, genus, family, order, class, phylum, kingdom, domain
 d. species, family, class, order, phylum, kingdom

12. By definition, organisms in the same _____ are more closely related than are those in the same _____.
 a. order, family
 b. class, phylum
 c. family, genus
 d. phylum, division

13. Which of the following are prokaryotic?
 a. bacteria
 b. archaea
 c. protists
 d. both a and b

14. Order the following items by size, using numbers: 1 = smallest and 8 = largest.
 _____ human immunodeficiency virus HIV
 _____ protozoan
 _____ rickettsia
 _____ protein
 _____ worm
 _____ coccus-shaped bacterium
 _____ spirochete
 _____ atom

15. Which of the following is not an emerging infectious disease?
 a. avian influenza
 b. Lyme disease
 c. common cold
 d. West Nile fever

16. How would you categorize a virus?
 a. as prokaryotic
 b. as eukaryotic
 c. as an archaeon
 d. none of these choices
 Explain your choice for question 16.

Case Study Review

1. What is plankton?
 a. nutrients dissolved in seawater
 b. organic matter in the ocean
 c. organisms living in the ocean sediments
 d. organisms free-floating in the aquatic environment

2. What aspect of the plankton was actually analyzed by the marine researchers to arrive at their conclusions?
 a. the total number of cells
 b. the types of eukaryotes
 c. the genetic material of cells
 d. the types of viruses

3. In what ways is biological "dark matter" similar to the dark matter of the universe?

Writing Challenge

For each question, compose a one- or two-paragraph answer that includes the factual information needed to completely address the question. Check Your Progress questions can also be used for writing-challenge exercises.

1. What does it mean to say microbes are ubiquitous?

2. What is meant by diversity with respect to organisms?

3. What events, discoveries, or inventions were probably the most significant in the development of microbiology and why?

4. Explain how microbiologists use the scientific method to develop theories and explanations for microbial phenomena.

5. Explain how microbes are classified into groups according to evolutionary relationships, provided with standard scientific names, and identified by specific characteristics.

6. a. What are some of the sources for "new" infectious diseases?
 b. Comment on the sensational ways that some tabloid media portray the dangers of infectious diseases.

Concept Mapping

An Introduction to Concept Mapping found at http://www.mhhe.com/talaro9 provides guidance for working with concept maps.

1. Supply your own linking words or phrases in this concept map, and provide the missing concepts in the empty boxes.

Level II. Application, Analysis, Evaluation, and Synthesis

These problems go beyond just restating facts and require higher levels of understanding and an ability to interpret, problem solve, transfer knowledge to new situations, create models, and predict outcomes.

Critical Thinking

Critical thinking is the ability to reason and solve problems using facts and concepts. These questions can be approached from a number of angles, and in most cases, they do not have a single correct answer.

1. What do you suppose the world would be like if there were cures for all infectious diseases and a means to destroy all microbes? What characteristics of microbes would prevent this from happening?

2. How would you describe the types of scientific reasoning in the various experiments for supporting and denying spontaneous generation?

3. Give the technical name of a microbiologist who researches or works with protozoa in a termite's gut, bacteria that live in volcanoes, the tapeworms of dogs, molds that cause food poisoning, emerging viral diseases, the metabolism of bacteria that live in acid swamps, the classification of *Paramecium*.

4. Name the six most common infectious agents on earth and the four microbes that cause the highest rates of cancer.

5. What does it mean to say that the human body is 90% prokaryotic?

6. What is the ultimate way that microbes will, as Pasteur said, have the "last word"?

7. Can you develop a scientific hypothesis and means of testing the cause of stomach ulcers? (Are they caused by an infection? By too much acid? By a genetic disorder?)

8. Construct the scientific name of a newly discovered species of bacterium using your name, a pet's name, a place, or a unique characteristic. Be sure to use proper notation and endings.

Visual Challenge

Use the following pattern to construct an outline of the scientific reasoning that was involved in developing the germ theory of disease similar to figure 1.10.

Observations

↓

Hypothesis

↓

Testing the Hypothesis

↓

Establishment of Theory

↓

Accepted Principle

CHAPTER **2** The Chemistry of Biology

A highly magnified view of a 4-billion-year-old Martian meteorite uncovers tiny rods that resemble earthly prokaryotes.

A view of Mars' Mount Sharp reveals stratified rock layers reminiscent of those on earth that could hold signs of ancient organisms.

CASE STUDY Part 1 Following the Water and Carbon on Mars

Throughout history, humans have gazed at the night sky and pondered about the possible existence of other life forms in the universe. Telescopes have allowed closer glimpses of celestial bodies, but they have never been able to show the details needed to verify the presence of **life.** As technology advanced in the 1970s, the National Aeronautics and Space Administration **(NASA)** began a series of voyages to directly explore our own solar system. Astronomers knew from sophisticated **chemical** and **physical** analyses that most of the planets in our solar system had far too extreme conditions to **support life** as we know it, with the possible exception of Mars. Mars has a profile somewhat similar to earth and is one of the closer planets, orbiting an average of 225 million miles away from earth. It is known to be very dry and cold (the temperature range is 80°F to –225°F), but there was a reasonable possibility that at least **simple organisms** could have developed there.

Starting in 1976, a series of space explorations was launched to find evidence that could point to signs of life on Mars. From these studies sprang a new science—**astrobiology**—which applies principles from biology, chemistry, and geology to investigate the possibilities of extraterrestrial life. One conclusion of NASA scientists that has driven many of their searches is that any life on Mars, if it has existed at all, has been microbial.

Among the significant questions being tackled by astrobiologists are: what are the basic requirements of life, and what would signs of

> "Any life on Mars, if it has existed at all, has been microbial."

life look like? Like so many ideas of a biological nature, they turned to **chemistry** for answers. One of their assumptions was that, because some of the same chemical substances on earth would likely exist on Mars, then Martian life forms would be expected to have a similar profile at least chemically. Attention was turned to substances that are part of all life on earth: mainly **water** and **carbon-based chemicals.**

The main goals of one of the first Mars space vehicles, *Viking Explorer*, were to sample for **water, carbon dioxide, organic compounds,** and to **culture microbes** from Martian soil. The results were mostly negative or inconclusive, except for one—that the atmosphere contained high levels of carbon dioxide gas. Not surprisingly, the samples yielded no Martian microbes. A discovery in 1996 of tiny rod-shaped objects in a 4-billion-year-old **Martian meteorite** from the Antarctic has been, and continues to be, the subject of much scientific scrutiny. This tantalizing image bears a resemblance to prokaryotic cells, but there is still a controversy about whether these are **ancient microbes** or geologic artifacts.

- ▶ *What chemical properties of water makes it essential for living processes?*
- ▶ *What characteristics of carbon make it the central building block of life?*

To continue the Case Study, go to page 54.

30 **Chapter 2** The Chemistry of Biology

2.1 Atoms: Fundamental Building Blocks of All Matter in the Universe

 Expected Learning Outcomes

1. Describe the properties of atoms and identify the relationships of the particles that they contain.
2. Characterize elements and their isotopes.
3. Explain the differences between atomic number, mass number, and atomic weight.
4. List the major elements that are associated with life.
5. Describe electron orbitals and energy shells and how they are filled.

The universe is composed of an infinite variety of substances existing in gaseous, liquid, and solid states. All such tangible materials that occupy space and have mass are called **matter.** The organization of matter—whether air, rocks, or bacteria—begins with individual building blocks called atoms. An **atom** is defined as a tiny particle that cannot be subdivided into smaller substances without losing its properties. Even in a science dealing with very small things, an atom's minute size is striking; for example, an oxygen atom is only 0.0000000013 mm (0.0013 nm) in diameter, and 1 million of them in a cluster would barely be visible to the naked eye.

Although scientists have not directly observed the detailed structure of an atom, the exact composition of atoms has been well established by extensive physical analysis using sophisticated instruments. In general, an atom derives its properties from a combination of subatomic particles called **protons** (p^+), which are positively charged; **neutrons** (n^0), which have no charge (are neutral); and **electrons** (e^-), which are negatively charged. The relatively larger protons and neutrons make up a central core, or atomic **nucleus,**[1] that is surrounded by 1 or more electrons (**figure 2.1**). The nucleus makes up the larger mass (weight) of the atom, whereas the electron region, sometimes called the "electron cloud," accounts for the greater volume. To get a perspective on proportions, consider this: If an atom were the size of a football stadium, the nucleus would be about the size of a marble! The stability of atomic structure is largely maintained by

- the mutual attraction of the protons and electrons (opposite charges attract each other), and
- the exact balance of proton number and electron number, which causes the opposing charges to cancel each other out.

At least in theory, then, isolated intact atoms do not carry a charge.

Different Types of Atoms: Elements and Their Properties

All atoms share the same fundamental structure. All protons are identical, all neutrons are identical, and all electrons are identical. But when these subatomic particles come together in specific, varied

1. Be careful not to confuse the nucleus of an atom with the nucleus of a cell.

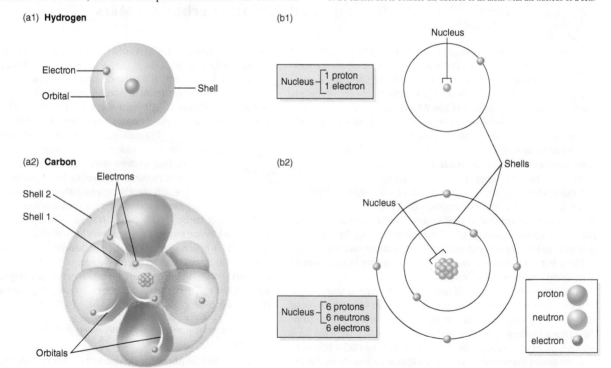

Figure 2.1 Models of atomic structure. Three-dimensional models of hydrogen and carbon that approximate their actual structure. The atomic nucleus is surrounded by electrons that travel within orbitals and occur in energy levels called shells. **(a1)** Hydrogen has just one orbital and one shell. **(a2)** Carbon has four orbitals and two shells. The outermost orbitals are most accurately portrayed as sets of lobe-shaped pairs rather than circles or spheres. **(b1, 2)** Simple models of hydrogen and carbon are not strictly accurate representations of atomic structure but are designed as a quick reference to the numbers and arrangements of shells and electrons, and the numbers of protons and neutrons in the nucleus. (Not to accurate scale.)

combinations, unique types of atoms called **elements** result. Each element is a pure substance that has a characteristic atomic structure and predictable chemical behavior. To date, 118 elements have been described. Ninety-four of them are naturally occurring, and the rest were artificially produced by manipulating the particles in the nucleus. By convention, an element is assigned a distinctive name with an abbreviated shorthand symbol. The elements essential to life, often called bioelements, are outlined in **table 2.1.** In some form or another, they make up the matter of all earth's organisms and viruses. Microorganisms have a particularly important relationship with most of these elements. This is due to the roles microbes play in the cycling processes that maintain the elements in forms usable by other organisms.

The vast majority of life forms require only about 20 of the 94 naturally occurring elements. The other 70 or so elements are not critical to life, and a number of them, such as arsenic and uranium, can be highly toxic to cells. As we will see in chapter 7, microbes have some incredible "survival skills" that make it possible to occupy extreme habitats containing large amounts of these elements. The word that describes such a microbe is *extremophile.** For additional information on the functions of elements and the involvement of microbes in their recycling, look ahead to table 7.1.

Quick Search
Find Carl Sagan's engaging overview of "The Chemical Elements" on YouTube.

The Major Elements of Life and Their Primary Characteristics

The unique properties of each element result from the numbers of protons, neutrons, and electrons it contains, and each element can be identified by certain physical measurements.

Each element is assigned an **atomic number (AN)** based on the number of protons it has. The atomic number is a valuable measurement because an element's proton number does not vary, and knowing it automatically tells you the usual number of electrons (recall that a neutral atom has an equal number of protons and electrons). Another useful measurement is the **mass number (MN),** equal to the number of protons and neutrons. If one knows the mass number and the atomic number, it is possible to determine the numbers of neutrons by subtraction. Hydrogen is a unique element because its common form has only one proton, one electron, and no neutron, making it the only element with the same atomic and mass number.

Isotopes are variant forms of the same element that differ in the number of neutrons and thus have different mass numbers. These multiple forms occur naturally in certain proportions. Carbon, for example, exists primarily as carbon 12 with 6 neutrons (MN = 12); but a small amount (about 1%) consists of carbon 13 with 7 neutrons and carbon 14 with 8 neutrons. Although isotopes have virtually the same chemical properties, some of them have unstable nuclei that spontaneously release energy in the form of radiation. Such *radioactive isotopes* play a role in a number of research and medical applications. Because they emit detectable energy, they can be used to trace the position of key atoms or molecules in chemical reactions, they are tools in diagnosis and treatment, and they are even applied in sterilization procedures (see chapter 11).

* An *extremophile* (ex-tree'-moh-fyl") is a microbe that can live in very severe conditions that would be harmful to other organisms.

TABLE 2.1	Chemical Characteristics of Major Elements of Life			
Element	Atomic Symbol*	Atomic Number	Atomic Mass**	Ionized Forms (See page 37).
Calcium	Ca	20	40.08	Ca^{2+}
Carbon	C	6	12.01	CO_3^{2-}
Carbon˙	C-14	6	14.0	
Chlorine	Cl	17	35.45	Cl^-
Cobalt	Co	27	58.93	Co^{2+}, Co^{3+}
Copper	Cu	29	63.54	Cu^+, Cu^{2+}
Hydrogen	H	1	1.00	H^+
Hydrogen˙	H-3	1	3.01	
Iodine	I	53	126.9	I^-
Iodine˙	I-131	53	131.0	
Iron	Fe	26	55.84	Fe^{2+}, Fe^{3+}
Magnesium	Mg	12	24.30	Mg^{2+}
Manganese	Mn	25	54.93	Mn^{2+}, Mn^{3+}
Nitrogen	N	7	14.0	NO_3^- (nitrate)
Oxygen	O	8	15.99	
Phosphorus	P	15	31.97	PO_4^{3-} (phosphate)
Phosphorus˙	P-32	15	32	
Potassium	K	19	39.10	K^+
Sodium	Na	11	22.99	Na^+
Sulfur	S	16	32.06	SO_4^{-2} (sulfate)
Zinc	Zn	30	65.38	Zn^{2+}

*Based on the Latin name of the element. The first letter is always capitalized; if there is a second letter, it is always lowercased.

**The atomic mass or weight is equal to the average mass number for the isotopes of that element.

˙An isotope of the element.

Clarifying Mass, Weight, and Related Terms

Mass refers to the quantity of matter that an atomic particle contains. The proton and neutron have almost exactly the same mass, which is about 1.66×10^{-24} grams, a unit of measurement known as a Dalton (Da) or unified atomic mass unit (U). All elements can be measured in these units. The terms *mass* and *weight* are often used interchangeably in biology, even though they apply to two different but related aspects of matter. Weight is a measurement of the gravitational pull on the mass of a particle, atom, or object. Consequently, it is possible for something with the same mass to have different weights. For example, an astronaut on the earth (normal gravity) would weigh more than the same astronaut on the moon (weak gravity). Atomic weight has been the traditional usage for biologists, because most chemical reactions and biological activities occur within the normal gravitational conditions on earth. This permits use of atomic weight as a standard of comparison. You will also see the terms *formula weight* and *molecular weight* used interchangeably, and they are indeed synonyms. They both mean the sum of atomic weights of all atoms in a molecule.

Figure 2.2 Examples of biologically important atoms. Featured element boxes contain information on symbol, atomic number, atomic mass, and electron shell patterns. Simple models show how the shells are filled by electrons as the atomic numbers increase. Chemists depict elements in shorthand form (red Lewis structures) that indicate only the valence electrons, because these are the electrons involved in chemical bonds. In the background is a partial display of the periodic table of elements showing the position of these elements in the periodic table.

Another important measurement of an element is its **atomic mass** or **weight.** This is given as the average mass numbers of all isotopic forms (table 2.1). You will notice that this number may not come out even, because most elements have several isotopes and differing proportions of them.

Electron Orbitals and Shells

The structure of an atom can be envisioned as a central nucleus surrounded by a cloud of electrons that constantly spin within confined pathways surrounding the nucleus at exceedingly high speed (see figure 2.1). The pathways taken by electrons are called **orbitals,** which are not actual objects or exact locations but represent volumes of three-dimensional space in which an electron is likely to be found. The position of an electron at any one instant is dictated by its energy level or **shell,** proceeding from the lower-level energy electrons nearest the nucleus to the higher-energy electrons in the outer shells.

Electrons fill the orbitals and shells in *pairs,* starting with the shell nearest the nucleus:

- The first shell contains one orbital and a maximum of 2 electrons.
- The second shell has four orbitals and up to 8 electrons.
- The third shell with nine orbitals can hold up to 18 electrons.
- The fourth shell with 16 orbitals contains up to 32 electrons.

The number of orbitals and shells and how completely they are filled depend on the numbers of electrons, so that each element will have a unique pattern. For example:

- Helium (AN = 2) has only a filled first shell of 2 electrons.
- Oxygen (AN = 8) has a filled first shell and a partially filled second shell of 6 electrons.
- Magnesium (AN = 12) has a filled first shell, a filled second one, and a third shell that has only one orbital, so is nearly empty.

As we will see, the chemical properties of an element are controlled mainly by the distribution of electrons in the outermost shell. **Figure 2.2** presents various simplified models of atomic structure and electron maps, superimposed over a partial display of the periodic table of elements.

 Check Your Progress SECTION 2.1

1. How are the concepts of an atom and an element related? What causes elements to differ?
2. What are subatomic particles and how do they contribute to the structure and character of atoms?
3. How are mass number and atomic number derived? What is the atomic mass or weight?
4. What is distinctive about isotopes of elements, and why are they important?
5. Why is an isolated atom neutral?
6. Describe the concept of the atomic nucleus, electron orbitals, and shells.

2.2 Bonds and Molecules

 Expected Learning Outcomes

6. Explain how elements make chemical bonds to form molecules and compounds.
7. State the relationship among an atom, molecule, and compound.
8. Identify the differences between covalent, ionic, and hydrogen bonds.
9. Summarize the concepts of valence, polarity, and diatomic elements.
10. Describe ionization and distinguish between anions and cations.
11. Compare oxidation and reduction and their effects.

Most elements do not exist naturally in pure, uncombined form but are bound together as molecules and compounds. A **molecule*** is a distinct chemical substance that results from the combination of two or more atoms. Molecules come in a great variety. A few of them such as oxygen (O_2) consist of the same element (see the Nature of Diatomic Elements on page 34). But most molecules, for example carbon dioxide (CO_2) and water (H_2O), contain two or more different elements and are more appropriately termed **compounds.** So compounds are one major type of molecule. Other examples of compounds are biological molecules such as proteins, sugars, and fats.

When atoms bind together in molecules, they lose the properties of the atom and take on the properties of the combined substance. In the same way that an atom has an atomic weight, a molecule has a **formula mass** or **molecular weight**[2] (MW), which is calculated from the sum of all of the atomic masses of the atoms it contains.

Chemical bonds of molecules are created when two or more atoms share, donate (lose), or accept (gain) electrons **(figure 2.3).** This capacity for making bonds, termed **valence,*** is determined by the number of electrons that an atom has to lose or share with other atoms during bond formation. The valence electrons determine the degree of reactivity and the types of bonds an element can make. Elements with a filled outer orbital are relatively nonreactive because they have no extra electrons to share with or donate to other atoms. For example, helium has one filled shell, with no tendency either to give up electrons or to take them from other elements, making it a stable, inert (nonreactive) gas. Elements with partially filled outer orbitals are less stable and are more apt to form some sort of bond.

Many chemical reactions are based on the tendency of atoms with unfilled outer shells to gain greater stability by achieving, or at least approximating, a filled outer shell. For example, an atom such as oxygen that can accept two additional electrons will bond readily with atoms (such as hydrogen) that can share or donate electrons. We explore some additional examples of the basic types of bonding in the following section.

In addition to reactivity, the number of electrons in the outer shell also dictates the number of chemical bonds an atom can make. For instance, hydrogen can bind with one other atom, oxygen can bind with up to two other atoms, and carbon can bind with four.

* *valence* (vay'-lents) L. *valentia,* strength. The binding qualities of an atom dictated by the number of electrons in its outermost shell.

* *molecule* (mol'-ih-kyool) L. *molecula,* little mass.
2. Biologists prefer to use this term.

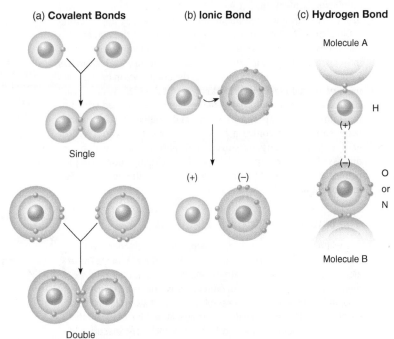

Figure 2.3 General representation of three types of bonding. (a) Covalent bonds, both single and double. **(b)** Ionic bond. **(c)** Hydrogen bond. Note that hydrogen bonds are represented in models and formulas by dotted lines, as shown in (c).

Figure 2.4 Examples of molecules with covalent bonding. (a) A hydrogen molecule is formed when two hydrogen atoms share their electrons and form a single bond. **(b)** In a double bond, the outer orbitals of two oxygen atoms overlap and permit the sharing of 4 electrons (one pair from each) and the saturation of the outer orbital for both. **(c)** Simple, three-dimensional, and working models of methane. Note that carbon has 4 electrons to share and hydrogens each have one thereby completing the shells for all atoms in the compound and creating 4 single bonds. Note that (a) and (b) also show the formation of diatomic molecules.

Covalent Bonds: Molecules with Shared Electrons

Covalent (cooperative valence) **bonds** form between atoms with valences that suit them to sharing electrons rather than to donating or receiving them. A simple example is hydrogen gas (H_2), which consists of two hydrogen atoms. A hydrogen atom has only a single electron, but when two of them combine, each will bring its electron to orbit about both nuclei, thereby approaching a filled orbital (2 electrons) for both atoms and thus creating a single covalent bond (**figure 2.4a**). Covalent bonding also occurs in oxygen gas (O_2), but with a difference. Because each atom has 2 electrons to share in this molecule, the combination creates two pairs of shared electrons, also known as a double covalent bond (**figure 2.4b**). The majority of the molecules associated with living things are composed of single and double covalent bonds between the most common biological elements (carbon, hydrogen, oxygen, nitrogen, sulfur, and phosphorus), which are discussed in more depth in chapter 7. A slightly more complex pattern of covalent bonding is shown for methane gas (CH_4) in **figure 2.4c**.

The Nature of Diatomic Elements

You will notice that hydrogen, oxygen, nitrogen, chlorine, and iodine are often shown in notation with a 2 subscript—H_2 or O_2. These elements are *diatomic* (two atoms), meaning that in their pure elemental state, they exist in pairs, rather than as a single atom. In every case, these elements are more stable as a pair of atoms joined by a covalent bond (a molecule) than as a single atom. The reason for this phenomenon can be explained by their valences. The electrons in the outer shell are configured so as to complete a full outer shell for both atoms when they bind. You can see this for yourself by observing figure 2.4. It is interesting that most of the diatomic elements are gases.

Polarity in Molecules

When atoms of different electronegativity[3] form covalent bonds, the electrons will not be shared equally and are pulled more toward one atom than another. This force causes one end of a molecule to assume a partial negative charge and the other end to assume a partial positive charge. A molecule with such an unequal distribution of charges is termed **polar** and shows polarity—meaning it has positive and negative poles.

Observe the water molecule shown in **figure 2.5** and note that, because the oxygen atom is larger and has more protons than the hydrogen atoms, it will have a stronger attraction for the shared electrons than the hydrogen atoms. Because the electrons will spend more time near the oxygen, it will express a partial negative charge. The electrons are less attracted to the hydrogen orbitals, causing the positive charge of the hydrogen's single proton to

3. Electronegativity—the ability of an atom or molecule to attract electrons.

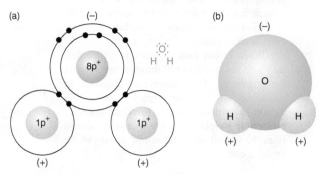

Figure 2.5 Polar molecule. (a) A simple model and **(b)** a three-dimensional model of a water molecule indicate the polarity, or unequal distribution, of electrical charge, which is caused by the pull of the shared electrons toward the oxygen side of the molecule.

dominate. The polar nature of water plays an extensive role in a number of biological reactions, which are discussed later. Polarity is a significant property of many large molecules in living systems and greatly influences both their reactivity and their structure.

When covalent bonds are formed between atoms that have the same or similar electronegativity, the electrons are shared equally between the two atoms. Because of this balanced distribution, no part of the molecule has a greater attraction for the electrons. This sort of electrically neutral molecule is termed **nonpolar.** Examples of nonpolar molecules are oxygen, methane (see figure 2.4), and lipids (see figure 2.18).

Ionic Bonds: Electron Transfer Among Atoms

In reactions that form **ionic bonds,** electrons are transferred completely from one atom to another and are not shared. These reactions invariably occur between atoms with complementary valences. This means that one atom has an unfilled outer shell that can readily accept electrons and the other atom has an unfilled outer shell that will readily give up electrons. A striking example is the reaction that occurs between sodium (Na) and chlorine (Cl). Elemental sodium is a soft, lustrous metal so reactive that it can burn flesh, and molecular chlorine is a very poisonous yellow gas. But when the two are combined, they form sodium chloride[4] (NaCl)—the familiar nontoxic table salt—a compound with properties quite different from either parent element (**figure 2.6).**

How does this transformation occur? Sodium has 11 electrons (2 in shell one, 8 in shell two, and only 1 in shell three), so it is 7 short of having a complete outer shell. Chlorine has 17 electrons (2 in shell one, 8 in shell two, and 7 in shell three), making it 1 short of a complete outer shell. When these two atoms come together, the sodium atom will readily donate its single valence electron and the chlorine atom will avidly receive it. The reaction is slightly more involved than a single sodium atom's combining with a single chloride atom, but the details do not negate the fundamental reaction as described here. The outcome of this reaction is a solid crystal complex that interlinks millions of sodium and chloride atoms (**figure 2.6c, d).** The binding of Na^+ and Cl^- exists in three dimensions. Each Na is surrounded by 6 Cls and vice versa. Their charges balance out, and no single molecule of NaCl is present.

Ionization: Formation of Charged Particles

Compounds with intact ionic bonds are electrically neutral, but they can produce charged particles when dissolved in a liquid called a solvent. This phenomenon, called **ionization,** occurs when the ionic bond is broken and the atoms dissociate (separate) into unattached, charged particles called **ions** (figure 2.7). To illustrate what imparts a charge to ions, let us look again at the reaction between sodium and chlorine. When a sodium atom reacts with chlorine and loses 1 electron, the sodium is left with 1 more proton than electrons. This imbalance produces a positively charged sodium ion (Na^+). Chlorine, on the other hand, has gained 1 electron and now has 1 more electron than protons, producing a negatively charged

(a)

Na Cl:

Sodium atom (Na) Chlorine atom (Cl)

(b) :Na:Cl: $\longrightarrow$ [Na]$^+$ [Cl]$^-$

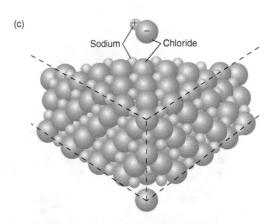

(c)

Sodium ⟨+⟩ ⟨−⟩ Chloride

(d)

Figure 2.6 Ionic bonding between sodium and chlorine.
(a) During the reaction, sodium loses its single outer orbital electron to chlorine, thereby filling chlorine's outer shell. (b) Simple model of ionic bonding. (c) Sodium and chloride ions form large molecules, or crystals, in which the two atoms alternate in a definite, regular, geometric pattern. (d) Note the cubic nature of NaCl crystals at the macroscopic level.

ion (Cl^-). Positively charged ions are termed **cations,**[*] and negatively charged ions are termed **anions.**[*] (A good mnemonic device is to think of the *t* in cation as a plus (+) sign and the first *n* in anion as a negative (−) sign.) Substances such as salts, acids, and bases that release ions when dissolved in water are termed **electrolytes** because their charges enable them to conduct an electrical current.

[*] *cation* (kat′-eye-on) A positively charged ion that migrates toward the negative pole, or cathode, of an electrical field.
[*] *anion* (an′-eye-on) A negatively charged ion that migrates toward the positive pole, or anode.

4. In general, when a salt is formed, the ending of the name of the negatively charged ion is changed to *-ide.*

Figure 2.8 **Hydrogen bonding in water.** Because of the polarity of water molecules, the negatively charged oxygen end of one water molecule is weakly attracted to the positively charged hydrogen end of an adjacent water molecule.

Figure 2.7 **Ionization.** When NaCl in the crystalline form is added to water, the ions are released from the crystal as separate charged particles (cations and anions) into solution. (See also figure 2.12.) In this solution, Cl⁻ ions are attracted to the hydrogen component of water, and Na⁺ ions are attracted to the oxygen (box).

Owing to the general rule that particles of like charge repel each other and those of opposite charge attract each other, we can expect ions to interact electrostatically with other ions and polar molecules. Such interactions are important in many cellular chemical reactions, in the formation of solutions, and in the reactions microorganisms have with dyes.

Hydrogen Bonding

Some types of bonding do not involve sharing, losing, or gaining electrons but instead are due to attractive forces between nearby molecules or atoms. One such bond is a **hydrogen bond,** a weak electrostatic force that forms between a hydrogen covalently bonded to one molecule and an oxygen or nitrogen atom on the same molecule or on a different molecule. This phenomenon occurs because a hydrogen atom in a covalent bond tends to be positively charged. Thus, it can attract a nearby negatively charged atom and form an easily disrupted bridge with it. This type of bonding is usually represented in molecular models with a dotted line. A simple example of hydrogen bonding occurs between water molecules **(figure 2.8).** More extensive hydrogen bonding is partly responsible for the structure and stability of proteins and nucleic acids, as you will see later on.

Weak molecular interactions similar to hydrogen bonds that play major roles in the shape and function of biological molecules are **van der Waals forces.** The basis for these interactions is also an attraction of two regions on atoms or molecules that are opposite in charge, but van der Waals forces can occur between nearly any types of molecules and not just those containing hydrogen, oxygen, and nitrogen. These forces come into play whenever the electrons in molecules move about their orbits and become unevenly distributed. This unevenness leads to short-term "sticky spots" in the molecule—some positively charged and others negatively charged. When such regions are located close together, their opposite charges pull them together. These forces can hold even large molecules together because of the cumulative effects of numerous sites of interaction. They not only function between molecules but may occur within different regions of the same large molecule. Van der Waals forces are a significant factor in protein folding and stability (see figure 2.23, steps 3 and 4).

Electron Transfer and Oxidation-Reduction Reactions

The metabolic work of cells, such as synthesis, movement, and digestion, revolves around energy exchanges and transfers. The management of energy in cells is almost exclusively dependent on chemical rather than physical reactions because most cells are far too delicate to operate with heat, radiation, and other more potent forms of energy. The outer-shell electrons are readily portable and easily manipulated sources of energy. It is in fact the movement of electrons from molecule to molecule that accounts for most energy exchanges in cells. Fundamentally, then, cells must have a supply of atoms that can gain or lose electrons if they are to carry out life processes.

The phenomenon in which electrons are transferred from one atom or molecule to another is termed an **oxidation-reduction** (shortened to **redox**) **reaction.** The term *oxidation* was originally adopted for reactions involving the addition of oxygen, but this is no longer the case. In current usage, *oxidation* includes any reaction that causes an atom to lose electrons. Because all redox reactions occur in pairs, it follows that *reduction* is the result of a

different atom gaining these same electrons. Keep in mind that because electrons are being added during reduction, the atom that receives them will become more negative; and that is the meaning of *reduction* in this context. It does not imply that an atom is getting smaller. In fact, reduction often results in a greater complexity of the molecule.

To analyze the phenomenon, let us again review the production of NaCl but from a different standpoint. When these two atoms, called the redox pair, react to form sodium chloride, a sodium atom gives up an electron to a chlorine atom. During this reaction, sodium is oxidized because it loses an electron, and chlorine is reduced because it gains an electron (**figure 2.9**). With this system, an atom such as sodium that can donate electrons and thereby reduce another atom is a **reducing agent.** An atom that can receive extra electrons and thereby oxidize another molecule is an **oxidizing agent.** You may find this concept easier to keep straight if you think of redox agents as partners: The reducing partner gives its electrons away and is oxidized; the oxidizing partner receives the electrons and is reduced.[5]

Redox reactions are essential to many of the biochemical processes discussed in chapter 8. In cellular metabolism, electrons are frequently transferred from one molecule to another as described here. In other reactions, oxidation and reduction occur with the transfer of a hydrogen atom (a proton and an electron) from one compound to another.

Figure 2.9 **Simplified diagram of the exchange of electrons during an oxidation-reduction reaction.** Numbers indicate the total electrons in that shell.

Reducing agent can donate an electron.

Oxidizing agent can accept an electron.

Oxidized cation donated an electron and converted to a positively charged ion.

Reduced anion accepted the electron and converted to a negatively charged ion.

 Check Your Progress SECTION 2.2

7. Explain how the concepts of molecules and compounds are related.
8. Distinguish between the general reactions in covalent, ionic, and hydrogen bonds.
9. Which kinds of elements tend to make covalent bonds?
10. Distinguish between a single and a double bond.
11. Define polarity and explain what causes it.
12. Which kinds of elements tend to make ionic bonds?
13. Differentiate between an anion and a cation, using examples.
14. Differentiate between oxidation and reduction, and between an oxidizing agent and a reducing agent, using examples.

2.3 Chemical Reactions, Solutions, and pH

Expected Learning Outcomes

12. Classify different forms of chemical shorthand and types of reactions.

13. Explain solutes, solvents, and hydration.

14. Differentiate between hydrophilic and hydrophobic.

15. Describe the pH scale and how it was derived; define acid, base, and neutral levels.

5. A mnemonic device to keep track of this is *LEO* says *GER: L*ose *E*lectrons *O*xidized; *G*ain *E*lectrons *R*educed.

Formulas, Models, and Equations

The atomic content of molecules can be represented by a few convenient formulas. We have already been using the molecular formula, which concisely gives the atomic symbols and the number of the atoms involved in subscripts (CO_2, H_2O). More complex molecules such as glucose ($C_6H_{12}O_6$) can also be symbolized this way, but this formula is not unique, because fructose and galactose also share it. Molecular formulas are useful, but they only summarize the atoms in a compound; they do not show the position of bonds between atoms. For this purpose, chemists use structural formulas illustrating the relationships of the atoms and the number and types of bonds (**figure 2.10**). Other structural models present the three-dimensional appearance of a molecule, illustrating the orientation of atoms (differentiated by color codes) and the molecule's overall shape (**figure 2.11**). Many complex molecules such as proteins are now represented by computer-generated images (see figure 2.23, step 4).

Molecules, including those in cells, are constantly involved in **chemical reactions,** leading to changes in the composition of the matter they contain. These changes generally involve the breaking and making of bonds and the rearrangement of atoms. The chemical substances that start a reaction and that are changed by the reaction are called the **reactants.** The substances that result from the reaction are called the **products.** Keep in mind that all of the matter in any reaction is retained in some form, and the same types and numbers of atoms going into the reaction will be present in the products. Chemists and biologists use shorthand to summarize the content of a reaction by means of a **chemical equation.** In an equation, the reactant(s) are on the left of an arrow and the product(s) on the right. The number of atoms of each element must be balanced on either side of the arrow. Note that the numbers of reactants and products are indicated by a coefficient in front of the formula (no coefficient means one). We have already reviewed the reaction with sodium and chloride, which would be shown with this equation:

$$2Na + Cl_2 \rightarrow 2NaCl$$

Most equations do not give the details or even exact order of the reaction but are meant to keep the expression a simple overview of the process being shown. Some of the common reactions in organisms are syntheses, decompositions, and exchanges.

Figure 2.10 Comparison of molecular and structural formulas. (a) Molecular formulas provide a brief summary of the elements in a compound. **(b1)** Structural formulas clarify the exact relationships of the atoms in the molecule, depicting single bonds by a single line and double bonds by two lines. **(b2)** In structural formulas of organic compounds, cyclic or ringed compounds may be completely labeled, or **(b3)** they may be presented in a shorthand form in which carbons are assumed to be at the angles and attached to hydrogens. See figure 2.16 for structural formulas of three sugars with the same molecular formula, $C_6H_{12}O_6$.

Figure 2.11 Three-dimensional, or space-filling, models of (a) water, (b) carbon dioxide, and (c) glucose. The red atoms are oxygen, the white ones hydrogen, and the black ones carbon.

In a **synthesis* reaction,** the reactants bond together in a manner that produces an entirely new molecule (reactant A plus reactant B yields product AB). An example is the production of sulfur dioxide, a by-product of burning sulfur fuels and an important component of smog:

$$S + O_2 \rightarrow SO_2$$

Some synthesis reactions are not such simple combinations. When water is synthesized, for example, the reaction does not really involve one oxygen atom combining with two hydrogen atoms, because elemental oxygen exists as O_2 and elemental hydrogen exists as H_2. A more accurate equation for this reaction is:

$$2H_2 + O_2 \rightarrow 2H_2O$$

In **decomposition reactions,** the bonds on a single reactant molecule are permanently broken to release two or more product molecules. A simple example can be shown for the common chemical hydrogen peroxide:

$$2H_2O_2 \rightarrow 2H_2O + O_2$$

* *synthesis* (sin'-thuh-sis) Gr. *synthesis*, putting together.

During **exchange reactions,** the reactants trade portions between each other and release products that are combinations of the two.

$$AB + XY \rightleftharpoons AY + XB$$

This type of reaction occurs between an acid and a base when they react to form water and a salt:

$$HCl + NaOH \rightarrow NaCl + H_2O$$

The reactions in biological systems can be reversible, meaning that reactants and products can be converted back and forth. These reversible reactions are symbolized with a double arrow, each pointing in opposite directions, as in the exchange reaction shown earlier. Whether a reaction is reversible depends on the proportions of these compounds, the difference in energy state of the reactants and products, and the presence of **catalysts** (substances that increase the rate of a reaction). Additional reactants coming from another reaction can also be indicated by arrows that enter or leave at the main arrow:

$$X + Y \longrightarrow XYD$$

Solutions: Homogeneous Mixtures of Molecules

A **solution** is a mixture of one or more substances called **solutes** uniformly dispersed in a dissolving medium called a **solvent.** An important characteristic of a solution is that the solute cannot be separated by filtration or ordinary settling. The solute can be gaseous, liquid, or solid, and the solvent is usually a liquid. Examples of solutions are salt or sugar dissolved in water and iodine dissolved

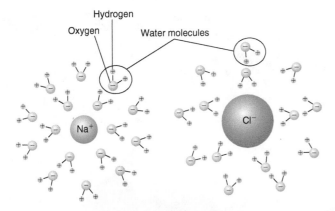

Hydrogen

Oxygen Water molecules

Na$^+$

Cl$^-$

Figure 2.12 **Hydration spheres formed around ions in solution.** In this example, a sodium cation attracts the negatively charged region of water molecules, and a chloride anion attracts the positively charged region of water molecules. In both cases, the ions become surrounded by spherical layers of specific numbers and arrangements of water molecules.

in alcohol. In general, a solvent will dissolve a solute only if it has similar electrical characteristics as indicated by the rule of solubility, expressed simply as "like dissolves like." For example, water is a polar molecule and will readily dissolve an ionic solute such as NaCl, yet a nonpolar solvent such as benzene will not dissolve NaCl.

Water is the most common solvent in natural systems, having several characteristics that suit it to this role. The polarity of the water molecule causes it to form hydrogen bonds with other water molecules, but it can also interact readily with charged or polar molecules.

When ionic solutes such as NaCl crystals are added to water, the Na$^+$ and Cl$^-$ are released into solution. Dissolution occurs because Na$^+$ is attracted to the negative pole of the water molecule and Cl$^-$ is attracted to the positive poles. In this way, they are drawn away from the crystal separately into solution. As it leaves, each ion becomes **hydrated,** which means that it is surrounded by a sphere of water molecules (**figure 2.12**). Molecules such as salt or sugar that attract water to their surface are termed **hydrophilic.*** Nonpolar molecules, such as benzene, that repel water are considered **hydrophobic.*** A third class of molecules, such as the phospholipids in cell membranes, are considered **amphipathic*** because they have both hydrophilic and hydrophobic properties.

Because most biological activities take place in aqueous (water-based) solutions, the concentration of these solutions can be very important (see chapter 7). The **concentration** of a solution expresses the amount of solute dissolved in a certain amount of solvent. It can be figured by percentage or molarity. Percentage is the ratio of solute in solution expressed as some combination of weight or volume.

A common way to calculate concentration by percentage is to use the weight of the solute, measured in grams (g), dissolved in a specified volume of solvent, measured in milliliters (ml). For example, dissolving 3 g of NaCl in the amount of water to produce 100 ml of solution is a 3% solution; dissolving 30 g in water up to

100 ml of solution produces a 30% solution; and dissolving 3 g in 1,000 ml (1 liter) produces a 0.3% solution.

A frequent way to express concentration of biological solutions is by its molar concentration, or *molarity* (M). A standard molar solution is obtained by dissolving 1 *mole,* defined as the molecular weight of the compound in grams, in 1 L (1,000 ml) of solution. To make a 1 M solution of sodium chloride, we would dissolve 58 g of NaCl to give 1 L of solution; a 0.1 M solution would require 5.8 g of NaCl in 1 L of solution.

Acidity, Alkalinity, and the pH Scale

Another factor with far-reaching impact on living things is the concentration of acidic or basic solutions in their environment. To understand how solutions become acidic or basic, we must look again at the behavior of water molecules. Hydrogens and oxygen tend to remain bonded by covalent bonds, but under certain conditions, a single hydrogen can break away as an ionic H$^+$, or **hydrogen ion,** leaving the remainder of the molecule in the form of an OH$^-$, or **hydroxide ion.** The H$^+$ ion is positively charged because it is essentially a hydrogen that has lost its electron; the OH$^-$ is negatively charged because it remains in possession of that electron. Ionization of water is constantly occurring, but in pure water containing no other ions, H$^+$ and OH$^-$ are produced in equal amounts, and the solution remains neutral. By one definition, a solution is considered **acidic** when one of its components (an acid) releases excess hydrogen ions.[6] A solution is **basic** when a component (a base) releases excess hydroxide ions, so that there is no longer a balance between the two ions. Another term used interchangeably with basic is **alkaline.**

To measure the acid and base concentrations of solutions, scientists use the **pH** scale, a graduated numerical scale that ranges from 0 (the most acidic) to 14 (the most basic). This scale is a useful standard for rating the relative acid or base content of a substance. Use **figure 2.13** to familiarize yourself with the pH readings of some common substances. It is not an arbitrary scale but actually a mathematical derivation based on the negative logarithm (reviewed in "Exponents" found at http://www.mhhe.com/talaro9) of the concentration of H$^+$ ions in moles per liter (symbolized as [H$^+$]) in a solution, represented as:

$$pH = -\log[H^+]$$

Acidic solutions have a greater concentration of H$^+$ than OH$^-$, starting with: pH 0, which contains 1.0 moles H$^+$/liter (L). Each of the subsequent whole-number readings in the scale reduces the [H$^+$] by tenfold:

- pH 1 contains [0.1 moles H$^+$/L].
- pH 2 contains [0.01 moles H$^+$/L].
- Continuing in the same manner up to pH 14, which contains [0.00000000000001 moles H$^+$/L].

These same concentrations can be represented more manageably by exponents:

- pH 2 has an [H$^+$] of 10^{-2} moles.
- pH 14 has an [H$^+$] of 10^{-14} moles (**table 2.2**).

* *hydrophilic* (hy-droh-fil'-ik) Gr. *hydros*, water, and *philos*, to love.
* *hydrophobic* (hy-droh-fob'-ik) Gr. *phobos*, fear.
* *amphipathic* (am'-fy-path'-ik) Gr. *amphi*, both.

6. Actually, it forms a hydronium ion (H$_3$O$^+$), but for simplicity's sake, we will use the notation of H$^+$.

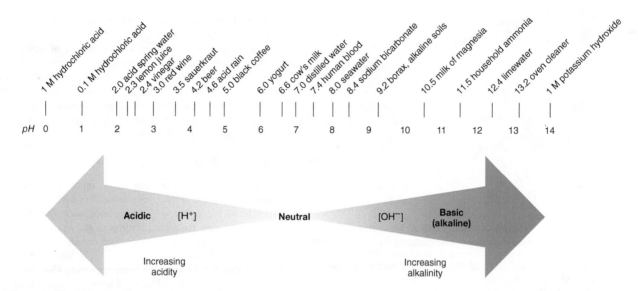

Figure 2.13 **The pH scale.** Shown are the relative degrees of acidity and alkalinity and the approximate pH readings for various substances.

TABLE 2.2	Hydrogen Ion and Hydroxide Ion Concentrations at a Given pH		
Moles/L of Hydrogen Ions	Logarithm	pH	Moles/L of OH⁻
1.0	10^0	0	10^{-14}
0.1	10^{-1}	1	10^{-13}
0.01	10^{-2}	2	10^{-12}
0.001	10^{-3}	3	10^{-11}
0.0001	10^{-4}	4	10^{-10}
0.00001	10^{-5}	5	10^{-9}
0.000001	10^{-6}	6	10^{-8}
0.0000001	10^{-7}	7	10^{-7}
0.00000001	10^{-8}	8	10^{-6}
0.000000001	10^{-9}	9	10^{-5}
0.0000000001	10^{-10}	10	10^{-4}
0.00000000001	10^{-11}	11	10^{-3}
0.000000000001	10^{-12}	12	10^{-2}
0.0000000000001	10^{-13}	13	10^{-1}
0.00000000000001	10^{-14}	14	10^0

It is evident that the pH units are derived from the exponent itself. Even though the basis for the pH scale is [H⁺], it is important to note that, as the [H⁺] in a solution decreases, the [OH⁻] increases in direct proportion. At midpoint—pH 7 or **neutrality**—the concentrations are exactly equal and neither predominates, this being the pH of pure water previously mentioned.

In summary, the pH scale can be used to rate or determine the degree of acidity or alkalinity of a solution. On this scale, a pH below 7 is acidic, and the lower the pH, the greater the acidity; a pH above 7 is basic, and the higher the pH, the greater the alkalinity. Incidentally, although pHs are given here in even whole numbers, more often, a pH reading exists in decimal form; for example, pH 4.5 or 6.8 (acidic) and pH 7.4 or 10.2 (basic). Because of the damaging effects of very concentrated acids or bases, most cells operate best under neutral, weakly acidic, or weakly basic conditions (see chapter 7).

Aqueous solutions containing both acids and bases may be involved in **neutralization** reactions, which give rise to water and other neutral by-products. For example, when equal molar solutions of hydrochloric acid (HCl) and sodium hydroxide (NaOH, a base) are mixed, the reaction proceeds as follows:

$$HCl + NaOH \rightarrow H_2O + NaCl$$

Here the acid and base ionize to H⁺ and OH⁻ ions, which form water, and other ions, Na⁺ and Cl⁻, which form sodium chloride. Any product other than water that arises when acids and bases react is called a salt. Many of the organic acids (such as lactic and succinic acids) that function in **metabolism*** are available as the acid and the salt form (such as lactate, succinate), depending on the conditions in the cell (see chapter 8).

 Check Your Progress SECTION 2.3

15. Review the types of chemical reactions and the general ways they can be expressed in equations.
16. Define solution, solvent, and solute.
17. What properties of water make it an effective biological solvent, and how does a molecule like NaCl become dissolved in it?
18. What is molarity? Tell how to make a 1 M solution of $Mg_3(PO_4)_2$ and a 0.1 M solution of $CaSO_4$.
19. What determines whether a substance is an acid or a base? Briefly outline the pH scale.

* *metabolism* (muh-tab´-oh-lizm) A general term referring to the totality of chemical and physical processes occurring in the cell.

2.4 The Chemistry of Carbon and Organic Compounds

 Expected Learning Outcomes

16. Describe the chemistry of carbon and the difference between inorganic and organic compounds.

17. Identify functional groups and know some examples.

18. Define what macromolecules, polymers, and monomers are.

So far, our main focus has been on the characteristics of atoms, ions, and small, simple substances that play diverse roles in the structure and function of living things. These substances are often lumped together in a category called **inorganic chemicals.** A chemical is usually inorganic if it does not contain **both** carbon and hydrogen. Examples of inorganic chemicals include H_2O, O_2, NaCl (sodium chloride), $Mg_3(PO_4)_2$ (magnesium phosphate), $CaCO_3$ (calcium carbonate), and CO_2 (carbon dioxide). In reality, however, most of the chemical reactions and structures of living things occur at the level of more complex molecules, termed **organic chemicals.** The minimum requirement for a compound to be considered organic is that it contains a basic framework of carbon bonded to hydrogens. Organic molecules vary in complexity from the simplest, methane (CH_4; see figure 2.4c), which has a molecular weight of 16, to certain antibody molecules (produced by an immune reaction) that have a molecular weight of nearly 1 million and are among the most complex molecules on earth. Most organic chemicals in cells contain other elements such as oxygen, nitrogen, and phosphorus in addition to the carbon and hydrogen.

The role of carbon as the fundamental element of life can best be understood if we look at its chemistry and bonding patterns. The valence of carbon makes it an ideal atomic building block to form the backbone of organic molecules; it has 4 electrons in its outer orbital to be shared with other atoms (including other carbons) through covalent bonding. As a result, it can form stable chains containing thousands of carbon atoms and still has bonding sites available for forming covalent bonds with numerous other atoms. The bonds that carbon forms are linear, branched, or ringed, and it can form four single bonds, two double bonds, or one triple bond (**figure 2.14**). Several unique kinds of molecules are made of pure carbon alone. You may be familiar with diamonds and graphite. A relatively new discovery, fullerene, is made by carbon atoms double-bonding with each other to produce a hollow sphere. Look ahead to **Clinical Connections** on page 44 to see a type of this molecule, which is considered one of the most common molecules in the universe, and one that may have many earthly uses.

Functional Groups of Organic Compounds

One important advantage of carbon's serving as the molecular skeleton for living things is that it is free to bind with a variety of special molecular groups or accessory molecules called **functional groups.** Functional groups help define the chemical class of certain groups of organic compounds and confer unique reactive properties on the whole molecule (**table 2.3**). Because each type of functional group behaves in a distinctive manner, reactions of an organic compound can be predicted by knowing the kind of

Figure 2.14 The versatility of bonding in carbon. In most compounds, each carbon makes a total of four bonds. **(a)** Single, double, and triple bonds can be made with other carbons, oxygen, and nitrogen; single bonds are made with hydrogen. Simple electron models show how the electrons are shared in these bonds. **(b)** Multiple bonding of carbons can give rise to long chains, branched compounds, and ringed compounds, many of which are extraordinarily large and complex.

TABLE 2.3	Representative Functional Groups and Organic Compounds That Contain Them	
Formula of Functional Group	**Name**	**Can Be Found in**
R* — O — H	Hydroxyl	Alcohols, carbohydrates
R — C (=O, OH)	Carboxyl	Fatty acids, proteins, organic acids
R — C (H, NH₂, H)	Amino	Proteins, nucleic acids
R — C (=O, O — R)	Ester	Lipids
R — C (H, SH, H)	Sulfhydryl	Cysteine (amino acid), proteins
R — C (=O, H)	Carbonyl, terminal end	Aldehydes, polysaccharides
R — C — C (=O)	Carbonyl, internal	Ketones, polysaccharides
R — O — P — OH (=O, OH)	Phosphate	DNA, RNA, ATP

*The R designation on a molecule is shorthand for remainder, and its placement in a formula indicates that what is attached at that site varies from one compound to another.

these groups are assembled from smaller molecular subunits, or building blocks, and because they are often very large compounds, they are termed **macromolecules.** All macromolecules except lipids are formed by polymerization, a process in which repeating subunits termed **monomers*** are bound into chains of various lengths termed **polymers.*** For example, amino acids (monomers), when arranged in a chain, form proteins (polymers). The large size and complex, three-dimensional shape of macromolecules enable them to function as structural components, molecular messengers, energy sources, enzymes (biochemical catalysts), nutrient stores, and sources of genetic information. In the following section and in later chapters, we consider numerous concepts relating to the roles of macromolecules in cells. Table 2.4 will also be a useful reference when you study metabolism in chapter 8.

 Check Your Progress SECTION 2.4

20. What atoms must be present in a molecule for it to be considered organic?
21. Name several inorganic compounds.
22. What characteristics of carbon make it ideal for the formation of organic compounds?
23. What are functional groups?
24. Differentiate between a monomer and a polymer. How are polymers formed?

2.5 Molecules of Life: Carbohydrates

 Expected Learning Outcomes

19. Define *carbohydrate* and know the functional groups that characterize carbohydrates.
20. Distinguish among mono-, di-, and polysaccharides, and describe how their bonds are made.
21. Discuss the functions of carbohydrates in cells.

functional group or groups it carries. Many synthesis, decomposition, and transfer reactions rely upon functional groups such as R—OH or R—NH₂. The R designation on a molecule is shorthand for remainder, and its placement in a formula indicates that the group attached at that site varies from one compound to another.

Organic Macromolecules: Superstructures of Life

The compounds of life fall into the realm of **biochemistry.** Biochemicals are organic compounds produced by (or components of) living things, and they include four main families: carbohydrates, lipids, proteins, and nucleic acids **(table 2.4).** The compounds in

The term **carbohydrate** originates from the way that most members of this chemical class resemble combinations of carbon and water. Carbohydrates can be generally represented by the formula $(CH_2O)_n$, in which n indicates the number of units that combine to make the finished carbohydrate. The basic structure of a simple carbohydrate monomer is a backbone of carbon bound to two or more hydroxyl groups. Because they also have either an aldehyde or a ketone group, they are often designated as *polyhydroxy* **aldehydes** or **ketones (figure 2.15).** In simple terms, a sugar such as glucose is an aldehyde with a terminal carbonyl group bonded to a hydrogen and another carbon. Fructose sugar is a ketone with a carbonyl group bonded between two carbons.

Carbohydrates exist in a great variety of configurations. The common term sugar **(saccharide*)** refers to a simple carbohydrate,

* *monomer* (mahn′-oh-mur) Gr. *mono,* one, and *meros,* part.
* *polymer* (pahl′-ee-mur) Gr. *poly,* many; also the root for polysaccharide, polypeptide, and polynucleotide.
* *saccharide* (sak′-uh-ryd) Gr. *sakcharon,* sweet.

TABLE 2.4	Macromolecules and Their Functions	
Macromolecule	**Description/Basic Structure**	**Examples/Notes**
Carbohydrates		
Monosaccharides	3- to 7-carbon sugars	Glucose, fructose / Sugars involved in metabolic reactions; building block of disaccharides and polysaccharides
Disaccharides	Two monosaccharides	Maltose (malt sugar) / Composed of two glucoses; an important breakdown product of starch
		Lactose (milk sugar) / Composed of glucose and galactose
		Sucrose (table sugar) / Composed of glucose and fructose
Polysaccharides	Chains of monosaccharides	Starch, cellulose, glycogen / Cell wall, food storage
Lipids		
Triglycerides	Fatty acids + glycerol	Fats, oils / Major component of cell membranes; storage
Phospholipids	Fatty acids + glycerol + phosphate	Membranes
Waxes	Fatty acids, alcohols	Mycolic acid / Cell wall of mycobacteria
Steroids	Ringed structure	Cholesterol, ergosterol / Membranes of eukaryotes and some bacteria
Proteins		
Polypeptides	Amino acids in a chain bound by peptide bonds	Enzymes; part of cell membrane, cell wall, ribosomes, antibodies / Metabolic reactions; structural components
Nucleic acids	Nucleotides, composed of pentose sugar + phosphate + nitrogenous base	Purines: adenine, guanine; Pyrimidines: cytosine, thymine, uracil
Deoxyribonucleic acid (DNA)	Contains deoxyribose sugar and thymine, not uracil	Chromosomes; genetic material of viruses / Inheritance
Ribonucleic acid (RNA)	Contains ribose sugar and uracil, not thymine	Ribosomes; mRNA, tRNA / Expression of genetic traits
Adenosine triphosphate (ATP)	Contains adenine, ribose sugar, and 3 phosphate groups	A high-energy compound that gives off energy to power reactions in cells

Figure 2.15 **Common classes of carbohydrates. (a)** Major saccharide groups, named for the number of sugar units each contains. **(b)** Three hexoses with the same molecular formula ($C_6H_{12}O_6$) and different structural formulas. Both linear and ring models are given. The linear form emphasizes aldehyde and ketone groups, although in solution the sugars exist in the ring form. Note that the carbons are numbered in red so as to keep track of reactions within and between monosaccharides.

CLINICAL CONNECTIONS

Nanoparticles—Molecule-Sized "Smart" Pills

In the near future, it may be possible to treat an infection or cancer by taking a single tiny dose of medicine by nose, mouth, or skin. This is just one of the revolutionary possibilities being explored by the science of **chemotherapy,** defined as the use of chemical compounds (drugs) to treat or prevent diseases. Traditionally, drugs have been swallowed in pill form or injected, but often, these methods leave a great deal to be desired. For example, a drug being swallowed may be absorbed in unpredictable amounts, and it may not reliably reach the site of action; or it may not be specific to the target cells and cause harm to healthy tissues.

For several years, pharmaceutical researchers have been exploring alternate ways to administer drugs using tiny delivery systems called **nanoparticles.*** This idea comes from the science of **nanotechnology,** defined as the study and application of molecule-sized devices or structures (look ahead to **3.1 Making Connections**). Of several molecule-sized systems under development, two that look very promising are liposomes and fullerenes. The structure of these two types of nanoparticles suits them well for carrying drugs to a precise location and controlling their release. In both cases, they display a spherical, hollow structure that provides spaces for holding drugs, and both have surfaces that could be manipulated to bind to a specific organ or cell type.

Liposomes are lipid-based molecules with the lipids arranged in a bilayer similar to a cell membrane **(figure a).** They are soluble in water, could carry a variety of drugs in their core, and readily fuse with the membrane of the cell they are targeting, immediately delivering their contents directly into the cytoplasm. Note also that liposomes can also display molecules that improve recognition and entry of the drug. Liposomes are being considered for treating tumors and viral infections, delivering antibiotics to infected tissues and organs, vaccine delivery, and even some types of genetic therapies.

Fullerenes represent an unusual group of molecules that consist only of carbon double-bonded to other carbons, forming a lattice network that can assume a number of configurations. The most adaptable configuration is the spheroid form called a buckyball,* composed of 60 carbons **(figure b).** These molecules can also have drugs loaded into their cores and be directed toward specific cells or organs, but they are not broken down in the body and can remain in place significantly longer than traditional drug carriers. They are being tested as a means of treating cancers with radioactive isotopes and delivering antiviral drugs into infected cells.

Nanomedicine is one of the most rapidly growing areas of research. What other applications could grow out of this use of such tiny delivery systems? *Answer available at http://www.mhhe.com/talaro9*

*nano for nanometer, which is one-billionth of a meter in length, about 1/80,000 the diameter of a human hair.

*This term and fullerene were chosen in honor of Buckminster Fuller, who designed the geodesic dome, an architectural structure that is constructed on the same plan as these tiny molecules.

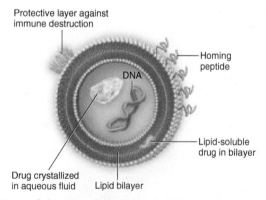

(a) Diagram of a liposome is shown carrying drugs and displaying specific surface molecules to help in homing to the target and drug delivery.

(b) Structure of a buckyball indicates its "soccer ball" appearance of hexagonal carbons.

such as a monosaccharide or a disaccharide, that has a sweet taste. A **monosaccharide** is a simple polyhydroxy aldehyde or ketone molecule containing from 3 to 7 carbons; a **disaccharide** is a combination of two monosaccharides; and a **polysaccharide** is a polymer of five or more monosaccharides bound in linear or branched chain patterns (figure 2.15). Monosaccharides and disaccharides are specified by combining a prefix that describes some characteristic of the sugar with the suffix -**ose.** For example, **hexoses** are composed of 6 carbons, and **pentoses** contain 5 carbons. **Glucose** (Greek for sweet) is the most common and universally important

hexose; **fructose** is named for fruit (one of its sources); and xylose, a pentose, derives its name from the Greek word for wood. Disaccharides are named similarly: **lactose** (Latin for milk) is an important component of milk; **maltose** means malt sugar; and **sucrose** (French for sugar) is common table sugar or cane sugar.

The Nature of Carbohydrate Bonds

The subunits of disaccharides and polysaccharides are linked by means of **glycosidic bonds,** in which carbons (each is assigned a

Figure 2.16 **Glycosidic bond in three common disaccharides.** (a) General scheme in the formation of a glycosidic bond by dehydration synthesis. (b) Formation of the 1,4 bond between two α glucoses to produce maltose. (c) Formation of the 1,2 bond between glucose and fructose to produce sucrose. (d) A 1,4 bond between a galactose and glucose produces lactose. Note that all three dehydration synthesis reactions release water.

number) on adjacent sugar units are bonded to the same oxygen atom like links in a chain **(figure 2.16).** For example:

- Maltose is formed when the number 1 carbon on a glucose bonds to the oxygen on the number 4 carbon on a second glucose.
- Sucrose is formed when glucose and fructose bind oxygen between their number 1 and number 2 carbons.
- Lactose is formed when glucose and galactose connect by their number 1 and number 4 carbons.

In order to form this bond, one carbon gives up its OH group and the other (the one contributing the oxygen to the bond) loses the

H from its OH group. Because a water molecule is produced, this reaction is known as **dehydration synthesis,** a process common to most polymerization reactions (see proteins, page 50). Three polysaccharides (starch, cellulose, and glycogen) are structurally and biochemically distinct, even though all are polymers of the same monosaccharide—glucose. The basis for their differences lies primarily in the exact way the glucoses are bound together, which greatly affects the characteristics of the end product **(figure 2.17).** The synthesis and breakage of each type of bond require a specialized catalyst called an enzyme (see chapter 8).

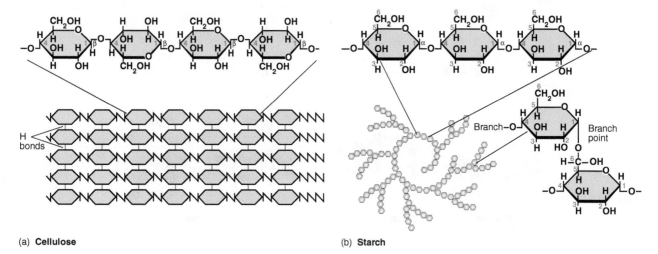

(a) **Cellulose**

(b) **Starch**

Figure 2.17 Polysaccharides. (a) Cellulose is composed of β glucose bonded in 1,4 bonds that produce linear, lengthy chains of polysaccharides that are H-bonded along their length. This accounts for fibrous support structures of plants. **(b)** Starch is also composed of glucose polymers, in this case α glucose. The main structure is amylose bonded in a 1,4 pattern, with side branches of amylopectin bonded by 1,6 bonds. The entire molecule is compact and granular.

The Functions of Carbohydrates in Cells

Carbohydrates are the most abundant biological molecules in nature. They play numerous roles in cell structure, adhesion, and metabolism.

Polysaccharides typically contribute to structural support and protection and serve as nutrient and energy stores. The cell walls in plants and many microscopic algae derive their strength and rigidity from **cellulose,** a long, fibrous polymer **(figure 2.17a)**. Because of this role, cellulose is probably one of the most common organic substances on the earth, yet it is digestible only by certain bacteria, fungi, and protozoa that produce the enzyme cellulase. These microbes, called decomposers, play an essential role in breaking down and recycling plant materials (see figure 7.2). Some bacteria secrete slime layers of a glucose polymer called *dextran.* This substance causes a sticky layer to develop on teeth that leads to plaque, described later in chapter 21.

Other structural polysaccharides can be conjugated (chemically bonded) to amino acids, nitrogen bases, lipids, or proteins. **Agar,** an indispensable polysaccharide in preparing solid culture media, is a natural component of certain seaweeds. It is a complex polymer of galactose and sulfur-containing carbohydrates. **Chitin** (ky-tun), a polymer of glucosamine (a sugar with an amino functional group), is a major compound in the cell walls of fungi and the exoskeletons of insects. **Peptidoglycan*** is one special class of compounds in which polysaccharides (glycans) are linked to peptide fragments (a short chain of amino acids). This molecule provides the main source of structural support to the bacterial cell wall. The cell wall of gram-negative bacteria also contains **lipopolysaccharide,** a complex of lipid and polysaccharide responsible for symptoms such as fever and shock (see chapters 4 and 13).

The outer surface of many cells has a delicate "sugar coating" composed of polysaccharides bound in various ways to proteins (the combination is called mucoprotein or glycoprotein). This structure,

called the **glycocalyx,*** functions in attachment to other cells or as a site for *receptors*—surface molecules that receive and respond to external stimuli. Small sugar molecules account for the differences in human blood types, and carbohydrates are a component of large protein molecules called antibodies. Some viruses have glycoproteins on their surface for binding to and invading their host cells.

Polysaccharides are usually stored by cells in the form of glucose polymers such as **starch (figure 2.17b)** or **glycogen** that are readily tapped as a source of energy and other metabolic needs. Because a water molecule is required for breaking the bond between two glucose molecules, digestion is also termed **hydrolysis.*** Starch is the primary storage food of green plants, microscopic algae, and some fungi; glycogen (animal starch) is a stored carbohydrate for animals and certain groups of bacteria and protozoa.

2.6 Molecules of Life: Lipids

 Expected Learning Outcomes

22. Define *lipid, triglyceride, phospholipid, fatty acid,* and *cholesterol.*

23. Describe how an ester bond is formed.

24. Discuss major functions of lipids in cells.

The term **lipid,** derived from the Greek word *lipos,* meaning fat, is not a chemical designation but an operational term for a variety of substances that are not soluble in polar solvents such as water (recall that oil and water do not mix) but will dissolve in nonpolar solvents such as benzene and chloroform. This property occurs because the substances we call lipids contain relatively long or complex C—H (hydrocarbon) chains that are nonpolar and thus

* *peptidoglycan* (pep-tih-doh-gly´-kan).

* *glycocalyx* (gly″-koh-kay´-lix) Gr. *glycos,* sweet and *calyx,* covering.
* *hydrolysis* (hy-drol´-eye-sis) Gr. *hydro,* water, and *lysis,* to dissolve.

Figure 2.18 Synthesis and structure of a triglyceride. (a) Because a water molecule is released at each ester bond, this is another form of dehydration synthesis. The jagged lines and R symbol represent the hydrocarbon chains of the fatty acids, which are commonly very long. **(b)** Structural models of two kinds of fatty acids. (1) A saturated fatty acid has long, straight chains that readily pack together. (2) An unsaturated fatty acid has at least one double bond and cannot pack densely due to the bends in the long chain caused by the double bonds. **(c)** Three-dimensional models of triglycerides containing saturated (1) and unsaturated fatty acids (2). Which of these two fats is an oil and which one is solid?

hydrophobic. The main groups of compounds classified as lipids are triglycerides, phospholipids, steroids, and waxes.

Important storage lipids are the **triglycerides,** a category that includes fats and oils. Triglycerides are composed of a single molecule of glycerol bound to three **fatty acids (figure 2.18). Glycerol** is a 3-carbon alcohol[7] with three OH groups that serve as binding sites. Fatty acids are long-chain unbranched hydrocarbon molecules with a carboxyl group (COOH) at one end that is free to bind to the glycerol. The bond that forms between the —OH group and the —COOH is defined as an **ester bond (figure 2.18a).** The hydrocarbon portion of a fatty acid can vary in length from 4 to 24 carbons and, depending on the fat, it may be *saturated* or *unsaturated.* A saturated fatty acid has all of the carbons in the chain bonded to hydrogens with single bonds. Fatty acids having at least one carbon—carbon double bond are considered unsaturated **(figure 2.18b).** Fats that contain such fatty acids are described with these terms as well. The structure

of fatty acids is what gives fats and oils (liquid fats) their greasy, insoluble nature. In general, solid fats (such as beef tallow) are more saturated, and oils (or liquid fats) are more unsaturated.

In most cells, triglycerides are stored in long-term concentrated form as droplets or globules. When the ester linkage is acted on by digestive enzymes called lipases, the fatty acids and glycerol are freed to be used in metabolism. Fatty acids are a superior source of energy, yielding twice as much per gram as other storage molecules (starch). Soaps are K^+ or Na^+ salts of fatty acids whose qualities make them excellent grease removers and cleaners (see chapter 11).

Membrane Lipids

The **phospholipids** serve as a major structural component of cell membranes. Although phospholipids also contain glycerol and fatty acids, they differ significantly from triglycerides. Phospholipids contain only two fatty acids attached to the glycerol, and the third glycerol binding site holds a phosphate group. The phosphate is in

7. Alcohols are hydrocarbons containing an —OH functional group.

Figure 2.19 Phospholipids—membrane molecules. (a) A model of a single molecule of a phospholipid. The phosphate-alcohol head lends a charge to one end of the molecule; its long, trailing hydrocarbon chain is uncharged. **(b)** Phospholipids in water-based solutions become arranged (1) in single layers called micelles, with the charged head oriented toward the water phase and the hydrophobic nonpolar tail buried away from the water phase, or (2) in double-layered systems with the hydrophobic tails sandwiched between two hydrophilic layers.

turn bonded to an alcohol, which varies from one phospholipid to another **(figure 2.19***a***)**. This class of lipids has a hydrophilic region from the charge on the phosphoric acid–alcohol "head" of the molecule and a hydrophobic region that corresponds to the long, uncharged "tail" (formed by the fatty acids). When exposed to an aqueous solution, the charged heads are attracted to the water phase, and the nonpolar tails are repelled from the water phase **(figure 2.19***b***)**. This property causes lipids to naturally assume single and double layers (bilayers), which contribute to their biological significance in membranes. When two single layers of polar lipids come together to form a double layer, the outer hydrophilic face of each single layer will orient itself toward the solution, and the hydrophobic portions will become immersed in the core of the bilayer. The structure of lipid bilayers confers characteristics on membranes such as selective permeability and fluid nature.

Miscellaneous Lipids

Steroids are complex ringed compounds commonly found in cell membranes and animal hormones. The best known of these is the sterol (meaning a steroid with an OH group) called **cholesterol (figure 2.20)**. Cholesterol reinforces the structure of the cell membrane in animal cells and in an unusual group of cell-wall-deficient bacteria called the mycoplasmas (see chapter 4).

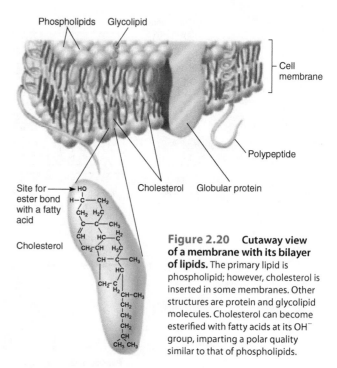

Figure 2.20 Cutaway view of a membrane with its bilayer of lipids. The primary lipid is phospholipid; however, cholesterol is inserted in some membranes. Other structures are protein and glycolipid molecules. Cholesterol can become esterified with fatty acids at its OH⁻ group, imparting a polar quality similar to that of phospholipids.

The cell membranes of fungi also contain a unique sterol, called ergosterol. *Prostaglandins* are fatty acid derivatives found in trace amounts that function in inflammatory and allergic reactions, blood clotting, and smooth muscle contraction. Chemically, a *wax* is an ester formed between a long-chain alcohol and a saturated fatty acid. The resulting material is typically pliable and soft when warmed but hard and water-resistant when cold (paraffin, for example). Among living things, fur, feathers, fruits, leaves, human skin, and insect exoskeletons are naturally waterproofed with a coating of wax. Bacteria that cause tuberculosis and leprosy produce a wax (wax D) that contributes to their pathogenicity.

The Structure and Functions of Membranes

The word **membrane** appears frequently in descriptions of cells in chapters 4 and 5. The word itself can be used to indicate a lining or covering including such multicellular structures as the mucous membranes of the body. At the cellular level, however, a membrane is a thin sheet of molecules composed of phospholipids and sterols (averaging about 40% of membrane content) and proteins (averaging about 60%). All cells have a membrane that completely encases the cytoplasm. Membranes are also components of eukaryotic organelles such as nuclei, mitochondria, and chloroplasts, and they appear in internal pockets of certain prokaryotic cells. Even some viruses, which are not cells, can have a membranous envelope.

A standard model of membrane structure has the lipids forming a continuous bilayer. The polar lipid heads face toward the aqueous phases and the nonpolar tails orient toward the center of the membrane. Embedded at numerous sites in this bilayer are various-sized globular proteins (figure 2.20). Some proteins are situated only at the surface; others extend fully through the entire membrane.

Membranes are dynamic and constantly changing because the lipid phase is in motion and many proteins can migrate freely about. This fluidity is essential to such activities as engulfment of food and discharge or secretion by cells. The structure of the lipid phase provides an impenetrable barrier that accounts for the selective permeability and transport of molecules. Membrane proteins function in receiving molecular signals (receptors), in binding and transporting nutrients, and as enzymes, topics to be discussed in chapters 7 and 8.

 Check Your Progress SECTIONS 2.5–2.6

25. What is the structure of carbohydrates and glycosidic bonds?
26. Differentiate between mono-, di-, and polysaccharides, and give examples of each.
27. What are some of the functions of polysaccharides in cells?
28. Draw simple structural molecules of triglycerides and phospholipids to compare their differences and similarities. What is an ester bond?

2.7 Molecules of Life: Proteins

 Expected Learning Outcomes

25. Describe the structures of peptides and polypeptides and how their bonds form.

26. Characterize the four levels of protein structure and describe the pattern of folding.

27. Summarize some of the essential functions of proteins.

The predominant organic molecules in cells are **proteins,** a fitting term adopted from the Greek word *proteios,* meaning first or prime. To a large extent, the structure, behavior, and unique qualities of each living thing are a consequence of the proteins they contain. To best explain the origin of the special properties and versatility of proteins, we must examine their general structure.

The building blocks of proteins are **amino acids,** which exist in 20 different naturally occurring forms. **Figure 2.21** provides examples of several common amino acids. See **Appendix A** for a table that shows all 20. Various combinations of these amino acids account for the nearly infinite variety of proteins. Amino acids have a basic skeleton consisting of a carbon (called the α carbon) linked to an amino group (NH_2), a carboxyl group (COOH), a hydrogen atom (H), and a variable R group. The variations among the amino acids occur at the R group, which is different in each amino acid and imparts the unique characteristics to the molecule and to the proteins that contain it. A covalent bond called a **peptide bond** forms between the amino group on one amino acid and the carboxyl group on another amino acid. As a result of peptide bond formation, it is possible to produce molecules varying in length from two amino acids to chains containing thousands of them.

Various terms are used to denote the nature of compounds containing peptide bonds. **Peptide*** usually refers to a molecule com-

* *peptide* (pep′-tyd) Gr. *pepsis,* digestion.

Amino Acid	Structural Formula
Alanine	
Valine	
Cysteine	
Phenylalanine	
Tyrosine	

Figure 2.21 Structural formulas of selected amino acids. The basic structure common to all amino acids is shown in blue type; and the variable group, or R group, is placed in a colored box. Note the variations in structure of this reactive component.

posed of short chains of amino acids, such as a dipeptide (two amino acids), a tripeptide (three), and a tetrapeptide (four) **(figure 2.22).** A **polypeptide** contains an unspecified number of amino acids but usually has more than 20 and is often a smaller subunit of a protein. A protein is the largest of this class of compounds and usually contains a minimum of 50 amino acids. It is common for the terms *polypeptide* and *protein* to be used interchangeably, though not all polypeptides are large enough to be considered proteins. In chapter 9, we see that protein synthesis is not just a random connection of amino acids; it is directed by information provided in DNA.

Figure 2.22 **The formation of peptide bonds in a tetrapeptide.**

Protein Structure and Diversity

The reason that proteins are so varied and specific is that they do not function in the form of a simple straight chain of amino acids (called the primary structure). A protein has a natural tendency to assume more complex levels of organization, called the secondary, tertiary, and quaternary structures (**figure 2.23**).

The **primary (1°) structure** of a protein is the fundamental chain of amino acids just described, but proteins vary extensively in the exact order, type, and number of amino acids. It is this quality that gives rise to the unlimited diversity in protein form and function.

A polypeptide does not remain in its primary state, but instead, it spontaneously arranges itself into a higher level of complexity called its **secondary (2°) structure.** The secondary state arises from numerous hydrogen bonds occurring between the C=O and N—H groups of peptide bonds. This bonding causes the whole chain to coil or fold into regular patterns. The coiled spiral form is called the α helix, and the folded, accordion form is called the β-pleated sheet. Polypeptides ordinarily will contain both types of configurations.

Once a chain has assumed the secondary structure, it goes on to form yet another level of folding and compacting—the **tertiary (3°) structure.** This structure arises through additional intrachain[8] forces and bonds between various parts of the α helix and β-pleated sheets. The chief actions in creating the tertiary structure are additional hydrogen bonds between charged functional groups, van der Waals forces between various parts of the polypeptide, and covalent disulfide bonds. The disulfide bonds occur between sulfur atoms on the amino acid **cysteine,*** and these bonds confer a high degree of stability to the overall protein structure. The result is a complex, three-dimensional protein that is now the completed functional state in many cases.

The most complex proteins assume a **quaternary (4°) structure,** in which two or more polypeptides interact to form a large, multiunit protein. The polypeptide units form loose associations based on weak van der Waals and other forces. The polypeptides in proteins with

quaternary structure can be the same or different. The arrangement of these individual polypeptides tends to be symmetrical and will dictate the exact form of the finished protein (**figure 2.23, step 4**).

The most important outcome of bonding and folding is that each different type of protein develops a unique shape, and its surface displays a distinctive pattern of pockets and bumps. As a result, a protein can react only with molecules that complement or fit its particular surface features. Such a degree of specificity can provide the functional diversity required for many thousands of different cellular activities. **Enzymes** serve as the catalysts for all chemical reactions in cells, and nearly every reaction requires a different enzyme (see chapter 8). **Antibodies** are complex glycoproteins with specific regions of attachment for bacteria, viruses, and other microorganisms. Certain bacterial toxins (poisonous proteins) react with only one specific organ or tissue. Proteins embedded in the cell membrane have reactive sites restricted to a certain nutrient. Some proteins function as *receptors* to receive stimuli from the environment.

The functional, three-dimensional form of a protein is termed the *native state,* and if it is disrupted by some means, the protein is said to be *denatured.* Such agents as heat, acid, alcohol, and some disinfectants disrupt (and thus denature) the stabilizing intrachain bonds and cause the molecule to become nonfunctional, as described in chapter 11.

 Check Your Progress SECTION 2.7

29. Describe the basic structure of an amino acid and the formation of a peptide bond.
30. Differentiate between a peptide, a polypeptide, and a protein.
31. Explain what causes the various levels of structure of a protein molecule.
32. What functions do proteins perform in a cell?

2.8 Nucleic Acids: A Program for Genetics

 Expected Learning Outcomes

28. Identify a nucleic acid and differentiate between DNA and RNA.
29. Describe the structures of nucleotides and list the nitrogen bases.
30. Explain how the DNA code may be copied, and describe the basic functions of RNA.

The nucleic acids, **deoxyribonucleic* acid (DNA)** and **ribonucleic* acid (RNA),** were originally isolated from the cell nucleus. Shortly thereafter, they were also found in other parts of nucleated cells, in cells with no nuclei (bacteria), and in viruses. The universal

8. **Intra**chain means within the chain; **inter**chain would be between two chains.
* *cysteine* (sis´-tuh-yeen) Gr. *Kystis,* sac. An amino acid first found in urine stones.

* *deoxyribonucleic* (dee-ox"-ee-ry"-boh-noo-klay´-ik).
* *ribonucleic* (ry"-boh-noo-klay´-ik) It is easy to see why the abbreviations are used!

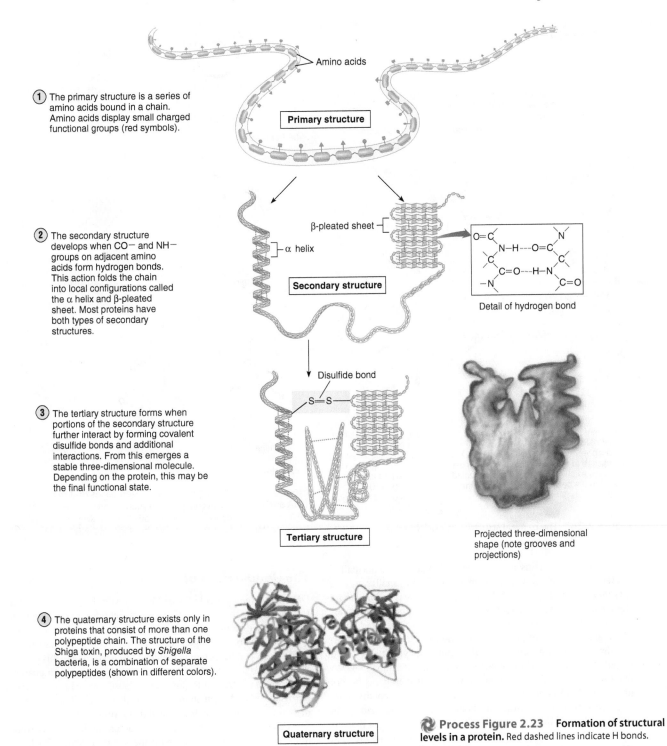

1 The primary structure is a series of amino acids bound in a chain. Amino acids display small charged functional groups (red symbols).

Amino acids

Primary structure

2 The secondary structure develops when CO— and NH— groups on adjacent amino acids form hydrogen bonds. This action folds the chain into local configurations called the α helix and β-pleated sheet. Most proteins have both types of secondary structures.

β-pleated sheet

α helix

Secondary structure

Detail of hydrogen bond

3 The tertiary structure forms when portions of the secondary structure further interact by forming covalent disulfide bonds and additional interactions. From this emerges a stable three-dimensional molecule. Depending on the protein, this may be the final functional state.

Disulfide bond

S=S

Tertiary structure

Projected three-dimensional shape (note grooves and projections)

4 The quaternary structure exists only in proteins that consist of more than one polypeptide chain. The structure of the Shiga toxin, produced by *Shigella* bacteria, is a combination of separate polypeptides (shown in different colors).

Quaternary structure

Process Figure 2.23 **Formation of structural levels in a protein.** Red dashed lines indicate H bonds.

occurrence of nucleic acids in all known cells and viruses emphasizes their important roles as informational molecules. DNA, the master instruction manual of cells, contains a coded genetic program with detailed and specific instructions for each organism's heredity. It transfers the details of its program to RNA, "helper"

molecules responsible for carrying out DNA's instructions and translating the DNA program into proteins that can perform life functions. For now, let us briefly consider the structure and some functions of DNA, RNA, and a close relative, adenosine triphosphate (ATP).

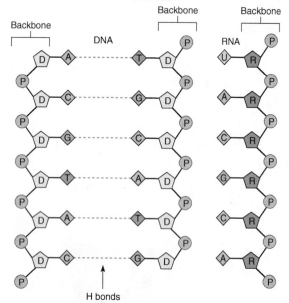

(a) A nucleotide, composed of a phosphate, a pentose sugar, and a nitrogen base (either A,T,C,G, or U) is the monomer of both DNA and RNA.

(b) In DNA, the polymer is composed of alternating deoxyribose (D) and phosphate (P) with nitrogen bases (A,T,C,G) attached to the deoxyribose. DNA almost always exists in pairs of strands, oriented so that the bases are paired across the central axis of the molecule.

(c) In RNA, the polymer is composed of alternating ribose (R) and phosphate (P) attached to nitrogen bases (A,U,C,G), but it is usually a single strand.

Figure 2.24 The general structure of nucleic acids.

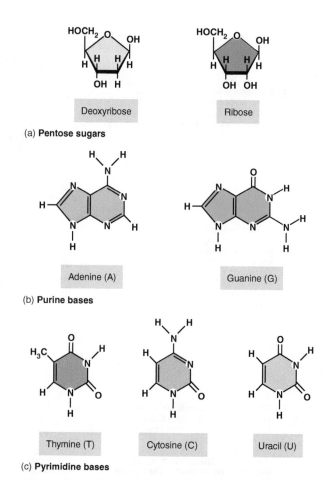

(a) **Pentose sugars**

(b) **Purine bases**

(c) **Pyrimidine bases**

Figure 2.25 The sugars and nitrogen bases that make up DNA and RNA. (a) DNA contains deoxyribose, and RNA contains ribose. **(b)** A and G purine bases are found in both DNA and RNA. **(c)** Pyrimidine bases are found in both DNA and RNA, but T is found only in DNA, and U is found only in RNA.

Both nucleic acids are polymers of repeating units called **nucleotides,** * each of which is composed of three smaller units: a **nitrogen base,** a pentose (5-carbon) sugar, and a *phosphate* (figure 2.24*a*). The nitrogen base is a cyclic compound that comes in two forms: *purines* (two rings) and *pyrimidines* (one ring). There are two types of purines—**adenine (A)** and **guanine (G)**—and three types of pyrimidines—**thymine (T), cytosine (C),** and **uracil (U) (figure 2.25).** A characteristic that differentiates DNA from RNA is that DNA contains all of the nitrogen bases except uracil, and RNA contains all of the nitrogen bases except thymine. The nitrogen base is covalently bonded to the sugar *ribose* in RNA and *deoxyribose* (because it has one fewer oxygen than ribose) in DNA. Phosphate (PO_4^{3-}), a derivative of phosphoric acid (H_3PO_4), provides the final covalent bridge that connects sugars in series. Thus, the backbone of a nucleic acid strand is a chain of alternating phosphate-sugar-phosphate-sugar molecules, and the nitrogen bases branch off the side of this backbone **(figure 2.24*b, c*).**

* *nucleotide* (noo′-klee-oh-tyd) From nucleus and acid.

The Double Helix of DNA

DNA is a huge molecule formed by two very long polynucleotide (meaning that it consists of many nucleotides joined together) strands linked along their length by hydrogen bonds between complementary pairs of nitrogen bases. The term complementary means that the nitrogen bases pair in matched sets according to this pattern: Adenine ordinarily pairs with thymine, and cytosine with guanine. The bases are attracted in this way because each pair has oxygen, nitrogen, and hydrogen atoms positioned precisely to favor the formation of hydrogen bonds between them. **(figure 2.26).**

For ease in understanding the structure of DNA, it is sometimes compared to a ladder, with the sugar-phosphate backbone representing the rails and the paired nitrogen bases representing the steps. The flat ladder is useful for understanding basic components and orientation, but in reality, DNA exists in a three-dimensional arrangement called a *double helix.* A better analogy may be a spiral staircase. In this model, the two strands (helixes) coil together, with the sugar-phosphate forming outer ribbons, and the paired bases

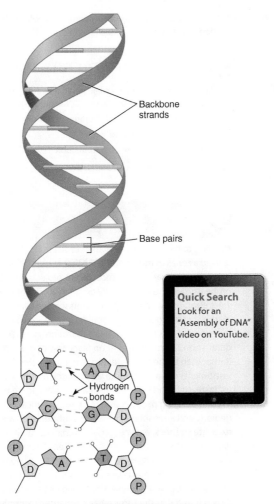

Figure 2.26 A structural representation of the double helix of DNA. At the bottom are the details of hydrogen bonds between the nitrogen bases of the two strands.

Figure 2.27 Simplified view of DNA replication in cells. The DNA in the cell's chromosome must be duplicated as the cell is dividing. This duplication is accomplished through the separation of the double DNA strand into two single strands. New strands are then synthesized using the original strands as guides to assemble the correct new complementary bases.

sandwiched between them (figure 2.26). As is true of protein, the structure of DNA is intimately related to its function. DNA molecules are usually extremely long, a feature that satisfies a requirement for storing genetic information in the sequence of base pairs the molecule contains. The hydrogen bonds between pairs can be disrupted when DNA is being copied, and the fixed complementary base pairing is essential to maintain the genetic code.

Making New DNA: Passing on the Genetic Message

The biological properties of cells and viruses are ultimately programmed by a master code composed of nucleic acids. This code is in the form of DNA in all cells and many viruses; a number of viruses are based on RNA alone. Regardless of the exact genetic makeup, both cells and viruses can continue to exist only if they can duplicate their genetic material and pass it on to

subsequent generations. **Figure 2.27** summarizes the main steps in this process in cells.

During its division cycle, the cell has a mechanism for making a copy of its DNA by **replication,*** using the original strand as a pattern. Note that replication is guided by the double-stranded nature of DNA and the precise pairing of bases that create the master code. Replication requires the separation of the double strand into two single strands by an enzyme that helps to split the hydrogen bonds along the length of the molecule. This event exposes the base code and makes it available for copying. Free nucleotides are used to synthesize matching strands that complement the bases in the code by adhering to the pairing requirements of A—T and C—G. The end result is two separate double strands with the same order of bases as the original molecule. With this type of replication, each new double strand contains one of the original single strands from the starting DNA.

RNA: Organizers of Protein Synthesis

Like DNA, RNA is a polynucleotide that consists of a long chain of nucleotides. However, RNA is a single strand containing ribose

* *replication* (reh″-plih-kay′-shun) A process that makes an exact copy.

sugar instead of deoxyribose and uracil instead of thymine (see figure 2.24). Several functional types of RNA are formed using the DNA template through a replication-like process. Three major types of RNA are important for protein synthesis. Messenger RNA (mRNA) is a copy of a gene from DNA that provides instructions for the order of amino acids; transfer RNA (tRNA) is a carrier that delivers the correct amino acids during protein synthesis; and ribosomal RNA (rRNA) is a major component of ribosomes, which are the sites of protein synthesis. More information on these important processes is presented in chapter 9.

ATP: The Energy Molecule of Cells

A relative of RNA involved in an entirely different cell activity is **adenosine triphosphate (ATP)**. ATP is a nucleotide containing adenine, ribose, and three phosphates rather than just one (**figure 2.28**). It belongs to a category of high-energy compounds (also including guanosine triphosphate, GTP) that give off energy when the bond is broken between the second and third (outermost) phosphate. The presence of these high-energy bonds makes it possible for ATP to release and store energy for cellular chemical reactions. Breakage of the bond of the terminal phosphate releases energy to do cellular work and also generates adenosine diphosphate (ADP). ADP can be converted back to ATP when the third phosphate is restored, thereby serving as an energy depot. Carriers for oxidation-reduction activi-

(a)

(b)

Figure 2.28 Model of an ATP molecule, the chemical form of energy transfer in cells. (a) Structural formula: The wavy lines connecting the phosphates represent bonds that release large amounts of energy when broken. **(b)** Ball-and-stick model shows the arrangement of atoms in three dimensions.

ties (nicotinamide adenine dinucleotide [NAD], for instance) are also derivatives of nucleotides (see chapter 8).

Check Your Progress SECTION 2.8

33. Describe a nucleotide and a polynucleotide, and compare and contrast the general structure of DNA and RNA.
34. Name the two purines and the three pyrimidines.
35. What are the functions of RNA?
36. What is ATP, and how does it function in cells?

CASE STUDY Part 2

Needing to move from speculation to scientific facts, NASA started a series of missions in 2002 that could perform more detailed investigations. The most recent projects were the *Phoenix* probe in 2008 and the *Curiosity* probe in 2012. Both spacecraft were equipped with a one-ton roving science lab to analyze the Martian surface geology and soil. An important component of rover design was to explore more thoroughly the idea that conditions conducive to life exist on Mars now or did in the past. Rather than trying to isolate microorganisms, the Mars rover's instruments serve like remote senses—the mouth, nose, and eyes to "taste, sniff, and observe" the Martian soil and ice by measuring and assaying pH, salts, and the basic chemical makeup of its geology and atmosphere. The rover's robotic arms are able to excavate soil, rock, and ice. Other equipment can break up and vaporize rocks and perform detailed chemical analyses on the contents. Early results show that the soil is salty and slightly acidic. Perhaps the most definitive evidence has been that deposits of ice were shown to be frozen water (and not carbon dioxide), and that the surface has remnants of an active streambed that carried liquid water.

A significant amount of methane also turned up in the samples, but more complex organic compounds have not yet been evident. Methane is formed by certain primitive prokaryotes but can also be the result of geologic activity. *Curiosity** is designed to monitor the methane content and possibly determine if it is from a biological or non-biological source. A future mission to Mars is planned that will return samples to earth for more detailed analysis.

> **Quick Search**
> Discover other curious unknown features of Mars by googling "The 7 Biggest Mysteries of Mars."

■ Why is inorganic carbon such as CO_2 not by itself an indicator of life?

■ For what reasons are complex organic carbon compounds considered strong evidence of living activities?

To conclude this Case Study, go to Perspectives on the Connect website.

*To learn more about the findings of the *Curiosity* rover, go to http://mars.jpl.nasa.gov/msl/.

 Chapter Summary with Key Terms

2.1 Atoms: Fundamental Building Blocks of All Matter in the Universe

A. Atomic Structure and Elements
 1. All **matter** in the universe is composed of minute particles called **atoms**—the simplest form of matter not divisible into a simpler substance by chemical means. Atoms are composed of smaller particles called **protons, neutrons,** and **electrons.**
 2. a. Protons are positively ($+$) charged, neutrons are without charge, and electrons are negatively ($-$) charged.
 b. Protons and neutrons form the **nucleus** of the atom.
 c. Electrons orbit the nucleus in energy shells.
 3. Atoms that differ in numbers of the protons, neutrons, and electrons are elements. **Elements** can be described by **mass number (MN),** equal to the number of protons and neutrons it has, and **atomic number (AN),** the number of protons in the nucleus, and each is known by a distinct name and symbol. Elements may exist in variant forms called **isotopes.** The **atomic mass** or **weight** is equal to the average of the isotope mass numbers.

2.2 Bonds and Molecules

A. Atoms interact to form **chemical bonds** and **molecules.** If the atoms combining to make a molecule are different elements, then the substance is termed a **compound.**
 1. The type of bond is dictated by the electron makeup of the outer orbitals (**valence**) of the atoms. Bond types include:
 a. **Covalent bonds,** with shared electrons. The molecule is formed by one atom sharing its electrons with another atom; the balance of charge will be **polar** if unequal or **nonpolar** if equally shared/electrically neutral.
 b. **Ionic bonds,** where one atom transfers its electron(s) to another atom that can come closer to filling up its outer orbital. Dissociation of these compounds leads to the formation of charged **cations** and **anions.**
 c. **Hydrogen bonds** involve weak attractive forces between hydrogen ($+$ charge) and nearby oxygens and nitrogens ($-$ charge).
 d. **Van der Waals forces** are also weak interactions between polarized zones of molecules such as proteins.

B. An **oxidation** is a loss of electrons and a **reduction** is a gain electrons. A substance that causes an oxidation by taking electrons is called an **oxidizing agent,** and a substance that causes a reduction by giving electrons is called a **reducing agent.**

2.3 Chemical Reactions, Solutions, and pH

A. Chemicals termed **reactants** can interact in a way to form different compounds termed **products.** Examples of reactions are synthesis and decomposition.

B. A **solution** is a combination of a solid, liquid, or gaseous chemical (the **solute**) dissolved in a liquid medium (the **solvent**). Water is the most common solvent in natural systems.

C. Ionization of water leads to the release of hydrogen ions (H^+) and hydroxyl (OH^-) ions. The **pH** scale expresses the concentration of H^+ such that a pH of less than 7.0 is considered **acidic,** and a pH of more than that, indicating fewer H^+, is considered **basic (alkaline).**

2.4 The Chemistry of Carbon and Organic Compounds

A. **Biochemistry** is the study of molecules that are found in living things. Most of these substances are **organic** compounds, which consist of carbon and hydrogen covalently bonded in various combinations. Some are **inorganic** compounds are composed of elements other than C and H.

B. Functional groups are small accessory molecules bonded to many organic compounds that impart unique characteristics.

C. **Macromolecules** are very large organic compounds and are generally assembled from single units called **monomers** by polymerization. Molecules of life fall into basic categories of carbohydrates, lipids, proteins, and nucleic acids.

2.5 Molecules of Life: Carbohydrates

A. **Carbohydrates** are composed of carbon, hydrogen, and oxygen and contain aldehyde or ketone groups.
 1. **Monosaccharides** such as glucose are the simplest carbohydrates with 3 to 7 carbons; these are the monomers of carbohydrates.
 2. **Disaccharides** such as lactose consist of two monosaccharides joined by **glycosidic bonds.**
 3. **Polysaccharides** such as **starch** and **peptidoglycan** are chains of five or more monosaccharides.

2.6 Molecules of Life: Lipids

A. **Lipids** contain long hydrocarbon chains and are not soluble in polar solvents such as water due to their nonpolar, hydrophobic character. Common components of fats are **fatty acids,** elongate molecules with a carboxylic acid group. Examples are **triglycerides, phospholipids,** sterols, and waxes.

2.7 Molecules of Life: Proteins

A. **Proteins** are highly complex macromolecules that are crucial in most, if not all, life processes.
 1. **Amino acids** are the basic building blocks of proteins. They all share a basic structure of an amino group, a carboxyl group, an R group, and hydrogen bonded to a carbon atom. There are 20 different R groups, which define the basic set of 20 amino acids, found in all life forms.
 2. A **peptide** is a short chain of amino acids bound by **peptide bonds:** a **protein** contains at least 50 amino acids.
 3. The structure of a protein is very important to its function. This is described by the **primary structure** (the chain of amino acids), the **secondary structure** (formation of α helices and β-sheets due to hydrogen bonding within the chain), **tertiary structure** (cross-links, especially disulfide bonds, between secondary structures), and **quaternary structure** (formation of multisubunit proteins). The incredible variation in shapes is the basis for the diverse roles proteins play as **enzymes, antibodies,** receptors, and structural components.

2.8 The Nucleic Acids: A Program for Genetics

A. **Nucleotides** are the building blocks of nucleic acids. They are composed of a **nitrogen base,** a pentose sugar, and a phosphate. Nitrogen bases are ringed compounds: **adenine (A), guanine (G), cytosine (C), thymine (T),** and **uracil (U).** Pentose sugars may be deoxyribose or ribose, depending on the type of nucleic acid.

56 **Chapter 2** The Chemistry of Biology

B. **Deoxyribonucleic acid (DNA)** is a polymer of nucleotides that occurs as a double-stranded helix with hydrogen bonding between pairs of bases on the helices. It has all of the bases except uracil, and the pentose sugar is deoxyribose. DNA is the master code for a cell's life processes and must be transmitted to the offspring through **replication.**

C. **Ribonucleic acid (RNA)** is a polymer of nucleotides where the sugar is ribose and **uracil** is the replacement base for thymine. It is almost always found single-stranded and is used to express the DNA code into proteins.

D. **Adenosine triphosphate (ATP)** is a nucleotide with 3 phosphates that serves as the energy molecule in cells.

Level I. Knowledge and Comprehension

These questions require a working knowledge of the concepts in the chapter and the ability to recall and understand the information you have studied.

? Multiple-Choice Questions

Select the correct answer from the answers provided. For questions with blanks, choose the combination of answers that most accurately completes the statement.

1. The smallest unit of matter with unique characteristics is
 a. an electron
 b. a molecule
 c. an atom
 d. a proton

2. The _____ charge of a proton is exactly balanced by the _____ charge of a (an) _____.
 a. negative, positive, electron
 b. positive, neutral, neutron
 c. positive, negative, electron
 d. neutral, negative, electron

3. Electrons move around the nucleus of an atom in pathways called
 a. shells
 b. orbitals
 c. circles
 d. rings

4. Which parts of an element do not vary in number?
 a. electrons
 b. neutrons
 c. protons
 d. All of these vary.

5. If a substance contains two or more elements of different types, it is considered
 a. a compound
 b. a monomer
 c. a molecule
 d. organic

6. Bonds in which atoms share electrons are defined as _____ bonds.
 a. hydrogen
 b. ionic
 c. double
 d. covalent

7. A hydrogen bond can form between _____ adjacent to each other.
 a. two hydrogen atoms
 b. two oxygen atoms
 c. a hydrogen atom and an oxygen atom
 d. negative charges

8. An atom that can donate electrons during a reaction is called
 a. an oxidizing agent
 b. a reducing agent
 c. an ionic agent
 d. an electrolyte

9. In a solution of NaCl and water, NaCl is the _____ and water is the _____.
 a. acid, base
 b. base, acid
 c. solute, solvent
 d. solvent, solute

10. A solution with a pH of 2 _____ than a solution with a pH of 8.
 a. has less H^+
 b. has more H^+
 c. has more OH^-
 d. is less concentrated

11. Fructose is a type of
 a. disaccharide
 b. monosaccharide
 c. polysaccharide
 d. amino acid

12. Bond formation in polysaccharides and polypeptides is accompanied by the removal of a
 a. hydrogen atom
 b. hydroxyl ion
 c. carbon atom
 d. water molecule

13. The monomer unit of polysaccharides such as starch and cellulose is
 a. fructose
 b. glucose
 c. ribose
 d. lactose

14. A phospholipid contains
 a. three fatty acids bound to glycerol
 b. three fatty acids, a glycerol, and a phosphate
 c. two fatty acids and a phosphate bound to glycerol
 d. three cholesterol molecules bound to glycerol

15. Proteins are synthesized by linking amino acids with _____ bonds.
 a. disulfide
 b. glycosidic
 c. peptide
 d. ester

16. The amino acid that accounts for disulfide bonds in the tertiary structure of proteins is
 a. tyrosine
 b. glycine
 c. cysteine
 d. serine

17. DNA is a hereditary molecule that is composed of
 a. deoxyribose, phosphate, and nitrogen bases
 b. deoxyribose, a pentose, and nucleic acids
 c. sugar, proteins, and thymine
 d. adenine, phosphate, and ribose

18. What is meant by the term *DNA replication?*
 a. synthesis of nucleotides
 b. cell division
 c. interpretation of the genetic code
 d. the exact copying of the DNA code into two new molecules

19. Proteins can function as
 a. enzymes
 b. receptors
 c. antibodies
 d. all of these

20. RNA plays an important role in what biological process?
 a. replication
 b. protein synthesis
 c. lipid metabolism
 d. water transport

 Case Study Review

1. Which of the following has not been an objective of Mars exploration?
 a. to analyze elements in soil
 b. to mine for gold
 c. to detect organic compounds
 d. to detect CO_2

2. What was a significant result of the Mars *Phoenix* project?
 a. culturing bacteria c. finding organic matter
 b. verifying water d. discovering precious metals

3. What other elements present in earth microorganisms would one expect to find on Mars?

 Writing Challenge

For each question, compose a one- or two-paragraph answer that includes the factual information needed to completely address the question. Check Your Progress questions can also be used for writing-challenge exercises.

1. Explain this statement: "All compounds are molecules, but not all molecules are compounds." Give an example.

2. What causes atoms to form chemical bonds? Why do some elements not bond readily?

3. Why are some covalent molecules polar and others nonpolar?

4. Explain why some elements are diatomic.

5. Exactly what causes the charges to form on atoms in ionic bonds?

6. Why are hydrogen bonds relatively weak?

7. What kind of substances will be expected to be hydrophilic and hydrophobic, and what makes them so?

8. How can a neutral salt be formed from acids and bases?

9. a. What characteristic of phospholipids makes them essential components of cell membranes?
 b. How are saturated and unsaturated fatty acids different?
 c. Why is the hydrophilic end of phospholipids attracted to water?

10. What makes the amino acids distinctive, and how many of them are there?

11. Why is DNA called a double helix?

12. Describe what occurs in a dehydration synthesis reaction.

13. How is our understanding of microbiology enhanced by a knowledge of chemistry?

 Concept Mapping

An Introduction to Concept Mapping found at http://www.mhhe.com/talaro9 provides guidance for working with concept maps.

1. Supply your own linking words or phrases in this concept map, and provide the missing concepts in the empty boxes.

2. Construct your own concept map of macromolecules using table 2.4 as a guide.

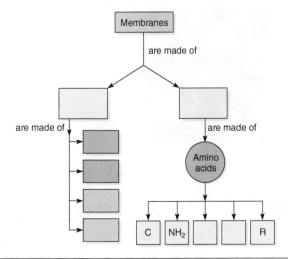

58 **Chapter 2** The Chemistry of Biology

Level II. Application, Analysis, Evaluation, and Synthesis

These problems go beyond just restating facts and require higher levels of understanding and an ability to interpret, problem solve, transfer knowledge to new situations, create models, and predict outcomes.

 Critical Thinking

Critical thinking is the ability to reason and solve problems using facts and concepts. These questions can be approached from a number of angles, and in most cases, they do not have a single correct answer.

1. The "octet rule" in chemistry helps predict the types of bonds that atoms will form. In general, an atom will be most stable if it fills its outer shell of 8 electrons. Atoms with fewer than 4 valence electrons tend to donate electrons and those with more than 4 valence electrons tend to accept additional electrons; those with exactly 4 can do both. Using this rule, determine what category each of the following elements falls into: N, S, C, P, O, H, Ca, Fe, and Mg. (You will need to work out the valence of the atoms.)

2. Predict the kinds of bonds that occur in ammonium (NH_3), phosphate (PO_4), disulfide (S—S), and magnesium chloride ($MgCl_2$). (Use simple models, such as those in figure 2.4.)

3. Work out the following problems:
 a. Will an H bond form between H_3C—CH═O and H_2O? Draw a simple figure to support your answer.
 b. Draw the following molecules and determine which are polar: Cl_2, NH_3, CH_4.
 c. What is the pH of a solution with a concentration of 0.00001 moles/ml (M) of H^+?
 d. What is the pH of a solution with a concentration of 0.00001 moles/ml (M) of OH^-?

 e. Draw the atomic structure of magnesium and predict what kinds of bonds it will make.
 f. What kind of ion would you expect magnesium to make on the basis of its valence?

4. Distinguish between polar and ionic compounds.

5. Is galactose an aldehyde or a ketone sugar?

6. a. How many water molecules are released when a triglyceride is formed?
 b. How many peptide bonds are in a hexapeptide?

7. Observe figure 2.26 and explain why adenine forms hydrogen bonds only with thymine and why cytosine forms them only with guanine.

8. For a and b, explain your choice.
 a. Is butter an example of a saturated or an unsaturated fat?
 b. Is olive oil an example of a saturated or an unsaturated fat?
 c. Explain why sterols like cholesterol can add "stiffness" to membranes that contain them.

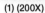 **Visual Challenge**

1. Figures 1 and 2 are both highly magnified views of biological substances. Using **figure 2.17** as your basis for comparison, speculate which molecules are shown and give the reasons for them having the microscopic appearance we see here.

(1) (200X) (2)

CHAPTER **3** **Tools of the Laboratory**
Methods of Studying Microorganisms

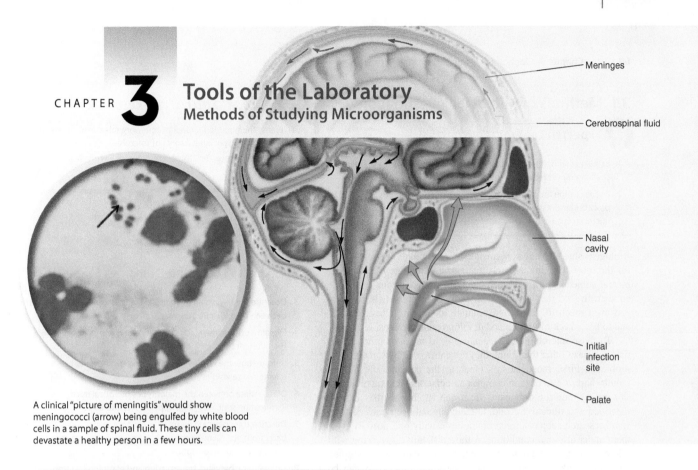

Meninges

Cerebrospinal fluid

Nasal cavity

Initial infection site

Palate

A clinical "picture of meningitis" would show meningococci (arrow) being engulfed by white blood cells in a sample of spinal fluid. These tiny cells can devastate a healthy person in a few hours.

CASE STUDY Part 1 Battling a Brain Infection

One Saturday evening in 2007, a 50-year-old woman named Kay Peterson began to suffer **flulike symptoms,** with **fever,** aching joints, sore throat, and a headache. Feeling miserable but not terribly concerned, she took some ibuprofen and went to bed. By the following morning, she began to feel increasingly ill and was unstable on her feet, **confused,** and complaining of **light-headedness.** Realizing this was more than just the flu, her husband rushed her immediately to the nearest emergency room.

An initial examination showed that most of Kay's vital signs were normal. Conditions that may provide some clues were rapid pulse and respiration, an **inflamed throat,** and a **stiff neck.** A **chest X ray** revealed no sign of **pneumonia,** and a blood test indicated an elevated **white blood cell** count. To rule out a possible brain infection, a puncture of the spinal canal was performed. As it turned out, the **cerebrospinal fluid (CSF)** the technician extracted appeared normal, microscopically and macroscopically.

Within an hour, Kay began to drift in and out of consciousness and was extremely lethargic. At one point, the medical team could

"Our intervention was truly a matter of life or death."

not find a pulse and noticed **dark brown spots** developing on her legs. When her condition appeared to be deteriorating rapidly, she was immediately taken to the intensive care unit and placed on **intravenous antibiotics.** One of the emergency doctors later reported that, "Her medical situation was so critical that our intervention was truly a matter of life or death."

Because Kay's symptoms pointed to a possible infection of the **central nervous system,** a second spinal puncture was performed. This time, the spinal fluid looked cloudy. A **Gram stain** was performed right away, and **cultures** were started.

▶ What are signs and symptoms of disease? Give examples from the case that appear to be the most diagnostically significant.

▶ What is the importance of a Gram stain in diagnosis of an infection like this?

To continue the Case Study, go to page 84.

3.1 Methods of Microbial Investigation

 Expected Learning Outcomes

1. Explain what unique characteristics of microorganisms make them challenging subjects for study.
2. Briefly outline the processes and purposes of the six types of procedures that are used in handling, maintaining, and studying microorganisms.

Biologists studying large organisms such as animals and plants can, for the most part, immediately see and differentiate their experimental subjects from the surrounding environment and from one another. In fact, they can use their senses of sight, smell, hearing, and even touch to detect and evaluate identifying characteristics and to keep track of growth and developmental changes.

Because microbiologists cannot rely as much as other scientists on senses other than sight, they are confronted by some unique problems. First, most habitats (such as the soil and the human mouth) harbor microbes in complex associations. It is often necessary to separate the organisms from one another so they can be identified and studied. Second, to maintain and keep track of such small research subjects, microbiologists usually will need to grow them under artificial conditions. A third difficulty in working with microbes is that they are not visible to the naked eye. This, coupled with their wide distribution means that undesirable ones can be inconspicuously introduced into an experiment, where they may cause misleading results.

To deal with the challenges of their tiny and sometimes elusive targets, microbiologists have developed several types of procedures for investigating and characterizing microorganisms. These techniques can be summed up succinctly as the **six "I's": inoculation, incubation, isolation, inspection, information gathering,** and **identification,** so-called because they all begin with the letter "I". The main features of the 6 "I's" are laid out in **figure 3.1** and **table 3.1.** Depending on the purposes of the particular investigator, these may be performed in several combinations and orders, but together, they serve as the major tools of the microbiologist's trade. As novice microbiologists, most of you will be learning some basic microscope, inoculation, culturing, and identification techniques. Many professional researchers use more advanced investigation and identification techniques that may not even require growth or absolute isolation of the microbe in culture (see 3.1 Secret World of Microbes). If you examine the example from the case file in chapter 1, you will notice that the researchers used only some of the 6 "I's", whereas the case file in this chapter includes all of them in some form.

The first four sections of this chapter cover some of the essential concepts that revolve around the 6 "I's", but not necessarily in the exact order presented in figure 3.1. Microscopes are so important to microbiological inquiry that we start out with the subject of microscopes, magnification, and staining techniques. This is followed by culturing procedures and media.

Quick Search

Take "A Tour of the Microbiology Lab" on YouTube to see the daily work performed there.

1. Name the notable features of microorganisms that have created a need for the specialized tools of microbiology.
2. In one sentence, briefly define what is involved in each of the six "I's".

3.2 The Microscope: Window on an Invisible Realm

 Expected Learning Outcomes

3. Describe the basic plan of an optical microscope, and differentiate between magnification and resolution.
4. Explain how the images are formed, along with the role of light and the different powers of lenses.
5. Indicate how the resolving power is determined and how resolution affects image visibility.
6. Differentiate between the major types of optical microscopes, their illumination sources, image appearance, and uses.
7. Describe the operating features of electron microscopes and how they differ from optical microscopes in illumination source, magnification, resolution, and image appearance.
8. Differentiate between transmission and scanning electron microsopes in image formation and appearance.

Imagine **Leeuwenhoek's** excitement and wonder when he first viewed a drop of rainwater and glimpsed an amazing microscopic world teeming with unearthly creatures. Beginning microbiology students still experience this sensation, and even experienced microbiologists remember their first view. The microbial existence is indeed another world, but it would remain largely uncharted without an essential tool: the microscope. Your efforts in exploring microbes will be more meaningful if you understand some essentials of **microscopy*** and specimen preparation.

Magnification and Microscope Design

The two key characteristics of a reliable microscope are **magnification,*** the ability to make objects appear enlarged, and **resolving power,** the ability to show detail.

A discovery by early microscopists that spurred the advancement of microbiology was that a clear, glass sphere could act as a lens to magnify small objects. Magnification in most microscopes results from a complex interaction between visible light waves and the curvature of the lens. When a beam or ray of light transmitted through air strikes and passes through the convex surface of glass, it experiences some degree of **refraction,*** defined as the bending

* *microscopy* (mye-kraw′-skuh-pee) Gr. The science that studies microscope techniques.
* *magnification* (mag′-nih-fih-kay″-shun) L. *magnus*, great, and *ficere*, to make.
* *refract, refraction* (ree-frakt′, ree-frak′-shun) L. *refringere*, to break apart.

INOCULATION

The sample is placed into a container of medium that will support its growth. The medium may be solid or liquid, and held in tubes, plates, flasks, and even eggs. The delivery tool is usually a loop, needle, swab, or syringe.

Streak plate

Blood bottle

Bird embryo

IDENTIFICATION

One goal of these procedures is to attach a name or identity to the microbe, using information gathered from inspection and investigation. Identification is accomplished through the use of keys, charts, and computer programs that analyze the data and arrive at a final conclusion.

Keys

INCUBATION

Inoculated media are placed in a controlled environment (incubator) to promote growth. During the hours or days of this process, a culture develops as the visible growth of the microbes in the container of medium.

Incubator

INFORMATION GATHERING

Additional tests for microbial function and characteristics may include inoculations into specialized media that determine biochemical traits, immunological testing, and genetic typing. Such tests will provide specific information unique to a certain microbe.

Biochemical tests

Drug sensitivity

DNA analysis

Immunologic tests

SPECIMEN COLLECTION

Microbiologists begin by sampling the object of their interest. It could be nearly any thing or place on earth. Very common sources are body fluids, foods, water, soil, plants, and animals, but even places like icebergs, volcanoes, and rocks can be sampled.

URINE

ISOLATION

Some inoculation techniques can separate microbes to create isolated colonies that each contain a single type of microbe. This is invaluable for identifying the exact species of microbes in the sample, and it paves the way for making pure cultures.

Pure culture of bacteria

Subculture

INSPECTION

Cultures are observed for the macroscopic appearance of growth characteristics. Cultures are examined under the microscope for basic details such as cell type and shape. This may be enhanced through staining and use of special microscopes.

Staining

Figure 3.1 An overview of some general laboratory techniques carried out by microbiologists. "The six "I's". Procedures start at the central "hub" of specimen collection and flow from there to inoculation, incubation, and so on. But not all steps are always performed, nor do they necessarily proceed exactly in this order. Some investigators go right from sampling to microscopic inspection or from sampling to DNA testing. Others may require only inoculation and incubation on special media or test systems. See table 3.1 for a brief description of each procedure, its purpose, and intended outcome.

TABLE 3.1	An Overview of Microbiology Techniques		
Technique	**Process Involves**	**Purpose and Outcome**	**See Pages**
Inoculation	Placing a sample into a container of medium that supplies nutrients for growth and is the first stage in culturing	To increase visibility; makes it possible to handle and manage microbes in an artificial environment and begin to analyze what the sample may contain	72, 73
Incubation	Exposing the inoculated medium to optimal growth conditions, generally for a few hours to days	To promote multiplication and produce the actual culture. An increase in microbe numbers will provide the higher quantities needed for further testing.	74
Isolation	Methods for separating individual microbes and achieving isolated colonies that can be readily distinguished from one another macroscopically*	To make additional cultures from single colonies to ensure they are pure; that is, containing only a single species of microbe for further observation and testing	74–76
Inspection	Observing cultures macroscopically for appearance of growth and microscopically for appearance of cells	To analyze initial characteristics of microbes in samples; stains of cells may reveal information on cell type and morphology	62–72
Information gathering	Testing of cultures with procedures that analyze biochemical and enzyme characteristics, immunologic reactions, drug sensitivity, and genetic makeup	To provide much specific data and generate an overall profile of the microbes. These test results and descriptions will become key determinants in the last category, identification.	75, 77–84
Identification	Analysis of collected data to help support a final determination of the types of microbes present in the original sample. This is accomplished by a variety of schemes.	This lays the groundwork for further research into the nature and roles of these microbes; it can also provide numerous applications in infection diagnosis, food safety, biotechnology, and microbial ecology.	75, 77

*Observable to the unaided or naked eye. This term usually applies to the cultural level of study.

or change in the angle of the light ray as it passes through a medium such as a lens. The greater the difference in the composition of the two substances the light passes between, the more pronounced is the refraction. When an object is placed a certain distance from the spherical lens and illuminated with light, an optical replica, or **image,** of it is formed by the refracted light. Depending upon the size and curvature of the lens, the image appears enlarged to a particular degree, which is called its power of magnification and is usually identified with a number combined with × (read "times"). This behavior of light is evident if one looks through an everyday object such as a glass ball or a magnifying glass (**figure 3.2).** It is basic to the function of all optical, or light, microscopes, though many of them have additional features that define, refine, and increase the size of the image.

The first microscopes were **simple,** meaning they contained just a single magnifying lens and a few working parts. Examples of this type of microscope are a magnifying glass, a hand lens, and Leeuwenhoek's basic little tool shown earlier in figure 1.9a. Among the refinements that led to the development of today's **compound** (two-lens) **microscope** were the addition of a second magnifying lens system, a lamp in the base to give off visible light and **illuminate*** the specimen, and a special lens called the **condenser** that converges or focuses the rays of light to a single point on the object. The fundamental parts of a modern compound light microscope are illustrated in **figure 3.3a.**

Figure 3.2 Effects of magnification. Demonstration of the magnification and image-forming capacity of clear glass "lenses." Given a proper source of illumination, a magnifying glass can deliver 2 to 10 times magnification.

* *illuminate* (ill-oo′-mih-nayt) L. *illuminatus,* to light up.

Principles of Light Microscopy

To be most effective, a microscope should provide adequate magnification, resolution, and clarity of image. Magnification of the object or specimen by a compound microscope occurs in two phases. The first lens in this system (the one closest to the specimen) is the objective lens, and the second (the one closest to the eye) is the ocular lens, or eyepiece **(figure 3.3b).** The objective forms the initial image of the specimen, called the **real image.** When the real image is projected to the plane of the eyepiece, the ocular lens magnifies it to produce a second image, the **virtual image.** The virtual image is the one that will be received by the eye and converted to a retinal and visual image. The magnifying power of the objective alone usually ranges from 4× to 100×, and the power of the ocular alone ranges from 10× to 20×. The total power of magnification of

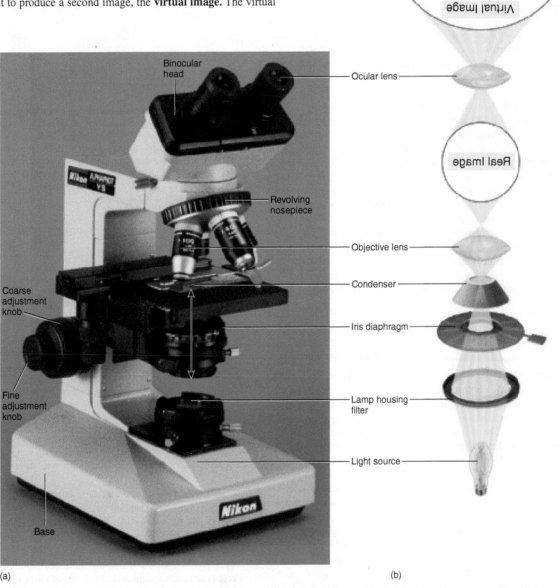

(a)

(b)

Figure 3.3 **(a) The main parts of a microscope.** This is a compound light microscope with two oculars for viewing (binocular). It usually has four objective lenses, a mechanical stage to move the specimen, a condenser, an iris diaphragm, and a built-in light source (lamp). **(b) Light pathway and image formation in light microscopes.** Light formed by the lamp is directed through the lamp filter and into the opening of the iris diaphragm; the condenser gathers the light rays and focuses them into a single point on the specimen; an enlarged image of the specimen—the real image—is next formed by the objective lens. This image is not seen but is projected into the ocular lens, which forms a final level of magnification called the virtual image. This image is observed in the field of view by the eye and perceived by the brain. Note that the lenses reverse the image and flip it upside down.

the final image formed by the combined lenses is a product of the separate powers of the two lenses:

Power of Objective	×	Usual Power of Ocular	=	Total Magnification
4× scanning objective		10×	=	40×
10× low power objective		10×	=	100×
40× high dry objective		10×	=	400×
100× oil immersion objective		10×	=	1,000×

Microscopes are equipped with a nosepiece holding three or more objectives that can be rotated into position as needed. The power of the ocular usually remains constant for a given microscope. Depending on the power of the ocular, the total magnification of standard light microscopes can vary from 40× with the lowest power objective (called the scanning objective) to 2,000×[1] with the highest power objective (the oil immersion objective).

Resolution: Distinguishing Magnified Objects Clearly In addition to magnification, a microscope must also have adequate **resolution, or resolving power.** Resolution defines the capacity of an optical system to distinguish two adjacent objects or points from one another. For example, at a distance of 25 cm (10 in), the lens in the human eye can resolve two small objects as separate points just as long as the two objects are no closer than 0.2 mm apart. The eye examination given by optometrists is in fact a test of the resolving power of the human eye for various-size letters read at a distance of 20 feet. Because microorganisms are extremely small and usually very close together, they will not be seen with clarity or any degree of detail unless the microscope's lenses can resolve them.

A simple equation in the form of a fraction expresses the main mathematical factors that influence the expression of resolving power.

$$\text{Resolving power (RP)} = \frac{\text{Wavelength of light in nm}}{2 \times \text{Numerical aperture of objective lens}}$$

From this equation, it is evident that the resolving power is a function of the wavelength of light that forms the image, along with certain characteristics of the objective. The light source for optical microscopes consists of a band of colored wavelengths in the visible spectrum. The shortest visible wavelengths are in the violet-blue portion of the spectrum (400 nm), and the longest are in the red portion (750 nm). Because the wavelength must pass between the objects that are being resolved, shorter wavelengths (in the 400–500 nm range) will provide better resolution (**figure 3.4**).

The other factor influencing resolution is the **numerical aperture (NA)**, a mathematical constant derived from the physical structure of the lens. This number represents the angle of light produced by refraction and is a measure of the quantity of light gathered by the lens. Each objective has a fixed numerical aperture reading ranging from 0.1 in the lowest power lens to approximately 1.25 in the highest power (oil immersion) lens. Lenses with higher NAs provide better resolving power because they increase the angle of refraction and widen the cone of light entering the lens. For the

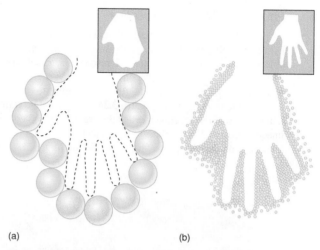

(a) (b)

Figure 3.4 Effect of wavelength on resolution. A simple model demonstrates how the wavelength influences the resolving power of a microscope. Here an outline of a hand represents the object being illuminated, and two different-size beads represent the wavelengths of light. In **(a)**, the longer waves are too large to penetrate between the finer spaces and produce a fuzzy, undetailed image. In **(b)**, shorter waves are small enough to enter small spaces and produce a much more detailed image that is recognizable as a hand.

Figure 3.5 Workings of an oil immersion lens. To maximize its resolving power, an oil immersion lens (the one with highest magnification) must have a drop of oil placed at its tip. This transmits a continuous cone of light from the condenser to the objective, thereby increasing the amount of light and, consequently, the numerical aperture. Without oil, some of the peripheral light that passes through the specimen is scattered into the air or onto the glass slide; this scattering decreases resolution.

oil immersion lens to arrive at its maximum resolving capacity, a drop of oil must be inserted between the tip of the lens and the specimen on the glass slide. Because immersion oil has the same optical qualities as glass, it prevents refractive loss that normally occurs as peripheral light passes from the slide into the air; this property effectively increases the numerical aperture (**figure 3.5**). There is an absolute limitation to resolution in optical microscopes, which can be demonstrated by calculating the resolution of the oil immersion lens using a blue-green wavelength of light:

$$RP = \frac{500 \text{ nm}}{2 \times 1.25}$$
$$= 200 \text{ nm (or } 0.2 \text{ } \mu\text{m)}$$

1. Some microscopes are equipped with 20× oculars or special annuli that can double their magnification.

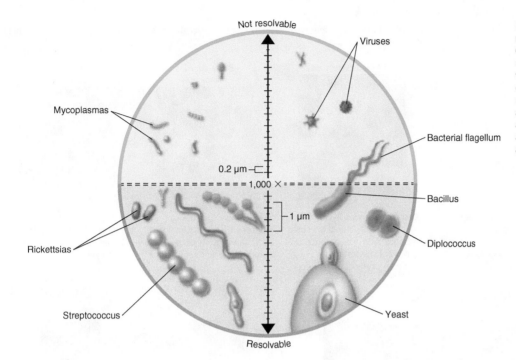

Figure 3.6 Effect of resolution on image visibility. Comparison of objects that would not be resolvable versus those that would be resolvable under oil immersion at 1,000× magnification. Note that in addition to differentiating two adjacent things, good resolution also means being able to observe an object with clarity.

In practical terms, this calculation means that the oil immersion lens can resolve any cell or cell part as long as it is at least 0.2 μm in diameter and that it can resolve two adjacent objects as long as they are no closer than 0.2 μm **(figure 3.6).** In general, organisms that are 0.5 μm or more in diameter are readily seen. This includes fungi and protozoa and some of their internal structures, and most bacteria. However, a few bacteria and most viruses are far too small to be resolved by the optical microscope and require electron microscopy (see figures 1.7 and 3.8). The factor that most limits the clarity of a microscope's image is its resolving power. Even if a light microscope were designed to magnify several thousand times, its resolving power could not be increased, and the image it produced would be enlarged but blurry.

Despite this limit, small improvements to resolution are possible. One is to place a blue filter over the microscope lamp, keeping the wavelength at the shortest possible value. Another comes from maximizing the numerical aperture. That is the effect of adding oil to the immersion lens, which effectively increases the NA from 1.25 to 1.4 and improves the resolving power to 0.17 μm.

Variations on the Optical Microscope

Optical microscopes that use visible light can be described by the nature of their **field of view,** or **field,** which is the circular area observed through the ocular lens. With special adaptations in lenses, condensers, and light sources, four special types of microscopes can be described: bright-field, dark-field, phase-contrast, and interference. A fifth type of optical microscope, the fluorescence microscope, uses ultraviolet radiation as the illuminating source, and a sixth, the confocal microscope, uses a laser beam. Each of these microscopes is adapted for viewing specimens in a particular way, as described in the next sections and summarized in **table 3.2.** Refer back to figure 1.4 for size comparisons of microbes and molecules.

Bright-Field Microscopy

The bright-field microscope is the most widely used type of light microscope. A bright-field microscope forms its image when light is transmitted through the specimen. The specimen, being denser and more opaque than its surroundings, absorbs some of this light, and the rest of the light is transmitted directly up through the ocular into the field. As a result, the specimen will produce an image that is darker than the surrounding brightly illuminated field. The bright-field microscope is a multipurpose instrument that can be used for both live, unstained material and preserved, stained material. The bright-field image is compared with that of other microscopes in table 3.2.

Dark-Field Microscopy

A bright-field microscope can be adapted as a dark-field microscope by adding a special disc called a *stop* to the condenser. The stop blocks all light from entering the objective lens except peripheral light that is reflected off the sides of the specimen itself. The resulting image is brightly illuminated specimens surrounded by a dark (black) field (table 3.2). The most effective use of dark-field microscopy is to visualize living cells that would be distorted by drying or heat, or cannot be stained with the usual methods. It can outline the organism's shape and permit rapid recognition of swimming cells that may appear in fresh specimens, but it does not reveal fine internal details.

Phase-Contrast and Interference Microscopy

If similar objects made of clear glass, ice, and plastic are immersed in the same container of water, an observer would have difficulty telling

TABLE 3.2 Comparisons of Types of Microscopy

I. Microscopes with visible light illumination
Maximum effective magnification = 1,000× to 2,000×*.
Maximum resolution = 0.2 μm.

A. Comparative Images from Optical Microscopes

The subject here is yeast cells examined at 1,000× with four types of microscopes. Notice the differences in the appearance of the field and the degree of detail shown in the four methods.

Bright-field microscope

Dark-field microscope

Phase-contrast microscope

Differential interference contrast microscope

Common multipurpose microscope for live and preserved stained specimens; specimen is dark, field is white; provides fair cellular detail.

Best for observing live, unstained specimens; specimen is bright, field is black; provides outline of specimen with reduced internal cellular detail.

Used for live specimens; specimen is contrasted against gray background; excellent for internal cellular detail.

Provides very detailed, highly contrasting, three-dimensional images of live specimens.

II. Microscopes with ultraviolet illumination
Maximum effective magnification = 1,000× to 2,000×*.
Maximum resolution = 0.2 μm.

B. Modifications of Optical Microscopes with Specialized Functions

Fluorescent Microscope

Confocal Microscope

Yeast cells stained with fluorescent dyes and viewed at 1,000× emit visible light; dye colors help differentiate live and dead cells. The specificity of this technique makes it a superior diagnostic tool.

Two views of *Paramecium* 1,500×, stained by fluorescent dyes, and scanned by a laser beam, form multiple images that are combined into a three-dimensional image. Note the fine detail of cilia and organelles.

III. Microscopes use a beam of electrons
Maximum effective magnification TEM = 1,000,000×.
Maximum effective magnification SEM = 650,000×.
Maximum resolution TEM = 0.5 nm.
Maximum resolution SEM = 10 nm.

C. Electron Microscopes Image Objects with High-Speed Electrons

Transmission electron microscope (TEM)

Scanning electron microscope (SEM)

Section of a bacterial cell being invaded by bacteriophage viruses 9,500×. This microscope provides the finest detail and resolution for cell and virus internal structure. It can be used only on preserved material.

View of a marine alga known as a coccolithophore, bearing an intricate cell wall 13,000×. The electron beam scans over the surface of the specimen and produces a dramatic three-dimensional image.

*The 2,000× maximum is achieved through the use of a 20× ocular or 2× annulus.

them apart because they have similar optical properties. In the same way, internal components of a live, unstained cell also lack sufficient contrast to distinguish readily. The phase-contrast microscope contains devices that transform the subtle changes in light waves passing through the specimen into differences in light intensity. For example, thicker cell parts such as organelles alter the pathway of light to a greater extent than thinner regions such as the cytoplasm, creating contrast. The amount of internal detail visible by this method is greater than by either bright-field or dark-field methods (table 3.2). The phase-contrast microscope is most useful for observing intracellular structures such as bacterial spores, granules, and organelles, as well as the locomotor structures of eukaryotic cells.

Like the phase-contrast microscope, the **differential interference contrast (DIC)** microscope provides a detailed view of unstained, live specimens by manipulating the light. But this microscope has additional refinements that can add contrasting colors to the image. DIC microscopes produce extremely well-defined images that are often vividly colored and appear three-dimensional (table 3.2).

Confocal Microscopes

Optical microscopes may be unable to form a clear image at higher magnifications, because samples are often too thick for conventional lenses to focus all levels of cells simultaneously. This is especially true of larger cells with complex internal structures. A newer type of microscope that overcomes this impediment is called the *scanning confocal microscope*. This microscope uses a laser beam of light to scan various depths in the specimen and deliver a sharp image focusing on just a single plane. It is thus able to capture a highly focused view at any level, ranging from the surface to the middle of the cell. It is most often used on fluorescently stained specimens, but it can also be used to visualize live unstained cells and tissues (table 3.2).

 CLINICAL CONNECTIONS

Fluorescent Techniques in Identification

Fluorescence microscopy has its most useful applications in diagnosing infections caused by specific bacteria, protozoans, and viruses. A staining technique with fluorescent dyes is commonly used to detect *Mycobacterium tuberculosis* (the agent of tuberculosis) in patients' specimens (see figure 19.20). In a number of diagnostic procedures, fluorescent dyes are bound to specific antibodies. These *fluorescent antibodies* can be used to identify the causative agents in such diseases as syphilis, chlamydia, trichomoniasis, herpes, and influenza. **Figure 3.7** displays the results of a fluorescent antibody technique used to highlight the spirochete of syphilis. A related technology uses fluorescent nucleic acid probes to differentiate between live and dead cells in mixtures or detect uncultured cells (see 3.1 Secret World of Microbes). A fluorescence microscope can be handy for locating specific microbes in complex mixtures because only those cells targeted by the technique will fluoresce.

Explain why fluorescent microscopic techniques can produce more specific results than other light microscopes. *Answer available at http://www.mhhe.com/talaro9*

Figure 3.7 Fluorescent staining of a sample of *Treponema pallidum*, the causative agent of syphilis. The specific fluorescent antibodies that attach only to the pathogen and fluoresce a bright green make it a valuable diagnostic stain. Note the spiral nature of the cells (1,000×).

Fluorescence Microscopy

The fluorescence microscope is a specially modified compound microscope furnished with an ultraviolet (UV) radiation source and filters that protect the viewer's eye from injury by these dangerous rays. The name for this type of microscopy is based on the use of certain dyes (acridine, fluorescein) and minerals that show **fluorescence.** This means that the dyes give off visible light when bombarded by shorter ultraviolet rays. For an image to be formed, the specimen must first be coated or placed in contact with a source of fluorescence. Subsequent illumination by ultraviolet radiation causes the specimen to emit visible light, producing an intense blue, yellow, orange, or red image against a black field.

Electron Microscopy

If conventional light microscopes are our windows on the microscopic world, then the electron microscope (EM) is our window on the tiniest details of that world. Unlike light microscopes, the electron microscope forms an image with a beam of electrons that can be made to travel in wavelike patterns when accelerated to high speeds. These waves are 100,000 times shorter than the waves of visible light. Knowing that resolving power is a function of wavelength makes it evident that the RP fraction and number will become very small. Indeed, it is possible to resolve atoms with an electron microscope, even though the practical resolution for most biological applications is approximately 0.5 nm. The degree of resolution allows magnification to be extremely high—usually between 5,000× and 1,000,000× for biological specimens and up to 5,000,000× in some applications. Its capacity for magnification and resolution makes the EM an invaluable tool for seeing the finest structure of cells and viruses. If not for electron microscopes, our understanding of biological structure and function would still be in its early theoretical stages.

In fundamental ways, the electron microscope is similar to the optical microscope. It employs components analogous to, but not

necessarily the same as, those in light microscopy **(table 3.3)**. For instance, it magnifies in stages by means of two lens systems, and it has a condensing lens, a specimen holder, and a focusing apparatus. Otherwise, the two types have numerous differences (table 3.3). An electron gun aims its beam through a vacuum to ring-shaped elec-

TABLE 3.3	Comparison of Light Microscopes and Electron Microscopes	
Characteristic	Light or Optical	Electron (Transmission)
Useful magnification	2,000×*	1,000,000× or more
Maximum resolution	200 nm (0.2 μm)	0.5 nm
Image produced by	Light rays	Electron beam
Image focused by	Glass objective lens	Electromagnetic objective lenses
Image viewed through	Glass ocular lens	Fluorescent screen
Specimen placed on	Glass slide	Copper mesh
Specimen may be alive.	Yes	Usually not
Specimen requires special stains or treatment.	Depends on technique	Yes
Shows natural color	Yes	No

*This maximum requires a 20× ocular.

tromagnets that focus this beam on the specimen. Specimens must be pretreated with chemicals or dyes to increase contrast and usually cannot be observed in a live state. The enlarged image is displayed on a viewing screen or photographed for further study rather than being observed directly through an eyepiece. Because images produced by electrons lack color, electron micrographs (a micrograph is a photograph of a microscopic object) are always shades of black, gray, and white. The color-enhanced micrographs seen in this and other textbooks have computer-added color.

Two general forms of EM are the **transmission electron microscope (TEM)** and the **scanning electron microscope (SEM)** (see table 3.2). Transmission electron microscopes are the method of choice for viewing the detailed structure of cells and viruses. This microscope produces its image by transmitting electrons through the specimen. Because electrons cannot readily penetrate thick preparations, the specimen must be stained or coated with metals that will increase image contrast and sectioned into extremely thin slices (20–100 nm thick). The electrons passing through the specimen travel to the fluorescent screen and display a pattern or image. The darker and lighter areas of the image correspond to more and less dense parts on the specimen **(figure 3.8a)**. The TEM can also be used to produce negative images and shadow casts of whole microbes (see figure 6.3).

Quick Search
Go to "25 Amazing Electron Microscope Images" for a unique visual experience.

The scanning electron microscope provides some of the most dramatic and realistic images in existence. This instrument can create an extremely detailed three-dimensional view of all things biological—from dental plaque to tapeworm heads. To produce its images, the SEM bombards the surface of a whole, metal-coated specimen with electrons while scanning back and forth over it. A shower of electrons deflected from the surface is picked up with great accuracy by a sophisticated detector, and the electron pattern is displayed as an image on a monitor screen. The contours of the specimens resolved with scanning electron micrography are very revealing and often surprising. Areas that look smooth and flat with the light microscope display intriguing surface features with the SEM **(figure 3.8b)**. Improved technology has continued to refine electron microscopes and to develop variations on the basic plan. Some inventive relatives of the EM are the scanning probe microscope and atomic force microscope **(3.1 Making Connections)**.

(a)

(b)

Figure 3.8 Micrographs from two types of electron microscopes. (a) Colorized TEM image of the H1N1 influenza virus, displaying its internal contents. This was a new strain of virus first observed in 2009. **(b)** SEM image of *Shewanella*, an unusual bacterium that derives energy from uranium and other radioactive materials. Note the fine nanowires it makes to carry electrical impulses and communicate with other cells.

3.1 MAKING CONNECTIONS

The Evolution in Resolution: Probing Microscopes

In the past, chemists, physicists, and biologists had to rely on indirect methods to provide information on the structures of the smallest molecules. But technological advances have created a new generation of microscopes that "see" atomic structure by actually feeling it. *Scanning probe microscopes* operate with a minute needle tapered to a tip that can be as narrow as a single atom! This probe scans over the exposed surface of a material and records an image of its outer texture. These revolutionary microscopes have such profound resolution that they have the potential to image single atoms and to magnify 100 million times. The scanning tunneling microscope (STM) was the first of these microscopes. It uses a tungsten probe that hovers near the surface of an object and follows its topography while simultaneously giving off an electrical signal of its pathway, which is then imaged on a screen. The STM is used primarily for detecting defects on the surfaces of electrical conductors and computer chips, but it has also provided the first incredible close-up views of DNA, the genetic material.

Another variety, the atomic force microscope (AFM), gently forces a diamond and metal probe down onto the surface of a specimen like a needle on a record. As it moves along the surface, any deflection of the metal probe is detected by a sensitive device that relays the information to an imager. The AFM is very useful in viewing the detailed functions of biological molecules such as antibodies and enzymes.

The latest versions of these microscopes have increased the resolving power to around 0.5 Å, which allowed technicians to image a pair of electrons! Such powerful tools for observing and positioning atoms have spawned a field called *nanotechnology*—the science of the "small." Scientists in this area use physics, chemistry, biology, and engineering to manipulate small molecules and atoms.

A section of graphene recently analyzed by the atomic force microscope, which clearly shows the carbon atoms that make up its structure. This image was so detailed that the bonds between the carbon atoms could be visualized and measured for the first time.

Working at these dimensions, researchers are currently creating tiny molecular tools to miniaturize computers and other electronic devices. A great deal of new research is also being devoted to the development of nanoparticles to deliver drugs, analyze DNA, and treat disease (look back at Clinical Connections, page 67).

Looking back at figure 2.1, name some other chemical features that may become visible using these high-power microscopes. *Answer available at http://www.mhhe.com/talaro9*

 Check Your Progress SECTION 3.2

3. Differentiate between the concepts of magnification, refraction, and resolution and explain how they contribute to the clarity of an image.

4. Briefly explain how an image is made and magnified.

5. On the basis of the formula for resolving power, explain why a smaller RP value is preferred to a larger one and explain what it means in practical terms if the resolving power is 1.0 μm.

6. What can be done to a microscope to improve resolution?

7. Compare bright-field, dark-field, phase-contrast, confocal, and fluorescence microscopy as to field appearance, specimen appearance, light source, and uses.

8. Compare and contrast the optical compound microscope with the electron microscope.

9. Why is the resolution so superior in the electron microscope?

10. Compare the way that the image is formed in the TEM and SEM.

3.3 Preparing Specimens for Optical Microscopes

 Expected Learning Outcomes

9. Explain the basic differences between fresh and fixed preparations for microscopy and how they are used.

10. Define dyes and describe the basic chemistry behind the process of staining.

11. Differentiate between negative and positive staining, giving examples.

12. Distinguish between simple, differential, and structural stains, including their applications.

13. Describe the process of Gram staining and how its results can aid the identification process.

A specimen for optical microscopy is generally prepared by mounting a sample on a suitable glass slide that sits on the stage between the condenser and the objective lens. The manner in which a slide

specimen, or mount is prepared depends upon: (1) the condition of the specimen, either in a living or preserved state; (2) the aims of the examiner, whether to observe overall structure, identify the microorganisms, or see movement; and (3) the type of microscopy available, whether it is bright-field, dark-field, phase-contrast, or fluorescence.

Fresh, Living Preparations

Live samples of microorganisms are used to prepare **wet mounts** so that they can be observed as near to their natural state as possible. The cells are suspended in a suitable fluid (water, broth, saline) that temporarily maintains viability and provides space and a medium for locomotion. A wet mount consists of a drop or two of the culture placed on a slide and overlaid with a cover glass. Although this preparation is quick and easy to make, it has certain disadvantages. The cover glass can damage larger cells, and the slide is very susceptible to drying and can contaminate the handler's fingers.

A more satisfactory alternative is the **hanging drop slide** (below) made with a special concave (depression) slide, an adhesive or sealant, and a coverslip from which a small drop of sample is suspended. These types of short-term mounts provide a true assessment of the size, shape, arrangement, color, and motility of cells. Greater cellular detail can be observed with phase-contrast or interference microscopy.

Coverslip

Hanging drop containing specimen

Vaseline

Depression slide

Fixed, Stained Smears

A more permanent mount for long-term study can be obtained by preparing fixed, stained specimens. The smear technique, developed by Robert Koch more than 100 years ago, consists of spreading a thin film made from a liquid suspension of cells on a slide and air-drying it. Next, the air-dried **smear** is usually heated gently by a process called **heat fixation** that simultaneously kills the specimen and secures it to the slide. Fixation also preserves various cellular components in a natural state with minimal distortion. Some types of fixation are performed with chemicals such as alcohol and formalin.

Like images on undeveloped photographic film, the unstained cells of a fixed smear are quite indistinct, no matter how great the magnification or how fine the resolving power of the microscope. The process of "developing" a smear to create contrast and make inconspicuous features stand out requires staining. Staining is any procedure that applies colored chemicals called dyes to specimens. Dyes impart a color to cells or cell parts by becoming affixed to them through a chemical reaction. In general, they are classified as **basic** (cationic) **dyes,** which have a positive charge, or **acidic** (anionic) **dyes,** which have a negative charge.

Negative Versus Positive Staining

Two basic types of staining technique are used, depending upon how a dye reacts with the specimen (summarized in **table 3.4**).

TABLE 3.4	Comparison of Positive and Negative Stains	
	Positive Staining	**Negative Staining**
Appearance of cell	Colored by dye	Clear and colorless
Background	Not stained (generally white)	Stained (dark gray or black)
Dyes employed	Basic dyes: Crystal violet, Methylene blue, Safranin, Malachite green	Acidic dyes: Nigrosin, India ink
Subtypes of stains	Several types: Simple stain, Differential stains, Gram stain, Acid-fast stain, Spore stain, Structural stains, One type of capsule stain, Flagella stain, Spore stain, Granules stain, Nucleic acid stain	Few types: Capsule, Spore, Negative stain of *Bacillus anthracis*

Most procedures involve a **positive stain,** in which the dye actually sticks to cells and gives them color. A **negative stain,** on the other hand, is just the reverse (like a photographic negative). The dye does not stick to the specimen but dries around its outer boundary, forming a silhouette. Nigrosin (blue-black) and India ink (a black suspension of carbon particles) are the dyes most commonly used for negative staining. The cells themselves do not stain because these dyes are negatively charged and are repelled by the negatively charged surface of the cells. The value of negative staining is its relative simplicity and the reduced shrinkage or distortion of cells, as the smear is not heat fixed. A quick assessment can thus be made regarding cellular size, shape, and arrangement. Negative staining is also used to accentuate the capsule that surrounds certain bacteria and yeasts (**figure 3.9**).

Staining Reactions of Dyes

Because many microbial cells lack contrast, it is necessary to use dyes to observe their detailed structure and identify them. Dyes are colored compounds carrying double-bonded groups such as $C=O$, $C=N$, and $N=N$. When these groups are illuminated, they emit specific colors. Most dyes form ions when dissolved in a compatible solvent. The color-bearing ion, termed a **chromophore,**

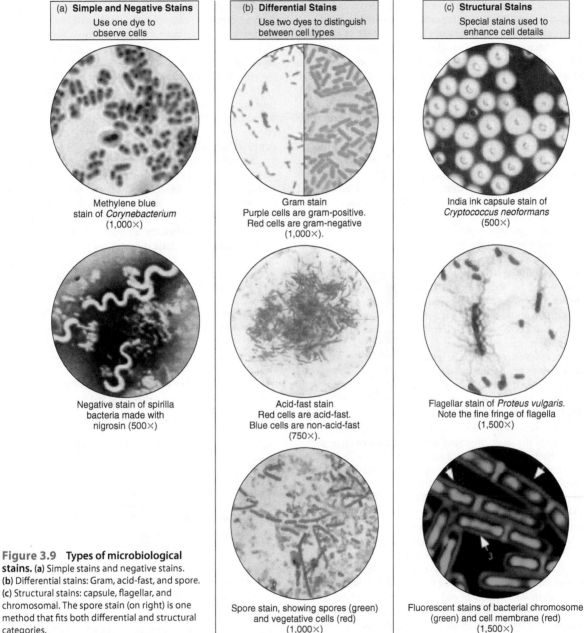

| (a) **Simple and Negative Stains** | (b) **Differential Stains** | (c) **Structural Stains** |
| Use one dye to observe cells | Use two dyes to distinguish between cell types | Special stains used to enhance cell details |

Methylene blue
stain of *Corynebacterium*
(1,000×)

Gram stain
Purple cells are gram-positive.
Red cells are gram-negative
(1,000×).

India ink capsule stain of
Cryptococcus neoformans
(500×)

Negative stain of spirilla
bacteria made with
nigrosin (500×)

Acid-fast stain
Red cells are acid-fast.
Blue cells are non-acid-fast
(750×).

Flagellar stain of *Proteus vulgaris*.
Note the fine fringe of flagella
(1,500×)

Figure 3.9 Types of microbiological stains. (a) Simple stains and negative stains. (b) Differential stains: Gram, acid-fast, and spore. (c) Structural stains: capsule, flagellar, and chromosomal. The spore stain (on right) is one method that fits both differential and structural categories.

Spore stain, showing spores (green)
and vegetative cells (red)
(1,000×)

Fluorescent stains of bacterial chromosome
(green) and cell membrane (red)
(1,500×)

has a charge that attracts it to certain cell parts bearing the opposite charge.

Basic dyes carry a positively charged chromophore and are attracted to negatively charged cell components (nucleic acids and proteins). Because bacteria contain large amounts of negatively charged substances, they stain readily with basic dyes such as methylene blue, crystal violet, fuchsin, and safranin.

The chromophores of acidic dyes have a negative charge and therefore bind to areas of a cell carrying a positive charge. One example is eosin, a red dye used to stain blood cells. Because bacterial cells have numerous acidic substances and carry a slightly negative charge on their surface, they tend to repel acidic dyes. Acidic dyes such as nigrosin and India ink can still be used successfully on bacteria using the negative stain method (table 3.4). With this technique, the dye settles around the cell and creates a dark background.

Simple Versus Differential Staining Positive staining methods are classified as simple, differential, or structural (figure 3.9). **Simple stains** require only a single dye and an uncomplicated procedure, while **differential stains** use two different-colored dyes, called the *primary dye* and the *counterstain,* to distinguish between cell types or parts.

These staining techniques tend to be more complex, sometimes requiring additional chemical reagents to produce the desired reaction.

Most simple staining techniques take advantage of the ready binding of bacterial cells to dyes like malachite green, crystal violet, basic fuchsin, and safranin. Simple stains cause all cells in a smear to appear more or less the same color, regardless of type, but they can still reveal characteristics such as shape, size, and arrangement. A simple stain with methylene blue is often used to stain granules in bacteria such as *Corynebacterium* (**figure 3.9a**), which can be a factor in identification.

Types of Differential Stains An effective differential stain uses dyes of contrasting color to clearly emphasize differences between two cell types or cell parts. Common combinations are red and purple, red and green, or pink and blue. Differential stains can also pinpoint other characteristics, such as the size, shape, and arrangement of cells. Typical examples include Gram, acid-fast, and endospore stains. Some staining techniques (spore, capsule) fall into more than one category.

Gram staining is a 130-year-old method named for its developer, **Hans Christian Gram.** Even today, it is an important diagnostic staining technique for bacteria. It permits ready differentiation of major categories based upon the color reaction of the cells: **gram-positive,** which are stained purple, and **gram-negative,** which are stained red (**figure 3.9b**). This difference in staining quality is due to structural variations

> **Quick Search**
> Visit "Microbiology-Bytes: The Gram Stain" to see a demonstration of this technique.

found in the cell walls of bacteria (look ahead to chapter 4). The Gram stain is the basis of several important bacteriologic topics, including bacterial taxonomy, cell wall structure, identification, and drug therapy. As we will see in the case file to continue, it is a critical step in diagnosing meningitis. Gram staining is discussed in greater detail in **3.2 Making Connections.**

The **acid-fast stain,** like the Gram stain, is an important diagnostic stain that differentiates acid-fast bacteria (pink) from non-acid-fast bacteria (blue). This stain originated as a specific method to detect *Mycobacterium tuberculosis* in specimens. It was determined that these bacterial cells have a particularly impervious outer wall that holds fast (tightly or tenaciously) to the dye (carbol fuchsin), even when washed with a solution containing acid or acid alcohol (figure 3.9b). This stain is used for other medically important mycobacteria such as the Hansen's disease (leprosy) bacillus and for *Nocardia,* an agent of lung or skin infections (see chapter 19).

The **endospore stain** (spore stain) is similar to the acid-fast method in that a dye is forced by heat into resistant survival cells called spores or endospores. These are formed in response to adverse conditions and are not reproductive (see chapter 4). This stain is designed to distinguish between spores and the vegetative cells that make them (figure 3.9b). Of significance in medical microbiology are the gram-positive, spore-forming members of the genus *Bacillus* (the cause of anthrax) and *Clostridium* (the cause of botulism and tetanus)—dramatic diseases of universal fascination that we consider in later chapters.

Structural stains are used to emphasize special cell parts such as capsules, endospores, and flagella that are not revealed by conventional staining methods. Capsule staining is a method of observing the microbial capsule, an unstructured protective layer surrounding the cells of some bacteria and fungi. Because the capsule does not react with most stains, it is often negatively stained with India ink, or it may be demonstrated by special positive stains. The fact that not all microbes exhibit capsules is a useful feature for identifying pathogens. One example is *Cryptococcus,* which causes a serious fungal meningitis in AIDS patients (**figure 3.9c**).

Flagellar staining is a method of revealing flagella, the tiny, slender filaments used by bacteria for locomotion. Because the width of bacterial flagella lies beyond the resolving power of the light microscope, in order to be seen, they must be enlarged by depositing a coating on the outside of the filament and then staining it. The presence, number, and arrangement of flagella can be helpful in identification of bacteria (figure 3.9c).

 Check Your Progress SECTION 3.3

11. Itemize the various staining methods, and briefly characterize each.
12. Explain what happens in positive staining to cause the reaction in the cell.
13. Explain what happens in negative staining that causes the final result.
14. For a stain to be considered differential, what must it do?
15. Outline the main differential stains and how they are used.

3.4 Additional Features of the Six "I's"

 Expected Learning Outcomes

14. Define *inoculation, media,* and *culture,* and describe sampling methods and instruments, and what events must be controlled.
15. Describe three basic techniques for isolation, including tools, media, incubation, and outcome.
16. Explain what an isolated colony is and indicate how it forms.
17. Differentiate between a pure culture, subculture, mixed culture, and contaminated culture. Define *contaminant.*
18. What kinds of data are collected during information gathering?
19. Describe some of the processes involved in identifying microbes from samples.

Inoculation, Growth, and Identification of Cultures

To cultivate, or **culture,*** microorganisms, one introduces a tiny sample (the inoculum) into a container of nutrient **medium*** (pl. media), which provides an environment in which they multiply. This process

* *culture* (kul'-chur) Gr. *cultus,* to tend or cultivate. It can be used as a verb or a noun.
* *medium* (mee'-dee-um) pl. media; L. middle.

3.2 MAKING CONNECTIONS

The Gram Stain: A Grand Stain

In 1884, Hans Christian Gram discovered a staining technique that could be used to make bacteria in infectious specimens more visible. His technique consisted of timed, sequential applications of crystal violet (the primary dye), Gram's iodine (IKI, the mordant), an alcohol rinse (decolorizer), and a contrasting counterstain—usually, the red dye, safranin. This color choice provides differentiation between bacteria that stain purple, called gram-positive, and those that stain red, called gram-negative.

Although these staining reactions involve an attraction of the cell to a charged dye, it is important to note that the terms *gram-positive* and *gram-negative* are not used to indicate the electrical charge of cells or dyes but whether or not a cell retains the primary dye-iodine complex after decolorization. There is nothing specific in the reaction of gram-positive cells to the primary dye or in the reaction of gram-negative cells to the counterstain. The different results in the Gram stain are due to differences in the structure of the cell wall and how it reacts to the series of reagents applied to the cells.

In the first step, crystal violet stains cells in a smear all the same purple color. The second and key differentiating step is the mordant—Gram's iodine. The mordant causes the dye to form large crystals that get trapped by the meshwork of the cell wall. Because this layer in gram-positive cells is thicker, the entrapment of the dye is far more extensive in them than in gram-negative cells. Application of alcohol in the third step dissolves lipids in the outer membrane of the gram-negative cells, which removes the dye from them. By contrast, the crystals of dye tightly embedded in the gram-positive bacteria are relatively inaccessible and resistant to removal. Because gram-negative bacteria are colorless after decolorization, their presence is demonstrated by applying the counterstain safranin in the final step.

This staining method remains an important basis for bacterial classification and identification. It permits differentiation of four major

Step	Microscopic Appearance of Cell		Chemical Reaction in Cell (very magnified view)	
	Gram (+)	Gram (–)	Gram (+)	Gram (–)
1 Crystal violet (primary dye)			Both cell walls stain with the dye.	
2 Gram's iodine (mordant)			Dye crystals trapped in cell	No effect of iodine
3 Alcohol (decolorizer)			Crystals remain in cell.	Outer wall is weakened; cell loses dye.
4 Safranin (red dye counterstain)			Red dye has no effect.	Red dye stains the colorless cell.

categories based upon color reaction and shape: gram-positive rods, gram-positive cocci, gram-negative rods, and gram-negative cocci (see table 4.4). The Gram stain can also be a practical aid in diagnosing infection and in guiding drug treatment. For example, Gram staining a fresh urine or throat specimen can point to a preliminary cause of infection, and in some cases, it is possible to begin drug therapy on the basis of this stain. Even in this day of elaborate and expensive medical technology, the Gram stain remains an important and unbeatable first tool in diagnosis.

Could the Gram stain be used to diagnose the flu? Why or why not?
Answer available at http://www.mhhe.com/talaro9

is called **inoculation.*** The observable growth that later appears in or on the medium is known as a culture. The nature of the sample being cultured depends on the objectives of the analysis. Clinical specimens for determining the cause of an infectious disease are obtained from body fluids (blood, cerebrospinal fluid), discharges (sputum, urine, feces), or diseased tissue. Samples subject to microbiological analysis can include nearly any natural material. Some common ones are soil, water, sewage, foods, air, and inanimate objects. The important concept of media will be covered in more detail in section 3.5.

A past assumption has been that most microbes could be teased out of samples and cultured, given the proper media. But this view has had to be greatly revised (**3.1 Secret World of Microbes**).

Some Special Requirements of Culturing

Inherent in these practices are the implementation of **sterile, aseptic, and pure culture**[2] techniques. Contamination during inoculation is a constant problem, so sterile techniques (media, transfer equipment) help ensure that only microbes that came from the sample are present. Another concern is the possible release of infectious agents from cultures into the environment, which is prevented by aseptic techniques. Many of these techniques revolve around keeping species in the pure culture form for further study, identification, or biotechnology applications.

* *inoculation* (in-ok″-yoo-lay′-shun) L. *in,* and *oculus,* eye.

2. *Sterile* means the complete absence of viable microbes; *aseptic* refers to prevention of infection; *pure culture* refers to growth of a single species of microbe.

3.1 Secret World of Microbes
The Uncultured

For some time, microbiologists have had abundant evidence that culture-based methods are unable to identify many kinds of bacteria. This was first confirmed by environmental researchers, who came to believe that only about 1% (and in some environments, it was 0.001%) of microbes present in lakes, soil, and saltwater environments could be grown in laboratories by the usual methods and, therefore, were unknown and unstudied. These microbes are termed **viable but nonculturable,** or **VBNC.**

Microbiologists have spent several decades concocting recipes for media and having great success in growing all kinds of bacteria from all kinds of environments. Just identifying and studying those kept them very occupied. But by the 1990s, a number of specific, nonculturing tools based on genetic testing had become widely available. When these methods were used to sample various environments, they revealed a vast "jungle" of new species that had never before been cultured. These were the techniques that Venter's team applied to ocean samples (see Case Study, page 1). This discovery seemed reasonable, because it may not yet be possible to exactly re-create the many correct media and conditions to grow such organisms in the lab.

Medical microbiologists have also missed a large proportion of microbes that are normal residents of the body. Stanford University scientists applied these techniques to subgingival plaque harvested from one of their own mouths. They used small, known fragments of DNA or probes that can highlight microbes in specimens. Oral biologists had previously recovered about 500 bacterial strains from this site; the Stanford scientists found 30 species that had never before been cultured or described. This discovery energized the medical world and spurred the use of non-culture-based methods to find VBNCs in the human body.

The new realization that our bodies are hosts to a wide variety of unknown microbes has several implications. As evolutionary microbiologist

A fluorescent micrograph of a biofilm of *Vibrio cholerae* (orange cells) taken from a water sample in India. After an attempt to culture these bacteria over 495 days, a few cells enlarged, but most remained inactive. This pathogen appears to remain dormant in water where it can serve as a source of cholera infection for people drinking the water.

Paul Ewald has asked, "What are all those microbes doing in there?" He points out that many oral microbes previously assumed to be innocuous are now associated with cancer and heart disease. Many of the diseases that we currently think of as noninfectious will likely be found to have an infectious cause once we continue to look for VBNCs.

Look ahead to chapter 13, we will explore some of the findings from the Human Microbiome Project, which recently did a comprehensive study of the microbial content of several body sites. One important finding was the essential functions these residents can have in protective immunities.

Do you think that all of the VBNCs are really not culturable? Suggest some other possibilities. *Answer available at http://www.mhhe.com/talaro9*

Isolation Techniques

Certain **isolation** techniques are based on the concept that if an individual bacterial cell is separated from other cells and provided adequate space on a nutrient surface, it will grow into a discrete mound of cells called a **colony (figure 3.10).** Because it arises from a single cell or cluster of cells, an isolated colony consists of just one species. Proper isolation requires that a small number of cells be inoculated into a relatively large volume or over an expansive area of medium. It generally requires the following materials: a medium that has a relatively firm surface (see description of agar on page 78) contained in a clear, flat covered plate called a *Petri dish,* and inoculating tools.

In the **streak plate method,** a small droplet of sample is spread with a tool called an **inoculating loop** over the surface of the medium according to a pattern that gradually thins out the sample and separates the cells spatially over several sections of the plate **(figure 3.11a, b).** Because of its ease and effectiveness, the streak plate is the method of choice for most applications.

In the **loop dilution,** or **pour plate, technique,** the sample is inoculated, also with a loop, into a series of cooled but still liquid agar tubes so as to dilute the number of cells in each successive tube in the series **(figure 3.11c, d).** Inoculated tubes are then plated out

(poured) into sterile Petri dishes and are allowed to solidify (harden). The number of cells per volume is so decreased that cells have ample space to form separate colonies in the second or third plate. One difference between this and the streak plate method is that in this technique, some of the colonies will develop deep in the medium itself and not just on the surface.

With the **spread plate technique,** a small volume of liquid from a diluted sample is pipetted onto the surface of the medium and spread around evenly by a sterile spreading tool (sometimes called a "hockey stick"). As with the streak plate, cells are spread over separate areas on the surface so that they can form individual colonies **(figure 3.11e, f).**

Once a container of medium has been inoculated, it is **incubated** in a temperature-controlled chamber (incubator) to encourage microbial growth. Although microbes have adapted to growth at temperatures ranging from freezing to boiling, the usual temperatures used in laboratory propagation fall between 20°C and 40°C. Incubators can also control the content of atmospheric gases such as oxygen and carbon dioxide that may be required for the growth of certain microbes. During the incubation period (ranging from a few hours to several weeks), the microbe multiplies and produces a culture with macroscopically observable growth.

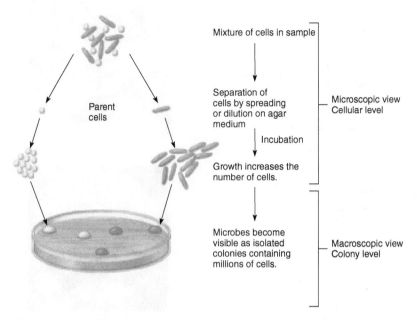

Figure 3.10 Isolation technique. Stages in the formation of an isolated colony, showing the microscopic events and the macroscopic result. Separation techniques such as streaking can be used to isolate single cells. After numerous cell divisions, a macroscopic mound of cells, or a colony, will be formed. This is a relatively simple yet successful way to separate different types of bacteria in a mixed sample.

Mixture of cells in sample

Separation of cells by spreading or dilution on agar medium

Incubation

Growth increases the number of cells.

Parent cells

Microscopic view Cellular level

Microbes become visible as isolated colonies containing millions of cells.

Macroscopic view Colony level

Microbial growth in a liquid medium materializes as cloudiness, sediment, a surface scum, or colored pigment. Growth on solid media may take the form of a spreading mat or separate colonies.

In some ways, culturing microbes is analogous to gardening. Cultures are formed by "seeding" tiny plots (media) with microbial cells. Extreme care is taken to exclude weeds (contaminants). A **pure culture** is a container of medium that grows only a single known species or type of microorganism **(figure 3.12c).** This type of culture is most frequently used for laboratory study, because it allows the precise examination and control of one microorganism by itself. Instead of the term *pure culture,* some microbiologists prefer the term axenic, meaning that the culture is free of other living things except for the one being studied. A standard method for preparing a pure culture is based on a **subculture** technique for making a second-level culture. A tiny bit of cells from a well-isolated colony is transferred into a separate container of media and incubated (see figure 3.1, isolation).

A **mixed culture (figure 3.12a)** is a container that holds two or more easily differentiated species of microorganisms, not unlike a garden plot containing both carrots and onions. A **contaminated culture (figure 3.12b)** has had **contaminants** (unwanted microbes of uncertain identity) introduced into it, like weeds into a garden. Because contaminants have the potential for disrupting experiments and tests, special procedures have been developed to control them, as you will no doubt witness in your own laboratory.

Identification Techniques

How does one determine what sorts of microorganisms have been isolated in cultures? Certainly microscopic appearance can be valu-

able in differentiating the smaller, simpler prokaryotic cells from the larger, more complex eukaryotic cells. Appearance can often be used to identify eukaryotic microorganisms to the level of genus or species because of their more distinctive appearance.

Bacteria are generally not as readily identifiable by these methods because very different species may appear quite similar. For them, we must include other techniques, some of which characterize their cellular metabolism. These methods, called **biochemical tests,** can determine fundamental chemical characteristics such as nutrient requirements, products given off during growth, presence of enzymes, and mechanisms for deriving energy. **Figure 3.13a** provides an example of a multiple-test, miniaturized system for obtaining physiological characteristics. Biochemical tests are discussed in more depth in chapter 17 and chapters that cover identification of pathogens.

Several modern diagnostic tools that analyze genetic characteristics can detect microbes based on their DNA. These DNA profiles can be extremely specific, even sufficient by themselves to identify some microbes (see chapters 10 and 17). Identification can be assisted by testing the isolate against known antibodies (immunologic testing). In the case of certain pathogens, further information is obtained by inoculating a suitable laboratory animal. By compiling physiological testing results with both macroscopic and microscopic traits, a complete picture of the microbe is developed. Expertise in final identification comes from specialists, manuals, and computerized programs. A traditional pathway in bacterial identification uses flowcharts or keys that apply the results of tests to a selection process **(figure 3.13b).** The top of the key provides a general category from which to begin a series of branching points, usually into two pathways at each new junction. The points of separation are based on having a positive or negative result for each test. Following the pathway that fits the characteristics leads to an end point where a name for an organism is given. This process of "keying out" the organism can simplify the identification process.

Check Your Progress SECTION 3.4

16. Clarify what is involved in inoculation, growth, and contamination.
17. Name two ways that pure, mixed, and contaminated cultures are similar and two ways that they differ from each other.
18. Explain what is involved in isolating microorganisms and why it may be necessary to do this.
19. Compare and contrast three common laboratory techniques for separating bacteria in a mixed sample.
20. Describe how an isolated colony forms.
21. Explain why an isolated colony and a pure culture are not the same thing.

Note: This method works best if the spreading tool (usually an **inoculating loop**) is resterilized (flamed) after each of steps 1–3.

Loop containing sample

1 2 3 4

(a) **Steps in a Streak Plate;** this one is a four-part or quadrant streak.

(b)

Loop containing sample

1 2 3

1 2 3

(c) **Steps in Loop Dilution;** also called a pour plate or serial dilution

(d)

"Hockey stick"

1 2

(e) **Steps in a Spread Plate**

(f)

Figure 3.11 Methods for isolating bacteria. (a) Steps in a quadrant streak plate and **(b)** resulting isolated colonies of bacteria. **(c)** Steps in the loop dilution method and **(d)** the appearance of plate 3. **(e)** Spread plate and **(f)** its result. Techniques in (a) and (c) use a loopful of culture, whereas (e) starts with a pre-diluted sample.

Figure 3.12 Various states of cultures. (a) A mixed culture of *Micrococcus luteus* and *Escherichia coli* can be readily differentiated by their colors. **(b)** This plate of *Serratia marcescens* was overexposed to room air and has developed a large white colony. Because this intruder is not desirable and not identified, the culture is now contaminated. **(c)** Tubes containing pure cultures of *E. coli* (white), *M. luteus* (yellow), and *S. marcescens* (red) made by subculturing isolated colonies.

(a)

(b)

(c)

Figure 3.13 Rapid mini testing with identification key for *Neisseria meningitidis.* **(a)** A test system for common gram-negative cocci uses 8 small wells of media to be inoculated with a pure culture and incubated. A certain combination of reactions will be consistent with this species. **(b)** A sample of a key that uses test data (positive or negative reactions) to guide identification of genera and species related to *N. meningitidis.*

(a)

Scheme for Differentating Gram-Negative Cocci and Coccobacilli

(b)

3.5 Media: The Foundations of Culturing

 Expected Learning Outcomes

20. Explain the importance of media for culturing microbes in the laboratory.

21. Name the three general categories of media, based on their inherent properties and uses.

22. Compare and contrast liquid, solid, and semisolid media, giving examples.

23. Analyze chemically defined and complex media, describing their basic differences and content.

24. Describe functional media; list several different categories, and explain what characterizes each type of functional media.

25. Identify the qualities of enriched, selective, and differential media; use examples to explain their content and purposes.

26. Explain what it means to say that microorganisms are not culturable.

27. Describe live media and the circumstances that require it.

A major stimulus to the rise of microbiology in the late 1800s was the development of techniques for growing microbes out of their natural habitats and in pure form in the laboratory. This milestone enabled the close examination of a microbe and its morphology, physiology, and genetics. It was evident from the very first that for successful cultivation, the microorganisms being cultured had to be provided with all of their required nutrients in an artificial medium.

Some microbes require only a very few simple inorganic compounds for growth; others need a complex list of specific inorganic and organic compounds. This tremendous diversity is evident in the types of media that can be prepared. At least 500 different types of media are used in culturing and identifying

microorganisms. Culture media are contained in test tubes, flasks, or Petri dishes, and they are inoculated by such tools as loops, needles, pipettes, and swabs. Media are extremely varied in nutrient content and consistency, and can be specially formulated for a particular purpose.

For an experiment to be properly controlled, sterile technique is necessary. This means that the inoculation must start with a sterile medium and inoculating tools with sterile tips must be used. Measures must be taken to prevent introduction of nonsterile materials, such as room air and fingers, directly into the media.

Types of Media

Most media discussed here are designed for bacteria and fungi, though algae and some protozoa can be propagated in media. Viruses can only be cultivated in live host cells. Media fall into three general categories based on their properties: physical state, chemical composition, and functional type (**table 3.5**).

Physical States of Media

Liquid media are defined as water-based solutions that do not solidify at temperatures above freezing and that tend to flow freely when the container is tilted (**figure 3.14**). These media, termed **broths,** milks, or infusions, are made by dissolving various solutes in distilled water. Growth occurs throughout the container and can then present a dispersed, cloudy, or flaky appearance. A common laboratory medium, *nutrient broth,* contains beef extract and peptone dissolved in water. Other examples of liquid media are methylene blue milk and litmus milk that contain whole milk and dyes. Fluid thioglycollate is a slightly viscous broth used for determining patterns of growth in oxygen (see figure 7.11).

At ordinary room temperature, **semisolid media** exhibit a clotlike consistency (**figure 3.15**) because they contain an amount of solidifying agent (agar or gelatin) that thickens them but does not produce a firm substrate. Semisolid media are used to determine the motility of bacteria and to localize a reaction at a specific site. Motility test medium and sulfur indole motility (SIM) medium both contain a small amount (0.3–0.5%) of agar. In both cases, the medium is stabbed carefully in the center with an inoculating needle and later observed for the pattern of growth around the stab line. In addition to motility, SIM can test for physiological characteristics used in identification (hydrogen sulfide production and indole reaction).

Solid media provide a firm surface on which cells can form discrete colonies (see figure 3.11) and are advantageous for isolating and culturing bacteria and fungi. They come in two forms: liquefiable and nonliquefiable. Liquefiable solid media, sometimes called reversible solid media, contain a solidifying agent that changes its physical properties in response to temperature. By far the most widely used and effective of these agents is **agar,**[3] a polysaccharide

isolated from the red alga *Gelidium.* The benefits of agar are numerous. It is solid at room temperature, and it melts (liquefies) at the boiling temperature of water (100°C or 212°F). Once liquefied, agar does not resolidify until it cools to 42°C (108°F), so it can be inoculated and poured in liquid form at temperatures (45°C to 50°C) that

| TABLE 3.5 | Three Categories of Media Classification | | |
|---|---|---|
| **Physical State (Medium's Normal Consistency)** | **Chemical Composition (Type of Chemicals Medium Contains)** | **Functional Type (Purpose of Medium)*** |
| 1. Liquid
2. Semisolid
3. Solid (can be converted to liquid)
4. Solid (cannot be liquefied) | 1. Synthetic (chemically defined)
2. Nonsynthetic (complex; not chemically defined) | 1. General purpose
2. Enriched
3. Selective
4. Differential
5. Anaerobic growth
6. Specimen transport
7. Assay
8. Enumeration |

*Some media can serve more than one function. For example, a medium such as brain-heart infusion is general purpose and enriched; mannitol salt agar is both selective and differential; and blood agar is both enriched and differential.

(a)

Figure 3.14 Sample liquid media.
(a) Liquid media tend to flow freely when the container is tilted. Urea broth is used to show a biochemical reaction in which the enzyme urease digests urea and releases ammonium. This raises the pH of the solution and causes the dye to become increasingly pink. Left: uninoculated broth, pH 7; middle: growth with no change; right: positive, pH 8.0. **(b)** Presence-absence broth is for detecting the presence of fecal bacteria in water samples. It contains lactose and bromcresol purple dye. As some fecal bacteria ferment lactose, they release acidic substances. This lowers the pH and changes the dye from purple to yellow (right is *Escherichia coli*). Nonfermenters such as *Pseudomonas* (left) grow but do not change the pH (purple color indicates neutral pH).

(b)

3. This material was first employed by Dr. Hesse (see the Significant Events in Microbiology Table found at http://www.mhhe.com/talaro9, 1881).

Figure 3.15 Sample semisolid media. (a) Semisolid media have more body than liquid media but are softer than solid media. They do not flow freely and have a soft, clotlike consistency. **(b)** Sulfur indole motility (SIM) medium. When this medium is stabbed with an inoculum the appearance of growth around the stab line can be used to determine nonmotility (2) or motility (3). Tube 1 is a control that has not been inoculated, and tube 4 shows a black precipitate that occurs around the stab when H_2S gas has been produced.

Figure 3.16 Solid media that are reversible to liquids. (a) Media containing 1%–5% agar are solid and do not move when containers are tilted or inverted. Because they are reversibly solid, they can be liquefied with heat, poured into a different container, and resolidified. **(b)** Nutrient gelatin contains enough gelatin (12%) to take on a solid consistency. The top tube shows it as a solid. The bottom tube indicates what happens when it is warmed or when microbial enzymes digest the gelatin and liquefy it.

will not harm the microbes or the handler (body temperature is about 37°C or 98.6°F). Agar is flexible and moldable, and it provides a basic matrix to hold moisture and nutrients. Another useful property is that it is not readily digestible and thus not a nutrient for most microorganisms.

Any medium containing 1% to 5% agar usually has the word *agar* in its name. *Nutrient agar* is a common one. Like nutrient broth, it contains beef extract and peptone, as well as 1.5% agar by weight. Many of the examples covered in the section on functional categories of media contain agar.

Although gelatin is not nearly as satisfactory as agar, it will create a reasonably solid surface in concentrations of 10% to 15%. The main drawback for gelatin is that it can be digested by microbes and will melt at room and warmer temperatures, leaving a liquid. Agar and gelatin media are illustrated in **figure 3.16.**

Nonliquefiable solid media do not melt. They include materials such as rice grains (used to grow fungi), cooked meat media (good for anaerobes), and egg or serum media that are permanently coagulated or hardened by moist heat.

Chemical Content of Media

Media with a **chemically defined** composition are termed **synthetic.** Such media contain pure chemical nutrients that vary little from one source to another and have a molecular content specified by means of an exact formula. Synthetic media come in many forms. Some media, such as minimal media for fungi, contain nothing more than a few salts and amino acids dissolved in water. Others contain dozens of precisely measured ingredients (**table 3.6A).** Such standardized and reproducible media are most useful in research and cell culture. But they can only be used when the exact

TABLE 3.6A	Chemically Defined Synthetic Medium for Growth and Maintenance of Pathogenic *Staphylococcus aureus*	
0.25 Grams Each of These Amino Acids	**0.5 Grams Each of These Amino Acids**	**0.12 Grams Each of These Amino Acids**
Cystine	Arginine	Aspartic acid
Histidine	Glycine	Glutamic acid
Leucine	Isoleucine	
Phenylalanine	Lysine	
Proline	Methionine	
Tryptophan	Serine	
Tyrosine	Threonine	
	Valine	

Additional ingredients

0.005 mole nicotinamide ⎤
0.005 mole thiamine ⎥
0.005 mole pyridoxine ⎬—Vitamins
0.5 micrograms biotin ⎦

1.25 grams magnesium sulfate ⎤
1.25 grams dipotassium hydrogen phosphate ⎥
1.25 grams sodium chloride ⎬—Salts
0.125 grams iron chloride ⎦

Ingredients are dissolved in 1,000 milliliters of distilled water and buffered to a final pH of 7.0.

TABLE 3.6B	Brain-Heart Infusion Broth: A Complex, Nonsynthetic Medium for Growth and Maintenance of Pathogenic *Staphylococcus aureus*

27.5 grams brain-heart extract, peptone extract
2 grams glucose
5 grams sodium chloride
2.5 grams disodium hydrogen phosphate

Ingredients are dissolved in 1,000 milliliters of distilled water and buffered to a final pH of 7.0.

nutritional needs of the test organisms are known. Recently a defined medium that was developed to grow the parasitic protozoan *Leishmania* required 75 different chemicals.

If even one component of a given medium is not chemically definable, the medium is a **nonsynthetic,** or **complex,**[4] **medium (table 3.6B).** The composition of this type of medium cannot be described by an exact chemical formula. Substances that can make it nonsynthetic are extracts from animal or plant tissues including such materials as ground-up cells and secretions. Other examples are blood, serum, meat extracts, infusions, milk, soybean digests, and peptone. Peptone is a partially digested protein, rich in amino acids, that is often used as a carbon and nitrogen source. Nutrient broth, blood agar, and MacConkey agar, though different in function and appearance, are all complex nonsynthetic media. They present a rich mixture of nutrients for microbes with complex nutritional needs.

Tables 3.6A and 3.6B provide a practical comparison of the two categories, using media to grow *Staphylococcus aureus*. Every substance in medium A is known to a very precise degree. The dominant substances in medium B are macromolecules that contain unknown (but potentially required) nutrients. Both A and B will satisfactorily grow the bacteria. (Which one would you rather make?)

Media to Suit Every Function

Microbiologists have many types of media at their disposal, with new ones being devised all the time. Depending upon what is added, a microbiologist can fine-tune a medium for nearly any purpose. Microbiologists have always been aware of microbes that could not be cultivated artificially, and now we can detect a single bacterium in its natural habitat without cultivation (see 3.1 Secret World of Microbes). But even with this new technology, it is highly unlikely that microbiologists will abandon culturing, simply because it provides a constant source of microbes for detailed study, research, and diagnosis.

General-purpose media are designed to grow a broad spectrum of microbes that do not have special growth requirements. As a rule, these media are nonsynthetic (complex) and contain a mixture of nutrients that could support the growth of a variety of bacteria and fungi. Examples include nutrient agar and broth, brain-heart infusion, and trypticase soy agar (TSA). TSA is a complex medium that contains partially digested milk protein (casein), soybean digest, NaCl, and agar.

An **enriched medium** contains complex organic substances such as blood, serum, hemoglobin, or special **growth factors** that certain species must be provided in order to grow. These growth factors are organic compounds such as vitamins and amino acids that the microbes cannot synthesize themselves. Bacteria that require growth factors and complex nutrients are termed **fastidious.** Blood agar, which is made by adding sterile animal blood (usually from sheep) to a sterile agar base (**figure 3.17a**) is widely employed

Growth of *Streptococcus pyogenes* showing beta hemolysis

(a) (b)

Figure 3.17 Examples of enriched media. (a) A blood agar plate growing the pathogenic bacterium *Streptococcus pyogenes*. It is the cause of "strep" throat and scarlet fever. Note that this medium can also differentiate among colonies by the types of hemolysis they display. Observe the colonies with clearly defined zones (beta hemolysis) and others with less defined zones (alpha hemolysis). **(b)** A culture of *Yersinia pestis* on chocolate agar, which gets its brownish color from cooked blood and does not produce hemolysis. It is used to grow fastidious pathogens like this notorious agent of bubonic plague.

4. *Complex* means that the medium has large molecules such as proteins, polysaccharides, lipids, and other chemicals that can vary greatly in exact composition.

to grow fastidious streptococci and other pathogens. Pathogenic *Neisseria* and *Yersinia* species are often subcultured on chocolate agar, which is made by heating blood agar and does not contain chocolate—it just has that appearance (**figure 3.17***b*).

Selective and Differential Media

Some of the cleverest and most inventive media recipes belong to the categories of selective and differential media (**figure 3.18**). These media are designed for special microbial groups, and they have extensive applications in isolation and identification. They can permit, in a single step, the preliminary identification of a genus or even a species.

A **selective medium (table 3.7)** contains one or more agents that inhibit the growth of a certain microbe or microbes (call them A, B, and C) but not another (D). This difference favors, or *selects,*

microbe D and allows it to grow by itself. Selective media are very important in primary isolation of a specific type of microorganism from samples containing mixtures of different species—for example, feces, saliva, skin, water, and soil. They hasten isolation by suppressing the unwanted background organisms and allowing growth of the desired ones.

Mannitol salt agar (MSA) contains a high concentration of NaCl (7.5%) that is quite inhibitory to most human pathogens. One exception is the genus *Staphylococcus,* which grows well in this medium and consequently can be amplified in mixed samples (**figure 3.19***a*).

Bile salts, a component of feces, inhibit most gram-positive bacteria while permitting many gram-negative rods to grow. Media for isolating intestinal pathogens (MacConkey agar, Hektoen enteric [HE] agar) contain bile salts as a selective agent (**figure 3.19***b*). Dyes such as methylene blue and crystal violet also inhibit certain gram-positive bacteria. Other agents that have selective properties are antimicrobial drugs and acid. Some selective media contain strongly inhibitory agents to favor the growth of a pathogen that would otherwise be overlooked because of its low numbers in a specimen. Selenite and brilliant green dye are used in media to isolate *Salmonella* from feces, and sodium azide is used to isolate enterococci from water and food.

Differential media grow several types of microorganisms but are designed to bring out visible differences among those microorganisms. Differences show up as variations in colony size or color, in media color changes, or in the formation of gas bubbles and precipitates (**table 3.8**). These variations come from the types of chemicals contained in the media and the ways that microbes react to them. For example, if microbe X metabolizes a certain substance not used by organism Y, then X

Broth culture with mixed sample of bacteria

(a) **General-purpose medium**
Is not selective and can be used to grow a wide variety of microbial types

(b) **Selective medium**
Growth is restricted to a particular group or type of microbe

(c) **Differential medium**
Permits growth of several types of microbes that show differing reactions

Figure 3.18 **Comparison of general-purpose media with selective and differential media.**
A mixed sample containing a number of different types of bacteria are streaked onto these plates: **(a)** a general-purpose nonselective medium, **(b)** a selective medium, and **(c)** a differential medium. Note the difference in the appearance and numbers of colonies with the three media. Medium (a) can grow a wider number and spectrum of colonies. Medium (b) produces only one or two types of colonies that look very similar. Medium (c) shows more variety than (b), and colonies are differentiated by a varying color reaction.

TABLE 3.7	**Examples of Selective Media, Agents, and Functions**	
Medium	**Selective Agent**	**Used For**
Mannitol salt agar	7.5% NaCl	Isolation of *Staphylococcus aureus* from infectious material
Enterococcus faecalis broth	Sodium azide, tetrazolium	Isolation of fecal enterococci
Phenylethanol agar (PEA)	Phenylethanol chloride	Isolation of staphylococci and streptococci
Tomato juice agar	Tomato juice, acid	Isolation of lactobacilli from saliva
MacConkey agar (MAC)	Bile, crystal violet	Isolation of gram-negative enterics
Eosin-methylene blue agar (EMB)	Bile, dyes	Isolation of coliform bacteria in specimens
Salmonella/Shigella (SS) agar	Bile, citrate, brilliant green	Isolation of *Salmonella* and *Shigella*
Sabouraud's agar (SAB)	pH of 5.6 (acid) inhibits bacteria	Isolation of fungi

(a)

(b)

Figure 3.19 Examples of media that are both selective and differential. (a) Mannitol salt agar can selectively grow *Staphylococcus* species from clinical samples. It contains 7.5% sodium chloride, an amount of salt that is inhibitory to most bacteria and molds found in humans. It is also differential because it contains a dye (phenol red) that changes color under variations in pH, and mannitol, a sugar that can be converted to acid. The left side shows *S. epidermidis,* a species that does not use mannitol (red); the right shows *S. aureus,* a pathogen that uses mannitol (yellow). **(b)** MacConkey agar differentiates between lactose-fermenting bacteria (indicated by a pink-red reaction in the center of the colony) and lactose-negative bacteria (indicated by an off-white colony with no dye reaction).

TABLE 3.8	**Examples of Differential Media**	
Medium	**Substances That Facilitate Differentiation**	**Differentiates**
Blood agar (BAP)	Intact red blood cells	Types of RBC damage (hemolysis)
Mannitol salt agar (MSA)	Mannitol and phenol red	Species of *Staphylococcus*
Hektoen enteric (HE) agar*	Brom thymol blue, acid fuchsin, sucrose, salicin, thiosulfate, ferric ammonium citrate, and bile	*Salmonella, Shigella,* and other lactose nonfermenters from fermenters; H₂S reactions are also observable
MacConkey agar (MAC)	Lactose, neutral red	Bacteria that ferment lactose (lowering the pH) from those that do not
Eosin-methylene blue (EMB)	Lactose, eosin, methylene blue	Same as MacConkey agar
Urea broth	Urea, phenol red	Bacteria that hydrolyze urea to ammonia and increase the pH
Sulfur indole motility (SIM)	Thiosulfate, iron	H₂S gas producers; motility; indole formation
Triple-sugar iron agar (TSIA)	Triple sugars, iron, and phenol red dye	Fermentation of sugars, H₂S production
XLD agar	Lysine, xylose, iron, thiosulfate, phenol red	Can differentiate *Enterobacter, Escherichia, Proteus, Providencia, Salmonella,* and *Shigella*

*Contains dyes and bile to inhibit gram-positive bacteria.

will cause a visible change in the medium and Y will not. The simplest differential media show two reaction types such as a color change in some colonies but not in others. Several newer forms of differential media contain artificial substrates called chromogens that release a wide variety of colors, each tied to a specific microbe. **Figure 3.20***b* shows the result from a urine culture containing six different bacteria. Other chromogenic agar is available for identifying *Staphylococcus, Listeria,* and pathogenic yeasts.

Dyes are effective differential agents because many of them are pH indicators that change color in response to the production of an acid or a base. For example, MacConkey agar contains neutral red, a dye that is yellow when neutral and pink or red when acidic. A common intestinal bacterium such as *Escherichia coli* that gives off acid when it metabolizes the lactose in the medium develops red to pink colonies, and one such as *Salmonella* that does not give off acid remains its natural color (off-white). Media shown in figure 3.19 (mannitol salt agar) and **figure 3.21** (fermentation broths) con-

tain phenol red dye that also changes color with pH: it is yellow in acid and red in neutral and basic conditions.

A single medium can be classified in more than one category depending on the ingredients it contains. MacConkey and EMB media, for example, appear in table 3.7 (selective media) and table 3.8 (differential media). Blood agar is both enriched and differential. Media companies have developed selective-differential media for numerous common pathogens, which makes it possible to identify them with a single streak plate. We will see examples of some of these media in later chapters.

Miscellaneous Media

A *reducing medium* contains a substance (thioglycollic acid or cystine) that absorbs oxygen or slows the penetration of oxygen in a medium, thus reducing its availability. Reducing media are important for growing anaerobic bacteria or for determining oxygen requirements

(a)

Figure 3.20 Media that differentiate multiple characteristics of bacteria. (a) Triple sugar iron agar (TSIA) inoculated on the surface and stabbed into the thicker region at the bottom (butt). This medium contains three sugars, phenol red dye to indicate pH changes (bright yellow is acid, various shades of red, basic), and iron salt to show H_2S gas production. Reactions are (1) no growth; (2) growth with no acid production (sugars not used); (3) acid production in the butt only; (4) acid production in all areas of the medium; (5) acid and H_2S production in butt (black precipitate). **(b)** A medium developed for culturing and identifying the most common urinary pathogens. CHROMagar Orientation™ uses color-forming reactions to distinguish at least seven species and permits rapid identification and treatment. In the example, the bacteria were streaked so as to spell their own names. Which bacterium was probably used to write the name at the top?

(b)

of isolates (described in chapter 7). Carbohydrate fermentation media contain sugars that can be fermented (converted to acids) and a pH indicator to show this reaction (see figure 3.19a and figure 3.21). Media for other biochemical reactions that provide the basis for identifying bacteria and fungi are presented in several later chapters.

Transport media are used to maintain and preserve specimens that have to be held for a period of time before clinical analysis or to sustain delicate species that die rapidly if not held under stable conditions. Stuart's and Amie's transport media contain buffers and

absorbants to prevent cell destruction but will not support growth. *Assay media* are used by technologists to test the effectiveness of antimicrobial drugs (see chapter 12) and by drug manufacturers to assess the effect of disinfectants, antiseptics, cosmetics, and preservatives on the growth of microorganisms. Enumeration media are used by industrial and environmental microbiologists to count the numbers of organisms in milk, water, food, soil, and other samples.

A number of significant microbial groups (viruses, rickettsias, and a few bacteria) will only grow on live cells or animals. These obligate parasites have unique requirements that must be provided by living animals such as rabbits, guinea pigs, mice, chickens, and the early life stages (embryos) of birds. Such animals can be an indispensable aid for studying, growing, and identifying microorganisms. Animal inoculation is an essential step in testing the effects of drugs and the effectiveness of vaccines before they are administered to humans. Animals are an important source of antibodies, antisera, antitoxins, and other immune products that can be used in therapy or testing.

Control tube

Gas bubble

Outline of Durham tube

Cloudiness indicating growth

Figure 3.21 Carbohydrate fermentation in broths. This medium is designed to show fermentation (acid production) using phenol red broth and gas formation by means of a small, inverted Durham tube for collecting gas bubbles. The tube on the left is an uninoculated negative control; the center tube is positive for acid (yellow) and gas (open space); the tube on the right shows growth but neither acid nor gas.

 Check Your Progress SECTION 3.5

22. Describe the main purposes of media, and compare the three categories based on physical state, chemical composition, and usage.
23. Differentiate among the ingredients and functions of enriched, selective, and differential media.
24. Explain the two principal functions of dyes in media.
25. Why are some bacteria difficult to grow in the laboratory? Relate this to what you know so far about the nutrients that are added to media.
26. What conditions are necessary to cultivate viruses in the laboratory?

 CASE STUDY **Part 2**

A Gram stain is one of the key tests for getting quick feedback on the kind of microbes that might be present in a sample. It is routine in meningitis because it can differentiate among several types of bacteria and detect certain other infectious agents, but it will not detect viruses. Within moments, a lab technician can possibly tell if there are bacterial cells, and they can observe their Gram reaction and shape.

Lab results from the Gram stain and culture were conclusive: Kay Peterson was infected by the meningococcus, *Neisseria*

*meningitidis,** which is an agent of both meningitis* and septicemia.* The microscopic examination yielded the classic appearance of tiny pairs of red cocci (diplococci) and white blood cells carrying the same cocci inside. A blood culture also showed growth, indicating that the bacteria had entered her bloodstream. Plates of agar inoculated with the CSF grew typical off-white, smooth isolated colonies that tested out as *N. meningitidis*. Kay remained on the antibiotic regimen for 10 days and was released, fortunately without long-term damage.

- What kinds of media would be used to culture and identify this microbe?
- What are some other potential microbes that could have caused this infection?

To conclude this Case Study, go to Perspectives on the Connect website.

For more information on the nature of this agent and its disease, see chapter 18 and log on to *http://www.meningitis.org/symptoms.*

* *Neisseria meningitidis* (ny-serr′ee-uh men′-in-jih′-tih-dis) From the German physician, *Neisser*, and Gr. *meninx*, a membrane.
* *meningitis* (men′-in-jy′-tis) Gr. *meninx*, a membrane, and *itis*, an inflammation. Specifically, an inflammation of the meninges, the membranes that surround the brain.
* *septicemia* (sep′-tih-see′-mee-uh) Gr. *septikos*, to make putrid, and *haima*, blood. The presence of infectious agents or their toxins in the blood.

Chapter Summary with Key Terms

3.1 Methods of Microbial Investigation

A. Microbiology as a science is very dependent on a number of specialized laboratory techniques.
 1. Initially, a specimen must be collected from a source, whether environmental or patient.
 2. **Inoculation** of a **medium** with the specimen is the first step in **culturing.**
 3. **Incubation** of the medium with the microbes under the right conditions creates a **culture** with visible growth.
 4. **Isolation** of the microbes in the sample into discrete, separate **colonies** is one desired goal.
 5. **Inspection** begins with macroscopic characteristics of the culture and continues with microscopic analysis.
 6. **Information gathering** involves acquiring additional data from physiological, immune, and genetic tests.
 7. **Identification** correlates the key characteristics that can pinpoint the actual species of microbe.

3.2 The Microscope: Window on an Invisible Realm

A. Optical, or light, microscopy depends on lenses that **refract** light rays, drawing the rays to a focus to produce a magnified image.
 1. A simple microscope consists of a single magnifying lens, whereas a compound microscope relies on two lenses: the ocular lens and the objective lens.
 2. The total power of magnification is calculated from the product of the ocular and objective magnifying powers.
 3. **Resolution,** or the **resolving power,** is a measure of a microscope's capacity to make clear images of very small objects. Resolution is improved with shorter wavelengths of illumination and with a higher **numerical aperture** of the lens. Light microscopes are limited by resolution to magnifications around 2,000×.
 4. Modifications in the lighting or the lens system give rise to the bright-field, dark-field, phase-contrast, interference, fluorescence, and confocal microscopes.

B. Electron microscopy depends on electromagnets that serve as lenses to focus electron beams. A **transmission electron microscope (TEM)** projects the electrons through prepared sections of the specimen, providing detailed structural images of cells, cell parts, and viruses. A **scanning electron microscope (SEM)** is more like dark-field microscopy, bouncing the electrons off the surface of the specimen to detectors.

3.3 Preparing Specimens for Optical Microscopes

A. Specimen preparation in optical microscopy varies according to the specimen, the purpose of the inspection, and the type of microscope being used.
 1. Wet mounts and hanging drop mounts permit examination of the characteristics of live cells, such as motility, shape, and arrangement.
 2. Fixed mounts are made by drying and heating a film of the specimen called a smear. This is then stained using dyes to permit visualization of cells or cell parts.

B. Staining uses either **basic** (cationic) **dyes** with positive charges or **acidic** (anionic) **dyes** with negative charges. The surfaces of microbes are negatively charged and attract basic dyes. This is the basis of **positive staining.** In

negative staining, the microbe repels the dye and it stains the background. Dyes may be used alone and in combination.

1. **Simple stains** use just one dye and highlight cell morphology.
2. **Differential stains** require a primary dye and a contrasting counterstain in order to distinguish cell types or parts. Important differential stains include the **Gram stain, acid-fast stain,** and the endospore stain.
3. **Structural stains** are designed to bring out distinctive characteristics. Examples include capsule stains and flagellar stains.

3.4 Additional Features of the Six "I's"

A. Inoculation of media followed by incubation produces visible growth in the form of **cultures.**
B. Techniques with solid media in Petri dishes provide a means of separating individual microbes by producing **isolated colonies.**
 1. With the **streak plate,** a loop is used to thin out the sample over the surface of the medium.
 2. With the **loop dilution** (pour plate), a series of tubes of media is used to dilute the sample.
 3. The **spread plate** method evenly distributes a tiny drop of inoculum with a special stick.
 4. Isolated colonies can be **subcultured** for further testing at this point. The goal is a **pure culture,** in most cases, or a **mixed culture. Contaminated cultures** can ruin correct analysis and study.

3.5 Media: The Foundations of Culturing

A. Artificial media allow the growth and isolation of microorganisms in the laboratory and can be classified by their physical state, chemical composition, and functional types. The nutritional requirements of microorganisms in the laboratory may be simple or complex.
B. Physical types of media include those that are **liquid,** such as **broths** and milk, those that are **semisolid,** and those that are solid. Solid media may be liquefiable, containing a solidifying agent such as **agar** or gelatin.
C. Chemical composition of a medium may be completely **chemically defined,** thus **synthetic. Nonsynthetic,** or **complex,** media contain ingredients that are not completely definable.
D. Functional types of media serve different purposes, often allowing biochemical tests to be performed at the same time. Types include **general-purpose, enriched, selective,** and **differential media.**
 1. Enriched media contain **growth factors** required by microbes.
 2. Selective media permit the growth of desired microbes while inhibiting unwanted ones.
 3. Differential media bring out visible variations in microbial growth.
 4. Others include anaerobic (reducing), assay, and enumeration media. Transport media are important for conveying certain clinical specimens to the laboratory.
E. In certain instances, microorganisms have to be grown in cell cultures or host animals.

Level I. Knowledge and Comprehension

These questions require a working knowledge of the concepts in the chapter and the ability to recall and understand the information you have studied.

 Multiple-Choice Questions

Select the correct answer from the answers provided. For questions with blanks, choose the combination of answers that most accurately completes the statement.

1. Which of the following is not one of the six "I's"?
 a. inspection d. incubation
 b. identification e. inoculation
 c. illumination

2. The term *culture* refers to the _____ growth of microorganisms in _____.
 a. rapid, an incubator
 b. macroscopic, media
 c. microscopic, the body
 d. artificial, colonies

3. A mixed culture is
 a. the same as a contaminated culture
 b. one that has been adequately stirred
 c. one that contains two or more known species
 d. a pond sample containing algae and protozoa

4. Agar is superior to gelatin as a solidifying agent because agar
 a. does not melt at room temperature
 b. solidifies at 75°C
 c. is not usually decomposed by microorganisms
 d. both a and c

5. The process that most accounts for magnification is
 a. a condenser c. illumination
 b. refraction of light rays d. resolution

6. A subculture is a
 a. colony growing beneath the media surface
 b. culture made from a contaminant
 c. culture made in an embryo
 d. culture made from an isolated colony

7. Resolution is _____ with a longer wavelength of light.
 a. improved c. not changed
 b. worsened d. not possible

8. A real image is produced by the
 a. ocular
 b. objective
 c. condenser
 d. eye

9. A microscope that has a total magnification of 1,500× when using the oil immersion objective has an ocular of what power?
 a. 150×
 b. 1.5×
 c. 15×
 d. 30×

10. The specimen for an electron microscope is always
 a. stained with dyes
 b. sliced into thin sections
 c. killed
 d. viewed directly

11. Motility is best observed with a
 a. hanging drop preparation
 b. negative stain
 c. streak plate
 d. flagellar stain

12. Bacteria tend to stain more readily with cationic (positively charged) dyes because bacteria
 a. contain large amounts of alkaline substances
 b. contain large amounts of acidic substances
 c. are neutral
 d. have thick cell walls

13. The primary difference between a TEM and SEM is in
 a. magnification capability
 b. colored versus black-and-white images
 c. preparation of the specimen
 d. type of lenses

14. A fastidious organism must be grown on what type of medium?
 a. general-purpose medium
 b. differential medium
 c. synthetic medium
 d. enriched medium

15. What type of medium is used to maintain and preserve specimens before clinical analysis?
 a. selective medium
 b. transport medium
 c. enriched medium
 d. differential medium

16. Which of the following is NOT an optical microscope?
 a. dark-field
 b. confocal
 c. atomic force
 d. fluorescent

17. **Multiple Matching.** For each type of medium, select all descriptions that fit. For media that fit more than one description, briefly explain why this is the case.

 ____ mannitol salt agar
 ____ chocolate agar
 ____ MacConkey agar
 ____ nutrient broth
 ____ brain-heart infusion broth
 ____ Sabouraud's agar
 ____ triple-sugar iron agar
 ____ SIM medium

 a. selective medium
 b. differential medium
 c. chemically defined (synthetic) medium
 d. enriched medium
 e. general-purpose medium
 f. complex medium
 g. transport medium

Case Study Review

1. Which of the following techniques from the six "I's" was not used in the diagnosis?
 a. incubation
 b. inoculation
 c. inspection
 d. All of them were used.

2. Which of these would not be a *sign* of meningitis?
 a. brown blotches on the skin
 b. stiff neck
 c. cloudy spinal fluid
 d. gram-negative cocci in specimens

3. Go to figure 3.13 and trace what information was used to "key out" and identify the bacterial species that caused meningitis in the Case Study.

Writing Challenge

For each question, compose a one- or two-paragraph answer that includes the factual information needed to completely address the question. Check Your Progress questions can also be used for writing-challenge exercises.

1. a. When buying a microscope, what features are most important to check for?
 b. What is probably true of a $20 microscope that claims to magnify 1,000×?

2. How can one obtain 2,000× magnification with a 100× objective?

3. Differentiate between microscopic and macroscopic methods of observing microorganisms, citing a specific example of each method.

4. Describe the steps of the Gram stain, and explain how it can be an important diagnostic tool for infections.

5. Describe the steps you would take to isolate, cultivate, and identify a microbial pathogen from a urine sample.

6. Trace the pathway of light from its source to the eye, explaining what happens as it passes through the major parts of the microscope.

7. Evaluate the following preparations in terms of providing information on microbial size, shape, motility, and differentiation: spore stain, negative stain, simple stain, hanging drop slide, and Gram stain.

 Concept Mapping

An Introduction to Concept Mapping found at http://www.mhhe.com/talaro9 provides guidance for working with concept maps.

1. Supply your own linking words or phrases in the concept map, and provide the missing concepts in the empty boxes.

 Level II. Application, Analysis, Evaluation, and Synthesis

These problems go beyond just restating facts and require higher levels of understanding and an ability to interpret, problem solve, transfer knowledge to new situations, create models, and predict outcomes.

Critical Thinking

Critical thinking is the ability to reason and solve problems using facts and concepts. These questions can be approached from a number of angles, and in most cases, they do not have a single correct answer.

1. A certain medium has the following composition:

 Glucose 15 g
 Yeast extract 5 g
 Peptone 5 g
 KH_2PO_4 2 g
 Distilled water 1,000 ml
 a. Tell what chemical category this medium belongs to, and explain why this is true.
 b. How could you convert *Staphylococcus* medium (table 3.6A) into a nonsynthetic medium?
2. a. Name four categories that blood agar fits.
 b. Name four differential reactions that TSIA shows.

c. Observe figure 3.15. Suggest what causes the difference in growth pattern between nonmotile and motile bacteria.
d. Explain what a medium that is both selective and differential does, using figure 3.18.
3. a. What kind of medium might you make to selectively grow a bacterium that lives in the ocean?
 b. One that lives in the human stomach?
 c. Why are intestinal bacteria able to grow on media containing bile?
4. Go back to page 6 and observe the six micrographs in figure 1.3. See if you can tell what kind of microscope was used to make the photograph based on magnification and appearance.
5. Could the Gram stain be used to diagnose the flu? Why or why not?

Visual Challenge

1. Examine figure 3.11*a, b*. If you performed the quadrant streak plate method using a broth culture that had 10× fewer cells than the broth used in the culture shown, which quadrant might you expect to yield isolated colonies? Explain your answer.
2. Look at figure 3.1 on page 61. Precisely which of the six "I's" were used in the Case Study, page 59? Which ones were used in the Case Study, page 1? Were any used in the Case Study, page 29?

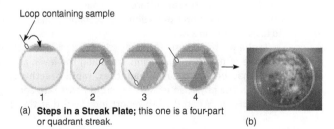

(a) **Steps in a Streak Plate;** this one is a four-part or quadrant streak.

(b)

www.mcgrawhillconnect.com
Enhance your study of this chapter with study tools and practice tests. Also ask your instructor about the resources available through ConnectPlus, including the media-rich eBook, interactive learning tools, and animations.

CHAPTER **4**

A Survey of Prokaryotic Cells and Microorganisms

Section of a prosthetic heart valve has a patch of MRSA biofilm attached (purple).

Looking as harmless as clusters of tiny purple grapes, the gram-positive pathogen *Staphylococcus aureus* is anything but.

CASE STUDY **Part 1** Heart Valves and Biofilms

On a summer morning in 2008, Mr. Maxwell Jones, a 65-year-old man, woke up complaining of abnormal **fatigue** and a **scratchy throat.** His wife said he felt hot and took his temperature. It was slightly elevated at 100°F. He dismissed his condition, saying he was probably tired from working in his garden and suffering one of his regular allergy attacks. Over the next few days, his symptom list grew. He lost his appetite, his **joints** and **muscles** were **sore,** and he woke up wringing wet from **night sweats.** He continued to have a **fever,** and his wife was worried over how pale he looked. She insisted he see a physician, who performed a physical and took a **throat culture.** Mr. Jones was sent home with instructions to take **oral penicillin** and acetaminophen (Tylenol), and to come back in a week.

At the next appointment, the patient reported that he still had some of the same symptoms, including the fever, and that now he had begun to have **headaches, rapid breathing,** and **coughing.** The physician recorded a **rapid heart rate** and slight **heart murmur.** When the lab report indicated that the throat

> "At least 65% of chronic infections are caused by microbial biofilms."

culture was **negative** for bacterial pathogens he had to look for other causes.

He began to wonder if the patient had a prior medical history of possible **risk factors.** From interviewing Mr. Jones, he learned that an **artificial valve** had been implanted in his heart 10 years before, a fact that had been omitted from his medical chart. This finding immediately caused alarm, and Mr. Jones was admitted to the intensive care unit and placed on a mixture of **intravenous antibiotics.** Tests for **blood cultures** and a **white blood cell count** were ordered as backup. By that evening, Mr. Jones had become confused and lost consciousness. He was rushed to the operating room but died during open heart surgery.

► *What appear to be the most important facts in this case?*

► *Explain why Mr. Jones' initial throat cultures were negative for infection.*

To continue the Case Study, go to page 118.

4.1 Basic Characteristics of Cells and Life Forms

 Expected Learning Outcomes

1. Describe the fundamental characteristics of cells.

2. Identify the primary properties that define life and living things.

There is a universal biological truth that the basic unit of life is the cell, whether the organism is a bacterium whose entire body is just a single cell or an elephant made up of trillions of cells. Regardless of their origins, all cells share a few common characteristics. They tend to assume cubical, spherical, or cylindrical shapes, and have a **cell membrane** that encases an internal matrix called the **cytoplasm.** All cells have one or more chromosomes containing DNA, ribosomes for protein synthesis, and they exhibit highly complex chemical reactions. As we learned in chapter 1, all cells discovered thus far are classified into one of two fundamentally different groups: the small, seemingly simple **prokaryotic cells** and the larger, structurally more complicated **eukaryotic cells.**

Eukaryotic cells are found in animals, plants, fungi, and protists. They contain a number of complex internal parts called **organelles** that perform useful functions for the cell. By convention, organelles are defined as cell components enclosed by membranes that carry out specific activities involving metabolism, nutrition, and synthesis. Organelles also partition the eukaryotic cell into smaller compartments. The most visible organelle is the nucleus, a roughly ball-shaped mass surrounded by a double membrane that contains the DNA of the cell. Other organelles include the Golgi apparatus, endoplasmic reticulum, vacuoles, and mitochondria (all discussed in chapter 5).

Prokaryotic cells are found only in the bacteria and archaea. Sometimes it may seem that prokaryotes are the microbial "havenots" because, for the sake of comparison, they are described by what they lack. They have no nucleus or other organelles. This apparent simplicity is misleading, because the fine structure of prokaryotes can be complex. Overall, prokaryotic cells can engage in nearly every activity that eukaryotic cells can, and many can function in ways that eukaryotes cannot.

We start this chapter with a description of the characteristics that impart the essence of life to cells, followed by a look at prokaryotic cell anatomy and a survey of major groups of prokaryotes. In chapter 5, we will similarly survey the eukaryotic world.

After you have studied the cells as presented in this chapter and chapter 5, refer to table 5.2 (page 133), which summarizes the major differences between prokaryotic and eukaryotic cells.

What Is Life?

Biologists have long debated over universal characteristics we see in organisms that are solid indicators of life or of being alive. What does a cell do that sets it apart from a nonliving rock? One of the first things that often comes to mind is the ability to move or to grow. Unfortunately, taken individually, these are not life signs. After all, inanimate objects can move and crystals can grow. There is probably no single property that we can hold up as the ultimate indicator of life. In fact, defining life requires a whole collection of behaviors and properties that even the simplest organisms will have. First and foremost on this list would be a self-contained and highly organized unit to carry out the activities of life, namely a **cell.** It is the cell that is the staging area for these life-supporting phenomena: heredity, reproduction, growth, development, metabolism, responsiveness, and transport **(figure 4.1).**

- **Heredity** is the transmission of an organism's genome* to the next generation by chromosomes, which carry DNA, the molecular blueprint of life.
- **Reproduction** involves the generation of offspring necessary to continue a species' line of evolution. All organisms manifest asexual reproduction, with one cell simply dividing into two new cells by fission or mitosis. Many organisms also display sexual reproduction, involving the union of sex cells from two parents.
- **Growth** has two general meanings in microbiology. In the usual sense, it means an increase in size of a population through reproduction. In another case, it refers to the enlargement of a single organism during maturation.
- **Development** includes all changes over the life span of an organism that complete the full expression of its genome.
- **Metabolism** encompasses the thousands of chemical reactions that all cells need to function. Generally, these reactions either synthesize new cell components or release energy that drives cellular activities. Both types of metabolism are supported and regulated by unique molecules of life called **enzymes.**
- **Responsiveness** is the capacity of cells to interact with external factors through irritability, communication, or movement. Cells demonstrate irritability by receiving and reacting to stimuli such as light and chemicals from their environment. They may also communicate with other cells by sending or receiving signals. Some cells show self-propulsion or motility using specialized locomotor structures.
- **Transport** is a system for controlling the flow of materials. This includes carrying nutrients and water from the external environment into the cell's interior. Without these raw materials, metabolism would cease. Cells also secrete substances, or expel waste, in the reverse direction. Movement of this type is the work of the cell membrane, which functions as the gatekeeper for cellular activities. Together, all of these life properties provide microorganisms with the capacity to adapt and evolve.

One of the main reasons that viruses are generally considered nonliving is that they are not cellular. Even if one argues that they are tiny units somewhat like cells, and that they do show some traits of life such as heredity, development, and evolution, they do not display these characteristics independent of their living host cell. Outside of their host, they lack most other features of life we just described, and are inactive and inert. We will return to this discussion about viruses in chapter 6.

* *genome* (gee′-nohm) The complete set of chromosomes and genes of an organism.

Figure 4.1 A summary of the major life-defining properties. The cell is central to the collective activities that are synonymous with being alive.

 Check Your Progress SECTION 4.1

1. Outline the primary indicators of life.
2. Name several general characteristics that could be used to define the prokaryotes.

4.2 Prokaryotic Profiles: The Bacteria and Archaea

 Expected Learning Outcomes

3. Describe the generalized anatomy of bacterial cells.
4. Distinguish among the types of external cell appendages.
5. Describe the structure and position of bacterial flagella and axial filaments, and their attachment patterns.
6. Explain how flagella influence motility and motile behavior.
7. Discuss the structure and functions of pili and fimbriae.
8. Define glycocalyx, and describe its different forms and functions.

In chapter 1, we introduced the two major types of prokaryotic cells: the bacteria and the archaea. Being the first type of cells on earth, prokaryotic cells have an evolutionary history that dates back over 3.5 billion years. At present, we cannot know the precise nature of these first cells, but many microbiologists speculate that they would be similar to present-day archaea living on sulfur compounds in deep, hot oceanic vents (see figure 4.33), extreme habitats they continue to dominate 3.5 billion years later. Having evolved over the same time frame as archaea, bacteria share a similar ancient history. Biologists have estimated that these two Domains together still account for at least half of the total mass of life forms on earth. The fact that these organisms have endured for so long in such a variety of habitats indicates cellular structure and function that are incredibly versatile and adaptable. The general structural plan of a prokaryotic cell can be represented with this flowchart:

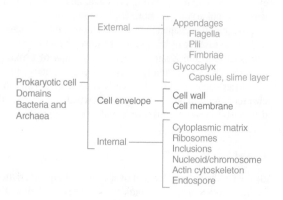

Structures that are essential to the functions of all prokaryotic cells are a cell membrane, cytoplasm, ribosomes, and one or occasionally more, chromosomes. The majority also have a cell wall

Figure 4.2 Structure of a typical bacterial cell. Cutaway view of a rod-shaped bacterium, showing major structural features. Note that not all components are found in all cells.

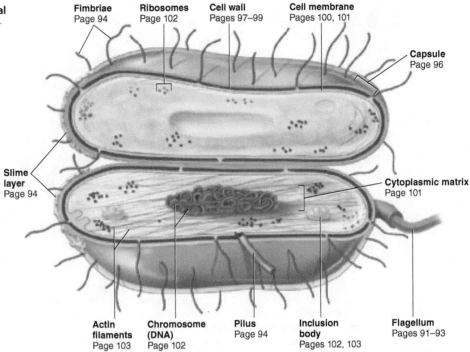

Fimbriae Page 94 · Ribosomes Page 102 · Cell wall Pages 97–99 · Cell membrane Pages 100, 101 · Capsule Page 96 · Slime layer Page 94 · Cytoplasmic matrix Page 101 · Actin filaments Page 103 · Chromosome (DNA) Page 102 · Pilus Page 94 · Inclusion body Pages 102, 103 · Flagellum Pages 91–93

and some form of surface coating or glycocalyx. Specific structures that are found in some, but not all, bacteria are flagella, pili, fimbriae, capsules, slime layers, inclusions, an actin cytoskeleton, and endospores.

The Structure of a Generalized Bacterial Cell

Prokaryotic cells appear featureless and two-dimensional when viewed with an ordinary microscope, but this is only because of their small size. Higher magnification provides increased insight into their intricate and often complex structure (see figures 4.18 and 4.28 in later sections). The descriptions of prokaryotic structure, except where otherwise noted, refer to the **bacteria,** a category of prokaryotes with peptidoglycan in their cell walls. **Figure 4.2** shows a three-dimensional illustration of a generalized (rod-shaped) bacterial cell with most of the structures from the flowchart. As we survey the principal anatomical features of this cell, we begin with the outer cell structures and proceed to the internal contents. In sections 4.6 and 4.7, we will cover prokaryotic taxonomy, discuss the differences between bacteria and archaea, and introduce the major characteristics of archaea.

Cell Extensions and Surface Structures

Bacteria often bear accessory **appendages** sprouting from their surfaces. Appendages can be divided into two major groups: those that provide motility (flagella and axial filaments) and those that provide attachments or channels (fimbriae and pili).

Flagella—Bacterial Propellers

The prokaryotic **flagellum*** is an appendage of phenomenal construction and is certainly unique in the biological world. Flagella provide the power of motility or self-propulsion. This allows a cell to swim freely through an aqueous habitat. The bacterial flagellum when viewed under high magnification displays three distinct parts: the filament, the hook (sheath), and the basal body **(figure 4.3).** The **filament** is a helical structure composed of a protein called flagellin. It is approximately 20 nm in diameter and varies from 1 to 70 μm in length. It is inserted into a curved, tubular hook. The hook is anchored to the cell by the **basal body,** a stack of rings firmly anchored through the cell wall to the cell membrane. The hook and its filament are free to rotate 360°—like a tiny propeller. This is in contrast to the flagella of eukaryotic cells, which undulate back and forth.

One can generalize that all spirilla, about half of the bacilli, and a small number of cocci are flagellated (these bacterial shapes are shown in figure 4.23). Flagella vary both in number and arrangement according to two general patterns: (1) In a **polar** arrangement, the flagella are attached at one or both ends of the cell. Three subtypes of this pattern are: **monotrichous*** with a single flagellum; **lophotrichous*** with small bunches or tufts of flagella emerging from the same site; and **amphitrichous*** with flagella at both poles of the cell. (2) In a **peritrichous*** arrangement, flagella are dispersed randomly over the surface of the cell **(figure 4.4).**

* *flagellum* (flah-jel′-em) pl. flagella; L., a whip.
* *monotrichous* (mah″-noh-trik′-us) Gr. *mono,* one, and *tricho,* hair.
* *lophotrichous* (lo″-foh-trik′-us) Gr. *lopho,* tuft or ridge.
* *amphitrichous* (am″-fee-trik′-us). Gr. *amphi,* on both sides.
* *peritrichous* (per″-ee-trik′-us) Gr. *peri,* around.

Figure 4.3 **Details of the flagellar basal body and its position in the cell wall.** The hook, rings, and rod function together as a tiny device that rotates the filament 360°. **(a)** Structure in gram-negative cells **(b)** Structure in gram-positive cells.

The presence of motility is one piece of information used in the laboratory identification of various groups of bacteria. Special stains or electron microscope preparations must be used to see the arrangement, because flagella are too minute to be seen in live preparations with a light microscope. Often it is sufficient to know simply whether a bacterial species is motile. One way to detect motility is to stab a tiny mass of cells into a soft (semisolid) medium in a test tube (see figure 3.15). Growth spreading rapidly through the entire medium is indicative of motility. Alternatively, cells can be observed microscopically with a hanging drop slide. A truly motile cell will flit, dart, or wobble around the field, making some progress, whereas one that is nonmotile jiggles about in one place but makes no progress.

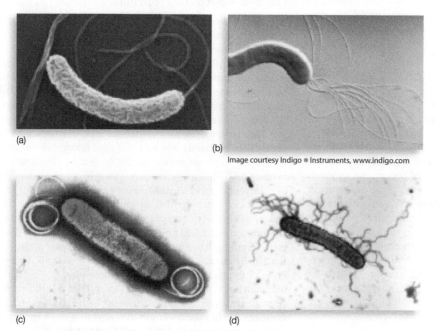

Image courtesy Indigo ® Instruments, www.indigo.com

Figure 4.4 **Electron micrographs depicting types of flagellar arrangements.** **(a)** Monotrichous flagellum on the pathogen *Vibrio cholerae* (10,000×). Note its highly textured glycocalyx. **(b)** Lophotrichous flagella on *Spirillum serpens*, a widespread aquatic bacterium (9,000×). **(c)** Unusual flagella on *Aquaspirillum* are amphitrichous and coil up into tight loops (7,500×). **(d)** An unidentified bacterium discovered living inside the cells of the protozoan *Paramecium* exhibits peritrichous flagella (7,500×).

Flagellar Responses Flagella often function as more than just a locomotor device. They are sensory appendages that can detect and respond to environmental signals. When the signal is of a chemical nature, the behavior is called **chemotaxis.*** Positive chemotaxis is movement of a cell in the direction of a favorable chemical stimulus (usually a nutrient); negative chemotaxis is movement away from a repellent (potentially harmful) compound.

The flagellum can guide bacteria in a certain direction because the system for detecting chemicals is linked to the mechanisms that drive the flagellum. Located in the cell membrane are clusters of receptors[1] that bind specific molecules coming from the immediate environment. The attachment of sufficient numbers of these molecules transmits signals to the flagellum and sets it into rotary motion. If several flagella are present, they become aligned and rotate

* *chemotaxis* (ke″-moh-tak′-sis) Gr. *chemo*, chemicals, and *taxis*, an ordering or arrangement.

1. Cell surface molecules that bind specifically with other molecules.

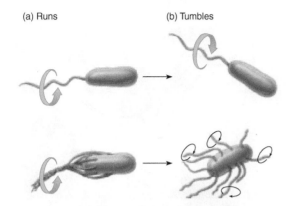

(a) Runs (b) Tumbles

Figure 4.5 The operation of flagella and the mode of locomotion in bacteria with polar and peritrichous flagella. (a) Runs. When a polar flagellum rotates in a counterclockwise direction, the cell swims forward in runs. In peritrichous forms, all flagella sweep toward one end of the cell and rotate as a single group. (b) Tumbles. When the flagellum reverses direction and rotates clockwise, the cell stops and tumbles. Peritrichous flagella also reverse direction and cause the cell to lose coordination and stop.

as a group (**figure 4.5**). As a flagellum rotates counterclockwise, the cell itself swims in a smooth linear direction toward the stimulus; this action is called a *run*. Runs are interrupted at various intervals by *tumbles* caused by the flagellum reversing its direction. This makes the cell stop and change its course. It is believed that attractant molecules inhibit tumbles, increase runs, and permit progress toward the stimulus (**figure 4.6**). Repellents cause numerous tumbles, allowing the bacterium to redirect itself away from the stimulus. Some photosynthetic bacteria exhibit *phototaxis,* a type of movement in response to light rather than chemicals.

Key

Tumble (T) Run (R) Tumble (T)

(a) **No attractant or repellent** (b) **Gradient of attractant concentration**

Figure 4.6 Chemotaxis in bacteria. (a) A cell moves via a random series of short runs and tumbles when there is no attractant or repellent. (b) The cell spends more time on runs as it gets closer to an attractant.

A few pathogenic bacteria use their flagella to invade the surface of mucous membranes during infections. *Helicobacter pylori,* the agent of gastric ulcers, bores through the stomach lining, and *Vibrio cholerae,* the cause of cholera, penetrates the small intestine with the help of its flagellum.

Periplasmic Flagella

Corkscrew-shaped bacteria called **spirochetes*** show a wormlike or serpentine mode of locomotion caused by two or more long, coiled threads, the periplasmic flagella or *axial filaments.* A periplasmic flagellum is a type of internal flagellum that is enclosed in the space between the outer sheath and the cell wall peptidoglycan (**figure 4.7**). The filaments curl closely around the spirochete coils yet are free to contract and impart a twisting or flexing motion to the cell. This form

* *spirochete* (spy'-roh-keet) Gr. *speira,* coil, and *chaite,* hair.

(a)

PF PC OS

(b)

Outer sheath (OS)

Protoplasmic cylinder (PC)

Periplasmic flagella (PF)

Peptidoglycan

Cell membrane

(c)

Figure 4.7 The orientation of periplasmic flagella on the spirochete cell. (a) Section through *Borrelia burgdorferi,* the spirochete of Lyme disease. The micrograph has been colorized to indicate the periplasmic flagella (yellow), the outer sheath (blue), and the protoplasmic cylinder (pink). (b) Longitudinal view with major cell parts labeled. (c) Cross section, indicating the position of the flagella with respect to other cell parts. Contraction of the filaments imparts a spinning and undulating pattern of locomotion.

(a)

E. coli cells

Fimbriae

Intestinal microvilli

G

(b)

Figure 4.8 Form and function of bacterial fimbriae. (a) Several cells of pathogenic _Escherichia coli_ covered with numerous fibers called fimbriae (30,000×). Note also the dark blue masses, which are chromosomes. **(b)** A row of _E. coli_ cells tightly adheres by their fimbriae to the surface of an intestinal cell (12,000×). This is how the bacterium clings and gains access to the inside of cells during an infection. (G = glycocalyx)

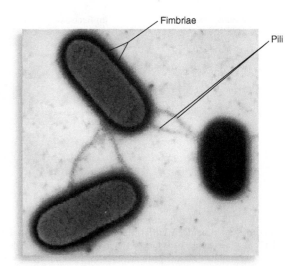

Fimbriae

Pili

Figure 4.9 Three bacteria in the process of conjugating. Clearly evident are the sex pili forming mutual conjugation bridges between a donor (upper cell) and two recipients (two lower cells). Fimbriae can also be seen on the donor cell.

of locomotion must be seen in live spirochetes to be truly appreciated (see Quick Search, page 105).

Nonflagellar Appendages: Fimbriae and Pili

The structures termed **fimbria*** and **pilus*** both refer to common bacterial surface appendages that are involved in interactions with other cells but do not provide locomotion, except for some specialized pili. Some microbiologists use the terms interchangeably, but we will refer to the smaller common appendages as fimbriae and the ones with specialized functions as pili.

Fimbriae are small, bristlelike fibers emerging from the surface of many types of bacterial cells (**figure 4.8**). Their exact composition varies, but most of them contain protein. Fimbriae have an inherent tendency to stick to each other and to surfaces. They may be responsible for the mutual clinging of cells that leads to biofilms and other thick aggregates of cells on the surface of liquids and for the microbial colonization of inanimate solids such as rocks and

glass (**4.1 Making Connections**). Some pathogens can colonize and infect host tissues because of a tight adhesion between their fimbriae and epithelial cells (**figure 4.8_b_**). For example, _Escherichia coli_ colonizes the intestine and begins its invasion of tissues by this means. Mutant forms of these pathogens that lack fimbriae are unable to cause infections.

Pili come in several varieties. A versatile form called the Type IV pilus is found only in gram-negative bacteria. This structure is a flexible tube made of the protein, pilin. Bacteria with pili participate in a mating process termed **conjugation,**[2] which uses the pilus (also called a sex pilus) as a connector for transferring DNA from a donor cell to a recipient (**figure 4.9**). This role of pili is discussed further in chapter 9.

Type IV pili are a major contributor to the infectiousness of _Neisseria gonorrhoeae,_ the agent of gonorrhea, by providing a mechanism for binding to the epithelial cells of the reproductive tract. Type IV pili found in _Pseudomonas_ bacteria carry out a remarkable sort of twitching motility. Cells can slide in jerking movements over moist surfaces by extending and then retracting pili in a repetitive motion. Microbiologists have found that this mechanism is every bit as complex and regulated as the flagellar mode of locomotion. This remarkable motility may be observed on YouTube by searching for "type IV pili twitching motility."

The Bacterial Surface Coating, or Glycocalyx

The bacterial cell surface is frequently exposed to severe environmental conditions. The **glycocalyx** develops as a coating of macromolecules to protect the cell and, in some cases, help it adhere to its environment. Glycocalyces differ among bacteria in thickness, organization, and chemical composition. Some bacteria are covered with a loose shield called a **slime layer** that protects them from

* _fimbria_ (fim′-bree-ah) pl. fimbriae; L., a fringe.
* _pilus_ (py′-lus) pl. pili; L., hair.

2. Although the term _mating_ is sometimes used for this process, it is not a form of reproduction.

4.1 MAKING CONNECTIONS

Biofilms—The Glue of Life

Microbes rarely live in isolation. More often they cling together in complex masses called **biofilms.** The formation of these living layers is actually a universal phenomenon that all of us have observed. Consider the scum that builds up in toilet bowls and shower stalls in a short time if they are not cleaned; or the algae that collect on the walls of swimming pools; and, more intimately, the constant deposition of plaque on teeth.

Fossils from ancient deposits tell us that microbes have been making biofilms for billions of years. It is through this process that they have colonized most habitats on earth and created stable communities that provide access to nutrients and other essential factors. Biofilms are often cooperative associations among several microbial groups (bacteria, fungi, algae, and protozoa) as well as plants and animals.

Substrates favorable to biofilm development have a moist, thin layer of organic material such as polysaccharides or glycoproteins deposited on their exposed surface. This has a sticky texture that attracts primary colonists, usually bacteria. These early cells attach and begin to multiply on the surface. Here, they lay down a glycocalyx consisting of fimbriae, pili, slime layers, or capsules. These substances bind the cells to the substrate and begin the development of the biofilm matrix.

As the biofilm evolves, it undergoes specific adaptations to the habitat in which it forms. In many cases, the earliest colonists contribute nutrients and create microhabitats for other microbes to attach and grow into the film, forming complete communities. The biofilm varies in thickness and complexity, depending upon where it occurs and how long it keeps developing. Complexity ranges from single cell layers to thick microbial mats with dozens of dynamic interactive layers.

Biofilms are a profoundly important force in the development of terrestrial and aquatic environments. They dwell permanently in bedrock and the earth's sediments, where they play essential roles in recycling elements, leaching minerals, and forming soil. Biofilms associated with plant roots promote the mutual exchange of nutrients between the microbes and roots. As we will learn in chapter 7, the microbes in these communities have "conversations" using a special chemical vocabulary, which greatly influences the actions of the biofilm.

Researchers are currently analyzing the effects of biofilms created by our own microbiota—microbes that live naturally on the body. These associations are common on the skin, the oral cavity, and large intestine. In these locations, microbes signal each other as well as human cells in ways that shape the conditions there.

Biofilms accumulate on damaged tissues (such as heart valves), hard tissues (teeth), and foreign materials (catheters, intrauterine devices [IUDs], artificial hip joints). Microbial biofilms play a key role in the majority of infections and diseases—for example, cholera, urinary tract infections, sexually transmitted infections, endocarditis, middle ear infections, and pneumonia. New evidence indicates that bacteria turn on different genes when they are in a biofilm than when they are "free-floating," or planktonic. This altered gene expression gives the bacteria a different set of characteristics, often making them impervious to antibiotics and disinfectants. For additional discussions of biofilms, see chapters 7 and 12.

> **Quick Search**
> Find "3D Architecture of Microbial Cities" with a browser and watch a dynamic animation about biofilms.

Describe some possible benefits of having biofilms form in or on the human body. *Answer available at http://www.mhhe.com/talaro9*

1. Attachment of free planktonic cells to surface

2–3. Growth of cells, synthesis of extracellular matrix, stable colonization of surface

4. Maturation of biofilm formation of thick layered deposits containing sessile cells

5. Mature biofilm completes cycle by dispersing planktonic cells, which swim free to start the process again in new habitats

dehydration and loss of nutrients, as well as serving in adhesion **(figure 4.10a).** Other bacteria produce **capsules** composed of repeating polysaccharide units, of protein, or of both. A capsule is bound more tightly to the cell than a slime layer is, and it has a thicker, gummy consistency that gives a prominently sticky (mucoid) character to the colonies of most encapsulated bacteria **(figure 4.11a).**

CLINICAL CONNECTIONS

The Glycocalyx and Infections

Capsules are formed by many pathogenic bacteria, such as *Streptococcus pneumoniae* (a cause of pneumonia, an infection of the lungs), *Haemophilus influenzae* (one cause of meningitis), and *Bacillus anthracis* (the cause of anthrax). Encapsulated bacterial cells generally have greater pathogenicity because capsules protect the bacteria against white blood cells called phagocytes. Phagocytes are a natural body defense that can engulf and destroy foreign cells, which helps to prevent infection. A capsular coating blocks the phagocytes from attaching to, engulfing, and killing bacteria. By escaping phagocytosis, the bacteria are free to multiply and infect body tissues. Encapsulated bacteria that mutate to nonencapsulated forms usually lose their pathogenicity.

Other types of glycocalyces can be important in formation of biofilm infections (see 4.1 Making Connections). The thick, white plaque that forms on teeth comes in part from the surface slimes produced by certain streptococci in the oral cavity. This slime protects them from being dislodged from the teeth and provides a niche for persistent colonization that, can lead to dental disease. The glycocalyx of some bacteria is so highly adherent that it is responsible for harmful biofilms developing on nonliving materials such as plastic catheters, intrauterine devices, and metal pacemakers that are in common medical use **(figure 4.12).**

Biofilms on heart valves can give rise to infections in other areas of the body. Explain how this happens by looking at the figure in 4.1 Making Connections. *Answer available at http://www.mhhe.com/talaro9*

(a)

Figure 4.10 Types of glycocalyces seen through cutaway views of cells. (a) The slime layer is a loose structure that is easily washed off. **(b)** The capsule is a thick, structured layer that is not readily removed.

Figure 4.11 Appearance of encapsulated bacteria. (a) Close-up view of colonies of *Bacillus* species with and without capsules. Even at the macroscopic level, the moist, slimy character of the capsule is evident. **(b)** Special staining reveals the microscopic appearance of a large, well-developed capsule (the clear "halo" around the cells) of *Klebsiella* (1,000×).

Figure 4.12 Magnified view of a biofilm. Scanning electron micrograph of a biofilm formed by a gram-negative bacterium, *Alkaligenes*, on a central venous catheter. Note the thick matrix of the biofilm caught in the fine fibers of the catheter.

Check Your Progress SECTION 4.2

3. What other microbial groups besides bacteria have prokaryotic cells?
4. Describe the structure of a flagellum and how it operates. What are the four main types of flagellar arrangement?
5. How does the flagellum dictate the behavior of a motile bacterium? Differentiate between flagella and periplasmic flagella.
6. Differentiate between the structure and functions of pili and fimbriae.
7. Explain the position of the glycocalyx.
8. How do slime layers and capsules differ in structure and functions?
9. How can a capsule or slime layer be detected even at the level of a colony?
10. Explain how the bacterial glycocalyx and certain surface appendages contribute to biofilm formation.

4.3 The Cell Envelope: The Outer Boundary Layer of Bacteria

Expected Learning Outcomes

9. Explain the concept of the cell envelope, and describe its structure.
10. Outline the structure and functions of cell walls, and explain the role of peptidoglycan.
11. Contrast the major structure of gram-positive and gram-negative cell walls.
12. Summarize how gram-positive and gram-negative cells differ in their reactions.
13. Relate the characteristics of other types of cell walls and wall-free cells.
14. Describe the structure of the cell membrane, and explain several of its major roles in bacterial cells.

The majority of bacteria have a chemically complex external covering, termed the cell envelope, that encloses the cytoplasm. It is composed of two main layers: the cell wall and the cell membrane. These layers are stacked together and often tightly bound into a unit like the outer husk and casings of a coconut. Although each envelope layer performs a distinct action, together they act as a single unit required for a cell's normal function and integrity.

Basic Types of Cell Envelopes

Long before the detailed anatomy of bacteria was even remotely known, a Danish physician named **Hans Christian Gram** developed a staining technique, the **Gram stain,**[3] which is

commonly used to delineate two different groups of bacteria known as the gram-positive bacteria and the gram-negative bacteria. You may wish to review this stain, described in 3.2 Making Connections. Because the Gram stain does not actually reveal the reasons that these two groups stain differently, we must turn to the electron microscope and to biochemical analysis of their structure.

The extent of the differences between gram-positive and gram-negative bacteria is evident in the physical appearance of their cell envelopes (**figure 4.13**). In **gram-positive** cells, a microscopic section resembles an open-faced sandwich with two layers: the thick cell wall, composed primarily of peptidoglycan (defined in the next section), and the cell membrane. A similar section of a gram-negative cell envelope shows a complete sandwich with three layers: an outer membrane, a thin peptidoglycan layer, and the cell membrane. The reactions of the Gram stain are the result of these basic differences. The thick peptidoglycan of the gram-positive cell traps the crystal violet-mordant complex and makes it inaccessible to the decolorizer, leaving the cells purple. Gram-negative cell walls are thinner, and the crystal violet is relatively easy to remove with the decolorizer. In addition, the alcohol dissolves the outer membrane of the cell, which increases this loss of dye. These factors create a colorless cell that will stain with a red counterstain. **Table 4.1** provides a summary of the major similarities and differences between the wall types.

Structure of Cell Walls

The cell wall accounts for a number of important bacterial characteristics. In general, it helps determine the shape of a bacterium, and it also provides the kind of strong structural support necessary to keep a bacterium intact despite constant changes in

(a)

(b)

Figure 4.13 Comparative views of the envelopes of gram-positive and gram-negative cells. (a) A section through a gram-positive cell wall/membrane with an interpretation of the main layers visible (85,000×). **(b)** A section through a gram-negative cell wall/membrane with an interpretation of its three sandwich-style layers (90,000×).

3. This text follows the American Society for Microbiology style, which calls for capitalization of the terms *Gram stain* and *Gram staining* and lowercase treatment of gram-negative and gram-positive, except in headings.

TABLE 4.1	Comparison of Gram-Positive and Gram-Negative Cell Walls	
Characteristic	**Gram-Positive**	**Gram-Negative**
Number of major layers	One	Two
Chemical composition	Peptidoglycan Teichoic acid Lipoteichoic acid Mycolic acids and polysaccharides*	Lipopolysaccharide (LPS) Lipoprotein Peptidoglycan Porin proteins
Overall thickness	Thicker (20–80 nm)	Thinner (8–11 nm)
Outer membrane	No	Yes
Periplasmic space	Narrow	Extensive
Permeability to molecules	More penetrable	Less penetrable

*In some cells.

(a) The peptidoglycan of a cell wall is a huge, three-dimensional latticework that is actually one giant molecule to surround and support the cell.

(b) This shows the molecular pattern of peptidoglycan. It has alternating glycans (NAG and NAM) bound together in long strands. The NAG stands for *N*-acetyl glucosamine, and the NAM stands for *N*-acetyl muramic acid. Adjacent muramic acid molecules on parallel chains are bound by a cross-linkage of peptides (brown spheres).

(c) An enlarged view of the links between the NAM molecules. Tetrapeptide chains branching off the muramic acids connect by amino acid interbridges. The amino acids in the interbridge can vary or may be lacking entirely. It is this linkage that provides rigid yet flexible support to the cell.

Figure 4.14 Structure of peptidoglycan component of cell walls.

environmental conditions. The cell walls of most bacteria gain their relative strength and stability from a unique macromolecule called **peptidoglycan (PG).** This compound is composed of a repeating framework of long **glycan*** chains cross-linked by short peptide fragments **(figure 4.14).** The amount and exact composition of peptidoglycan vary among the major bacterial groups.

Because many bacteria live in aqueous habitats with a low solute concentration, they are constantly absorbing excess water by osmosis. Were it not for the structural support of the peptidoglycan in the cell wall, they would rupture from internal pressure. Several types of drugs used to treat infection (penicillin, cephalosporins) are effective because they target the peptide cross-links in the peptidoglycan, thereby disrupting its integrity. With their cell walls incomplete or missing, such cells have very little protection from **lysis.*** Lysozyme, an enzyme contained in tears and saliva, provides a natural defense against certain bacteria by hydrolyzing the bonds in the glycan chains and causing the wall to break down. Chapters 11 and 12 provide more information on the actions of antimicrobial chemical agents and drugs.

The Gram-Positive Cell Wall

The bulk of the gram-positive cell wall is a thick, homogeneous sheath of peptidoglycan ranging from 20 to 80 nm in thickness. It also contains tightly bound acidic polysaccharides, including teichoic acid directly attached to the peptidoglycan and lipoteichoic acid **(figure 4.15).** Cell wall **teichoic acid** is a polymer of ribitol or glycerol and phosphate embedded in the peptidoglycan sheath. Lipoteichoic acid is similar in structure but is attached to the lipids in the plasma membrane. These molecules appear to function in cell wall maintenance, enlargement during cell division, and

* *glycan* (gly′-kan) Gr., sugar. These are large polymers of simple sugars.
* *lysis* (ly′-sis) Gr., to loosen. A process of cell destruction, as occurs in bursting.

Figure 4.15 **A comparison of the detailed structure of gram-positive and gram-negative cell envelopes and walls.**

binding of some pathogens to tissues. The cell wall of gram-positive bacteria is loosely adherent to the cell membrane, but at their junction lies a small compartment called the **periplasmic* space.** This is analogous to the larger space in gram-negatives, but it has different functions. It is a site for temporary storage of enzymes that have been released by the cell membrane. More recent studies have found that this space serves as the major site for peptidoglycan synthesis.

The Gram-Negative Cell Wall

The gram-negative cell wall is more complex in morphology because it is composed of an **outer membrane (OM)** and a thinner shell of peptidoglycan (see figures 4.13 and 4.15). The outer membrane is somewhat similar in construction to the cell membrane, except that it contains specialized types of **lipopolysaccharides (LPS)** and **lipoproteins.** Lipopolysaccharides consist of lipid molecules bound to polysaccharides. The lipids form the matrix of the top layer of the OM, and the polysaccharide strands project from the lipid surface. The lipid portion may become toxic when it is released during infections. Its role as an endotoxin is described in chapter 13. The polysaccharides give rise to the somatic (O) antigen in gram-negative pathogens and can be used in identification. They may also function as receptors and interfere with host defenses.

Two types of proteins are located in the OM. The **porins** are inserted in the upper layer of the outer membrane. They have some

regulatory control over molecules entering and leaving the cell. Many qualities of the selective permeability of gram-negative bacteria to bile, disinfectants, and drugs are due to the porins. Some structural proteins are also embedded in the upper layer of the OM. The bottom layer of the outer membrane is similar to the cell membrane in its overall structure and is composed of phospholipids and lipoproteins.

The bottom layer of the gram-negative wall is a single, thin (1–3 nm) sheet of peptidoglycan. Although it acts as a somewhat rigid protective structure, as previously described, its thinness gives gram-negative bacteria a relatively greater flexibility and sensitivity to lysis. There is a well-developed **periplasmic space** above and below the peptidoglycan. This space in gram-negative bacteria is a site of many metabolic reactions related to synthesis and transport of proteins, actions of enyzmes, and energy release.

Nontypical Cell Walls

Several bacterial groups lack the cell wall structure of gram-positive or gram-negative bacteria, and some bacteria have no cell wall at all. Although these exceptional forms can stain positive or negative in the Gram stain, examination of their fine structure and chemistry shows that they do not fit the descriptions for typical gram-negative or gram-positive cells. For example, the cells of *Mycobacterium* and *Nocardia* contain peptidoglycan and stain gram-positive, but the bulk of their cell wall is composed of unique types of lipids. One of these is a very-long-chain fatty acid called *mycolic acid,* or cord factor, that contributes to the pathogenicity of this group. The thick, waxy nature imparted to the cell wall by these lipids is also responsible for a high degree of resistance to certain chemicals and dyes.

* *periplasmic* (per″-ih-plaz′-mik) Gr. *peri,* around, and *plastos,* the fluid substances of a cell.

 CLINICAL CONNECTIONS

The Cell Wall and Infections

Variations in cell wall anatomy contribute to several differences between the two cell types besides staining reactions. The outer membrane contributes an extra barrier in gram-negative bacteria that makes them more impervious to some antimicrobic chemicals such as dyes and disinfectants, so they are generally more difficult to inhibit or kill than are gram-positive bacteria. One exception is for alcohol-based compounds, which can dissolve the lipids in the outer membrane and disturb its integrity. Treating infections caused by gram-negative bacteria often requires different drugs than for gram-positive infections, because of the special requirement that the drugs must cross the outer membrane.

The cell wall or its parts can interact with human tissues and contribute to disease. The lipopolysaccharides have been referred to as *endotoxins* because they stimulate fever and shock reactions in gram-negative infections such as meningitis and typhoid fever. Proteins attached to the outer portion of the cell wall of several gram-positive species, including *Corynebacterium diphtheriae* (the agent of diphtheria) and *Streptococcus pyogenes* (the cause of strep throat), also have toxic properties. The lipids in the cell walls of certain *Mycobacterium* species are harmful to human cells as well. Because most macromolecules in the cell walls are foreign to humans, they stimulate antibody production by the immune system (see chapter 15).

Explain why penicillin can be an effective drug to treat gram-positive bacterial infections but is ineffective against most gram-negative bacteria. *Answer available at http://www.mhhe.com/talaro9*

Such resistance is the basis for the **acid-fast stain** used to diagnose tuberculosis and leprosy. In this stain, hot carbol fuchsin dye becomes tenaciously attached (is held fast) to these cells so that an acid-alcohol solution will not remove the dye.

Mycoplasmas and Other Cell-Wall-Deficient Bacteria

Mycoplasmas are bacteria that naturally lack a cell wall. Although other bacteria require an intact cell wall to prevent the bursting of the cell, the mycoplasma cell membrane contains sterols that make it resistant to lysis. These extremely tiny bacteria range from 0.1 to 0.5 μm in size. They range in shape from filamentous to coccus or doughnut-shaped. This property of extreme variations in shape is a type of **pleomorphism.*** They can be grown on artificial media, although added sterols are required for the cell membranes of some species. Mycoplasmas are found in many habitats, including plants, soil, and animals. The most important medical species is *Mycoplasma pneumoniae* (**figure 4.16**), which adheres to the epithelial cells in the lung and causes an atypical form of pneumonia in humans.

Figure 4.16 **Scanning electron micrograph of *Mycoplasma pneumoniae* (10,000X).** Cells exhibit extreme variation in shape due to the lack of a cell wall.

Some bacteria that ordinarily have a cell wall can lose it during part of their life cycle. These wall-deficient forms are referred to as **L forms** or L-phase variants (for the Lister Institute, where they were discovered). L forms arise naturally from a mutation in the wall-forming genes, or they can be induced artificially by treatment with a chemical such as lysozyme or penicillin that disrupts the cell wall. When a gram-positive cell is exposed to either of these two chemicals, it will lose the cell wall completely and become a **protoplast,*** a fragile cell bounded only by a membrane that is highly susceptible to lysis. A gram-negative cell exposed to these same substances loses its peptidoglycan but retains its outer membrane, leaving a less fragile but nevertheless weakened **spheroplast.*** Evidence points to a role for L forms in certain chronic infections.

Cell Membrane Structure

A layer in the cell envelope appearing just beneath the cell wall is the **cell,** or **cytoplasmic, membrane,** a very thin (5–10 nm), flexible sheet structured as one complete sheath around the cytoplasm. In general composition, it is a lipid bilayer with proteins embedded to varying degrees (**figure 4.17**). This configuration, first proposed by S. J. Singer and G. L. Nicolson, is called the **fluid mosaic model.** The model describes a membrane as a continuous bilayer formed by lipids with the polar heads oriented toward the outside and the nonpolar tails toward the center of the membrane. Embedded at numerous sites in this bilayer are various-size proteins. Peripheral proteins are situated only at the surface and are readily removed. Integral proteins extend fully through the entire membrane and are often fixed in place. The configuration of the inner and outer sides of the membrane can be quite different because of the variations in protein shape and position.

Membranes are dynamic and constantly changing because the lipid phase is in motion, which allows some proteins to migrate to specific locations where they are needed. This fluidity

* *pleomorphism* (plee″-oh-mor′-fizm) Gr. *pleon,* more, and *morph,* form or shape. The tendency for cells of the same species to vary to some extent in shape and size.

* *protoplast* (proh′-toh-plast) Gr. *proto,* first, and *plastos,* formed.
* *spheroplast* (sfer′-oh-plast) Gr. *sphaira,* sphere.

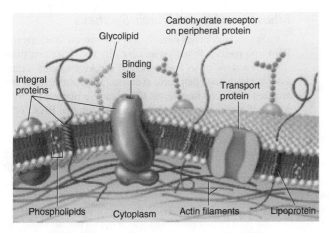

Figure 4.17 Cell membrane structure. A generalized version of the fluid mosaic model of a cell membrane indicates a bilayer of lipids with proteins embedded to some degree in the lipid matrix. Molecules attached to the proteins provide surface features for cell responsiveness and binding. This structure explains many characteristics of membranes, including flexibility, permeability, specificity, and transport.

is essential to such activities as cell enlargement and discharge or secretion by cells. The structure of the lipid phase provides an impenetrable barrier to many substances. This property accounts for the selective permeability and capacity to regulate transport of molecules. Bacterial cell membranes contain primarily phospholipids (making up about 30%–40% of the membrane mass) and proteins (contributing 60%–70%). Major exceptions to this description are the membranes of mycoplasmas, which contain high amounts of sterols—rigid lipids that stabilize and reinforce the membrane—and the membranes of archaea, which contain unique branched hydrocarbons rather than fatty acids. Look back at figure 2.20 to observe eukaryotic membrane structure, which is very similar to bacteria, except for the presence of cholesterol in the eukaryotic variety.

Although bacteria lack complex internal membranous organelles, some members develop stacked layers of internal membranes that carry out physiological processes related to energy and synthesis. These membranes are usually an outgrowth of the cell membrane extending into the cytoplasm, which can increase the membrane surface area available for these reactions. Examples of cells with internal membranes are cyanobacteria, whose thylakoid membranes are the sites of photosynthesis (figure 4.28c). Even eukaryotic mitochondria, considered bacterial in origin, function by means of a series of internal membranes (look ahead to 5.1 Making Connections).

Functions of the Cell Membrane

Because bacteria have none of the eukaryotic organelles, the cell membrane provides a site for energy reactions, nutrient processing, and synthesis. A major action of the cell membrane is to regulate *transport,* that is, the passage of nutrients into the cell and the discharge of wastes. Although water and small uncharged molecules can diffuse across the membrane unaided, the membrane is a *selec-*

tively permeable structure with special carrier mechanisms for passage of most molecules (see chapter 7). The glycocalyx and cell wall can bar the passage of large molecules, but they are not the primary transport apparatus. The cell membrane is also involved in *secretion,* or the release of a metabolic product into the extracellular environment.

The membranes of bacteria are an important site for a number of metabolic activities. For example, most enzymes that handle the energy reactions of respiration reside in the cell membrane (see chapter 8). Enzyme structures located in the cell membrane also help synthesize structural macromolecules to be incorporated into the cell envelope and appendages. Other products (enzymes and toxins) are secreted by the membrane into the extracellular environment.

 Check Your Progress SECTION 4.3

11. Compare the basic structure of the cell envelopes of gram-positive and gram-negative bacteria.
12. Explain the function of peptidoglycan and give a simple description of its structure.
13. What happens to a cell that has its peptidoglycan disrupted or removed?
14. How does the precise structure of the cell walls differ between gram-positive and gram-negative bacteria?
15. What other properties besides staining are different in gram-positive and gram-negative bacteria?
16. What is the periplasmic space, and what is its function?
17. Describe the medical impact of the cell walls of gram-negative and gram-positive bacteria.
18. Describe the structure of the cell membrane, and explain why it is considered selectively permeable.
19. List five essential functions that the cell membrane performs in bacteria.

4.4 Bacterial Internal Structure

 Expected Learning Outcomes

15. List the contents of the cell cytoplasm.
16. Describe features of the bacterial chromosome and plasmids.
17. Characterize the bacterial ribosomes and cytoskeleton.
18. Describe inclusion bodies and granules, and explain their importance to cells.
19. Describe the life cycle of endospore-forming bacteria, including the formation and germination of endospores.
20. Discuss the resistance and significance of endospores.

Contents of the Cell Cytoplasm

The cell membrane surrounds a complex solution referred to as **cytoplasm,** or cytoplasmic matrix. This chemical "pool" is a prominent site for many of the cell's biochemical and synthetic

activities. Its major component is water (70%–80%), which serves as a solvent for a complex mixture of nutrients including sugars, amino acids, and other organic molecules and salts. The components of this pool serve as building blocks for cell synthesis or as sources of energy. The cytoplasm also holds larger, discrete bodies such as the chromosome, ribosomes, granules, and actin strands.

Bacterial Chromosomes and Plasmids: The Sources of Genetic Information

The hereditary material of most bacteria exists in the form of a single circular strand of DNA designated as the **bacterial chromosome,** although a few bacteria have multiple or linear chromosomes. By definition, bacteria do not have a true nucleus. Their DNA is not enclosed by a nuclear membrane but instead is aggregated in a central area of the cell called the **nucleoid.** The chromosome is actually an extremely long molecule of DNA that is tightly coiled to fit inside the cell compartment. Arranged along its length are genetic units (genes) that carry information required for bacterial maintenance and growth. When exposed to special stains or observed with an electron microscope, chromosomes have a granular or fibrous appearance (**figure 4.18**).

Although the chromosome is the minimal genetic requirement for bacterial survival, many bacteria contain other, nonessential pieces of DNA called **plasmids.** These tiny strands exist apart from the chromosome, although at times they can become integrated into it. During bacterial reproduction, they are duplicated and passed on to offspring. They are not essential to bacterial growth and metabolism, but they often confer protective traits such as resisting drugs and producing toxins and enzymes (see chapter 9). Because they can be readily manipulated in the laboratory and transferred from one bacterial cell to another, plasmids are an important agent in modern genetic engineering techniques.

Ribosomes: Sites of Protein Synthesis

A bacterial cell contains thousands of **ribosomes,** which are made of RNA and protein. When viewed even by very high magnification, ribosomes show up as fine, spherical specks dispersed throughout the cytoplasm that often occur in chains (polysomes). Many are also attached to the cell membrane. Chemically, a ribosome is a combination of a special type of RNA called ribosomal RNA, or rRNA (about 60%), and protein (40%).

One method of characterizing ribosomes is by S, or Svedberg,[4] units, which rate the molecular sizes of various cell parts that have been spun down and separated by molecular weight and shape in a centrifuge. Heavier, more compact structures sediment faster and are assigned a higher S rating. Combining this method of analysis with high-resolution electron micrography has revealed that the prokaryotic ribosome, which has an overall rating of 70S, is actually composed of two smaller subunits (**figure 4.19**). They fit together to form a miniature "factory" where protein synthesis occurs. We examine the more detailed functions of ribosomes in chapter 9.

Inclusions, or Granules: Storage Bodies

Most bacteria are exposed to severe shifts in the availability of food. During periods of nutrient abundance, some can compensate by storing nutrients as **inclusion bodies,** or **inclusions,** of varying size, number, and content. As the environmental source of these nutrients becomes depleted, the bacterial cell can mobilize its own storehouse as required. Some inclusion bodies contain condensed, energy-rich organic substances, such as glycogen and poly β-hydroxybutyrate (PHB), within special single-layered membranes (**figure 4.20a**). A unique type of inclusion found in some aquatic bacteria is gas vesicles that provide buoyancy and flotation. Other inclusions, also called **granules,** contain crystals

4. Named in honor of T. Svedberg, the Swedish chemist who developed the ultracentrifuge in 1926.

Figure 4.18 Bacterial cells stained to highlight their chromosomes. The individual cocci of *Deinococcus radiodurans* contain one or more prominent bodies that are the chromosomes or nucleoids (1,200×). Some cells are in the process of dividing. Notice how much of the cell's space the chromosomes (light blue bodies) occupy.

Ribosome (70S)

Large subunit (50S)

Small subunit (30S)

Figure 4.19 A model of a prokaryotic ribosome, showing the small (30S) and large (50S) subunits, both separate and joined.

Figure 4.21 Bacterial cytoskeleton of *Bacillus*. Fluorescent stain of actin fibers appears as fine helical ribbons wound inside the cell. The inset provides a three-dimensional interpretation of its structure.

(b)

Figure 4.20 Bacterial inclusion bodies. (a) Large particles (pink) of polyhydroxybutyrate are deposited in an insoluble, concentrated form that provides an ample, long-term supply of that nutrient (32,500×). **(b)** A section through *Aquaspirillum* reveals a chain of tiny iron magnets (magnetosomes = MP). These unusual bacteria use these inclusions to orient within their habitat (123,000×).

framework involved in support and shape. Research into the fine structure of certain rod- and spiral-shaped bacteria has provided several new insights. It is now evident that many of them possess an internal network of protein polymers associated with the wall. Several of these cytoskeleton systems have been studied, but the best understood is made of actin filaments that curl within the body of the cell and help maintain its shape during cell enlargement **(figure 4.21).** Other cytoskeletal elements appear to be active in cell division.

What Exactly Is A Spore?

The word *spore* can have more than one usage in microbiology. It is a generic term that refers to any tiny compact cells that are produced by vegetative or reproductive structures of microorganisms. Spores can be quite variable in origin, form, and function. The bacterial type discussed next is also called an endospore, because it is produced inside a cell. It functions in *survival*, not in reproduction, because no increase in cell numbers is involved in its formation. In contrast, the fungi produce many different types of spores for both survival and reproduction (see chapter 5).

Bacterial Endospores: An Extremely Resistant Life Form

Ample evidence indicates that the anatomy of bacteria helps them adjust rather well to adverse habitats. But of all microbial structures, nothing can compare to the bacterial **endospore** (or simply spore) for withstanding hostile conditions and facilitating survival. Endospores are dormant bodies produced by *Bacillus, Clostridium,* and several other bacterial genera. These bacteria have a two-phase life cycle that shifts between a **vegetative cell (figure 4.22, step 1)** and an endospore **(figure 4.22, step 8).** The vegetative cell is the metabolically active and growing phase. When exposed to certain

of inorganic compounds and are not enclosed by membranes. Sulfur granules of photosynthetic bacteria and polyphosphate granules of *Corynebacterium* and *Mycobacterium* are of this type. The latter represent an important source of building blocks for nucleic acid and ATP synthesis. They have been termed **metachromatic granules** because they stain a contrasting color (red, purple) in the presence of methylene blue dye.

Perhaps the most remarkable cell granule is involved not in nutrition but rather in navigation. Magnetotactic bacteria contain crystalline particles of iron oxide (magnetosomes) that have magnetic properties **(figure 4.20*b*).** These granules occur in a variety of bacteria living in oceans and swamps. Their primary function is to orient the cells in the earth's magnetic field, somewhat like a compass. It is thought that magnetosomes direct these bacteria into locations with favorable oxygen levels or nutrient-rich sediments.

The Bacterial Cytoskeleton

Until recently, bacteriologists thought bacteria lacked any real form of cytoskeleton.[5] The cell wall was considered to be the sole

5. An intracellular framework of fibers and tubules that bind and support eukaryotic cells.

① Process Figure 4.22 **A typical sporulation cycle in *Bacillus* species from the active vegetative cell to release and germination.** This process takes, on average, about 10 hours. Inset is a high magnification (10,000×) cross section of a single spore showing the dense protective layers that surround the core with its chromosome.

environmental signals, it forms an endospore by a process termed **sporulation.** The spore exists in an inert, resting condition that is capable of extreme resistance and very long-term survival.

Endospore Formation and Resistance

The major stimulus for endospore formation is the depletion of nutrients, especially amino acids. Once this stimulus has been received by the vegetative cell, it converts to a committed sporulating cell called a **sporangium.** Complete transformation of a vegetative cell into a sporangium and then into an endospore requires 6 to 12 hours in most spore-forming species. Figure 4.22 illustrates some major physical and chemical events in this process.

Bacterial endospores are the hardiest of all life forms, capable of withstanding extremes in heat, drying, freezing, radiation, and chemicals that would readily kill ordinary cells. Their survival under such harsh conditions is due to several factors. The heat resistance of spores has been linked to their high content of calcium and *dipicolinic acid,* although the exact role of these chemicals is not yet clear. We know, for instance, that heat destroys cells by inactivating proteins and DNA and that this process requires a certain

amount of water in the protoplasm. Because the deposition of calcium dipicolinate in the endospore removes water and leaves the endospore very dehydrated, it is less vulnerable to the effects of heat. It is also metabolically inactive and highly resistant to damage from further drying. The thick, impervious cortex and spore coats provide additional protection against radiation and chemicals.

The longevity of bacterial spores verges on immortality! One record describes the isolation of viable endospores from a fossilized bee that was 25 million years old. More recently, microbiologists unearthed a viable endospore from a 250-million-year-old salt crystal. Initial analysis of this ancient microbe indicates it is a species of *Bacillus* that is genetically different from known species.

The Germination of Endospores

After lying in a state of inactivity, endospores can be revitalized when favorable conditions arise. The breaking of dormancy, or **germination,** happens in the presence of water and a specific germination agent. Once initiated, it proceeds to completion quite rapidly (1½ hours). Although the specific germination

 CLINICAL CONNECTIONS

The Impact of Endospores

Although the majority of spore-forming bacteria are relatively harmless, several bacterial pathogens are sporeformers. In fact, some aspects of the diseases they cause are related to the persistence and resistance of their spores. Spores of *Bacillus anthracis,* the agent of anthrax, are classified as a high level bioterrorism agent. The genus *Clostridium* includes even more pathogens, including *C. tetani,* the cause of tetanus (lockjaw), and *C. perfringens,* the cause of gas gangrene. When the spores of these species are embedded in a wound that contains dead tissue, they can germinate, grow, and release potent toxins. Another toxin-forming species, *C. botulinum,* is the agent of botulism, a deadly form of food poisoning. These diseases are discussed further in chapter 19.

Because they inhabit the soil and dust, endospores are a constant intruder where sterility and cleanliness are important. They resist ordinary cleaning methods that use boiling water, soaps, and disinfectants, and they frequently contaminate cultures and media. Hospitals and clinics must take precautions to guard against the potential harmful effects of endospores in wounds. Endospore destruction is a particular concern of the food-canning industry. Several endospore-forming species cause food spoilage or poisoning. Ordinary boiling (100°C) will usually not destroy such spores, so canning is carried out in pressurized steam at 120°C for 20 to 30 minutes. Such rigorous conditions will ensure that the food is sterile and free from viable bacteria.

***Clostridium difficile* is an emerging pathogen that causes thousands of intestinal infections in hospital patients every year. What qualities of this bacterium make it such a serious concern?** *Answer available at http://www.mhhe.com/talaro9*

agent varies among species, it is generally a small organic molecule such as an amino acid or an inorganic salt. This agent stimulates the formation of hydrolytic (digestive) enzymes by the endospore membranes. These enzymes digest the cortex and expose the core to water. As the core rehydrates and takes up nutrients, it begins to grow out of the endospore coats. In time, it reverts to a fully active vegetative cell, resuming the vegetative cycle (figure 4.22).

 Check Your Progress SECTION 4.4

20. Compare the functions of the bacterial chromosome (nucleoid) and plasmids.
21. What is unique about the structure of bacterial ribosomes, what is their function, and where are they located?
22. Compare and contrast the structure and function of inclusions and granules.
23. What are metachromatic granules, and what do they contain?
24. Describe the way endospores are formed, their structure, and their importance in the life cycle.
25. Explain why an endospore is not considered a reproductive body.
26. Why are spores so difficult to destroy?

4.5 Bacterial Shapes, Arrangements, and Sizes

 Expected Learning Outcomes

21. Describe the shapes of bacteria and their possible variants.
22. Identify several arrangements of bacteria and how they are formed.
23. Indicate the size ranges in bacteria in comparison to other organisms.

For the most part, bacteria function as independent single-celled, or unicellular, organisms. Although it is true that an individual bacterial cell can live attached to others in colonies or other such groupings, each one is fully capable of carrying out all necessary life activities, such as reproduction, metabolism, and nutrient processing unlike the more specialized cells of a multicellular organism.

Bacteria exhibit considerable variety in shape, size, and colonial arrangement. It is convenient to describe most bacteria by one of three general shapes as dictated by the configuration of the cell wall (**figure 4.23**). If the cell is spherical or ball-shaped, the bacterium is described as a **coccus.*** Cocci can be perfect spheres, but they also can exist as oval, bean-shaped, or even pointed variants.

A cell that is cylindrical (longer than wide) is termed a rod, or **bacillus.*** There is also a genus named *Bacillus* named for its rod shape. As might be expected, rods are also quite varied in their actual form. Depending on the bacterial species, they can be blocky, spindle-shaped, round-ended, long and threadlike (filamentous), or even clubbed or drumstick-shaped. When a rod is short and plump, it is called a **coccobacillus;** if it is gently curved, it is a **vibrio.***

A bacterium having the shape of a curviform or spiral-shaped cylinder is called a **spirillum,*** a rigid helix, twisted twice or more along its axis (like a corkscrew). Another spiral cell mentioned earlier in conjunction with periplasmic flagella is the **spirochete,** a more flexible form that resembles a spring. Refer to **table 4.2** for a comparison of other features of the two helical bacterial forms. Because bacterial cells look two-dimensional and flat with traditional staining and microscope techniques, they are best observed using a scanning electron microscope to emphasize their striking three-dimensional forms (figure 4.23).

> **Quick Search**
> To appreciate their differences, look for "Spirochetes That Cause Lyme Disease" and "Motile Spirilla" on YouTube.

It is common for cells of a single species to show **pleomorphism* (figure 4.24).** This is due to individual variations in cell wall structure caused by nutritional or slight hereditary differences. For example, although the cells of *Corynebacterium diphtheriae* are generally considered rod-shaped, in culture they display club-shaped, swollen, curved, filamentous, and coccoid variations. Pleomorphism reaches an extreme in the mycoplasmas, which entirely lack cell walls and thus display extreme variations in shape (see figure 4.16).

* *coccus* (kok′-us) pl. cocci (kok′-seye) Gr. *Kokkos,* berry.
* *bacillus* (bah-sil′-lus) pl. bacilli (bah-sil′-eye) L. *bacill,* small staff or rod.
* *vibrio* (vib′-ree-oh) L. *vibrare,* to shake.
* *spirillum* (spy-ril′-em) pl. spirilla; L. *spira,* a coil.
* *pleomorphism* (plee″-oh-mor′-fizm) Gr. *Pleon,* more, and *morph,* form or shape.

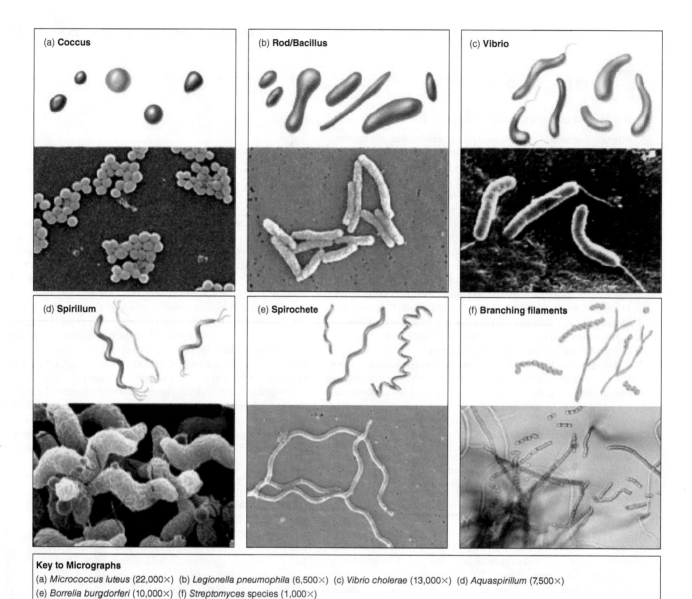

Key to Micrographs

(a) *Micrococcus luteus* (22,000×) (b) *Legionella pneumophila* (6,500×) (c) *Vibrio cholerae* (13,000×) (d) *Aquaspirillum* (7,500×)
(e) *Borrelia burgdorferi* (10,000×) (f) *Streptomyces* species (1,000×)

Figure 4.23 Common bacterial shapes. Drawings show examples of shape variations for cocci, rods, vibrios, spirilla, spirochetes, and branching filaments. Below each shape is a micrograph of a representative example.

TABLE 4.2	Comparison of the Two Spiral-Shaped Bacteria				
	Overall Appearance	Mode of Locomotion	Number of Helical Turns	Gram Reaction (Cell Wall Type)	Examples of Important Types
Spirilla	Rigid helix Spirilla	Polar flagella; cells swim by rotating around like corkscrews; do not flex; have one to several flagella; can be in tufts	Varies from 1 to 20	Gram-negative	Most are nonpathogenic. One species, *Spirillum minor,* causes rat bite fever.
Spirochetes	Flexible helix Curved or spiral forms: Spirillum/Spirochete	Periplasmic flagella within sheath; cells flex; can swim by rotation or by creeping on surfaces; have 2 to 100 periplasmic flagella	Varies from 3 to 70	Gram-negative	*Treponema pallidum,* cause of syphilis; *Borrelia* and *Leptospira,* important pathogens

Palisades arrangement

Metachromatic granules

Pleomorphism

Metachromatic granules

Palisades arrangement

Figure 4.24 Pleomorphism and other morphological features of *Corynebacterium*. Cells are irregular in shape and size (800×). This genus typically exhibits a palisades arrangement, with cells in parallel array (inset). Close examination will also reveal darkly stained metachromatic granules.

Bacterial cells can also be categorized according to **arrangement,** or style of grouping. The main factors influencing the arrangement of a particular cell type are its pattern of division and how the cells remain attached afterward. The greatest variety in arrangement occurs in cocci (**figure 4.25**). They may exist as singles, in pairs (**diplococci***), in **tetrads** (groups of four), in irregular clusters (both **staphylococci*** and **micrococci),** or in chains of a few to hundreds of cells (**streptococci**). An even more complex grouping is a cubical packet of 8, 16, or more cells called a **sarcina.*** These different coccal groupings are the result of the division of a coccus in a single plane, in two perpendicular planes, or in several intersecting planes; after division, the resultant daughter cells remain attached.

Bacilli are less varied in arrangement because they divide only in the transverse plane (perpendicular to the axis). They occur either as single cells, as a pair of cells with their ends attached (**diplobacilli),** or as a chain of several cells (**streptobacilli**). A **palisades*** arrangement, typical of the corynebacteria, is formed when the cells of a chain remain partially attached by a small hinge region at the ends. The cells tend to fold (snap) back upon each other, forming a row of cells oriented side by side (see figure 4.24). The reaction can be compared to the behavior of boxcars on a jack-knifed train, and the result looks superficially like an irregular picket fence. Spirilla are occasionally found in short chains, but spirochetes rarely remain attached after division. Comparative sizes of typical cells are presented in **figure 4.26.**

* *diplococci* (dih-plo-kok-seye) Gr. *diplo,* double.
* *staphylococci* (staf″-ih-loh-kok′-seye) Gr. *staphyle,* a bunch of grapes.
* *sarcina* (sar′-sin-uh) L. *sarcina,* a packet.
* *palisades* (pal′-ih-saydz) L. *pale,* a stake. A fence made of a row of stakes.

(a) Division in one plane — Diplococci (two cells) — Streptococci (variable number of cocci in chains)

(b) Division in two perpendicular planes — Tetrad (cocci in packets of four) — Sarcina (packet of 8–64 cells)

(c) Division in several planes — Irregular clusters (number of cells varies)

Staphylococci and Micrococci

Figure 4.25 Arrangement of cocci resulting from different planes of cell division. (a) Division in one plane produces diplococci and streptococci. **(b)** Division in two planes at right angles produces tetrads and packets. **(c)** Division in several planes produces irregular clusters.

Check Your Progress SECTION 4.5

27. Classify bacteria according to their basic shapes.
28. How are spirochetes and spirilla different?
29. What are vibrios and coccobacilli?
30. Describe pleomorphism, and give examples of bacteria with this trait.
31. What is the difference between the use of the shape bacillus and the name *Bacillus*? *Staphylococcus* and staphylococcus?
32. Rank the size ranges of bacteria according to shape, and compare bacterial size with viruses and eukaryotic cells.

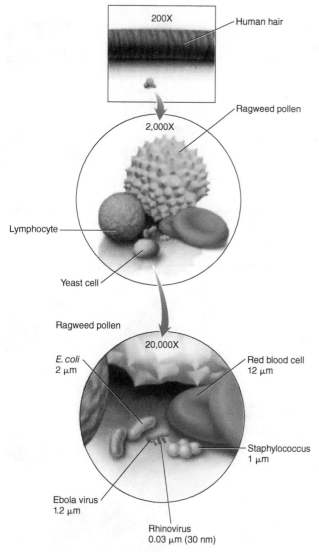

Figure 4.26 The dimensions of bacteria. The sizes of bacteria range from those just barely visible with light microscopy (0.2 μm) to those measuring a thousand times that size. Cocci measure anywhere from 0.5 to 3.0 μm in diameter; bacilli range from 0.2 to 2.0 μm in diameter and from 0.5 to 20 μm in length. Note the range of sizes as compared with eukaryotic cells and viruses. Comparisons are given as average sizes.

4.6 Classification Systems of Prokaryotic Domains: Archaea and Bacteria

 Expected Learning Outcomes

24. Describe the purposes of classification and taxonomy in the study of prokaryotes.

25. Summarize characteristics used to classify bacteria.

26. Outline a basic system of bacterial taxonomy.

27. Explain the species and subspecies levels for bacteria.

Classification systems serve both practical and academic purposes. They aid in differentiating and identifying unknown species in medical and applied microbiology. They are also useful in organizing bacteria and as a means of studying their relationships and evolutionary origins. Since classification was first initiated around 200 years ago, several thousand species of bacteria and archaea have been identified, named, and catalogued.

Tracing the origins of and evolutionary relationships among bacteria has not been an easy task. As a rule, tiny, relatively soft organisms do not form fossils very readily. Several times since the 1960s, however, scientists have discovered billion-year-old fossils of prokaryotes that look very much like modern bacteria (see figure 4.28c).

One of the questions that has plagued taxonomists is, What characteristics are reliable indicators of closeness in ancestry? Early bacteriologists found it convenient to classify bacteria according to shape, variations in arrangement, growth characteristics, and habitat. However, as more species were discovered and as techniques for studying their biochemistry were developed, it soon became clear that similarities in cell shape, arrangement, and staining reactions do not automatically indicate relatedness. Even though gram-negative rods look alike, there are hundreds of different species with highly significant differences in biochemistry and genetics. If we attempted to classify them on the basis of Gram stain and shape alone, we could not assign them to a more specific level than Phylum! As a result, the newer classification schemes are incorporating more specific genetic and molecular data to increase accuracy.

In general, the methods that a microbiologist uses to identify bacteria to the level of genus and species fall into the categories of morphology (microscopic and macroscopic), bacterial physiology or biochemistry, serological analysis, and genetic techniques (chapter 17 and **Appendix table C.1**). Data from a cross section of such tests can produce a unique profile of each species. Many identification systems are automated and computerized to process data and provide a "best fit" identification. However, not all methods are used on all bacteria. A few bacteria can be identified by a special technology that analyzes only the kind of fatty acids they contain; in contrast, some are identifiable by a Gram stain and a few physiological tests; others may require a diverse spectrum of morphological, biochemical, and genetic analysis.

Bacterial Taxonomy: A Work in Progress

There is no single official system for classifying the prokaryotes. Indeed, most plans are in a state of flux as new information and methods of analysis become available. One widely used reference is *Bergey's Manual of Systematic Bacteriology,* a major resource that covers all known prokaryotes. In the past, the classification scheme in this guide has been based mostly on characteristics such as Gram stain and metabolic reactions. This is called a **phenetic,** or phenotypic, method of classification.

The second edition of this large collection now includes genetic information that clarifies the **phylogenetic** (evolutionary) history and relationships of the thousands of known species **(figure 4.27).** This change has redefined our presentation of their classification, so that prokaryotes are now placed in five major subgroups and 25 different phyla instead of two domains split into

Figure 4.27 A master classification scheme based on ribosomal analysis. This pattern displays the major Phyla within Domains Bacteria and Archaea. Branches indicate the origins of each group, and their relative positions estimate ancestral relationships. Major groups of Domain Eukarya are shown here for comparison.

four divisions. The Domains Archaea and Bacteria based on genetic characteristics have been retained, but the bacteria of clinical importance are no longer as closely aligned, and the 250 or so species that cause disease in humans are found within seven or eight of the revised phyla. The grouping by Gram reaction remains significant but primarily at the lower taxonomic levels. This being an introduction to the subject, we will follow a pragmatic organization that simplifies the presentation and avoids increasingly complex and often conflicting taxonomy.

The major categories of this revised taxonomic scheme are presented in **table 4.3,** which provides a brief survey of characteristics of the major taxonomic groups, along with examples of representative members (A–O). For a complete version of the major taxonomic groups and genera, go to **Appendix table C.2.**

A Diagnostic Scheme for Medical Use

Many medical microbiologists prefer an informal working system that outlines the major families and genera (**table 4.4**). This scheme uses the phenotypic qualities of bacteria in identification. It is restricted to bacterial disease agents and depends less on nomenclature. It also divides the bacteria into gram-positive, gram-negative, and those without cell walls and then subgroups them according to cell shape, arrangement, and certain physiological traits such as oxygen usage: *Aerobic* bacteria use oxygen in metabolism; *anaerobic* bacteria do not use oxygen in metabolism; and facultative bacteria may or may not use oxygen. Further tests not listed on the table

would be required to separate closely related genera and species. Many of these are included in later chapters on specific bacterial groups.

Species and Subspecies in Bacteria

Among most organisms, the **species** level is a distinct, readily defined, and natural taxonomic category. In animals, for instance, a species is a distinct type of organism that can produce viable offspring only when it mates with others of its own kind. This definition does not work for bacteria primarily because they do not exhibit a typical mode of sexual reproduction. They can accept DNA from unrelated forms, and they can also alter their genetic makeup by a variety of mechanisms. Thus, it is necessary to use a modified definition for a bacterial species. Theoretically, it is a collection of bacterial cells, all of which share an overall similar pattern of traits, in contrast to other groups whose pattern differs significantly. Although the boundaries that separate two closely related species in a genus can be somewhat arbitrary, this definition still serves as a method to separate the bacteria into various kinds that can be cultured and studied. As additional information on bacterial genomes is discovered, it may be possible to define species according to specific combinations of genetic codes found only in a particular isolate. Some bacterial taxonomists use a criterion for bacterial species that examples must share at least 97% of their genome and ribosomal RNA. Many species can currently be identified on the basis of their unique ribosomal RNA profiles.

Because the individual members of given species can show variations, we must also define levels within species (subspecies) called **strains** and **types.** A strain or variety of bacteria is a culture derived from a single parent that differs in structure or metabolism from other cultures of that species (also called biovars or morphovars). For example, there are pigmented and nonpigmented strains of *Serratia marcescens* and flagellated and nonflagellated strains of *Pseudomonas fluorescens.* A type is a subspecies that can show differences in antigenic makeup (serotype or serovar), in susceptibility to bacterial viruses (phage type), and in pathogenicity (pathotype).

 Check Your Progress SECTION 4.6

33. What general characteristics are used to classify bacteria?
34. What are the most useful characteristics for categorizing bacteria into phyla?
35. Explain some of the ways the species level in bacteria is defined, and name at least three ways bacteria are classified below the species level.

TABLE 4.3	**Overview of a Classification System for Prokaryotes Based on *Bergey's Manual*, 2nd Edition (See Appendix Table C.2 for a full outline.)**

Volume 1 Domain Archaea Includes prokaryotes with unusual morphology, ecology, and modes of nutrition. Many of the known members are adapted to a habitat with extremes of temperature (hyperthermophiles), salt (halophiles), acidity (acidophiles), pressure, or lack of oxygen (anaerobic), and sometimes combinations of these. The domain has great ecological importance due to its actions in biogeochemical cycling. More coverage can be found in section 4.7.

Phylum Crenarchaeota Members depend on sulfur for growth and may inhabit hot and acidic sulfur pools and vents. Some species have adapted to cold habitats. See examples in **figures A** and 4.33.

Phylum Nanoarchaeota A newly discovered group of extremely small archaea found in salt mines and caves (see 4.1 Secret World of Microbes).

Phylum Euryarchaeota The largest and best-studied group of archaea; members' adaptations include methane production (methanogens), high saline or salt (halobacteria or halophiles), high temperature (thermophiles), and reduction of sulfur compounds. An example is *Methanocaldococcus* (**figure B**).

A. Unidentified thermophilic crenarchaeotes isolated from a deep-sea thermal vent at 160°F (71°C).

B. *Methanocaldococcus*—a hyperthermophile inhabiting hydrothermal vents at near-boiling temperature

Volume 1 Domain Bacteria I This domain contains deeply branching and photosynthetic bacteria that are considered the oldest evolutionary lines still in existence. It contains a wide diversity of prominent bacteria, including photosynthesizers (cyanobacteria), thermophiles, radiation-resistant bacteria, halophiles, and sulfur metabolizers.

Phylum Aquificae This group contains small thermophilic rods that inhabit underwater volcanoes.

Phylum Thermotogae A phylum similar to Aquificae; includes thermophilic halophiles that live in deep-sea vents. An example is *Desulfurobacterium* (**figure C**).

Phylum Chlorobi Also known as green sulfur bacteria, this phylum consists of anaerobic bacteria that live in the muddy layers of lakes and ponds, where they photosynthesize and metabolize sulfides.

Phylum Deinococcus-Thermus A small phylum of extremophiles whose members range from being highly radiation- and desiccation-resistant cocci that live in soil and fresh water to rods that live in very hot aquatic habitats, such as hot springs and pools. *Deinococcus* can be seen in figure 4.18.

Phylum Cyanobacteria Very ubiquitous photosynthetic bacteria found in aquatic habitats, soil, and often associated with plants, fungi, and other organisms; blue-green, green, yellow, red, and orange in color. An example is *Gloeotrichia* (**figure D**; see section 4.7 for more coverage).

C. *Desulfurobacterium*—a tiny anaerobic, halophilic rod that reduces sulfur compounds

D. *Gloeotrichia*—can form colonies of radiating filaments that float in lakes and ponds

Volume 2 Domain Bacteria II This domain, along with the phyla that are covered in volumes 3, 4, and 5, contains bacteria that have the greatest medical impact.

Phylum Proteobacteria This phylum contains five classes representing an extremely varied cross section of over 2,000 identified species of bacteria. Though all share the characteristic of a gram-negative cell wall, the group contains bacteria with a wide range of adaptations, shapes, habitats, and ecology. Medically significant members include the obligately parasitic rickettsias; *Neisseria;* enterics such as *Escherichia coli* and *Salmonella; Vibrio* species; and other bacteria that live in the intestinal tracts of animals. The myxobacteria have the unique characteristic of being the only bacteria that can aggregate into multicellular structures (see figure 4.30; see also **figures E, F,** and **G** for examples).

E. A *Rickettsia rickettsii* cell (cause of Rocky Mountain spotted fever) being engulfed by a host cell

F. *Escherichia coli* O157:H7—a food-borne pathogen

G. A vibrio-shaped thermophile, *Desulfovibrio,* living in a pond biofilm

TABLE 4.3 *(continued)*

Volume 3 Phylum Firmicutes This collection of mostly gram-positive bacteria is characterized by having a low G + C content* (less than 50%). The three classes in the phylum display significant diversity, and a number of the members are pathogenic. Endospore-forming genera include *Bacillus* and *Clostridium.* Other important pathogens are found in genera *Staphylococcus* and *Streptococcus.* Although they lack a cell wall entirely, mycoplasmas (see figure 4.17) have been placed with the Firmicutes because of their genetic relatedness. (See **figures H** and **I.**)

H. *Bacillus anthracis*—SEM micrograph showing the rod-shaped cells next to a red blood cell

I. *Streptococcus pneumoniae*—image displays the diplococcus arrangement of this species

Volume 4 Phylum Actinobacteria This taxonomic category includes the high G + C (over 50%) gram-positive bacteria. Members of this small group differ considerably in life cycles and morphology. Prominent members include the branching filamentous Actinomycetes, the spore-bearing Streptomycetes, *Corynebacterium* (see figure 4.24), *Mycobacterium,* and *Micrococcus* (see figure 4.23a). (See **figures J** and **K.**)

J. *Streptomyces* species—common soil bacteria; often the source of antibiotics

K. *Mycobacterium tuberculosis*—the bacillus that causes tuberculosis

Volume 5 This represents a mixed assemblage of nine phyla, all of which are gram-negative but otherwise widely varied. The following is a selected array of examples.

Phylum Chlamydiae Another group of obligate intracellular parasites that reproduce inside host cells. These are among the smallest of bacteria, with a unique mode of reproduction. Several species cause diseases of the eyes, reproductive tract, and lungs. An example is *Chlamydia* (**figure L**).

Phylum Spirochetes These bacteria are distinguished by their shape and mode of locomotion. They move their slender, twisted cells by means of periplasmic flagella. Members live in a variety of habitats, including the bodies of animals and protozoans, fresh and marine water, and even muddy swamps. Important genera are *Treponema* (**figure M**) and *Borrelia* (see figure 4.23e).

Phylum Planctomycetes This group lives in fresh and marine water habitats and reproduces by budding. Many have a stalk that they use to attach to substrates. A unique feature is having a membrane around their DNA and special compartments enclosed in membranes. This has led to the speculation that they are similar to an ancestral form that gave rise to eukaryotes. An example is *Gemmata* (**figure N**).

Phylum Bacteriodetes These are widely distributed gram-negative anaerobic rods inhabiting soil, sediments, and water habitats, and frequently found as normal residents of the intestinal tracts of animals. They may be grouped with related Phyla Fibrobacteres and Chlorobi. Several members play an important role in the function of the human gut and some are involved in oral and intestinal infections. An example is *Bacteroides* (**figure O**).

L. View of an infected host cell revealing a vacuole containing *Chlamydia* cells in various stages of development

M. *Treponema pallidum*—spirochetes that cause syphilis

N. *Gemmata*—view of a budding cell through a fluorescent microscope (note the large blue nucleoid)

O. *Bacteroides* species—may cause intestinal infections

*G + C base composition The overall percentage of guanine and cytosine in DNA is a general indicator of relatedness because it is a trait that does not change rapidly. Bacteria with a significant difference in G + C percentage are less likely to be genetically related. This classification scheme is partly based on this percentage.

TABLE 4.4	Important Families and Genera of Pathogenic Bacteria, with Notes on Some Diseases*

I. Bacteria with gram-positive cell wall structure (Phyla Firmicutes and Actinobacteria)

A. Cocci in clusters or packets that are aerobic or facultative

Family Staphylococcaceae: *Staphylococcus* (members cause boils, skin infections)

B. Cocci in pairs and chains that are facultative

Family Streptococcaceae: *Streptococcus* (species cause strep throat, dental caries)

C. Anaerobic cocci in pairs, tetrads, irregular clusters

Family Peptococcaceae: *Peptococcus, Peptostreptococcus* (involved in wound infections)

D. Spore-forming rods

Family Bacillaceae: *Bacillus* (anthrax), *Clostridium* (tetanus, gas gangrene, botulism)

E. Non-sporeforming rods

Family Lactobacillaceae: *Lactobacillus, Listeria* (food infection), *Erysipelothrix* (erysipeloid)

Family Propionibacteriaceae: *Propionibacterium* (involved in acne)

Family Corynebacteriaceae: *Corynebacterium* (diphtheria)

Family Mycobacteriaceae: *Mycobacterium* (tuberculosis, leprosy)

Family Nocardiaceae: *Nocardia* (lung abscesses)

Family Actinomycetaceae: *Actinomyces* (dental infections)

Family Streptomycetaceae: *Streptomyces* (important source of antibiotics)

II. Bacteria with gram-negative cell wall structure (Phyla Proteobacteria, Bacteriodetes, Fusobacterium, Spirochaetes, Chlamydiae)

F. Aerobic cocci

Family Neisseraceae: *Neisseria* (gonorrhea, meningitis)

G. Aerobic coccobacilli

Family Moraxellaceae: *Moraxella, Acinetobacter*

H. Anaerobic cocci

Family Veillonellaceae: *Veillonella* (dental disease)

I. Aerobic rods

Family Pseudomonadaceae: *Pseudomonas* (pneumonia, burn infections)

Miscellaneous rods (different families): *Brucella* (undulant fever), *Bordetella* (whooping cough), *Francisella* (tularemia), *Coxiella* (Q fever) *Legionella* (Legionnaires' disease)

J. Facultative rods and vibrios

Family Enterobacteriaceae: *Escherichia, Edwardsiella, Citrobacter, Salmonella* (typhoid fever), *Shigella* (dysentery), *Klebsiella, Enterobacter, Serratia, Proteus, Yersinia* (one species causes plague)

J. Facultative rods and vibrios (*continued*)

Family Vibronaceae: *Vibrio* (cholera, food infection)

Family Campylobacteraceae: *Campylobacter* (**enteritis**)

Family Helicobacteraceae: *Helicobacter* (ulcers)

Miscellaneous genera: *Flavobacterium, Haemophilus* (meningitis), *Pasteurella* (bite infections), *Streptobacillus*

K. Anaerobic rods

Family Bacteroidaceae: *Bacteroides, Fusobacterium* (anaerobic wound and dental infections)

L. Helical and curviform bacteria

Family Spirochaetaceae: *Treponema* (syphilis), *Borrelia* (Lyme disease), *Leptospira* (kidney infection)

M. Obligate and facultative intracellular bacteria

Family Rickettsiaceae: *Rickettsia* (Rocky Mountain spotted fever)

Family Anaplasmataceae: *Ehrlichia* (human ehrlichosis)

Family Chlamydiaceae: *Chlamydia* (sexually transmitted infection)

Family Bartonellaceae: *Bartonella* (trench fever, cat scratch disease)

III. Bacteria with no cell walls (Class Mollicutes)

Family Mycoplasmataceae: *Mycoplasma* (pneumonia), *Ureaplasma* (urinary infection)

*Details of pathogens and diseases in later chapters.

4.7 Survey of Prokaryotic Groups with Unusual Characteristics

 Expected Learning Outcomes

28. Differentiate various groups of photosynthetic bacteria.
29. Characterize the types of obligate intracellular bacteria.
30. Summarize the basic characteristics of archaea.
31. Compare Domain Archaea with Domains Bacteria and Eukarya.
32. Explain archaeal adaptations that place them in the category of extremophiles.

So far in our introduction to the bacterial world, we have covered a rich variety of members with exceptional modes of living and behaving. And yet, we are still in the early phases of discovery. Investigations of unexplored areas of the earth continue to surprise and instruct us about the adaptations and importance of these remarkable organisms. Doing justice to such incredible diversity would require more space than we can set aside in an introductory textbook, but in this section we have selected some of the more prominent and unusual groups to present. In this minisurvey, we consider some medically important groups and some representatives of bacteria living free in the environment that are ecologically important. Many of the bacteria mentioned here do not have the morphology typical of bacteria discussed previously, and in a few cases, they are vividly different (**4.1 Secret World of Microbes**).

Free-Living Nonpathogenic Bacteria

Photosynthetic Bacteria

The nutrition of many bacteria is heterotrophic, meaning that they feed primarily off nutrients from other organisms. Photosynthetic bacteria, however, are independent cells that contain special light-trapping pigments and can use the energy of sunlight to synthesize all required nutrients from simple inorganic compounds. The two general types of photosynthetic bacteria are those that produce oxygen during photosynthesis and those that produce some other substance, such as sulfur granules or sulfates.

Cyanobacteria: Microbial Marvels

Cyanobacteria, gram-negative phototrophic* bacteria in the Phylum Cyanobacteria, are among the most dominant microorganisms on earth, with a long list of significant contributions to the planet. They are ancient in origin, probably having existed in some form for around 3 billion years. We can still find remnants of these early cells in fossil biofilms called stromatolites (**figure 4.28b1,2**). Many evolutionary microbiologists theorize that, because cyanobacteria were the very first photosynthesizers, they were responsible for converting the atmosphere from anaerobic to aerobic through their production of oxygen, which made it possible for the evolution of aerobic eukaryotes. Other contributions they have made to eukaryotic evolution include the chloroplasts of algae and plants. When

literally "to feed with light."

(a1)

(a2)

Stromatolite
(b1)

(b2)

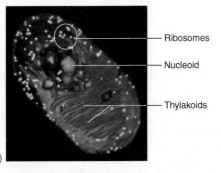
— Ribosomes

— Nucleoid

— Thylakoids

(c)

Figure 4.28 **Cyanobacterial characteristics.** (**a**) Striking colors and arrangements of cells (1) *Trichodesmium* is one of the dominant planktonic forms on earth. (2) *Merismopedia* displays a slimy sheath around its regular packets of cells. (**b**) Ancient signs of cyanobacteria. (1) A sectioned stromatolite displays layers of a cyanobacterial biofilm laid down over a billion years ago. (2) A microfossil of a billion-year-old filament found in Siberian fossils. (**c**) An electron micrograph of a single cell (10,000×) reveals layers of thylakoids that are the sites of photosynthesis.

4.1 Secret World of Microbes
Redefining Bacterial Size

Microbiologists keep being reminded how far we are from having a complete assessment of the bacterial world, mostly because the world is so large and bacteria are so small. There seem to be frequent reports of exceptional bacteria discovered in places like the deep-ocean volcanoes or Antarctic ice. Among the most remarkable are giant and dwarf bacteria.

Big Bacteria Break Records

In 1985, biologists discovered a new bacterium living in the intestine of surgeonfish that at the time was a candidate for the *Guinness Book of World Records*. The large cells, named *Epulopiscium fishelsoni* ("guest at a banquet of fish"), measure around 100 μm in length, although some specimens were as large as 300 μm. This record was broken when a marine microbiologist discovered an even larger species of bacteria living in ocean sediments near the African country of Namibia. These gigantic cocci are arranged in strands that look like pearls and contain hundreds of golden sulfur granules, inspiring their name, *Thiomargarita namibia* ("sulfur pearl of Namibia") (see photo). The size of the individual cells ranges from 100 up to 750 μm (0.75 mm), and many are large enough to see with the naked eye. By way of comparison, if the average bacterium were the size of a mouse, *Thiomargarita* would be as large as a blue whale!

These bacteria are found in such large numbers in the sediments that it is thought that they are essential to the ecological cycling of H_2S and other substances in this region, converting them to less toxic substances.

Miniature Microbes—Are They for Real?

At the other extreme, microbiologists are being asked to reevaluate the lower limits of bacterial size. Up until now it has been generally accepted that the smallest cells on the planet are some form of mycoplasma with dimensions of 0.2 to 0.3 μm, which is right at the limit of resolution with light microscopes. A new controversy is brewing over the discovery of tiny cells that look like dwarf bacteria but are 10 times smaller than mycoplasmas and 100 times smaller than the average bacterial cell. These minute cells have been given the name **nanobacteria** or **nanobes** (Gr. *nanos,* one-billionth).

Nanobacteria-like forms were first isolated from blood and serum samples. The tiny cells appear to grow in culture, have cell walls, and

Thiomargarita namibia—giant cocci. Approximately how many times larger is *Thiomargarita* than the nanobe shown on the right?

Three-dimensional micrograph of an ARMAN measuring about 0.25 μm across. These are fully functioning cells with a tiny nucleoid (yellow) and a small number of ribosomes (blue dots).

contain protein and nucleic acids, but their size range is only from 0.05 to 0.2 μm. Similar nanobes have been extracted by minerologists studying deposits in the ocean at temperatures up to 170°C. Many geologists are convinced that these nanobes are real cells, that they are probably similar to the first microbes on earth, and that they play a strategic role in the development of the earth's crust.

Microbiologists have been more skeptical. Experts have postulated that the minimum cell size to contain a functioning genome and reproductive and synthetic machinery is approximately 0.14 μm, which means that some of the nanobes could be artifacts or bits of larger cells that have broken free. It seems that the archaea may be the ultimate definers of smallness in prokaryotes. Microbiologists exploring acid mines in California have discovered ultrasmall archaea living in pink biofilms. These extremophiles, called ARMAN, are at the lower limits of size, between 100 and 400 nm. They are real cells, complete with a tiny genome and a reduced number of ribosomes, and are perhaps the first indisputable nanobes. Additional studies are needed to test this curious question of nanobes and possibly to answer some questions about the origins of life on earth and elsewhere in the universe.

What are some of the adaptations that a giant *Thiomargarita* would require for its survival? *Answer available at http://www.mhhe.com/talaro9*

chloroplasts are subjected to genetic analysis, it turns out that they are close relatives of some of the oldest groups of cyanobacteria, and probably arose through endosymbiosis (see chapter 5). So the green color of a forest or a field of corn actually comes from these tiny bacteria that became a part of photosynthetic eukaryotes billions of years ago. The earth would be an entirely different place if it were not for these microorganisms.

Cyanobacteria are very diverse in distribution and morphology. They flourish in every type of aquatic environment, whether ocean, hot springs, or Antarctic ice, and they can also survive in a wide range of terrestrial habitats. Because of this widespread distribu-

tion, they are huge contributors to worldwide productivity. Two species of cyanobacteria alone—*Prochlorococcus* and *Trichodesmium*—account for 30% to 40% of biomass formation and 50% of oxygen production through photosynthesis in the oceans. They are also one of a few groups of microbes that can convert nitrogen gas (N_2) into ammonium (NH_4^+) that can be used by plants, making them essential players in the nitrogen cycle.

Their structure and arrangement are varied, from coccoid, rodlike, and spiral-shaped cells, with arrangements in filaments, clusters, and sheets, usually surrounded by a gelatinous sheath **(figure 4.28a2).** Although their primary photosynthetic pigments

include green chlorophyll *b* and the bluish pigment phycocyanin, they may take on shades of yellow, orange, and red derived from other pigments.

Within an individual cell are found extensive specialized membranes called **thylakoids,** the locations of pigments and the sites of photosynthesis (**figure 4.28c**). They also have gas vesicles that keep the cells suspended high in the water column to facilitate photosynthesis. Cyanobacteria periodically overgrow in aquatic environments to form blooms that are harmful to fish and other inhabitants, and some produce toxins that could cause illness if ingested, but they are generally not medically important.

> **Quick Search**
>
> Find out about the little cyanobacterium *"Gloeocapsa,* which went to outer space and survived a year and a half."

Green and Purple Sulfur Bacteria

The green and purple bacteria are also photosynthetic and contain pigments. They differ from the cyanobacteria in having a different type of chlorophyll called *bacteriochlorophyll* and by not giving off oxygen as a product of photosynthesis. They live in sulfur springs, freshwater lakes, and swamps that are deep enough for the anaerobic conditions they require yet where their pigment can still absorb wavelengths of light (**figure 4.29**). These bacteria are named for their predominant colors, but they can also develop brown, pink, purple, blue, and orange coloration. Both groups utilize sulfur compounds (H_2S, S) in their metabolism.

Gliding, Fruiting Bacteria

The gliding bacteria are a mixed collection of gram-negative bacteria in Phylum Proteobacteria that live in water and soil. The name is derived from the tendency of members to glide over moist surfaces. The gliding property evidently involves rotation of filaments or fibers just under the outer membrane of the cell wall. They do not have flagella. Several morphological forms exist, including slender rods, long filaments, cocci, and some miniature,

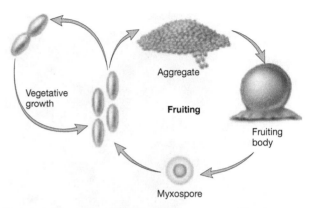

Figure 4.30 Life cycle of *Myxococcus*. This multicellular bacterium goes through several developmental stages in response to environmental signals.

tree-shaped fruiting bodies. Probably the most intriguing and exceptional members of this group are the slime bacteria, or myxobacteria. What sets the myxobacteria apart from other bacteria is the complexity and advancement of their life cycle. During this cycle, the vegetative cells respond to chemotactic signals by swarming together and differentiating into a many-celled, colored structure called the fruiting body, making it one of the few bacteria that can generate a multicellular body form (**figure 4.30**). The fruiting body is a survival structure that makes spores by a method very similar to that of certain fungi. These fruiting structures are often large enough to be seen with the unaided eye on tree bark and plant debris.

Unusual Forms of Medically Significant Bacteria

Most bacteria are free-living or parasitic forms that can metabolize and reproduce by independent means. Two groups of bacteria—the rickettsias and chlamydias—have adapted to life inside their host cells, where they are considered **obligate intracellular parasites.**

Rickettsias

Rickettsias[6] are distinctive, very tiny, gram-negative bacteria (**figure 4.31**). Although they are somewhat typical in morphology, they are atypical in their life cycle and other adaptations. Most are pathogens that alternate between a mammalian host and blood-sucking arthropods,[7] such as fleas, lice, or ticks. Rickettsias cannot survive or multiply outside a host cell and cannot carry out metabolism completely on their own, so they are closely attached to their hosts. Several important human diseases are caused by rickettsias. Among these are Rocky Mountain spotted fever, caused by *Rickettsia rickettsii* (transmitted by ticks), and endemic typhus, caused by

Figure 4.29 Photosynthetic bacteria. Purple-colored masses in a fall pond contain a concentrated bloom of purple sulfur bacteria (inset 1,500×). The pond also harbors a mixed population of algae (green clumps).

6. Named for Howard Ricketts, a physician who first worked with these organisms and later lost his life to typhus.

7. An arthropod is an invertebrate with jointed legs, such as an insect, tick, or spider.

Rickettsial cells Nucleus of cell

Figure 4.31 **Transmission electron micrograph of *Rickettsia conorii* inside its host cell (100,000X).** This species causes tick-borne Mediterranean fever.

Rickettsia typhi (transmitted by lice). It is worth noting, in advance of chapter 5, that the mitochondrion, a eukaryotic organelle, is a close genetic relative to rickettsias, indicating an evolutionary link between them.

Chlamydias

Bacteria of the genera *Chlamydia* and *Chlamydophila*, termed **chlamydias,** are similar to the rickettsias in that they require host cells for growth and metabolism. But they are not closely related to them and are not transmitted by arthropods. Because of their tiny size and obligately parasitic lifestyle, they were at one time considered a type of virus (see Table 4.3L). Species that carry the greatest medical impact are *Chlamydia trachomatis,* the cause of both a severe eye infection (trachoma) that can lead to blindness and one of the most common sexually transmitted diseases, and *Chlamydophila pneumoniae,* an agent in lung infections.

Diseases caused by rickettsias and chlamydias are described in more detail in the infectious disease chapters.

Archaea: The Other Prokaryotes

The discovery and characterization of novel prokaryotic cells that have unusual anatomy, physiology, and genetics changed our views of microbial taxonomy and classification (see chapter 1 and table 4.3). These single-celled, simple organisms, called **archaea,** or **archaeons,** are considered a third cell type in a separate superkingdom (the Domain Archaea). We include them in this chapter because they are prokaryotic in general structure and they do share many bacterial characteristics. But evidence is accumulating that they are actually more closely related to Domain Eukarya than to bacteria. For example, archaea and eukaryotes share a number of ribosomal RNA sequences that are not found in bacteria, and their protein synthesis and ribosomal subunit structures are similar. **Table 4.5** outlines selected points of comparison of the three domains.

Other ways that the archaea differ significantly from other cell types are that certain genetic sequences are found only in their ribosomal RNA. Their cell walls are also quite different, being composed of polysaccharide or protein and lacking peptidoglycan, and some lack cell walls altogether (see figure 4.33). It is likely that the archaea are the most ancient of all life forms and have retained characteristics of the first cells that originated on the earth nearly 4 billion years ago. The early earth is thought to have contained a hot, anaerobic "soup" with sulfuric gases and salts in abundance. Many of the present-day archaea occupy the remaining habitats on the earth that have some of the same extreme conditions. It is for this reason that they are considered **extremophiles,** or **hyperextremophiles,** meaning that they "love" the most extreme habitats on earth. Although there are some examples of extremophilic bacteria as well (refer to table 4.3), they are not as widespread as archaea in ultra extreme environments.

Metabolically, the archaea exhibit nearly incredible adaptations to what would be deadly conditions for other organisms.

TABLE 4.5	Comparison of Three Cellular Domains		
Characteristic	**Bacteria**	**Archaea**	**Eukarya**
Cell type	Prokaryotic	Prokaryotic	Eukaryotic
Chromosomes	Single, or few, circular	Single, circular	Several, linear
Types of ribosomes	70S	70S but structure is similar to 80S	80S
Unique ribosomal RNA signature sequences	+	+	+
Number of RNA sequences shared with Eukarya	One	Three	
Protein synthesis similar to Eukarya	−	+	
Presence of peptidoglycan in cell wall	+	−	−
Cell membrane lipids	Fatty acids with ester linkages	Long-chain, branched hydrocarbons with ether linkages	Fatty acids with ester linkages
Sterols in membrane	− (some exceptions)	−	+

Many of these hardy microbes are living in severe combinations of extremes as well—for instance, high acidity and high temperature, high salt and alkalinity, low temperature and high pressure. Included in this group are methane producers, hyperthermophiles, extreme halophiles, and sulfur reducers. It is worth noting that not all archaea are adapted to extremes, and many are widely distributed in more moderate environments such as soils, oceans, and even animal intestines. By some estimates, archaea are the most common cells on the earth, and they have made major contributions to the development of the earth itself.

Members of the group called **methanogens** can convert CO_2 and H_2 into methane gas (CH_4) through unusual and complex pathways. These archaea are common inhabitants of anaerobic mud and the bottom sediments of lakes and oceans. Some are even found in the oral cavity and large intestine of humans. The gas they produce in aquatic habitats collects in swamps and may become a source of fuel. Methane may also contribute to the "greenhouse effect," which maintains the earth's temperature and can contribute to global warming.

Other types of archaea—the **extreme halophiles**—require salt to grow and may have such a high salt tolerance that they can multiply in sodium chloride solutions (36% NaCl) that would destroy most cells. They exist in the saltiest places on the earth—inland seas, salt lakes, and salt mines. They are not particularly common in the ocean because the salt content is not high enough to support them. Many of the "halobacteria" use a red pigment to synthesize ATP in the presence of light. These pigments are responsible for "red herrings," the color of the Red Sea, and the red color of salt ponds (**figure 4.32**).

Archaea adapted to growth at very low temperatures are described as *psychrophilic* (loving cold temperatures); those growing at very high temperatures are *hyperthermophilic* (loving very high temperatures). **Hyperthermophiles** flourish at temperatures between 80°C and 121°C (boiling temperature) and cannot grow at 50°C. They live in volcanic waters and soils and submarine vents, and are often salt- and acid-tolerant as well (**figure 4.33**). Researchers sampling sulfur vents in the deep ocean discovered thermophilic archaea flourishing at temperatures up to 250°C—150° above the temperature of boiling water! Not only were these archaea growing prolifically at this high temperature, but they were also living at 265 atmospheres of pressure. (On the earth's surface, pressure is about 1 atmosphere.) For additional discussion of the unusual adaptations of archaea, see chapter 7.

✅ *Check Your Progress* SECTION 4.7

36. Discuss several ways in which bacteria are medically and ecologically important.

37. Name two main groups of obligate intracellular parasitic bacteria and explain why these groups can't live independently.

38. Explain the characteristics of archaea that indicate that they constitute a unique domain of living things that is neither bacterial nor eukaryotic.

39. What is meant by the terms extremophile and hyperextremophile?

40. Describe the three major archaeal lifestyles and adaptations to extreme habitats.

(a)

(b)

Figure 4.32 Halophiles around the world. (a) An aerial view of a salt pond at San Francisco Bay, California. The archaea that thrive in this warm, highly saline habitat produce brilliant red, pink, and orange pigments. **(b)** A sample taken from a saltern in Australia viewed by fluorescence microscopy (1,000×). Note the range of cell shapes (cocci, rods, and squares) found in this community.

Figure 4.33 The hottest life forms on earth. This member of the Crenarchaeota thrives in habitats above the temperature of boiling water and can even survive being autoclaved. (S = slime layer; CM = cell membrane)

CASE STUDY Part 2

During an autopsy of Mr. Jones's body, the pathologist observed that the prosthetic valve was covered with small patches he called vegetations. The later blood cultures grew a strain of *Staphylococcus aureus** known as MRSA. Microscopic examination of the valve revealed a thick biofilm coating containing that same bacterium. The pathologist concluded that the patient had infective endocarditis,* and that vegetations on the valve lesions had broken loose and entered the circulation. This event created emboli that blocked arteries in his brain and gave rise to a massive stroke. Upon closer review of Mr. Jones's case, the physician discovered that he had suffered from a skin infection the previous spring that had been treated and cured by a different physician. It turned out to be caused by the MRSA type of *Staphylococcus aureus.*

* *Staphylococcus aureus* (staf'-uh-loh-cok'-us ar-ee-us) Gr. *staphyle*, a bunch of grapes, *kokkus*, berry, and *aurum*, golden.
* *endocarditis* (en'-doh-car-dye'-tis) Gr. *endon*, within, *kardia*, heart, and *itis*, an inflammation. An inflammation of the lining of the heart and its valves usually caused by infection.

Most bacteria can form structured multicellular communities, or biofilms, on objects in a moist environment. This is even true of bacterial pathogens in the body. The CDC estimates that at least 65% of chronic infections are caused by microbial biofilms. In this case, the MRSA bacteria in the patient's skin infection must have entered the circulation and colonized the artificial valve over several weeks to months. Most cases of chronic endocarditis are caused by biofilms on valves. When the biofilm grows into larger vegetations, portions of it break loose into the circulation. These infect the blood and are spread into organs, causing fever and other signs and symptoms, including the ones that were fatal. MRSA is an emerging pathogen that started as a problem in the hospital, but it is now prominent in nonhospital settings as well.

- What does the acronym MRSA mean, and what is its significance?

- Why wasn't penicillin effective in treating the infection?

For more background on MRSA and endocarditis, see chapter 18.

To conclude this Case Study, go to Perspectives on the Connect website.

Chapter Summary with Key Terms

4.1 Basic Characteristics of Cells and Life Forms

A. All living things are composed of **cells,** which are complex collections of macromolecules that carry out living processes. All cells must have the minimum structure of an outer **cell membrane, cytoplasm,** a **chromosome,** and **ribosomes.**

B. Cells can be divided into two basic types: **prokaryotes** and **eukaryotes.**

1. Prokaryotic cells are the basic structural unit of bacteria and archaea. They lack a nucleus or **organelles.** They are highly successful and adaptable single-cell life forms.

2. Eukaryotic cells contain a membrane-surrounded nucleus and a number of organelles that function in specific ways. A wide variety of organisms, from single-celled protozoans to humans, are composed of eukaryotic cells.

3. Viruses are not generally considered living or cells, and rely on host cells to replicate.

C. Cells show the basic essential characteristics of life. Parts of cells and macromolecules do not show these characteristics independently.

1. The primary life indicators are heredity, reproduction, growth, metabolism, responsiveness, and transport.

4.2 Prokaryotic Profiles: The Bacteria and Archaea

A. Prokaryotes consist of two major groups, the bacteria and the archaea. Life on earth would not be possible without them.

B. Prokaryotic cells lack the membrane-surrounded organelles and nuclear compartment of eukaryotic cells but are still complex in their structure and function. All prokaryotes have a cell membrane, cytoplasm, ribosomes, and a chromosome.

C. **Appendages:** Some bacteria have projections that extend from the cell.

1. **Flagella** and internal **axial filaments** found in spirochetes are used for motility.

2. **Fimbriae** function in adhering to the environment; **pili** can be involved in adhesion, movement, and genetic exchange.

3. The **glycocalyx** may be a slime layer or a capsule.

4.3 The Cell Envelope: The Boundary Layer of Bacteria

A. Most prokaryotes are surrounded by a protective envelope that consists of the cell wall and the **cell membrane.**

B. The wall is relatively rigid due to **peptidoglycan.**

C. Structural differences give rise to **gram-positive** and **gram-negative** cells, as differentiated by the **Gram stain.**

1. Gram-positive bacteria contain a thick wall composed of peptidoglycan and teichoic acid in a single layer.

2. Gram-negative bacteria have a thinner two-layer cell wall with an **outer membrane,** thin layer of peptidoglycan, and a well-developed **periplasmic space.**

3. Wall structure gives rise to differences in staining, toxicity, and effects of drugs and disinfectants.

4. The cell or cytoplasmic membrane is a flexible sheet that surrounds the cytoplasm. It is composed of a bilayer of lipids with attached proteins. It is a multifunctional structure involved in transport, synthesis, and energy reactions.

4.4 Bacterial Internal Structure

The cell cytoplasm contains some or all of the following internal structures in bacteria: the **chromosome**(s) condensed in the **nucleoid; ribosomes,** which serve as the sites of protein synthesis and are 70S in size; extra genetic information in the form of **plasmids;** storage structures known as **inclusions;** a **cytoskeleton** of **bacterial actin,** which helps give the bacterium its shape; and in some bacteria an **endospore,** which is a highly resistant structure for survival, not reproduction.

4.5 Bacterial Shapes, Arrangements, and Sizes

 A. Most bacteria are unicellular and are found in a great variety of shapes, arrangements, and sizes. General shapes include **cocci, bacilli,** and helical forms such as **spirilla** and **spirochetes.** Some show great variation within the species in shape and size and are **pleomorphic.** Other variations include **coccobacilli, vibrios,** and filamentous forms.

 B. Prokaryotes divide by binary fission and do not utilize mitosis. Various **arrangements** result from cell division and are termed **diplococci,** streptococci, **staphylococci, tetrads,** and **sarcina** for cocci; bacilli may form pairs, chains, or **palisades.**

 C. Variant members of bacterial species are called **strains** and **types.**

4.6 Classification Systems of the Prokaryotic Domains: Archaea and Bacteria

 A. An important taxonomic system is standardized by *Bergey's Manual of Systemic Bacteriology,* which presents the prokaryotes in five major groups, as organized by volume.

 Volume 1 Domain Archaea
 Domain Bacteria: Deeply Branching and
 Phototropic Bacteria
 Domain Bacteria
 Volume 2 Phylum Proteobacteria
 Volume 3 Phylum Firmicutes
 Volume 4 Phylum Actinobacteria
 Volume 5 Phyla Chlamydiae, Spirochaetes, Planctomyces, Bacteriodetes, and others

4.7 Survey of Prokaryotic Groups with Unusual Characteristics

 A. Several groups of bacteria have unusual adaptations and life cycles.

 1. Medically important bacteria: **Rickettsias** and **chlamydias** are within the gram-negative group but are small **obligate intracellular parasites** that replicate within cells of the hosts they invade.

 2. Nonpathogenic bacterial groups: The majority of bacterial species are free-living and not involved in disease. Unusual groups include photosynthetic bacteria such as **cyanobacteria,** which provide oxygen to the environment, and the green and purple bacteria.

 B. **Archaea** share many characteristics with bacteria but vary in certain genetic aspects and structures such as the cell wall and ribosomes.

 1. Many are extremophiles, adapted to extreme environments similar to the earliest of earth's inhabitants.

 2. They are not considered medically important but are of ecological and potential economic importance.

Level I. Knowledge and Comprehension

These questions require a working knowledge of the concepts in the chapter and the ability to recall and understand the information you have studied.

 Multiple-Choice Questions

Select the correct answer from the answers provided. For questions with blanks, choose the combination of answers that most accurately completes the statement.

1. Which structure is not a component of all cells?
 a. cell wall c. genetic material
 b. cell membrane d. ribosomes

2. Viruses are not considered living things because
 a. they are not cells
 b. they cannot reproduce by themselves
 c. they lack metabolism
 d. All of these are correct.

3. Which of the following is not found in all bacterial cells?
 a. cell membrane c. ribosomes
 b. a nucleoid d. actin cytoskeleton

4. The major locomotor structures in bacteria are
 a. flagella b. pili c. fimbriae d. cilia

5. Pili are appendages in _____ bacteria that serve as a means of _____.
 a. gram-positive, genetic exchange
 b. gram-positive, attachment
 c. gram-negative, genetic exchange
 d. gram-negative, protection

6. An example of a glycocalyx is
 a. a capsule c. outer membrane
 b. pili d. a cell wall

7. Which of the following is a primary bacterial cell wall function?
 a. transport c. support
 b. motility d. adhesion

8. Which of the following is present in both gram-positive and gram-negative cell walls?
 a. an outer membrane c. teichoic acid
 b. peptidoglycan d. lipopolysaccharides

9. Metachromatic granules are concentrated _____ found in _____.
 a. fat, *Mycobacterium* c. sulfur, *Thiobacillus*
 b. dipicolinic acid, *Bacillus* d. PO_4, *Corynebacterium*

10. Which of the following prokaryotes lacks cell walls?
 a. rickettsias c. *Mycobacterium*
 b. mycoplasmas d. archaea

120 **Chapter 4** A Survey of Prokaryotic Cells and Microorganisms

11. The LPS layer in gram-negative cell walls releases _____ that cause _____.
 a. enzymes, pain
 b. endotoxins, fever
 c. techoic acid, inflammation
 d. phosphates, lysis

12. Bacterial endospores function in
 a. reproduction
 b. survival
 c. protein synthesis
 d. storage

13. An arrangement in packets of eight cells is described as a _____.
 a. micrococcus
 b. diplococcus
 c. tetrad
 d. sarcina

14. The major difference between a spirochete and a spirillum is
 a. presence of flagella
 b. the presence of twists
 c. the nature of motility
 d. size

15. Which phylum contains bacteria with a gram-positive cell wall?
 a. Proteobacteria
 b. Chlorobi
 c. Firmicutes
 d. Spirochetes

16. To which taxonomic group do cyanobacteria belong?
 a. Domain Archaea
 b. Phylum Actinobacteria
 c. Domain Bacteria
 d. Phylum Fusobacteria

17. Which stain is used to distinguish differences between the cell walls of medically important bacteria?
 a. simple stain
 b. acridine orange stain
 c. Gram stain
 d. negative stain

18. The first living cells on earth would most likely resemble which of these?
 a. a cyanobacterium
 b. an endospore former
 c. a gram-positive cell
 d. an archaeon

Case Study Review

1. What is true of the condition endocarditis?
 a. It occurs in the heart muscle.
 b. It is caused by microbes growing in the internal organs.
 c. It is an infection of the heart valves and lining.
 d. It can be transmitted to others.

2. Where did the MRSA pathogen likely originate?
 a. from the artificial valve itself
 b. from his earlier skin infection
 c. from the surgery
 d. from the patient's wife

3. What is a biofilm, and how did it form on the heart valve?

Writing Challenge

For each question, compose a one- or two-paragraph answer that includes the factual information needed to completely address the question. Check Your Progress questions can also be used for writing-challenge exercises.

1. Label the parts on the bacterial cell featured here and write a brief description of its function.

2. Discuss the collection of properties that are used to define life and the prokaryotic cell structures that are involved in carrying out these life processes.

3. Describe the basic process of biofilm formation.

4. What leads microbiologists to believe the archaea are more closely related to eukaryotes than to bacteria?

5. What is required to kill endospores? How do you suppose archaeologists were able to date some spores as being thousands (or millions) of years old?

Concept Mapping

An Introduction to Concept Mapping found at http://www.mhhe.com/talaro9 provides guidance for working with concept maps.

1. Construct your own concept map using the following words as the *concepts*. Supply the linking words between each pair of concepts.

genus	species
strain	domain
Borrelia	*burgdorferi*
Spirochaetes	phylum

Level II. Application, Analysis, Evaluation, and Synthesis

These problems go beyond just restating facts and require higher levels of understanding and an ability to interpret, problem solve, transfer knowledge to new situations, create models, and predict outcomes.

Critical Thinking

Critical thinking is the ability to reason and solve problems using facts and concepts. These questions can be approached from a number of angles, and in most cases, they do not have a single correct answer.

1. Using clay, demonstrate how cocci can divide in several planes and show the outcome of this division. Show how the arrangements of bacilli occur, including palisades.

2. Using a corkscrew and a spring to compare the flexibility and locomotion of spirilla and spirochetes, explain which cell type is represented by each object.

3. Under the microscope, you see a rod-shaped cell that is swimming rapidly forward.
 a. What do you automatically know about that bacterium's structure?
 b. Propose another function of flagella besides locomotion.

4. Name an acid-fast bacterium and explain what characteristics make this bacterium different from other gram-positive bacteria.

5. a. Name a bacterial group that uses chlorophyll to photosynthesize.
 b. Describe the two major groups of photosynthetic bacteria and how they are similar and different.

6. Propose a hypothesis to explain how bacteria and archaea could have, together, given rise to eukaryotes.

7. Explain or illustrate exactly what will happen to the cell wall if the synthesis of the interbridge is blocked by penicillin.

8. Ask your lab instructor to help you make a biofilm and examine it under the microscope. One possible technique is to suspend a glass slide in an aquarium for a few weeks, then carefully air-dry, fix, and Gram stain it. Observe the diversity of cell types.

9. Describe the shapes and arrangements of bacteria in figure 4.23*a*, *b*, *e*, and *f*.

Visual Challenge

1. From **chapter 3, figure 3.20***b***.** Which bacteria has a well-developed capsule: "*Klebsiella*" or "*S. aureus*"? Defend your answer.

2. What kinds of cells are shown here? Explain what causes the colors and appearance of the stages you see.

CHAPTER **5** A Survey of Eukaryotic Cells and Microorganisms

Hookworm larvae burrowing into the intestine (20×)

Larval schistosome, a parasitic roundworm (200×)

Trypanosoma, a flagellated protozoan (1,500×)

Examples of microorganisms that cause neglected diseases, distributed across the earth's tropical and subtropical zones (bands of blue)

 CASE STUDY Part 1 Neglected Tropical Diseases

Some of the greatest suffering in the world originates from a group of ancient infectious diseases that exist primarily in the **tropical** and **subtropical** regions of Africa, India, Latin America, and Asia. Nearly 1.4 billion people worldwide, sometimes referred to as the **"bottom billion,"** experience disability or death as a result of 13 common diseases.

These **neglected tropical diseases,** or **NTDs,** have received less attention than highly publicized diseases such as **AIDS, malaria,** and **tuberculosis,** and they have been largely ignored by the medical establishment in many countries. Unfortunately, they also tend to occur in the poorest rural areas, where access to treatment is often severely limited. "Almost everyone in the bottom billion has at least one of these diseases," said Dr. Peter Hotez, a **parasitologist** and medical doctor at George Washington University. Taken together, NTDs rank second only to HIV/AIDS in their medical, social, and economic impact.

Eleven of the 13 neglected disease pathogens are **eukaryotic parasites,** either parasitic **helminth worms** or **protozoans.** The leading parasitic worm infections are **ascariasis,* trichiuriasis, hookworm,** and **schistosomiasis,** and the leading protozoan infections are **Chagas disease, African trypanosomiasis,** and **leishmaniasis.**

> "Almost everyone in the bottom billion has at least one of these diseases."

The **chronic, progressive** actions of these infectious agents can cause debility and disfigurement. Consider Chagas disease, caused by the protozoan *Trypanosoma cruzi,* which over time **lodges in the heart and other organs,** destroys health, and shortens life. Some forms of leishmaniasis affect the skin and give rise to growths that **deform** the face and other body parts. The growth of **hookworms** causes **blood loss,** saps strength, and impairs development. Some parasites cause **blindness** and others **disfigure the limbs.** In addition to medical effects, people often lose their abilities to go to school and work, and become victims of harsh ostracizing by their communities.

▶ *What subjects are studied by the science of parasitology?*

▶ *What can you conclude about the total number of NTD cases, given that everyone in the bottom billion has at least one infection?*

To continue the Case Study, go to page 153.

*Some diseases are named by adding the suffix *-iasis* to the name of the organism that causes it.

5.1 The History of Eukaryotes

 Expected Learning Outcomes

1. Describe the evolutionary history of eukaryotic cells.
2. Provide a substantial theory regarding how eukaryotic cells originated and how multicellularity came to be.
3. List the eukaryotic groups and their body plans.

Using evidence from ancient sediments, paleontologists estimate that the earliest eukaryotic cells first evolved around 2 billion years ago. Other intriguing evidence comes from fossilized cells discovered in shale deposits from China and Russia that are 600 million to nearly a billion years old. It is remarkable how much they resemble modern-day algae or protozoa (**figure 5.1**).

When biologists began to focus on the possible origins of these cells, they turned to an analysis of modern cells, and from these studies emerged convincing evidence that eukaryotic cells evolved from prokaryotic cells through a process of intracellular **symbiosis*** (**5.1 Making Connections**). This essentially means that two different kinds of prokaryotes came together, merged, and formed a completely unique cell type. The starting event probably occurred when a larger prokaryotic cell engulfed smaller prokaryotic cells and kept them alive. Over hundreds of millions of years, this combination evolved into a stable, beneficial partnership. Some of the small cells trapped inside these evolving cells became **organelles*** that are the distinguishing feature of eukaryotic cells. The structure of these early cells was so versatile that eukaryotic microorganisms soon spread out into available habitats and adopted greatly diverse styles of living.

The first primitive eukaryotes were probably single-celled, independent microorganisms, but, over time, some forms began to cluster in permanent groupings called colonies. With further evolution, some of the cells within colonies became *specialized,* or adapted to perform a particular function advantageous to the whole colony, such as locomotion, feeding, or reproduction. Complex multicellular organisms evolved as individual cells in the organism lost the ability to survive apart from the intact colony. Although a multicellular organism is composed of many cells, it is more than just a disorganized assemblage of cells like a colony. Rather, it is composed of distinct groups of cells that cannot exist independently of the rest of the body. The cell groupings of multicellular organisms that have a specific function are termed *tissues,* and groups of tissues make up *organs.*

Looking at modern eukaryotic organisms, we find examples of many levels of cellular complexity (**table 5.1**). All protozoa, as well as numerous algae and fungi, are unicellular. Truly multicellular organisms are found only among plants and animals and some of the fungi (mushrooms) and algae (seaweeds). Only certain eukaryotes are traditionally studied by microbiologists—primarily the protozoa, the microscopic algae and fungi, and animal parasites, or helminths.

* *symbiosis* (sim-beye-oh′-sis) Gr. *sym,* together, and *bios,* to live. A close association between two organisms.
* *organelles* (or-gan′-elz) Gr. *organa,* tool, and *ella,* little. Structures inside cells that perform specific functions.

(a) (b)

Figure 5.1 Ancient eukaryotic protists discovered in fossilized rocks. (a) A cell preserved in Siberian shale deposits dates from 850 million to 950 million years ago. **(b)** A disclike cell was recovered from a Chinese rock dating 590 million to 610 million years ago. Both cells are relatively simple, with (a) showing chloroplast-like bodies like algae. Example (b) has a cell wall with spines, very similar to the modern algae *Pediastrum.*

TABLE 5.1	Eukaryotic Organisms Studied in Microbiology	
Unicellular, a Few Colonial	May Be Unicellular, Colonial, or Multicellular	Multicellular Except Reproductive Stages
Protozoa	Fungi	Helminths (parasitic worms)
	Algae	Arthropods (animal vectors of diseases)

5.2 Form and Function of the Eukaryotic Cell: External Structures

 Expected Learning Outcomes

4. Describe the plan of a basic eukaryotic cell and organelles, and indicate the structures all cells possess and those found only in some groups.
5. Describe the types of eukaryotic locomotor appendages.
6. Differentiate the structure and functions of flagella and cilia, and the types of cells that possess them.
7. Define the glycocalyx for eukaryotic cells and list its basic functions.
8. Characterize the cell wall and membrane of eukaryotic cells.

The cells of eukaryotic organisms are so varied that no one member can serve as a typical example, so a composite structure of a eukaryotic cell is depicted in **figure 5.2.** No single type of microbial cell would contain all structures represented. It is evident that the organelles impart much greater complexity and compartmentalization compared to a prokaryotic cell. Differences among fungi, protozoa, algae, and animal cells are introduced in later sections.

5.1 MAKING CONNECTIONS

The Extraordinary Evolution of Eukaryotic Cells

For years, biologists have grappled with the problem of how a cell as complex as the eukaryotic cell originated. One of the most fascinating theories is that of **endosymbiosis.** This theory states that eukaryotic cells arose when a much larger prokaryotic cell engulfed smaller prokaryotic cells that began to live and reproduce inside the prokaryotic cell, rather than being destroyed. As the smaller cells took up permanent residence, they came to perform specialized functions for the larger cell, such as food synthesis and oxygen utilization, that enhanced the cell's versatility and survival. In time, the cells evolved into a single functioning entity, and the relationship became obligatory.

At first, the idea of endosymbiosis was greeted with some controversy; however, we now know that associations of this sort are rather common in the microbial world. The interrelationships range from temporary nondependent endosymbiosis to interdependent associations in which the two microbes share genes and physiology (see insects and *Wolbachia* below).

The biologist most responsible for validation of the theory of endosymbiosis is *Dr. Lynn Margulis.* Using molecular techniques, she accumulated convincing evidence of the relationships between the organelles of modern eukaryotic cells and the structure of bacteria. In many ways, the mitochondrion of eukaryotic cells behaves as a tiny cell within a cell. It is capable of independent division, contains a circular chromosome with bacterial DNA sequences, and has ribosomes that are clearly prokaryotic. Mitochondria also have bacterial membranes and can be inhibited by drugs that affect only bacteria.

Genetic studies indicate that chloroplasts likely originated from endosymbiotic cyanobacteria that provided their host cells with a built-in feeding mechanism. Evidence is seen in a modern flagellated protist that harbors specialized chloroplasts with cyanobacterial chlorophyll and thylakoids. Dr. Margulis also has convincing evidence that eukaryotic cilia and flagella have arisen from endosymbiosis between spiral bacteria and the cell membrane of early eukaryotic cells. Most notable is a protozoan found in termites with spirochetes functioning as flagella.

The accompanying figure shows a possible sequence of events. A large archaeal cell with its flexible envelope could engulf a smaller bacterial cell. The archaeon would contribute its cytoplasmic ribosomes and some unique aspects of protein synthesis, as predicted by known characteristics (see table 4.5). Folds in the cell membrane could wrap around the chromosome to form a nuclear envelope. For its part, the bacterial cell would forge a metabolic relationship with the archaea, making use of archaeal molecules and contributing energy through aerobic respiration. Evolution of a stable mutualistic existence would maintain both cell types and create the eukaryotic cell and its organelles. This scenario also has the advantage of explaining the relationships among the major domains. So well accepted is the theory that bacteriologists have placed both mitochondria and chloroplasts on the family tree of bacteria (see figure 1.15). In fact, the closest relative of mitochondria are rickettsias, which are also obligate intracellular bacteria!

Explain some of the ways the early mitochondria and chloroplasts could have assisted the survival of the larger cell. *Answer available at http://www.mhhe.com/talaro9*

A larger prokaryotic cell, possibly an archaea, containing a flexible outer envelope and folded internal membranes.

A smaller prokaryotic cell, related to modern rickettsias, that can live intracellularly.

Membrane forms around the DNA, creating a primitive nucleus.

The larger cell engulfs the smaller one; smaller one survives and remains surrounded by the vacuolar membrane.

Smaller bacterium becomes a permanent resident of its host's cytoplasm; it multiplies and is passed on during cell division. It utilizes aerobic metabolism and increases energy availability for the host.

Early endoplasmic reticulum

Early mitochondria

Ancestral eukaryotic cell develops additional membrane pouches that become the endoplasmic reticulum and Golgi apparatus.

Ancestral cell

Photosynthetic bacteria (ancient cyanobacteria) are also engulfed; they develop into chloroplasts.

Chloroplast

Cell wall

Many protozoa, animals

Some groups of algae, higher plants

Fluorescent image of *Wolbachia* (orange bacteria) in the cells of the malarial mosquito (green nuclei). This tiny parasite is a permanent resident of many insect cells and is known to control major parts of insects' life cycles.

Quick Search

Look up "an interactive tour of the cell" at the National Science Foundation website to explore the dynamics of cell structure.

Cell wall*
Page 127

Mitochondrion
Pages 130, 131

Cell membrane
Page 127

Golgi apparatus
Pages 129, 130

Rough endoplasmic
reticulum with
ribosomes
Pages 127, 129

Microfilaments
Page 132

Flagellum
or cilium*
Pages 127, 129

Nuclear
envelope
with pores
Pages 127, 128

Nucleus
Page 127

Lysosome
Page 131

Nucleolus
Pages 127, 128

Smooth
endoplasmic
reticulum
Page 127

Microtubules
Page 132

Microvilli

Chloroplast*
Pages 131, 132

Centrioles*
Page 128

***Structure not present in all cell types**

Glycocalyx
Page 126

Figure 5.2 Overview of composite eukaryotic cell. This drawing represents all structures associated with eukaryotic cells, but no microbial cell possesses all of them. See figures 5.15, 5.22, and 5.24 for examples of individual cell types.

The flowchart shown here maps the structural organization of a eukaryotic cell. Compare this outline to the one found on page 90 in chapter 4.

In general, eukaryotic microbial cells have a cytoplasmic membrane, nucleus, mitochondria, endoplasmic reticulum, Golgi apparatus, vacuoles, cytoskeleton, and glycocalyx. A cell wall, locomotor appendages, and chloroplasts are found only in some groups. In the following sections, we cover the microscopic structure and functions of the eukaryotic cell. As with the prokaryotes, we begin on the outside and proceed inward through the cell.

Locomotor Appendages: Cilia and Flagella

Motility allows a microorganism to locate life-sustaining nutrients and to migrate toward positive stimuli such as sunlight; it also permits avoidance of harmful substances and stimuli. Locomotion by means of flagella is common in protozoa, algae, and a few fungal and animal cells. Cilia are found only in protozoa and animal cells.

Eukaryotic cell

External structures — Glycocalyx / Capsules / Slimes

Boundary of cell — Cell wall / Cell/cytoplasmic membrane

Organelles and other components within the cell membrane — Cytoplasmic matrix

Nucleus — Nuclear envelope / Nucleolus / Chromosomes

Organelles — Endoplasmic reticulum / Golgi complex / Mitochondria / Chloroplasts

Locomotor organelles — Flagella / Cilia

Ribosomes

Cytoskeleton — Microtubules / Microfilaments

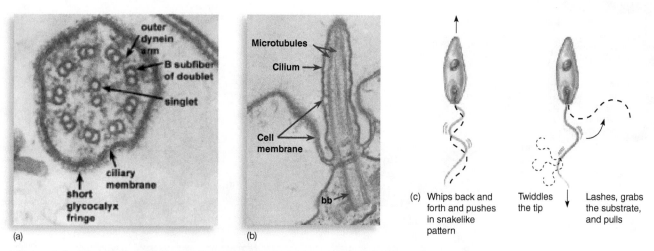

Figure 5.3 The structure of cilia and flagella. (a) A cross section through a protozoan cilium reveals the typical 9 + 2 arrangement of microtubules seen in both cilia and flagella. **(b)** Longitudinal section through a cilium, showing the lengthwise orientation of the microtubules and the basal body (bb) from which they arise. Note the membrane that surrounds the cilium that is an extension of the cell membrane and shows that it is indeed an organelle. **(c)** Locomotor patterns seen in flagellates.

Although they share the same name, eukaryotic flagella are much different from those of prokaryotes. The eukaryotic flagellum is thicker (by a factor of 10), has a much different construction, and is covered by an extension of the cell membrane. A flagellum is a long, sheathed cylinder containing regularly spaced hollow tubules—microtubules—that extend along its entire length **(figure 5.3b).** A cross section reveals nine pairs of closely attached microtubules surrounding a single central pair. This scheme, called the 9 + 2 arrangement, is a typical pattern of flagella and cilia **(figure 5.3a).** The nine pairs are linked together and anchored to the pair in the center. This architecture permits the microtubules to "walk" by sliding past each other, whipping the flagellum back and forth. Although details of this process are too complex to discuss here, it involves expenditure of energy and a coordinating mechanism in the cell membrane. Flagella can move the cell by pushing it forward like a fishtail or by pulling it by a lashing or twirling motion **(figure 5.3c).** The placement and number of flagella can be useful in identifying flagellated protozoa and certain algae.

Cilia are very similar in overall architecture to flagella, but they are shorter and more numerous (some cells have several thousand). They are found only in certain protozoa and animal cells. In the ciliated protozoa, the cilia occur in rows over the cell surface, where they beat back and forth in regular oarlike strokes **(figure 5.4)** and provide rapid motility. The fastest ciliated protozoan can swim up to 2,500 μm/s—a meter and a half per minute! On some cells, cilia also function as feeding and filtering structures.

Quick Search
Find videos using the search words amoebic, flagellate, and ciliate movement on YouTube.

The Glycocalyx

Most eukaryotic microbes have a **glycocalyx,** an outermost boundary that comes into direct contact with the environment. This structure is usually composed of polysaccharides and appears as a network of fibers, a slime layer, or a capsule much like the glycocalyx of pro-

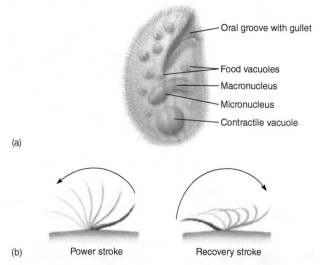

Figure 5.4 Locomotion in ciliates. (a) A simple ciliate, *Balantidium*, has regular rows of cilia over its surface and within its oral groove and gullet for capturing and transporting food. **(b)** Cilia beat in coordinated waves, driving the cell forward and backward. The pattern of ciliary movement is like a swimmer's arms, with a power forward stroke and a repositioning stroke. Ciliary moves are made possible by the microtubules they contain.

karyotes. From its position as the exposed cell layer, the glycocalyx serves a variety of functions. Most prominently, it promotes adherence to environmental surfaces and the development of biofilms and mats. It also serves important receptor and communication functions and offers some protection against environmental changes.

The nature of the layer beneath the glycocalyx varies among the several eukaryotic groups. Fungi and most algae have a thick, rigid cell wall surrounding a cell membrane. Protozoa, a few algae, and all animal cells lack a cell wall and are encased primarily by a cell membrane.

Form and Function of the Eukaryotic Cell: Boundary Structures

The Cell Wall

The cell walls of the fungi and algae are rigid and provide structural support and shape, but they are different in chemical composition from prokaryotic cell walls. Fungal cell walls have a thick, inner layer of polysaccharide fibers composed of chitin or cellulose and a thin outer layer of mixed glycans. The cell walls of algae are quite varied in chemical composition. Substances commonly found among various algal groups are cellulose, pectin,[1] mannans,[2] and minerals such as silicon dioxide and calcium carbonate.

The Cytoplasmic Membrane

The cytoplasmic (cell) membrane of eukaryotic cells is a typical bilayer of phospholipids in which protein molecules are embedded (see figures 2.20 and 4.17). In addition to phospholipids, eukaryotic membranes also contain *sterols* of various kinds. Sterols are different from phospholipids in both structure and behavior, as you may recall from chapter 2. Their relative rigidity confers stability on eukaryotic membranes. This strengthening feature is extremely important in cells that lack a cell wall. Cytoplasmic membranes of eukaryotes are functionally similar to those of prokaryotes, serving as selectively permeable barriers in transport. Unlike prokaryotes, eukaryotes have extensive membrane-bound organelles that can account for 60% to 80% of their volume.

 Check Your Progress SECTIONS 5.1 AND 5.2

1. Briefly explain how the eukaryotic cell could have evolved from prokaryotic ones.
2. Which kingdoms of the five-kingdom system contain eukaryotic microorganisms?
3. How do unicellular, colonial, and multicellular organisms differ from each other? Give examples of each type.
4. How are flagella and cilia similar? How are they different?
5. Which eukaryotic cells have a cell wall?
6. What are the functions of the glycocalyx, cell wall, and membrane?

5.3 Form and Function of the Eukaryotic Cell: Internal Structures

 Expected Learning Outcomes

9. Describe the structure of the nucleus and its outstanding features.
10. Outline the stages in cell division and mitosis.
11. Describe the structure of the two types of endoplasmic reticulum and their functions.
12. Identify the parts of the Golgi apparatus, and explain its basic actions and uses in the cell.

1. A polysaccharide composed of galacturonic acid subunits.
2. A polymer of the sugar known as mannose.

13. Summarize the stages in processing by the nucleus, endoplasmic reticulum, and Golgi apparatus involved in synthesis, packaging, and export.
14. Describe the structure of a mitochondrion, and explain its importance and functions.
15. Describe the structure of chloroplasts, and explain their importance and functions.
16. Discuss features of eukaryotic ribosomes.
17. Indicate the basic structure of the cytoskeleton, and explain its main features and functions.

The Nucleus: The Control Center

The nucleus is a compact sphere that is the most prominent organelle of eukaryotic cells. It is separated from the cell cytoplasm by an external boundary called a **nuclear envelope** or membrane. The envelope has a unique architecture. It is composed of two parallel membranes separated by a narrow space, and it is perforated with small, regularly spaced openings, or pores, at sites where the two membranes unite **(figure 5.5)**. The pores are structured to serve as selective passageways for molecules to migrate between the nucleus and cytoplasm. The main body of the nucleus consists of a matrix called the nucleoplasm and a granular mass, the **nucleolus.** The nucleolus is the site for ribosomal RNA synthesis and a collection area for ribosomal subunits. The subunits are transported through the nuclear pores into the cytoplasm for final assembly into ribosomes.

A prominent feature of the nucleoplasm in stained preparations is a network of dark fibers known as **chromatin** because of its attraction for dyes. Analysis has shown that chromatin actually comprises the eukaryotic **chromosomes,** large units of genetic information in the cell. The chromosomes in the nucleus of nondividing cells are not readily visible because they are long, linear DNA molecules bound in varying degrees to **histone** proteins, and they are far too fine to be resolved as distinct structures without extremely high magnification. During **mitosis,** however, when the duplicated chromosomes are separated equally into daughter cells, the chromosomes themselves become readily visible as discrete bodies **(figure 5.6)**. This appearance arises when the DNA becomes highly condensed by forming coils and supercoils around the histones to prevent the chromosomes from tangling as they are separated into new cells. This process is described in more detail in chapter 9.

Although we correctly view the nucleus as the primary genetic center, it does not function in isolation. As we show in the next three sections, it is closely tied to cytoplasmic organelles that perform elaborate cell functions.

Endoplasmic Reticulum: A Passageway and Production System for Eukaryotes

The **endoplasmic reticulum (ER)** is an interconnected network of membranous, hollow sacs that synthesize and transport cell substances **(figure 5.7a)**. Originating from, and continuous with, the outer membrane of the nuclear envelope, the ER serves as a passageway for materials between the nucleus and the cytoplasm. It also provides significant compartmentalization for numerous cell activities. The two types of endoplasmic reticulum are the **rough endoplasmic reticulum (RER)** and the **smooth endoplasmic**

Figure 5.5 The nucleus. (a) Electron micrograph section of an interphase nucleus, showing its most prominent features. **(b)** Cutaway three-dimensional view of the relationships of the nuclear envelope, pores, and endoplasmic reticulum.

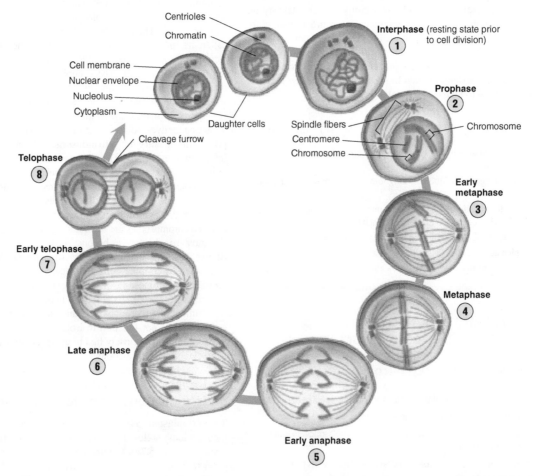

📷 Process Figure 5.6 Changes in the cell and nucleus during mitosis of a eukaryotic cell (1) Before mitosis (at interphase), chromosomes are visible only as chromatin. **(2)** As mitosis proceeds (early prophase), chromosomes take on a fine, threadlike appearance as they condense, and the nuclear membrane and nucleolus are temporarily disrupted. **(3)–(4)** By metaphase, the chromosomes are fully visible as X-shaped structures. The shape is due to duplicated chromosomes attached at a central point, the centromere. **(5)–(6)** Spindle fibers attach to these and facilitate the separation of individual chromosomes during anaphase. **(7)–(8)** Telophase completes chromosomal separation and division of the cell proper into daughter cells. Note: This mechanism is how wall-free cells divide. Cells with walls will have a different pattern.

Figure 5.7 The origin and structures of the rough endoplasmic reticulum (RER) and Golgi apparatus. (a) Schematic view of the origin of the endoplasmic reticulum from the outer membrane of the nuclear envelope. **(b)** Three-dimensional projection of the RER. **(c)** Detail of the orientation of a ribosome on the RER membrane. Proteins are collected within the RER cisternae and distributed through its network to other destinations. **(d)** The flattened layers of the Golgi apparatus receive protein-carrying transport vesicles from the RER, process their contents, and transport condensing vesicles to sites of various cellular functions.

reticulum (SER). These two ER networks are similar in origin and are directly connected to each other, but they differ in some aspects of structure and function.

The RER consists of parallel, flattened sacs called **cisternae,*** and it appears "rough" in electron micrographs because its outer surface is studded with ribosomes **(figure 5.7b).** This architecture ties in with its role in synthesis of proteins, which are collected in the lumen **(figure 5.7c)** of the cisternae and processed for further transport to the Golgi apparatus **(figure 5.7d).** The SER lacks ribosomes and is more tubular in structure (see figures 5.2 and 5.7a). Although it communicates with the RER and also transports molecules within the cell, it has specialized functions. Most important among them are the synthesis of nonprotein molecules such as lipids, and detoxification of metabolic waste products and other toxic substances.

Golgi Apparatus: A Packaging Machine

The **Golgi**[3] **apparatus,** also called the **Golgi complex** or body, is the site in the cell that collects proteins and and packages them for transport to their final destinations. It is a discrete organelle consisting of layers of flattened, disc-shaped sacs also called cisternae, giving an appearance of a stack of pita breads. These sacs have outer limiting membranes and cavities like those of the endoplasmic reticulum, but they do not form a continuous network (figure 5.7d). This organelle is always closely associated with the endoplasmic reticulum both in its location and function. At a site where it borders on the Golgi apparatus, the endoplasmic reticulum buds off tiny membrane-bound packets of protein called **transport vesicles** that are picked up by the forming face of the Golgi apparatus. Once

* *cisternae* (siss-tur'-nee) L., *cisterna,* reservoir.

3. (gol'-jee) Named for C. Golgi, an Italian histologist who first described the apparatus in 1898.

in the complex itself, the proteins are further modified for transport by the addition of polysaccharides and lipids. The final action of this apparatus is to pinch off finished **condensing vesicles** that will be conveyed to organelles such as lysosomes or transported outside the cell as **secretory vesicles (figure 5.8).**

Nucleus, Endoplasmic Reticulum, and Golgi Apparatus: Nature's Assembly Line

As the keeper of the eukaryotic genetic code, the nucleus ultimately governs and regulates all cell activities. But because the nucleus remains fixed in a specific cellular site, it must direct these activities through a structural and chemical network (figure 5.8). This network includes ribosomes, which originate in the nucleus, and the rough endoplasmic reticulum, which is continuously connected with the nuclear envelope.

Initially, a segment of the genetic code of DNA containing the instructions for producing a protein is copied into RNA and passed out through the nuclear pores directly to the ribosomes on the endoplasmic reticulum. Here, specific proteins are synthesized from the RNA code and deposited in the lumen (space) of the endoplasmic reticulum. Details of this process are covered in chapter 9. After being transported to the Golgi apparatus, the protein products are chemically modified and packaged into **vesicles*** that can be used by the cell in a variety of ways. Some of the vesicles contain

* *vesicle* (ves'-ik-l) L. *vesios*, bladder. A small sac containing fluid.

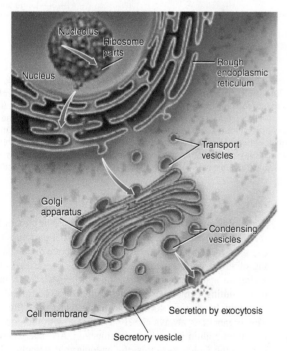

Figure 5.8 The synthesis and transport machine. Function requires cooperation and interaction among the system of organelles. The nucleolus provides a constant supply of ribosomes that travel through the nuclear pores to the RER. Once in place, ribosomes synthesize proteins that are assembled by the RER into vesicles and moved to the nearby Golgi. Finished vesicles leave the Golgi after processing and migrate to the cell membrane. From there they may be secreted (as here) or act internally.

enzymes to digest food inside the cell; other vesicles are secreted to digest materials outside the cell; and yet others are important in the enlargement and repair of the cell wall and membrane.

A **lysosome*** is one type of vesicle originating from the Golgi apparatus that contains a variety of enzymes. Lysosomes are involved in intracellular digestion of food particles and in protection against invading microorganisms. They also participate in digestion and removal of cell debris in damaged tissue.

Other types of vesicles include **vacuoles,*** which are membrane-bound sacs containing fluids or solid particles to be digested, excreted, or stored. They are formed in phagocytic cells (certain white blood cells and protozoa) in response to food and other substances that have been engulfed. The contents of a food vacuole are digested through the merger of the vacuole with a lysosome. This merged structure is called a phagosome **(figure 5.9).** Other types of vacuoles are used in storing reserve food such as fats and glycogen. Protozoa living in freshwater habitats regulate osmotic pressure by means of contractile vacuoles, which regularly expel excess water that has diffused into the cell (described later).

Mitochondria: Energy Generators of the Cell

None of the cellular activities of the genetic assembly line could proceed without a constant supply of energy, the bulk of which is generated in most eukaryotes by **mitochondria.*** When viewed with light microscopy, mitochondria appear as tiny round or elongated particles scattered throughout the cytoplasm. Higher magnification reveals that a mitochondrion consists of a smooth, continuous outer membrane that forms the external contour and an inner, folded membrane nestled neatly within the outer membrane **(figure 5.10***b***).** The folds on the inner membrane, called **cristae,*** vary in exact structure among eukaryotic cell types. Plant, animal, and fungal mitochondria have lamellar cristae folded into shelflike layers. Those of algae and protozoa are tubular, fingerlike projections or flattened discs.

The cristae membranes hold the enzymes and electron carriers of aerobic respiration. This is an oxygen-using process that extracts chemical energy contained in nutrient molecules and stores it in the form of high-energy molecules, or ATP. More detailed functions of mitochondria are covered in chapter 8. The spaces around the cristae are filled with a chemically complex fluid called the **matrix,*** which holds ribosomes, DNA, and a pool of enzymes and other compounds involved in the metabolic cycle. Mitochondria (along with chloroplasts) are unique among organelles in that they divide independently of the cell, contain circular strands of DNA, and have prokaryote-sized 70S ribosomes. These findings have given support to the endosymbiotic theory of their evolutionary origins discussed in 5.1 Making Connections.

Chloroplasts: Photosynthesis Machines

Chloroplasts are remarkable organelles found in algae and plant cells that are capable of converting the energy of sunlight into chemical energy through photosynthesis. The photosynthetic role

* *lysosome* (ly'-soh-sohm) Gr. *lysis*, dissolution, and *soma*, body.
* *vacuole* (vak'-yoo-ohl) L. *vacuus*, empty. Any membranous space in the cytoplasm.
* *mitochondria* (my''-toh-kon'-dree-uh) sing. mitochondrion; Gr. *mitos*, thread, and *chondrion*, granule.
* *cristae* (kris'-te) sing. crista; L. *crista*, a comb.
* *matrix* (may'-triks) L. *mater*, mother or origin.

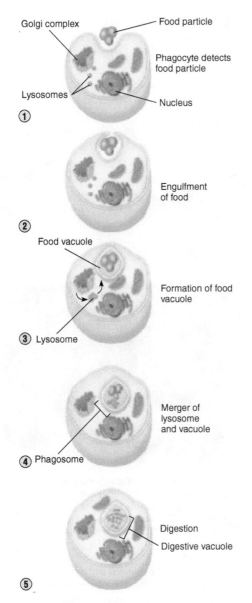

Figure 5.9 **The functions of lysosomes during phagocytosis.**

Golgi complex
Food particle
Phagocyte detects food particle
Lysosomes
Nucleus
①

Engulfment of food
②

Food vacuole
Formation of food vacuole
③ Lysosome

Merger of lysosome and vacuole
④ Phagosome

Digestion
Digestive vacuole
⑤

(a)
Cristae (darker lines)
Matrix (lighter spaces)

(b)
Circular DNA strand
70S ribosomes
Matrix
Cristae
Inner membrane
Outer membrane

Figure 5.10 **General structure of a mitochondrion. (a)** An electron micrograph of a longitudinal section. In most cells, mitochondria are elliptical or spherical, and occasionally filament-like. **(b)** A cutaway three-dimensional illustration details the double membrane structure and the extensive foldings of the inner membrane.

of chloroplasts makes them important primary producers of organic nutrients upon which all other organisms (except certain bacteria and archaea) ultimately depend. Another important photosynthetic product of chloroplasts is oxygen gas. Although chloroplasts resemble mitochondria, chloroplasts are larger, contain special pigments, and are much more varied in shape. Be reminded that chloroplasts are thought to have originated from intracellular cyanobacteria and resemble them in many ways.

There are differences among various algal chloroplasts, but most are generally composed of two membranes, one enclosing the other. The smooth, outer membrane completely covers an inner membrane folded into small, disclike sacs called **thylakoids** that are stacked upon one another into **grana.** These structures carry the green pigment chlorophyll and sometimes additional pigments as well. Surrounding the thylakoids is a ground substance called the **stroma* (figure 5.11).** The role of the photosynthetic pigments is to absorb and transform solar energy into chemical energy, which is then used during reactions in the stroma to synthesize carbohydrates. We further explore some important aspects of photosynthesis in chapters 7 and 8.

Ribosomes: Protein Synthesizers

In an electron micrograph of a eukaryotic cell, ribosomes are numerous, tiny particles that give a "dotted" appearance to the cytoplasm. Ribosomes are distributed in two ways: Some are scattered freely in the cytoplasm and cytoskeleton; others are intimately associated with the rough endoplasmic reticulum, as previously described. Multiple ribosomes are often found arranged in short chains called polyribosomes (polysomes). The basic structure of eukaryotic ribosomes is similar to that of prokaryotic ribosomes, described in chapter 4. Both are composed of large and small subunits of ribonucleoprotein (see figure 5.7). By contrast, however, the ribosomes of eukaryotes (except in the mitochondria and

* *stroma* (stroh′-mah) Gr. *stroma,* mattress or bed.

(a)

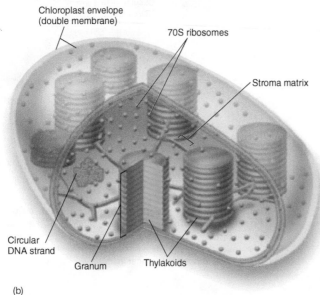

Chloroplast envelope (double membrane)

70S ribosomes

Stroma matrix

Circular DNA strand

Granum Thylakoids

(b)

Figure 5.11 Details of an algal chloroplast. (a) An electron microscope image of a single alga—*Phaeocystis*—with two hemispherical-shaped chloroplasts, each bearing several layers of thylakoids (25,000×). **(b)** An artist's three-dimensional rendition of a chloroplast and its major features.

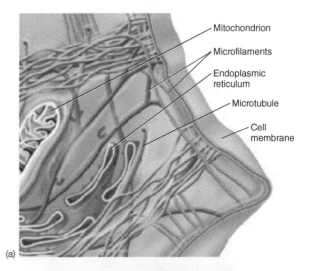

Mitochondrion

Microfilaments

Endoplasmic reticulum

Microtubule

Cell membrane

(a)

(b)

Figure 5.12 A model of the cytoskeleton. (a) Depicted is the relationship between microtubules, microfilaments, and organelles. (Not to scale.) **(b)** The cytoskeleton of a large eukaryotic cell is highlighted by fluorescent dyes. Microtubules are stained green, microfilaments are red, and the nucleus is blue.

chloroplasts) are of the larger 80S variety that is a combination of 60S and 40S subunits. As in the prokaryotes, eukaryotic ribosomes are the staging areas for protein synthesis.

The Cytoskeleton: A Support Network

All cells share a generalized region encased by the cell membrane called the cytoplasm or, in eukaryotic cells, the **cytoplasmic matrix.** This complex area houses the organelles and sustains major metabolic and synthetic activities. It also contains the framework of support in cells lacking walls. The matrix is interwoven by a flexible framework of molecules called the **cytoskeleton (figure 5.12).** This framework appears to have several functions, such as anchoring

organelles, providing support, and permitting shape changes and movement in some cells. The two main types of cytoskeletal elements are *microfilaments* and *microtubules.*

Microfilaments are thin strands composed of the protein actin that attach to the cell membrane and form a network through the cytoplasm. Some microfilaments are responsible for movements of the cytoplasm, often made evident by the streaming of organelles around the cell in a cyclic pattern. Other microfilaments are active in *amoeboid motion,* a type of movement typical of cells such as amoebas and phagocytes that produces extensions of the cell membrane (pseudopods) into which the cytoplasm flows.

Microtubules are long, hollow tubes that maintain the shape of eukaryotic cells such as protozoa that lack cell walls. They may also serve as an alternative transport system for molecules. The spindle fibers that play an essential role in mitosis are actually microtubules that attach to chromosomes and separate them into daughter cells. As indicated earlier, microtubules are also responsible for the movement of cilia and flagella.

 Check Your Progress SECTION 5.3

7. In what ways does the nucleus function like the "brain" of the cell?

8. Explain how ribosomes and the nucleolus are related.

9. How does the nucleus communicate with the cytoplasm?

10. Compare and contrast the smooth ER, the rough ER, and the Golgi apparatus in structure and function.

11. Compare the structures and functions of the mitochondrion and the chloroplast.

12. What makes the mitochondrion and chloroplast unique among the organelles?

13. Describe some of the ways that organisms use lysosomes.

14. For what reasons would a cell need a "skeleton"?

5.4 Eukaryotic-Prokaryotic Comparisons and Taxonomy of Eukaryotes

 Expected Learning Outcomes

18. Compare and contrast prokaryotic cells, eukaryotic cells, and viruses.

19. Outline the basics of eukaryotic taxonomy.

20. Explain what is meant by the term *protist*, and outline the types of organisms belonging to this designation.

Now that we have introduced the major characteristics of eukaryotic cells, this section will serve to summarize their major characteristics and to compare and contrast them with prokaryotic cells (see chapter 4), especially from the standpoints of structure, physiology, and other traits (**table 5.2**). We have included viruses for the purposes of summarizing the biological characteristics of all microbes and to show you just how much viruses differ from cells. We will explore this fascinating group of microbes in chapter 6.

Overview of Taxonomy

Exploring the origins of eukaryotic cells with molecular technology has significantly clarified our understanding of relationships among the organisms in Domain Eukarya. The phenetic characteristics traditionally used for placing plants, animals, and fungi into separate kingdoms are general cell type, level of organization or body plan, and nutritional type. It now appears that these criteria really do reflect accurate differences among these organisms and give rise to the same basic kingdoms as do genetic tests using ribosomal RNA (see figure 1.15).

Because our understanding of the phylogenetic relationships is still in development, there is not yet a single official system of taxonomy for presenting all of the eukaryotes. One of the proposed alternate plans of classification is shown in **figure 5.13**. This simplified system, also based on data from ribosomal RNA analysis, retains some of the traditional kingdoms.

TABLE 5.2	A General Comparison of Prokaryotic and Eukaryotic Cells and Viruses			
Function or Structure	**Characteristic***	**Prokaryotic Cells**	**Eukaryotic Cells**	**Viruses***
Genetics	Nucleic acids	+	+	+
	True nucleus	−	+	−
	Nuclear envelope	−	+	−
	Nucleoid	+	−	−
Reproduction	Mitosis	−	+	−
	Production of sex cells	+/−	+	−
	Binary fission	+	+	−
Biosynthesis	Independent	+	+	−
	Golgi apparatus	−	+	−
	Endoplasmic reticulum	−	+	−
	Ribosomes	+***	+	−
Respiration	Enzymes	+	+	−
	Mitochondria	−	+	−
Photosynthesis	Pigments	+/−	+/−	−
	Chloroplasts	−	+/−	−
Motility/locomotor structures	Flagella	+/−***	+/−	−
	Cilia	−	+/−	−
Shape/protection	Cell membrane	+	+	+/−
	Cell wall	+/−***	+/−	− (have capsids instead)
	Capsule	+/−	+/−	−
Size (in general)		0.5–3 µm****	2–100 µm	< 0.2 µm

*+ means most members of the group exhibit this characteristic; − means most lack it; +/− means some members have it and some do not.

**Viruses cannot participate in metabolic or genetic activity outside their host cells.

***The prokaryotic type is structurally very different.

****Much smaller and much larger bacteria exist; see 4.1 Secret World of Microbes.

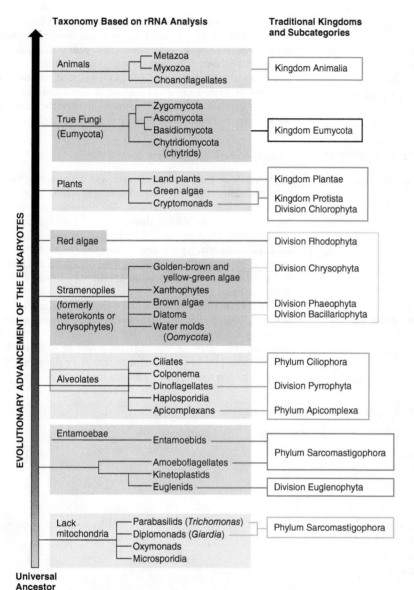

Figure 5.13 RNA-based phylogenetic tree and taxonomy of Domain Eukarya. A comparison of two possible systems for presenting the taxonomy of major eukaryotic groups. This textbook will largely follow the simpler system on the right, using Kingdoms, Divisions, and Phyla to separate the groups of eukaryotes.

The one group that has created the greatest challenge in establishing reliable relationships is **Kingdom Protista**—the protists. Any simple eukaryotic cell that lacked multicellular structure or cell specialization has been placed into the Kingdom Protista generally as an alga (photosynthetic) or protozoan (nonphotosynthetic). Although exceptions arise with this classification scheme—notably multicellular algae and the photosynthetic protozoans—most eukaryotic microbes have been readily accommodated in the Kingdom Protista as traditionally presented.

Newer genetic data reveal that the organisms we call protists may be as different from each other as plants are different from animals. They are highly complex organisms that are likely to have evolved from a number of separate ancestors.

Microbiologists prefer to set up taxonomic systems that reflect true relationships based on all valid scientific data, including genotypic, molecular, morphological, physiological, and ecological. As a result, several alternative taxonomic strategies are being proposed to deal with this changing picture. Suggestions have ranged from distributing the protists among five new kingdoms to 25 kingdoms or more.

Note that figure 5.13 compares an rRNA-based system as first outlined in chapter 1 alongside the original Kingdom Protista with its assorted phyla and divisions. One advantage of this original plan is that it continues to use most of the original taxa at the phylum, division, and lower levels, especially as they relate to medically significant microbial groups. We feel the term **protist** is still a useful shorthand reference and will continue to use it for any eukaryote that is not a fungus, animal, or plant.

In the interest of space and ease in presentation, we have adopted a system of taxonomy that emphasizes natural groupings with the least complexity. A final note about taxonomy: No one system is perfect or permanent. Let your instructor guide you as to which one is satisfactory for your course.

With the general structure of the eukaryotic cell in mind, let us next examine the range of adaptations that this cell type has undergone. The following sections contain a general survey of the principal eukaryotic microorganisms—fungi, algae, protozoa, and parasitic worms—while also introducing elements of their structure, life history, classification, identification, and importance. A survey of diseases associated with some of these microbes is found in chapters 22 and 23.

5.5 The Kingdom of the Fungi

 Expected Learning Outcomes

21. Describe the basic characteristics of the Kingdom Fungi in terms of general types of cells and organisms, structure, and nutrition.

22. Differentiate between characteristics of yeasts and molds, and define fungal spores.

23. Classify types of fungal spores and explain their functions.

24. Discuss the main features of fungal classification and representative examples of each group.

25. Explain how fungi are identified.

26. Discuss the importance of fungi in ecology, agriculture, commerce, and medicine.

The position of the **fungi*** in the biological world has been debated for many years. They were originally classified with the green plants (along with algae and bacteria), and later they were placed in a group with algae and protozoa (the Protista). Even at that time, however, many microbiologists were struck by several unique qualities of fungi that warranted placement into a separate kingdom. Confirmation of their status by genetic testing eliminated any question that they belong in a kingdom of their own.

The **Kingdom Fungi,** or **Eumycota,** is filled with organisms of great variety and complexity that have survived on earth for approximately 650 million years. About 100,000 species are known, although experts estimate a count much higher than this—perhaps even 1.5 million different types. For practical purposes, mycologists divide the fungi into two groups: the *macroscopic fungi* (mushrooms, puffballs, gill fungi) and the *microscopic fungi* (molds, yeasts). Although the majority of fungi are either unicellular or colonial, a few complex forms such as mushrooms and puffballs are considered multicellular.

Chemical traits of fungal cells include the possession of a polysaccharide, **chitin,** in their cell walls and the sterol, ergosterol, in their cell membranes. Cells of the microscopic fungi exist in two basic morphological types: hyphae and yeasts. **Hyphae*** are long, threadlike cells that make up the bodies of filamentous fungi, or **molds (figure 5.14).** A **yeast** cell is distinguished by its round to oval shape and by its mode of asexual reproduction. It grows swellings on its surface called buds, which then become separate cells

* *fungi* (fun′-jy) sing. fungus; Gr. *fungos,* mushroom.
* *hypha* (hy′-fuh) pl. hyphae (hy′-fee); Gr. *hyphe,* a web.

(figure 5.15a). Some species form a **pseudohypha,*** a chain of yeasts formed when buds remain attached in a row **(figure 5.15c).** Because of its manner of formation, it is not a true hypha like that of molds. Although some fungal cells exist only in a yeast form and others occur primarily as hyphae, a few, called **dimorphic,*** can take either form, depending upon growth conditions, such as changing temperature. This variability in growth form is particularly characteristic of some pathogenic molds.

Fungal Nutrition

All fungi are **heterotrophic.*** They acquire nutrients from a wide variety of organic sources or **substrates (figure 5.16).** Most fungi are **saprobes,*** meaning that they obtain these substrates from the remnants of dead plants and animals in soil or aquatic habitats. Fungi can also be parasites on the bodies of living animals or plants, although very few fungi absolutely require a living host. In general, the fungus penetrates the substrate and secretes enzymes that reduce it to small molecules that can be absorbed. Fungi have enzymes for digesting an incredible array of substances, including feathers, hair, cellulose, petroleum products, wood, even rubber. It is likely that every naturally occurring organic material on the earth can be attacked by some type of fungus.

* *pseudohypha* (soo″-doh-hy′-fuh) pl. pseudohyphae; Gr. *pseudo,* false, and *hyphe.*
* *dimorphic* (dy-mor′-fik) Gr. *di,* two, and *morphe,* form.
* *heterotrophic* (het-ur-oh-tro′-fik) Gr. *hetero,* other, and *troph,* to feed. A type of nutrition that relies on an organic nutrient source.
* *saprobe* (sap′-rohb) Gr. *sapros,* rotten, and *bios,* to live. Also called saprotroph or saprophyte.

(a)

(b)

Septum

(c) As in *Penicillium*

Septa
Septate hyphae
Septum with pores
Nucleus

Nonseptate hyphae
Nuclei

As in *Rhizopus*

Figure 5.14 Macroscopic and microscopic views of molds.
(a) A container of food (left too long in the refrigerator) has developed a miniature forest of mold colonies. Note the various textures of mycelia and the array of color differences due to spores. **(b)** Close-up of hyphal structure (1,200×). **(c)** Basic structural types of hyphae. The septate hyphae develop small pores that allow communication between cells. Nonseptate hyphae lack septa and are single, long multinucleate cells.

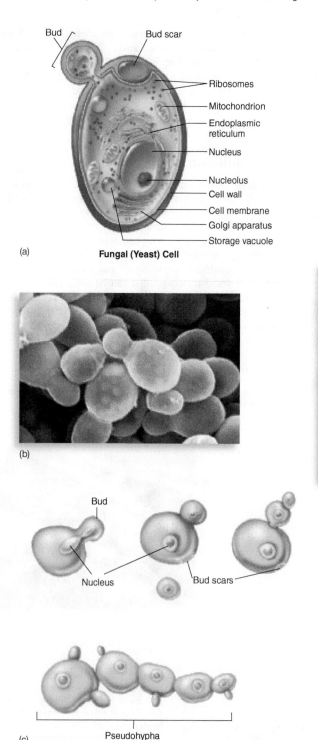

(a)

Fungal (Yeast) Cell

(b)

Bud

Nucleus

Bud scars

(c)

Pseudohypha

Figure 5.15 **Microscopic morphology of yeasts. (a)** General structure of a yeast cell, representing major organelles. Note the presence of a cell wall and lack of locomotor organelles. **(b)** Scanning electron micrograph of *Malassezia furfur*, a yeast that causes a type of superficial skin infection (25,000×). **(c)** Formation and release of yeast buds and pseudohypha (a chain of budding yeast cells).

(a)

(b)

Figure 5.16 **Nutritional sources (substrates) for fungi. (a)** *Penicillium notatum* mold, a very common decomposer of citrus fruit, is known for its velvety texture and typical blue-green color. Microscopic inset shows the brush arrangement of *Penicillium* phialospores (220×), the asexual phase. **(b)** The appearance of athlete's foot, an infection caused by *Trichophyton rubrum*. The inset is a 1,000× magnification revealing its hyphae (blue) and conidia (brown). septate hyphae and conidia.

Fungi are often found in nutritionally poor or adverse environments. Various fungal types thrive in substrates with higher salt, sugar, or acid content, at relatively high temperatures, and even in snow and glaciers.

The medical and agricultural impact of fungi is extensive. A number of species cause **mycoses** (fungal infections) in animals, and thousands of species are important plant pathogens. Fungal toxins may cause disease in humans, and airborne fungi are a frequent cause of allergies and other medical conditions (**5.1 Secret World of Microbes**).

Organization of Microscopic Fungi

The cells of most microscopic fungi grow in loose associations or colonies. The colonies of yeasts are much like those of bacteria in

5.1 Secret World of Microbes

Fungi: A Force of Nature

Life in the Fungal Jungle

Fungi are among the most prolific microbes on earth. So dominant are they that, by one estimate, the average topsoil contains nearly 9 tons of fungal mycelia per acre. In this habitat, they associate with a wide variety of other organisms, from bacteria to animals to plants.

The activities of fungi under natural conditions include nutritional and protective interactions with plants and algae, decomposition of organic matter and recycling of the minerals it contains, and contributions to biofilm networks that are needed to successfully colonize new habitats.

Some fungi have developed into normal residents of plants called endophytes. These fungi live inside the tissues of the plant itself and protect it against disease, presumably by secreting chemicals that deter infections by other pathogenic fungi. Understanding the roles of endophytes promises to open up a new field of biological control to inoculate plants with harmless fungi rather than using more toxic fungicides.

Lichens are unusual hybrid organisms that form when a fungus combines with a photosynthetic microbe, either an alga or cyanobacterium. The fungus acquires nutrients from its smaller partner and probably provides a protective haven that favors survival of the lichen body. Lichens occur in most habitats on earth, but they are especially important as early invaders of rock and in soil formation. Fungi also interact with animals in their habitats, most notably with small roundworms, called nematodes, and insects. Several species of molds prey upon or parasitize nematodes.

Is There a Fungus in the House?

The fact that fungi are so widespread also means that they frequently share human living quarters, especially in locations that provide ample moisture and nutrients. Often their presence is harmless and limited to a film of mildew on shower stalls or in other moist environments.

In some cases, depending on the amount of contamination and the type of mold, these indoor fungi can also give rise to various medical problems. Such common air contaminants as *Aspergillus, Cladosporium,* and *Stachybotrys* all have the capacity to give off airborne spores and toxins that, when inhaled, cause a whole spectrum of symptoms sometimes referred to as "sick

Mycelium and spores in the ascomycete *Stachybotrys.* This black mold (400×) is implicated in building contamination that leads to toxic diseases.

A little brown bat suffering from white nose syndrome. Note the fungus on the snout, wings, and body.

building syndrome." The usual source of harmful fungi is the presence of chronically water-damaged walls, ceilings, and other building materials that have come to harbor these fungi. People exposed to these houses or buildings report symptoms that range from skin rash, flulike reactions, sore throat, and headaches to fatigue, diarrhea, allergies, and immune suppression.

Bat Populations Decimated by Fungal Infections

Starting in 2007, wildlife personnel and others began reporting mass deaths of bats in caves throughout the Northeast and some parts of the southern United States. At first, the cause was not clear, but workers had observed a whitish growth on the muzzle of the dead bats and called the condition "white nose syndrome." Closer inspection revealed that the white growth was *Geomyces,* a newly recognized fungal pathogen that inhabits the same caves where bats hibernate. The animals apparently became infected in the winter, and by spring, they were already dead or sick and dying. Up to 6 million bats have been killed—as high as 95% of some cave populations. Unfortunately, little can be done at this point, because the infection is spread from bat to bat and no viable treatment is possible.

What characteristics of fungi allow them to spread into such a wide variety of habitats? *Answer available at http://www.mhhe.com/talaro9*

that they have a soft, uniform texture and appearance. The colonies of filamentous fungi are noted for the striking cottony, hairy, or velvety textures that arise from their microscopic organization and morphology. The woven, intertwining mass of hyphae that makes up the body or colony of a mold is called a **mycelium.***

Although hyphae contain the usual eukaryotic organelles, they also have some unique organizational features. In most fungi, the hyphae are divided into segments by cross walls, or **septa,** a condition called septate (see figure 5.14*c*). The nature of the septa varies from solid partitions with no communication between the compartments to partial walls with small pores that

allow the flow of organelles and nutrients between adjacent compartments. Nonseptate hyphae consist of one long, continuous cell *not* divided into individual compartments by cross walls. With this construction, the cytoplasm and organelles move freely from one region to another, and each hyphal element can have several nuclei (see figure 5.14*c*).

Hyphae can also be classified according to their particular function. Vegetative hyphae (mycelia) are responsible for the visible mass of growth that appears on the surface of a food source and penetrates it to digest and absorb nutrients. During the development of a fungal colony, the vegetative hyphae give rise to structures called reproductive, or fertile, hyphae that branch off vegetative mycelium. These hyphae are responsible for the production of fungal

* *mycelium* (my′-see-lee-yum) pl. mycelia; Gr. *mykes,* root word for fungus.

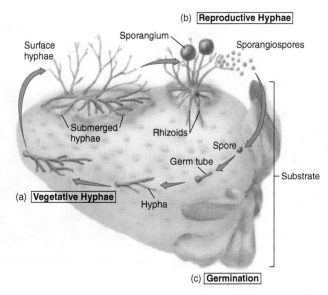

Figure 5.17 Functional types of hyphae using the mold
Rhizopus **as an example. (a)** Vegetative hyphae are those surface and submerged filaments that digest, absorb, and distribute nutrients from the substrate. This species also has special anchoring structures called rhizoids. **(b)** Later, as the mold matures, it sprouts reproductive hyphae that produce asexual spores called sporangiospores. **(c)** During the asexual life cycle, the free mold spores settle on a substrate and send out germ tubes that elongate into hyphae that produce an extensive mycelium. So prolific are the fungi that a single colony of mold can easily contain 5,000 spore-bearing structures. If each of these released 2,000 single spores and if every spore were able to germinate, we would soon find ourselves in a sea of mycelia. Most spores do not germinate, but enough are successful to keep the numbers of fungi and their spores very high in most habitats.

reproductive bodies called spores, discussed next. Other specializations of hyphae are illustrated in **figure 5.17.**

Reproductive Strategies and Spore Formation

Fungi have many complex and successful reproductive strategies. Most can propagate by the simple outward growth of existing hyphae or by fragmentation, in which a separated piece of mycelium can generate a whole new colony. But the primary reproductive mode of fungi involves the production of various types of **spores.** Do not confuse fungal spores with the extremely resistant, nonreproductive bacterial endospores. Fungal spores function not only in multiplication but also in survival, providing genetic variation, and dissemination. Because of their compactness and relatively light weight, fungal spores are dispersed widely through the environment by air, water, and living things. Upon encountering a favorable substrate, a spore will germinate and produce a new fungus colony in a very short time (figure 5.17).

The fungi exhibit such a marked diversity in spores that they are largely classified and identified by their spores and spore-forming structures. Although there are some elaborate systems for naming and classifying spores, we present only a basic overview of the principal types. The most general subdivision is based on the way the spores arise. Asexual spores are the products of mitotic division of a

single parent cell, and sexual spores are formed through a process involving the fusing of two parental nuclei followed by meiosis.

Asexual Spore Formation

On the basis of the nature of the reproductive hypha and the manner in which the spores originate, there are two subtypes of asexual spore (**figure 5.18**):

1. **Sporangiospores (figure 5.18*a*)** are formed by successive cleavages within a saclike head called a **sporangium,*** which is attached to a stalk, the sporangiophore. These spores are initially enclosed but are released when the sporangium ruptures. Some sporangiospores are the end result of the sexual phase of the life cycle as seen in figure 5.19.

2. **Conidia*** (conidiospores) are free spores not enclosed by a spore-bearing sac (**figure 5.18*b*).** They develop either by pinching off the tip of a special fertile hypha or by segmentation of a preexisting vegetative hypha. Conidia are the most common asexual spores, and they occur in these forms:

arthrospore (ar′-thro-spor) Gr. *arthron*, joint. A rectangular spore formed when a septate hypha fragments at the cross walls.

chlamydospore (klam-ih′-doh-spor) Gr. *chlamys*, cloak. A spherical conidium formed by the thickening of a hyphal cell. It is released when the surrounding hypha fractures, and it serves as a survival or resting cell.

blastospore. A spore produced by budding from a parent cell that is a yeast or another conidium; also called a bud.

phialospore (fy′-ah-lo-spor) Gr. *phialos*, a vessel. A conidium budded from the mouth of a vase-shaped spore-bearing cell called a phialide or *sterigma*, leaving a small collar.

microconidium and *macroconidium*. The smaller and larger conidia formed by the same fungus under varying conditions. Microconidia are one-celled, and macroconidia have two or more cells.

porospore. A conidium that grows out through small pores in the spore-bearing cell; some are composed of several cells.

Sexual Spore Formation

Because fungi can propagate successfully by producing millions of asexual spores, it is natural to wonder about the survival potential of sexual spores. The answer lies in important variations that occur when fungi of different genetic makeup combine their genetic material. As in plants and animals, a union of genes from two parents creates offspring with combinations of genes different from that of either parent. The offspring from such a union can have slight variations in form and function that are potentially advantageous to the adaptation and evolution of their species.

The majority of fungi produce sexual spores at some point. The nature of this process varies from the simple fusion of fertile hyphae of two different strains to a complex union of differentiated male and female structures and the development of special fruiting structures. We consider the three most common sexual spores:

* *sporangium* (spo-ran′-jee-um) pl. sporangia; Gr. *sporos*, seed, and *angeion*, vessel.
* *conidia* (koh-nid′-ee-uh) sing. conidium; Gr. *konidion*, a particle of dust.

Figure 5.18 Types of asexual mold spores. (a) Sporangiospores: (1) *Absidia*, (2) *Syncephalastrum*, (table 5.3) **(b)** Conidia: (1) arthrospores (e.g., *Coccidioides*), (2) chlamydospores and blastospores (e.g., *Candida albicans*), (3) phialospores (e.g., *Aspergillus*, table 5.3), (4) macroconidia and microconidia (e.g., *Microsporum*, table 5.3), and (5) porospores (e.g., *Alternaria*).

zygospores, ascospores, and basidiospores. These spore types provide an important basis for classifying the major fungal divisions.

Zygospores* are sturdy diploid spores formed when hyphae of two opposite strains (called the plus and minus strains) fuse and create a diploid zygote that swells and becomes covered by strong, spiny walls **(figure 5.19).** When its wall is disrupted and moisture and nutrient conditions are suitable, the zygospore germinates and forms a mycelium that gives rise to a sporangium. Meiosis of diploid cells of the sporangium results in haploid nuclei that

* *zygospores* (zy'-goh-sporz) Gr. *zygon,* yoke, to join.

Figure 5.19 Formation of zygospores in *Rhizopus stolonifer.* Sexual reproduction occurs when two mating strains of hyphae grow together, fuse, and form a mature diploid zygospore. Germination of the zygospore involves production of a haploid sporangium that looks just like the asexual one shown in figure 5.18, but the individual spores contain genes from two different parents. So, in this case, the sporangiospores are the result of sexual recombination.

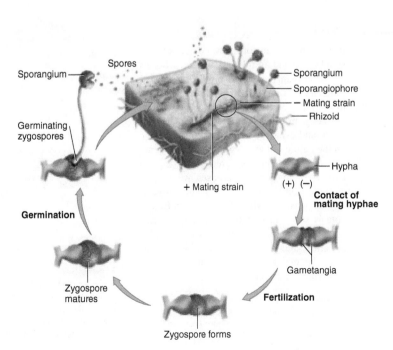

develop into sporangiospores. Both the sporangia and the sporangiospores that arise from sexual processes are outwardly identical to the asexual type, but because the spores arose from the union of two separate fungal parents, they are not genetically identical.

In general, haploid spores called **ascospores*** are created inside a special fungal sac, or **ascus** (pl. asci) (**figure 5.20**). Although details can vary among types of fungi, the ascus and ascospores are formed when two different strains or sexes join together to produce offspring. In many species, the male sexual organ fuses with the female sexual organ. The end result is a number of terminal cells called *dikaryons,* each containing a diploid nucleus. Through differentiation, each of these cells enlarges to form an ascus, and its diploid nucleus undergoes meiosis (often followed by mitosis) to form four to eight haploid nuclei that will mature into ascospores. A ripe ascus breaks open and releases the ascospores. Some species form an elaborate fruiting body to hold the asci (inset, figure 5.20).

Basidiospores* are haploid sexual spores formed on the outside of a club-shaped cell called a **basidium (figure 5.21)**. In general, spore formation follows the same pattern of two mating types coming together, fusing, and forming terminal cells with diploid nuclei. Each of these cells becomes a basidium, and its nucleus produces, through meiosis, four haploid nuclei. These nuclei are extruded through the top of the basidium, where they develop into basidiospores. Notice the location of the basidia along the gills in mushrooms, which are often dark from the spores they contain. It may be a surprise to discover that the fleshy part of a mushroom is actually a fruiting body designed to protect and help disseminate its sexual spores.

Fungal Classification

It is often difficult for microbiologists to assign logical and useful classification schemes to microorganisms that also reflect their evolutionary relationships. This difficulty is due to the fact that the organisms do not always perfectly fit the neat categories made for them, and even experts cannot always agree on the nature of the categories. The fungi are no exception, and there are several ways to classify them. For our purposes, we adopt a classification scheme with a medical mycology emphasis, in which the Kingdom Eumycota is subdivided into several phyla based upon the type of sexual reproduction, hyphal structure, and genetic profile. **Table 5.3** outlines the major phyla, their characteristics, and typical members.

* *ascospores* (as'-koh-sporz) Gr. *ascos,* a sac.
* *basidiospores* (bah-sid'-ee-oh-sporz) Gr. *basidi,* a pedestal.

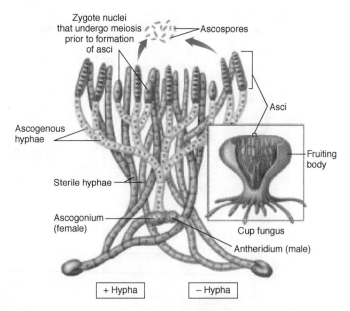

Figure 5.20 **Production of ascospores in a cup fungus.** Inset shows the cup-shaped fruiting body that houses the asci.

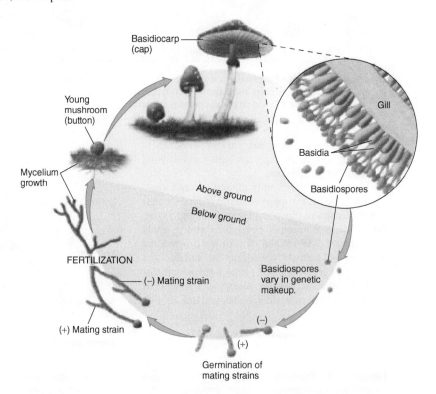

Figure 5.21 **The cycle of sexual spore formation in basidiomycota.** A mushroom is one example to observe formation of the sexual spores. Following mating between parental hyphae underground, the mycelium gives rise to the fruiting body that we commonly identify as a mushroom. Under the cap are gills bearing club-shaped basidia which form and release basidiospores. Because they are genetically-different, these basidiospores produce different parental hyphae that begin the cycle again.

TABLE 5.3	**A Survey of Fungal Groups, Characteristics, and Representative Members**

Phylum I—Zygomycota (also Zygomycetes)

- Sexual spores: zygospores
- Asexual spores: mostly sporangiospores, some conidia
- Hyphae are usually nonseptate. If septate, the septa are complete
- Most species are free-living saprobes; some are animal parasites
- Can be obnoxious contaminants in the laboratory, food spoilage agents, and destructive to crops
- Examples of common molds: *Rhizopus,* a black bread mold; *Mucor; Absidia; Circinella* (**figure A,** *Syncephalastrum,* and **figure B,** *Circinella*)

A. *Syncephalastrum,* a common inhabitant of soil and plants (400×)

B. A beautiful mold, *Circinella* is known for its curved sporangiophore (500×)

Phylum II—Ascomycota (also Ascomycetes)

- Sexual spores: most produce ascospores in asci
- Asexual spores: many types of conidia, formed at the tips of conidiophores
- Hyphae with porous septa
- Examples: This is by far the largest phylum. Members vary from macroscopic mushrooms to microscopic molds and yeasts.
 - *Penicillium* is one source of antibiotics (see figure 5.16).
 - *Aspergillus* is a common airborne mold that may be involved in respiratory infections and toxicity (**figure C).**
 - *Saccharomyces* is a yeast used in making bread and beer (**figure D).**
 - Includes many human and plant pathogens, such as *Pneumocystis (carinii) jiroveci,* a pathogen of AIDS patients.
 - *Histoplasma* is the cause of Ohio Valley fever (see figure 1.3).
 - *Microsporum* is one cause of ringworm, which is a common name for certain fungal skin infections that often grow in a ringed pattern (see figure 22.18).
 - *Coccidioides immitis* is the cause of Valley fever; *Candida albicans* is the cause of various yeast infections; and *Stachybotrys* is a toxic mold (see 5.1 Secret World of Microbes).

C. *Aspergillus fumigatus,* displaying its flowery conidial heads (600×)

D. X-ray photograph of *Saccharomyces* with a prominent nucleus (blue sphere) and bud (5,000×)

Phylum III—Basidiomycota (also Basidiomycetes)

Many members are familiar macroscopic forms such as mushrooms and puffballs, but this phylum also includes a number of microscopic plant pathogens called rusts and smuts that attack and destroy major crops, This has extensive impact on agriculture and global food production.

- Sexual reproduction by means of basidia and basidiospores
- Asexual spores: conidia
- Incompletely septate hyphae
- Some plant parasites and one human pathogen
- Fleshy fruiting bodies are common.
- Examples: mushrooms (**figure E**), puffballs, bracket fungi, and plant pathogens (rusts and smuts)
- The one human pathogen, the yeast *Cryptococcus neoformans,* causes an invasive systemic infection in several organs, including the skin, brain, and lungs (**figure F**).

E. *Armillaria* (honey) mushrooms, sprouting from the base of a tree, arose from a vast underground mycelium that covers 2,200 acres and stretches 3.5 miles across.

F. *Cryptococcus neoformans—* a yeast that causes cryptococcosis (400×). Note the capsule around each cell.

Phylum IV—Chytridimycota

Members of this phylum are unusual, primitive fungi commonly called **chytrids.*** Their cellular morphology ranges from single cells to clusters and colonies. They generally do not form hyphae or yeast-type cells. The one feature that most characterizes them is the presence of special flagellated spores, called zoospores and gametes. Most chytrids are saprobic and free-living in soil, water, and decaying matter. A significant number are parasites of plants, animals, and other microbes (**figure G**), but they are not known to cause human disease. They are known to be serious frog pathogens, often responsible for destroying whole populations in some habitats.

G. Parasitic chytrid fungi. The filamentous diatom *Chaetoceros* is attacked by flagellated chytrids that dissolve and destroy their host (400×).

* *chytrid* (kit′-rid) Gr. *chytridion,* little pot.

Fungi That Produce Only Asexual Spores (Imperfect)

From the beginnings of fungal classification, any fungus that lacked a sexual state was called "imperfect" and was placed in a catchall category, the Fungi Imperfecti. A species would remain classified in that category until its sexual state was described. Gradually, many species were found to make sexual spores, and they were assigned to the taxonomic grouping that best fit those spores. In other cases, they have been reassigned because genetic analysis indicated they belonged to an established phylum, usually to Ascomycota. This means that there is really no need for the "imperfect" taxon.

Fungal Identification and Cultivation

Fungi are identified in medical specimens by first being isolated on special types of media and then being observed macroscopically and microscopically. Examples of media for cultivating fungi are cornmeal, blood, and Sabouraud's agar. The latter medium is useful in isolating fungi from mixed samples because of its low pH, which inhibits the growth of bacteria but not of most fungi. Because the fungi are classified into general groups by the presence and type of sexual spores, it would seem logical to identify them in the same way, but sexual spores are rarely if ever demonstrated in the laboratory setting. As a result, the asexual spore-forming structures and spores are usually used to identify organisms to the level of genus and species. Other characteristics that contribute to identification are hyphal type, colony texture and pigmentation, physiological characteristics, and genetic makeup.

Fungi in Medicine, Nature, and Industry

Nearly all fungi are free-living and do not require a host to complete their life cycles. Even among those fungi that are pathogenic, most human infection occurs through accidental contact with an environmental source such as soil, water, or dust. Humans are generally quite resistant to fungal infection, except for two main types of fungal pathogens: the primary pathogens, which can infect even healthy persons, and the opportunistic pathogens, which attack persons who are already weakened in some way.

Mycoses (fungal infections) vary in the way the agent enters the body and the degree of tissue involvement **(table 5.4).** The list of opportunistic fungal pathogens has been increasing in the past few years because of newer medical techniques that keep immunocompromised patients alive. Even so-called harmless species found in the air and dust around us may be able to cause opportunistic infections in patients who already have AIDS, cancer, or diabetes.

Fungi are involved in other medical conditions besides infections. Fungal cell walls give off chemical substances that can cause allergies. The toxins produced by poisonous mushrooms can induce neurological disturbances and even death. The mold *Aspergillus flavus* synthesizes a potentially lethal poison called aflatoxin,[4]

4. From **aspergillus, flavus, toxin.**

CLINICAL CONNECTIONS

An Outbreak of Fungal Meningitis

Most fungi are not invasive and do not ordinarily cause serious infections unless a patient's immune system is compromised or the fungus is accidentally introduced into sterile tissues. In 2012, we witnessed how a simple medical procedure could turn into a medical nightmare because a common, mostly harmless fungus got into the wrong place at the wrong time. It all started when a small compounding pharmacy in Massachusetts unknowingly sent out hundreds of mold-contaminated medication vials to medical facilities for injections to control pain. These vials were sent to 23 states and used to inject the drug into the spinal column or joints of around 14,000 patients. By the time any problems were reported, several hundred cases of infection had occurred, half of which settled in the meninges. The most drastic outcome was the deaths of 39 patients from complications of meningitis. After months of investigation, the CDC isolated a black mold, *Exserohilum rostratum*, from both the patients and drug vials.

This mold resides in plants and soil, from which it spreads into the air and many human habitats. But it is not considered a human pathogen, and infections with it are very rare. Examination of the compounding facility uncovered negligence and poor quality control, along with dirty preparation rooms. Mold spores were introduced during filling of the vials, and because the medication lacked preservatives, they survived and grew.

This case drives home several important facts about fungi: (1) They can grow rapidly even in low nutrient environments; (2) just a single spore introduced into a sterile environment, whether it is a vial of medicine or the human body, can easily multiply into millions of fungal cells; and (3) even supposedly "harmless" fungi are often opportunistic, meaning that they will infect tissues "if given an opportunity." This case also emphasizes the need for zero tolerance for microbes of any kind in a drug that is being injected—such a procedure demands sterility. When you think of it, the patients were actually being inoculated in a way that assured the development of serious mycoses.

Explain how a supposedly harmless, airborne mold could get all the way into the brain and cause meningitis. *Answer available at http://www.mhhe.com/talaro9*

which is the cause of a disease in domestic animals that have eaten grain contaminated with the mold and is also a cause of liver cancer in humans.

Fungi pose an ever-present economic hindrance to the agricultural industry. A number of species are pathogenic to field plants such as corn and grain, and fungi also rot fresh produce during shipping and storage. It has been estimated that as much as 40% of the yearly fruit crop is consumed not by humans but by fungi.

On the beneficial side, however, fungi play an essential role in decomposing organic matter and returning essential minerals to the soil. They form stable associations with plant roots (mycorrhizae) that increase the ability of the roots to absorb water and nutrients. Industry has tapped the biochemical potential of fungi to produce large quantities of antibiotics, alcohol, organic acids, and vitamins. Some fungi are eaten or used to impart flavorings to food. The yeast *Saccharomyces* produces the alcohol in beer and

TABLE 5.4	Major Fungal Infections of Humans	
Degree of Tissue Involvement and Area Affected	**Name of Infection**	**Name of Causative Fungus**
Superficial (not deeply invasive)		
Outer epidermis	Tinea versicolor	*Malassezia furfur*
Epidermis, hair, and dermis can be attacked	Dermatophytosis, also called tinea or ringworm of the scalp, body, feet (athlete's foot), toenails	*Microsporum, Trichophyton,* and *Epidermophyton*
Mucous membranes, skin, nail	Candidiasis, or yeast infection	*Candida albicans**
Systemic (deep; organism enters lungs; can invade other organs)		
Lung	Coccidioidomycosis (San Joaquin Valley fever)	*Coccidioides immitis*
	North American blastomycosis (Chicago disease)	*Blastomyces dermatitidis*
	Histoplasmosis (Ohio Valley fever)	*Histoplasma capsulatum*
	Cryptococcosis (torulosis)	*Cryptococcus neoformans*
Lung, skin	Paracoccidioidomycosis (South American blastomycosis)	*Paracoccidioides brasiliensis*

*This fungus can cause severe, invasive systemic infections in patients with cancer, AIDS, or other debilitating diseases.

wine and the gas that causes bread to rise. Blue cheeses, soy sauce, and cured meats derive their unique flavors from the actions of fungi.

 Check Your Progress SECTIONS 5.4 AND 5.5

15. Review the major differences and similarities between prokaryotic and eukaryotic cells.

16. Compare the structures of yeast and hyphal cells and differentiate between yeasts and molds.

17. Tell how fungi obtain nutrients, and in what habitats one would expect to find them.

18. Describe the two main types of asexual fungal spores and how they are formed. Name several types of conidia.

19. Describe the three main types of sexual spores, and construct a simple diagram to show how each is formed.

20. Explain general features of fungal classification, give examples of the four fungal phyla, and describe their structure and significance.

21. Define the term mycosis and explain the levels of invasion of the body by fungi.

5.6 Survey of Protists: Algae

 Expected Learning Outcomes

27. Discuss the major characteristics of algae, and explain how they are classified.

28. Describe several ways that algae are important microorganisms.

Even though the terms *algae* and *protozoa* do not have taxonomic status, they are still scientifically useful. These are terms, like *protist,* that provide a shorthand label for certain eukaryotes. Microbiologists use such general terms to reference organisms that possess a collection of predictable characteristics. For example, protozoa are considered unicellular eukaryotic protists that lack tissues and share similarities in cell structure, nutrition, life cycles, and biochemistry. They are all microorganisms, and most of them are motile. Algae are eukaryotic protists, usually unicellular or colonial, that photosynthesize with chlorophyll *a*. They lack vascular systems for transport and have simple reproductive structures.

The Algae: Photosynthetic Protists

The **algae** are a group of photosynthetic organisms most readily recognized by their larger members, such as seaweeds and kelps. In addition to being beautifully colored and diverse in appearance, they vary in length from a few micrometers to 100 meters. Algae occur in unicellular, colonial, and filamentous forms, and the larger forms can possess tissues and simple organs. Examples of algal forms are shown in **figure 5.22** and **table 5.5.** An algal cell exhibits most of the organelles (**figure 5.22***a***).** The most noticeable of these are the chloroplasts, which contain, in addition to the green pigment chlorophyll, a number of other pigments that create the yellow, red, and brown coloration of some groups.

Algae are widespread inhabitants of fresh and marine waters. They are one of the main components of the large floating community of microscopic organisms called **plankton.** In this capacity, they play an essential role in the aquatic food web and contribute significantly to the oxygen content of the atmosphere through photosynthesis. One of the most prevalent groups on earth are single-celled chrysophyta called *diatoms* (**figure 5.22***b***).** These beautiful algae have silicate cell walls and golden pigment in their chloroplasts.

Quick Search
Find the video "Brink: Algae to Oil" on the Science Channel to learn about a new source of "green" products.

Other algal habitats include the surface of soil, rocks, and plants; and several species are even hardy enough to live in hot springs or snowbanks. A desert-adapted green alga blooms during spring rains and survives by forming resistant spores (**figure 5.22***c, d***).**

Animal tissues would be rather inhospitable to algae, so algae are rarely infectious. One exception, *Prototheca,* is an unusual nonphotosynthetic alga associated with skin and subcutaneous infections in humans and animals.

The primary medical threat from algae is due to a type of food poisoning caused by the toxins of marine algae such as dinoflagellates.

(a) Algal Cell

Ribosomes
Flagellum
Mitochondrion
Nucleus
Nucleolus
Chloroplast
Golgi apparatus
Cytoplasm
Cell membrane
Starch vacuoles
Cell wall

(b)

(c)

(d)

Figure 5.22 **Representative microscopic algae. (a)** Structure of *Chlamydomonas,* a motile green alga, indicating major organelles. **(b)** A strew of beautiful algae called diatoms shows the intricate and varied structure of their silica cell wall. **(c)** A member of the Chlorophyta, *Oedogonium,* displaying its green filaments and reproductive structures, including eggs (clear spheres) and zygotes (dark spheres) (200✕). **(d)** Spring pond with mixed algal bloom. Active photosynthesis and oxygen release are evident in surface bubbles.

TABLE 5.5	Summary of Algal Characteristics			
Division/Common Name	**Organization**	**Cell Wall**	**Pigmentation**	**Ecology/Importance**
Euglenophyta (euglenids)	Mainly unicellular, motile by flagella	None, pellicle instead	Chlorophyll, carotenoids, xanthophyll	Some are close relatives of Mastigophora
Pyrrophyta (dinoflagellates)	Unicellular, dual flagella	Cellulose or atypical wall	Chlorophyll, carotenoids	Cause of "red tide"
Chrysophyta (diatoms or golden-brown algae)	Mainly unicellular, some filamentous forms, unusual form of motility	Silicon dioxide	Chlorophyll, fucoxanthin	Diatomaceous earth, major component of plankton
Phaeophyta (brown algae—kelps)	Multicellular, vascular system, holdfasts	Cellulose, alginic acid	Chlorophyll, carotenoids, fucoxanthin	Source of an emulsifier, alginate
Rhodophyta (red seaweeds)	Multicellular	Cellulose	Chlorophyll, carotenoids, xanthophyll, phycobilin	Source of agar and carrageenan, a food additive
Chlorophyta (green algae, grouped with plants)	Varies from unicellular, colonial, filamentous, to multicellular	Cellulose	Chlorophyll, carotenoids, xanthophyll	Precursor of higher plants

During particular seasons of the year, the overgrowth of these motile algae imparts a brilliant red color to the water, which is referred to as a "red tide" (see figure 26.16). When intertidal animals feed, their bodies accumulate toxins given off by the algae that can persist for several months. Paralytic shellfish poisoning is caused by eating exposed clams or other invertebrates. It is marked by severe neurological symptoms and can be fatal. Ciguatera is a serious intoxication caused by algal toxins that have accumulated in fish such as bass and mackerel. Cooking does not destroy the toxin, and there is no antidote.

Several episodes of a severe infection caused by *Pfiesteria piscicida,* a toxic algal form, have been reported over the past several years in the United States. The disease was first reported in fish and was later transmitted to humans. This newly identified species occurs in at least 20 forms, including spores, cysts, and amoebas, that can release potent toxins. Both fish and humans develop neurological symptoms and bloody skin lesions. The cause of the epidemic has been traced to nutrient-rich agricultural runoff water that promoted the sudden "bloom" of *Pfiesteria.* These microbes first attacked and killed millions of fish and later people whose occupations exposed them to fish and contaminated water.

5.7 Survey of Protists: Protozoa

 Expected Learning Outcomes

29. Summarize the main characteristics of protozoan form, nutrition, and locomotion.

30. Describe the general life cycle and mode of reproduction in protozoans.

31. Explain how protozoans are identified and classified.

32. Outline a classification scheme for protozoans, and provide examples of important members of each group.

33. Explain some biological properties of parasites, and list some common protozoan pathogens.

If a poll were taken to choose the most engrossing and vivid group of microorganisms, many biologists would choose the protozoa. Although their name comes from the Greek for "first animals," they are far from being simple, primitive organisms. The protozoa constitute a diverse large group (about 65,000 known species) of single-celled creatures that display startling properties when it comes to movement, feeding, and behavior. Although most members of this group are harmless, free-living inhabitants of water and soil, a few species are parasites collectively responsible for hundreds of millions of infections of humans each year.

Protozoan Form and Function

Most protozoan cells are single cells containing the major eukaryotic organelles except chloroplasts. Their organelles can be highly specialized for feeding, reproduction, and locomotion. The cytoplasm is usually divided into a clear outer layer called the **ectoplasm** and a granular inner region called the *endoplasm*. Ectoplasm is involved in locomotion, feeding, and protection. Endoplasm houses the nucleus, mitochondria, and food and contractile vacuoles. Some ciliates and flagellates[5] even have organelles that work somewhat like a primitive nervous system to coordinate movement. Because protozoa lack a cell wall, they have a certain amount of flexibility. Their outer boundary is a cell membrane that regulates the movement of food, wastes, and secretions. Cell shape can remain constant (as in most ciliates) or can change constantly (as in amoebas). Certain amoebas (foraminiferans) encase themselves in hard shells made of calcium carbonate. The size of most protozoan cells falls within the range of 3 to 300 μm. Some notable exceptions are giant amoebas and ciliates that are large enough (3–4 mm in length) to be seen swimming in pond water.

Nutritional and Habitat Range

Protozoa are heterotrophic and usually require their food in a complex organic form. Free-living species graze on live cells of bacteria and algae, and even scavenge dead plant or animal debris. Some species have special feeding structures such as oral grooves, which carry food particles into a passageway or gullet that packages the captured food into vacuoles for digestion. A remarkable feeding adaptation can be seen in the ciliate *Didinium* (see table 5.6, figure E), which can easily devour another microbe that is nearly its size. Some protozoa absorb food directly through the cell membrane. Parasitic species live on the fluids of their host, such as plasma and digestive juices, or they can actively feed on tissues.

Although protozoa have adapted to a wide range of habitats, their main limiting factor is the availability of moisture. Their predominant habitats are fresh and marine water, soil, plants, and animals. Even extremes in temperature and pH are not a barrier to their existence; hardy species are found in hot springs, ice, and habitats with low or high pH.

Styles of Locomotion

Except for one group (the Apicomplexa), protozoa are motile by means of **pseudopods** ("false foot"), **flagella,** or **cilia.** A few species have both pseudopods (also called pseudopodia) and flagella. Some unusual protozoa move by a gliding or twisting movement that does not appear to involve any of these locomotor structures. Pseudopods are blunt, branched, or long and pointed, depending on the particular species. The flowing action of the pseudopods results in amoeboid motion, and pseudopods also serve as feeding structures in many amoebas.

The structure and behavior of flagella and cilia were discussed in section 5.1. Flagella vary in number from one to several, and in certain species, they are attached along the length of the cell by an extension of the cytoplasmic membrane called the *undulating membrane* (see figure 5.26a). In most ciliates, the cilia are distributed over the surface of the cell in characteristic patterns. Because of the tremendous variety in ciliary arrangements and functions, ciliates are among the most diverse and awesome cells in the biological

5. The terms *ciliate* and *flagellate* are common names of protozoan groups that move by means of cilia and flagella.

world. In certain protozoa, cilia line the oral groove and function in feeding; in others, they fuse together to form stiff props that serve as primitive rows of walking legs.

Life Cycles and Reproduction

Most protozoa are recognized by a motile feeding stage called the **trophozoite*** that requires ample food and moisture to remain active. A large number of species are also capable of entering into a dormant, resting stage called a **cyst** when conditions in the environment become unfavorable for growth and feeding. During *encystment,* the trophozoite cell rounds up into a sphere, and its ectoplasm secretes a tough, thick cuticle around the cell membrane **(figure 5.23).** Because cysts are more resistant than ordinary cells to heat, drying, and chemicals, they can survive adverse periods. They can be dispersed by air currents and may even be an important factor in the spread of diseases such as amebic dysentery. If provided with moisture and nutrients, a cyst breaks open and releases the active trophozoite.

The life cycles of protozoans vary from simple to complex. Several protozoan groups exist only in the trophozoite state. Many alternate between a trophozoite and a cyst stage, depending on the conditions of the habitat. The life cycle of a parasitic protozoan dictates its mode of transmission to other hosts. For example, the flagellate *Trichomonas vaginalis* causes a common sexually transmitted infection. Because it does not form cysts, it is more delicate and must be transmitted by intimate contact between sexual partners. In contrast, intestinal pathogens such as

Entamoeba histolytica and *Giardia lamblia* form cysts and are readily transmitted in contaminated water and foods.

All protozoa reproduce by relatively simple, asexual methods, usually mitotic cell division. Several parasitic species, including the agents of malaria and toxoplasmosis, reproduce asexually inside a host cell by multiple fission. Sexual reproduction also occurs during the life cycle of most protozoa. Ciliates participate in **conjugation,** a form of genetic exchange in which members of two different mating types fuse temporarily and exchange nuclei. This process of sexual recombination yields new and different genetic combinations that can be advantageous in evolution.

Protozoan Identification and Cultivation

Taxonomists have not escaped problems classifying protozoa. They, too, are very diverse and frequently frustrate attempts to generalize or place them in neat groupings. We will use a simple system of four groups, based on method of motility, mode of reproduction, and stages in the life cycle.

The unique appearance of most protozoa makes it possible for a knowledgeable person to identify them to the level of genus and often species by microscopic morphology alone. Characteristics to consider in identification include the shape and size of the cell; the type, number, and distribution of locomotor structures; the presence of special organelles or cysts; and the number of nuclei. Medical specimens taken from blood, sputum, cerebrospinal fluid, feces, or the vagina are smeared directly onto a slide and observed with or without special stains. Occasionally, protozoa are cultivated on artificial media or in laboratory animals for further identification or study.

* *trophozoite* (trof′-oh-zoh′-yte) Gr. *trophonikos,* to nourish, and *zoon,* animal.

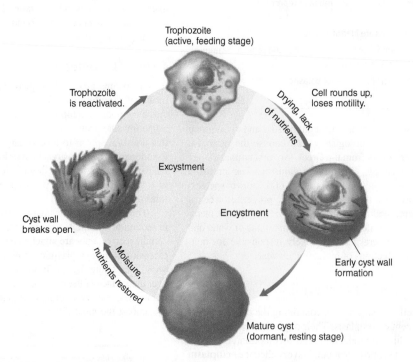

Trophozoite
(active, feeding stage)

Trophozoite
is reactivated.

Cell rounds up,
loses motility.

Drying, lack of nutrients

Excystment

Encystment

Cyst wall
breaks open.

Moisture, nutrients restored

Early cyst wall
formation

Mature cyst
(dormant, resting stage)

Figure 5.23 The general life cycle exhibited by many protozoa. All protozoa have a trophozoite form, but not all produce cysts.

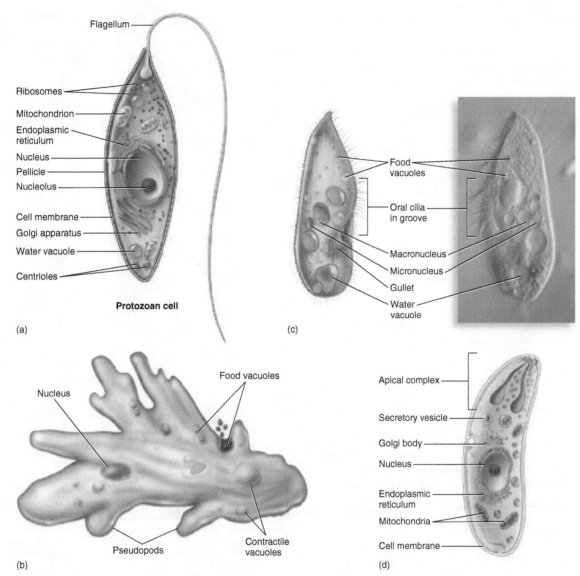

Flagellum

Ribosomes
Mitochondrion
Endoplasmic reticulum
Nucleus
Pellicle
Nucleolus

Cell membrane
Golgi apparatus
Water vacuole
Centrioles

Protozoan cell

(a)

Food vacuoles
Oral cilia in groove
Macronucleus
Micronucleus
Gullet
Water vacuole

(c)

Nucleus
Food vacuoles
Pseudopods
Contractile vacuoles

(b)

Apical complex
Secretory vesicle
Golgi body
Nucleus
Endoplasmic reticulum
Mitochondria
Cell membrane

(d)

Figure 5.24 Comparisons of the trophozoite structure of four Phyla of protozoa. (a) General structure of a mastigophoran such as *Peranema.* The outer pellicle is flexible and allows for some shape changing in this group. **(b) Structural appearance of a typical amoeba.** Pseudopods are active in both movement and feeding. **(c) Ciliate structure.** Image and artist's interpretation of the ciliate *Blepharisma,* a common inhabitant of pond water. Note the pattern of ciliary movement evident on the left side of the cell and the details of its internal structure. **(d) Apicomplexan trophozoite structure.** Apicomplexans have many of the usual protozoan organelles but also contain an unusual body, the apical complex, involved in feeding. Unlike other protozoa, they lack specialized motility organelles.

Classification of Selected Medically Important Protozoa

Most protozoa fit the basic morphology of one of four types of cells: the flagellated mastigophorans, the pseudopod-bearing amoebas, the ciliated ciliophorans, and the nonmotile apicomplexans. **Figure 5.24** depicts various aspects of these protozoan types. The overall taxonomy we are using here classifies the protozoa into four Phyla based on motility and other cell characteristics that are outlined with examples in **table 5.6.**

Important Protozoan Pathogens

Although protozoan infections are very common, they are actually caused by only a small number of species often restricted geographically to the tropics and subtropics **(table 5.7).** In this survey, we look at examples from two protozoan groups that illustrate some of the main features of protozoan diseases.

Quick Search
Look for "What Are Malaria Protozoa" on YouTube to learn about the most dominant parasitic protozoan.

TABLE 5.6 Selected Taxonomy of Protozoa, with Group Characteristics and Examples

The Mastigophora (Also Called Zoomastigophora)

- Motility is primarily by flagella alone or by both flagellar and amoeboid motion.
- Single nucleus
- Sexual reproduction, when present, by syngamy; division by longitudinal fission
- Several parasitic forms lack mitochondria and Golgi apparatus.
- Most species form cysts and are free-living; the group also includes several parasites
- Some species are found in loose aggregates or colonies, but most are solitary.
- Members include: *Trypanosoma* and *Leishmania*, important blood pathogens spread by insect vectors (see figure 5.26); *Giardia*, an intestinal parasite spread in water contaminated with feces (see **figure B**); *Trichomonas*, a parasite of the reproductive tract of humans spread by sexual contact (see figure 23.6)
- A large symbiont found in termites, *Trichonympha*, sprouts masses of flagella from its oral cavity (**figure A**)

A. *Trichonympha*—a common symbiotic flagellate in termite intestines, displaying numerous flagella (400×)

B. Trophozoite of *Giardia lamblia*—a widespread intestinal pathogen (2,000×)

The Sarcodina* (Amoebas)

- Cell form is primarily an amoeba (see figure 5.24*b*).
- Major locomotor organelles are pseudopods, although some species have flagellated reproductive states.
- Asexual reproduction by fission
- Mostly uninucleate; usually encyst
- Most amoebas are free-living and not infectious (**figure C**).
- *Entamoeba* is a parasite of humans (**figure D**).

C. *Polychaos*—a giant amoeba uses several pseudopods to feed on diatoms (100×)

D. Trophozoite of *Entamoeba histolytica*—the cause of amebic dysentery (1,000×)

The Ciliophora (Ciliates)

- Trophozoites are motile by cilia.
- Some have cilia in tufts for feeding and attachment; most develop cysts.
- Have both macronuclei and micronuclei; division by transverse fission
- Most have a definite mouth and feeding organelle.
- Show relatively advanced behavior (**figure E**)
- The majority of ciliates are free-living and harmless.
- One pathogen is *Balantidium* (**figure F**).

E. *Didinium* (predator, right)—preparing to attack and engulf *Paramecium* (prey, left) in an age-old ciliate struggle (1,200×)

F. *Balantidium coli*—a parasite of swine that can also cause intestinal infections in humans

The Apicomplexa (Sporozoa)

- Motility is absent in most cells except male gametes.
- Life cycles are complex, with well-developed asexual and sexual stages.
- Sporozoa produce special sporelike cells called **sporozoites*** (**figures G** and **H**) following sexual reproduction, which are important in transmission of infections.
- Most form thick-walled zygotes called oocysts; entire group is parasitic.
- *Plasmodium*, the most prevalent protozoan parasite, causes 100 million to 300 million cases of malaria each year worldwide. It is an intracellular parasite with a complex cycle alternating between humans and mosquitoes (figure H).
- *Toxoplasma gondii* causes an acute infection (toxoplasmosis) in humans, which is acquired from cats and other animals (see figure 23.16).
- *Cryptosporidium* is an emerging intestinal pathogen transmitted by contaminated water (see figure G).

Cytostome Food vacuoles Nucleus

G. Sporozoite of *Cryptosporidium*—a common water-borne pathogen

H. Sporozoite of *Plasmodium*—the agent of malaria, migrating through the gut of a mosquito

*Some biologists prefer to combine Mastigophora and Sarcodina into the phylum Sarcomastigophora. Because the algal group Euglenophyta has flagella, it may also be included in the Mastigophora.

* *sporozoite* (spor″-oh-zoh′-yte) Gr. *sporos*, seed, and *zoon*, animal.

CLINICAL CONNECTIONS

The Parasitic Way of Life

Protozoa are traditionally studied along with the helminths in the science of parasitology. Although a parasite is usually defined as an organism that obtains food and other requirements at the expense of a host, the term *parasite* is also used to denote protozoan and helminth pathogens. The range of host-parasite relationships can be very broad. At one extreme are the so-called "good" parasites, which occupy their host with little harm. An example is *Trichomonas tenax*, a flagellate found in the mouth that may infect and damage the gingiva in people with poor oral hygiene. At the other extreme are parasites (*Plasmodium, Trypanosoma*) that multiply in host tissues such as the blood or brain, causing severe damage and disease. Between these two extremes are parasites of varying pathogenicity, depending on their particular adaptations.

Most human parasites go through three general stages:

- The microbe is transmitted to the human host from a source such as soil, water, food, other humans, or animals.
- The microbe invades and multiplies in the host, producing more parasites that can infect other suitable hosts.
- The microbe leaves the host in large numbers by a specific means and must enter a new host to survive.

There are numerous variations on this theme. For instance, the microbe can invade more than one host species (alternate hosts) and undergo several changes as it cycles through these hosts, such as sexual reproduction or encystment. Some microbes are spread from human to human by means of **vectors,** * defined as animals such as insects that carry diseases. Others can be spread through bodily fluids and feces.

What correlation can be made between the geographic location of a parasite and its vector? *Answer available at http://www.mhhe.com/talaro9*

* *vector* (vek′-tur) L. *vectur,* one who carries.

Pathogenic Flagellates: Trypanosomes

Trypanosomes are protozoa belonging to the genus *Trypanosoma.** The two most important representatives are *T. brucei* and *T. cruzi,* species that are closely related but geographically restricted. *Trypanosoma brucei* occurs in Africa, where it causes an estimated 50,000 new cases of sleeping sickness each year. *Trypanosoma cruzi,* the cause of Chagas disease,[6] is endemic to South and Central America, where it infects several million people a year. Both species have long, crescent-shaped cells with a single flagellum that is sometimes attached to the cell body by an undulating membrane. Both occur in the blood during infection and are transmitted by blood-sucking vectors. We use *T. cruzi* to illustrate the phases of a trypanosomal life cycle and to demonstrate the complexity of parasitic relationships.

The trypanosome of Chagas disease relies on the close relationship of a warm-blooded mammal and an insect that feeds on mammalian blood. The mammalian hosts are numerous, including

* *Trypanosoma* (try″-pan-oh-soh′-mah) Gr. *Trypanon,* borer, and *soma,* body.
6. Named for Carlos Chagas, the discoverer of *T. cruzi.*

TABLE 5.7	Major Pathogenic Protozoa, Infections, and Primary Sources	
Protozoan/Disease		**Reservoir/Source**
Amoeboid Protozoa		
Amoebiasis: *Entamoeba histolytica*		Human/water and food
Brain infection: *Naegleria, Acanthamoeba*		Free-living in water
Ciliated Protozoa		
Balantidiosis: *Balantidium coli*		Zoonotic in pigs
Flagellated Protozoa		
Giardiasis: *Giardia lamblia*		Zoonotic/water and food
Trichomoniasis: *T. hominis, T. vaginalis*		Human
Hemoflagellates		
Trypanosomiasis: *Trypanosoma brucei, T. cruzi*		Zoonotic/vector-borne
Leishmaniasis: *Leishmania donovani, L. tropica, L. brasiliensis*		Zoonotic/vector-borne
Apicomplexan Protozoa		
Malaria: *Plasmodium vivax, P. falciparum, P. malariae*		Human/vector-borne
Toxoplasmosis: *Toxoplasma gondii*		Zoonotic/vector-borne
Cryptosporidiosis: *Cryptosporidium*		Free-living/water and food
Cyclosporiasis: *Cyclospora cayetanensis*		Water/fresh produce

dogs, cats, opossums, and armadillos. The vector is the *reduviid* * bug, an insect that is sometimes called the "kissing bug" because of its habit of biting its host at the corner of the mouth. Transmission occurs from bug to mammal and from mammal to bug but usually not from mammal to mammal, except across the placenta during pregnancy. The general phases of this cycle are presented in **figure 5.25.**

The trypanosome trophozoite multiplies in the intestinal tract of the reduviid bug and is harbored in the feces. The bug seeks a host and bites the mucous membranes, usually of the eye, nose, or lips, releasing the trypanosome in feces near the bite. Ironically, the victims themselves inadvertently contribute to the entry of the microbe by scratching the bite wound. Once in the body, the trypanosomes become established and multiply in muscle and white blood cells. Periodically, these parasitized cells rupture, releasing large numbers of new trophozoites into the blood. Eventually, the trypanosomes can spread to many systems, including the lymphoid organs, heart, liver, and brain. Manifestations of the resultant disease range from mild to very severe and include fever, inflammation, and heart and brain damage. In many cases, the disease has an extended course and can cause death.

Infective Amoebas: Entamoeba

Several species of amoebas cause disease in humans, but probably the most common disease is amoebiasis, or amebic

* *reduviid* (ree-doo′-vee-id) A member of a large family of flying insects with sucking, beaklike mouths.

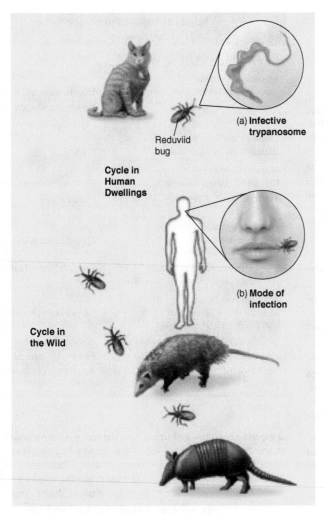

Figure 5.25 Cycle of transmission in Chagas disease.
Trypanosomes (**inset a**) are transmitted among domestic and wild mammalian hosts and human hosts by means of a bite from the kissing bug (**inset b**).

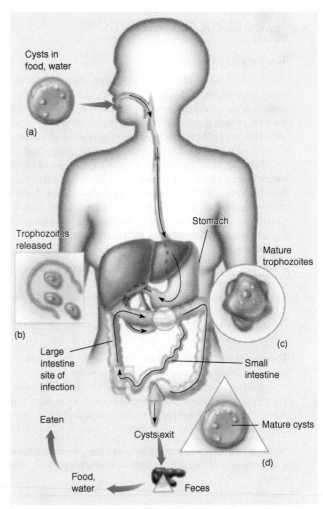

Figure 5.26 Stages in the infection and transmission of amebic dysentery. Arrows show the route of infection; insets show the appearance of *Entamoeba histolytica*. (**a**) Cysts are eaten. (**b**) Trophozoites (amoebas) emerge from cysts. (**c**) Trophozoites invade the large intestinal wall (see table 5.6, figure D.) (**d**) Mature cysts are released in the feces and may be spread through contaminated food and water.

dysentery,* caused by *Entamoeba histolytica*. This microbe is widely distributed in the world, from northern zones to the tropics, and is nearly always associated with humans. Amebic dysentery is the fourth most common protozoan infection in the world. This microbe has a life cycle quite different from the trypanosomes in that it does not involve multiple hosts and a blood-sucking vector. It lives part of its cycle as a trophozoite and part as a cyst. Because the cyst is the more resistant form and can survive in water and soil for several weeks, it is the more important stage for transmission. The primary way that people become infected is by ingesting food or water contaminated with human feces.

Figure 5.26 shows the major features of the amebic dysentery cycle, starting with the ingestion of cysts. The viable, heavy-walled

cyst passes through the stomach unharmed. Once inside the small intestine, the cyst germinates into a large multinucleate amoeba that subsequently divides to form small amoebas (the trophozoite stage). These trophozoites migrate to the large intestine and begin to feed and grow. From this site, they can penetrate the lining of the intestine and invade the liver, lungs, and skin. Common symptoms include gastrointestinal disturbances such as nausea, vomiting, and diarrhea, leading to weight loss and dehydration. The cycle is completed in the infected human when certain trophozoites in the feces begin to form cysts, which then pass out of the body with fecal matter. Knowledge of the amoebic cycle and role of cysts has been helpful in controlling the disease. Important preventive measures include sewage treatment, curtailing the use of human feces as fertilizer, and adequate sanitation of food and water.

* *dysentery* (dis′-en-ter″-ee) Any inflammation of the intestine accompanied by bloody stools. It can be caused by a number of factors, both microbial and nonmicrobial.

5.8 The Parasitic Helminths

 Expected Learning Outcomes

34. Describe the major groups of helminths and their basic morphology and classification.

35. Explain the elements of helminth biology, life cycles, and reproduction.

36. Discuss the importance of the helminth parasites.

Tapeworms, flukes, and roundworms are collectively called *helminths,* from the Greek word meaning "worm." Adult animals are usually large enough to be seen with the naked eye, and they range from the longest tapeworms, measuring up to about 25 m in length, to roundworms less than 1 mm in length. Traditionally, they have been included among microorganisms because of their infective abilities and because the microscope is necessary to identify their eggs and larvae.

On the basis of morphological form, the two major groups of parasitic helminths are the **flatworms** (Phylum Platyhelminthes), with a very thin, often segmented body plan (**figure 5.27**), and the **roundworms** (Phylum Aschelminthes, also called **nematodes**),* with an elongate, cylindrical, unsegmented body (**figure 5.28**). The flatworm group is subdivided into the **cestodes,** * or tapeworms, named for their long, ribbonlike arrangement, and the **trematodes,** * or flukes, characterized by flat, ovoid bodies. Not all flatworms and roundworms are parasites by nature; many live free in soil and water.

General Worm Morphology

All helminths are multicellular animals equipped to some degree with organs and organ systems. In parasitic helminths, the most

* *nematode* (neem'-ah-tohd) Gr. *nemato,* thread, and *eidos,* form.
* *cestode* (sess'-tohd) L. *cestus,* a belt, and *ode,* like.
* *trematode* (treem'-a-tohd) Gr. *trema,* hole. Named for the appearance of having tiny holes.

developed organs are those of the reproductive tract, with some degree of reduction in the digestive, excretory, nervous, and muscular systems. In particular groups, such as the cestodes, reproduction is so dominant that the worms are reduced to little more than a series of flattened sacs filled with ovaries, testes, and eggs (**figure 5.27a**). Not all worms have such extreme adaptations as cestodes, but most have a highly developed reproductive potential, thick cuticles for protection, and mouth glands for breaking down the host's tissue.

Life Cycles and Reproduction

The complete life cycle of helminths includes the fertilized egg (embryo), larval, and adult stages. In the majority of helminths, adults derive nutrients and reproduce sexually in a host's body. In nematodes, the sexes are separate and usually different in appearance; in trematodes, the sexes can be either separate or **hermaphroditic,** meaning that male and female sex organs are in the same worm; cestodes are generally hermaphroditic. For a parasite's continued survival as a species, it must complete the life cycle by transmitting an infective form, usually an egg or larva, to the body of another host, either of the same or a different species. By convention, the host in which larval development occurs is the intermediate (secondary) host, and adulthood and mating occur in the **definitive (final) host.** A transport host is an intermediate host that experiences no parasitic development but is an essential link in the completion of the cycle.

In general, sources for human infection are contaminated food, soil, water, or infected animals, and routes of infection are by oral intake or penetration of unbroken skin. Humans are the definitive hosts for many of the parasites, and in about half the diseases, they are also the sole biological reservoir. In other cases, animals or insect vectors serve as reservoirs or are required to complete worm development. In the majority of helminth infections, the worms must leave their host to complete the entire life cycle.

Fertilized eggs are usually released to the environment and are provided with a protective shell and extra food to aid their development into larvae. Even so, most eggs and larvae are vulnerable to

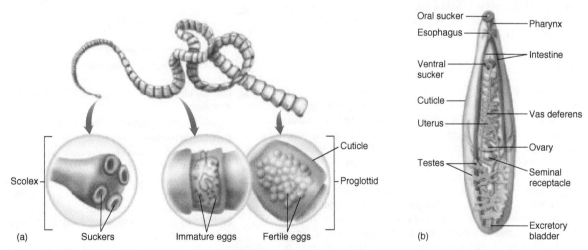

Figure 5.27 Parasitic flatworms. (a) A cestode (beef tapeworm), showing the scolex; long, tapelike body; and magnified views of immature and mature proglottids (body segments). **(b)** The structure of a trematode (liver fluke). Note the suckers that attach to host tissue and the dominance of reproductive and digestive organs.

152 **Chapter 5** A Survey of Eukaryotic Cells and Microorganisms

Figure 5.28 **The life cycle of the pinworm, a roundworm.** Eggs are the infective stage and are transmitted by unclean hands. Children frequently reinfect themselves and also pass the parasite on to others.

heat, cold, drying, and predators, and are destroyed or unable to reach a new host. To counteract this formidable mortality rate, certain worms have adapted a reproductive capacity that borders on the incredible: A single female *Ascaris*[7] can lay 200,000 eggs a day, and a large female can contain over 25 million eggs at varying stages of development! If only a tiny number of these eggs makes it to another host, the parasite will have been successful in completing its life cycle.

A Helminth Cycle: The Pinworm

To illustrate a helminth cycle in humans, we use the example of a roundworm, *Enterobius vermicularis,* the pinworm or seatworm. This worm causes a very common infestation of the large intestine (**figure 5.28**). Worms range from 2 to 12 mm long and have a tapered, curved cylinder shape. The condition they cause, enterobiasis, is usually a simple, uncomplicated infection that does not spread beyond the intestine.

A cycle starts when a person swallows microscopic eggs picked up from another infected person by direct contact or by touching contaminated surfaces. The eggs hatch in the intestine and then release larvae that mature into adult worms within about one month. Male and female worms mate, and the female migrates out

to the anus to deposit eggs, which cause intense itchiness that is relieved by scratching. Herein lies a significant means of dispersal: Scratching contaminates the fingers, which, in turn, transfers eggs to bedclothes and other inanimate objects. This person becomes a host and a source of eggs, and can spread them to others in addition to reinfesting himself. Enterobiasis occurs most often among families and in other close living situations. Its distribution is worldwide among all socioeconomic groups, but it seems to attack younger people more frequently than older ones.

Helminth Classification and Identification

The helminths are classified according to their shape; their size; the degree of development of various organs; the presence of hooks, suckers, or other special structures; the mode of reproduction; the kinds of hosts; and the appearance of eggs and larvae. They are identified in the laboratory by microscopic detection of the adult worm or its larvae and eggs, which often have distinctive shapes or external and internal structures. Occasionally, they are cultured in order to verify all of the life stages.

Distribution and Importance of Parasitic Worms

About 50 species of helminths parasitize humans. They are distributed in all areas of the world that support human life. Some worms are restricted to a given geographic region, and many have a higher incidence in tropical areas. This knowledge must be tempered with the realization that jet-age travel, along with human migration, is gradually changing the patterns of worm infections, especially of those species that do not require alternate hosts or special climatic conditions for development. The yearly estimate of worldwide cases numbers in the billions, and these are not confined to developing countries. A conservative estimate places 50 million helminth infections in North America alone. The primary targets are malnourished children.

 Check Your Progress SECTIONS 5.6–5.8

22. What is a working definition of a "protist"?
23. Describe the principal characteristics of algae that separate them from protozoa.
24. How are algae important? Give examples of algae with medical importance.
25. Explain the general characteristics of the protozoan life cycle.
26. Describe the protozoan adaptations for feeding.
27. Briefly outline the characteristics of the four protozoan groups and name important pathogens in each group.
28. What characteristics set the apicomplexa apart from the other protozoan groups?
29. Discuss the adaptations of parasitic worms to their lifestyles, and explain why these adaptations are necessary or advantageous to the worms' survival.
30. Outline the basic steps in an infection cycle of a pathogenic protozoan and a helminth.

7. *Ascaris* is a genus of parasitic intestinal roundworms.

CASE STUDY Part 2

There is much more to the story of neglected diseases of poverty. Most victims first become infected as children and continue to harbor the parasite for years, even for a lifetime. The chronic nature of the infection adds enormously to the accumulated damage that occurs. Infected people may become involved in an ongoing cycle that continues to produce more parasites and increase their survival and transmission. Many protozoans produce resistant survival cells called cysts, and worms go through complex reproductive phases with eggs and larvae. Some parasites are spread by direct contact with an infected person, some burrow into the skin, and others are ingested in contaminated soil or water. A significant factor in transmission of several parasites is the involvement of arthropod vectors such as mosquitoes and flies.

For most of these diseases, there is effective drug therapy, but getting the drugs to the poorest of the poor has been difficult. Many of the countries are not only deeply impoverished,

but are involved in civil wars and other conflicts, creating upheaval in an already overburdened system. One billion of the world's poorest live on less than $1 per day, and 2.7 billion live on less than $2 per day. In most cases, they are "out of sight and out of mind"—often living in remote rural areas far removed from medical facilities. NTDs are not given much priority for funding because they are not high-profile diseases with noticeable, acute symptoms requiring immediate medical care. Any progress in controlling these NTDs will require a global partnership that brings together resources from many countries.

- What is the definition of a vector, and how are vectors involved in these diseases?

- What are some possible solutions to the problem of neglected diseases?

To conclude this Case Study, go to Perspectives on the Connect website.

To read about a program to improve the conditions of the bottom billion go to http://www.globalnetwork.org/just50cents.

 Chapter Summary with Key Terms

5.1 The History of Eukaryotes

5.2 and 5.3 Form and Function of the Eukaryotic Cell: External and Internal Structures

 A. Eukaryotic cells are complex and compartmentalized into individual organelles.
 B. Major organelles and other structural features include: appendages (cilia, flagella), **glycocalyx,** cell wall, cytoplasmic (or cell) membrane, **organelles** (nucleus, **nucleolus, endoplasmic reticulum, Golgi complex, mitochondria, chloroplasts**), ribosomes, **cytoskeleton (microfilaments, microtubules).**

5.4 Eukaryotic-Prokaryotic Comparisons and Taxonomy of Eukaryotes

 A. The eukaryotic cell can be compared with the prokaryotic cell in structure, size, metabolism, motility, and shape.
 B. Taxonomic groups of the Domain Eukarya are based on level of organization, body plan, cell structure, nutrition, metabolism, and certain genetic characteristics.

5.5 The Kingdom of the Fungi

 Common names of the macroscopic fungi are mushrooms, bracket fungi, and puffballs. Microscopic fungi are known as yeasts and molds.

 A. *Overall Morphology:* At the cellular (microscopic) level, fungi are typical eukaryotic cells, with thick cell walls. Yeasts are single cells that form buds and **pseudohyphae. Hyphae** are long, tubular filaments that can be septate or nonseptate and grow in a network called a **mycelium;** hyphae are characteristic of the filamentous fungi called molds.
 B. *Nutritional Mode/Distribution:* All are **heterotrophic.** The majority are harmless **saprobes** living off organic **substrates** such as dead animal and plant tissues. A few are **parasites,** living on the tissues of other organisms, but none is obligate. Distribution is extremely widespread in many habitats.

 C. *Reproduction:* Primarily through **spores** formed on special reproductive hyphae. In asexual reproduction, spores are formed through budding, partitioning of a hypha, or in special sporogenous structures; examples are **conidia** and **sporangiospores.** In sexual reproduction, spores are formed following fusion of male and female strains and the formation of a sexual structure; sexual spores are one basis for classification.
 D. *Major Groups:* The four main phyla among the terrestrial fungi, given with sexual spore type, are **Zygomycota (zygospores), Ascomycota (ascospores), Basidiomycota (basidiospores),** and **Chytridiomycota** (motile zoospores).
 E. *Importance:* Fungi are essential decomposers of plant and animal detritis in the environment. Economically beneficial as sources of antibiotics; used in making foods and in genetic studies. Adverse impacts include: decomposition of fruits and vegetables, and human infections, or **mycoses;** some produce substances that are toxic if eaten.

5.6 Survey of Protists: Algae

 General group that traditionally includes single-celled and colonial eukaryotic microbes that lack organization into tissues.

 A. *Overall Morphology:* Are unicellular, colonial, filamentous or larger forms such as seaweeds.
 B. *Nutritional Mode/Distribution:* Photosynthetic; freshwater and marine water habitats; main component of **plankton.**
 C. *Importance:* Provide the basis of the food web in most aquatic habitats and are major producers of oxygen. Certain algae produce neurotoxins that are harmful to humans and animals.

5.7 Survey of Protists: Protozoa

 Include large single-celled organisms; a few are pathogens.

 A. *Overall Morphology:* Most are unicellular; lack a cell wall. The cytoplasm is divided into ectoplasm and endoplasm. Many convert to a resistant, dormant stage called a **cyst.**

B. *Nutritional Mode/Distribution:* All are heterotrophic. Most are free-living in a moist habitat (water, soil); feed by engulfing other microorganisms and organic matter.

C. *Reproduction:* Asexual by binary fission and **mitosis,** budding; sexual by fusion of free-swimming gametes, conjugation.

D. *Major Groups:* Protozoa are subdivided into four groups based upon mode of locomotion and type of reproduction: **Mastigophora,** the flagellates, motile by flagella; **Sarcodina,** the amoebas, motile by pseudopods; **Ciliophora,** the ciliates, motile by cilia; **Apicomplexa,** motility not well developed; produce unique reproductive structures.

E. *Importance:* Ecologically important in food webs and decomposing organic matter. Medical significance: hundreds of millions of people are afflicted with one of the many protozoan infections (malaria, trypanosomiasis, amoebiasis). Can be spread from host to host by insect **vectors.**

5.8 The Parasitic Helminths
Includes three categories: roundworms, tapeworms, and flukes.

A. *Overall Morphology:* Animal cells; multicellular; individual organs specialized for reproduction, digestion, movement, protection, though some of these are reduced.

B. *Reproductive Mode:* Includes embryo, larval, and adult stages. Majority reproduce sexually. Sexes may be hermaphroditic.

C. *Epidemiology:* Developing countries in the tropics are hardest hit by helminth infections; transmitted via ingestion, vectors, and direct contact with infectious stages. They afflict billions of humans.

Level I. Knowledge and Comprehension

These questions require a working knowledge of the concepts in the chapter and the ability to recall and understand the information you have studied.

(?) Multiple-Choice Questions

Select the correct answer from the answers provided. For questions with blanks, choose the combination of answers that most accurately completes the statement.

1. Both flagella and cilia are found primarily in
 a. algae c. fungi
 b. protozoa d. both b and c

2. Features of the nuclear envelope include
 a. ribosomes
 b. a double membrane structure
 c. pores that allow communication with the cytoplasm
 d. b and c
 e. all of these

3. The cell wall is usually found in which eukaryotes?
 a. fungi c. protozoa
 b. algae d. a and b

4. What is embedded in rough endoplasmic reticulum?
 a. ribosomes c. chromatin
 b. Golgi apparatus d. vesicles

5. Yeasts are _____ fungi, and molds are _____ fungi.
 a. macroscopic, microscopic
 b. unicellular, filamentous
 c. motile, nonmotile
 d. water, terrestrial

6. In general, fungi derive nutrients through
 a. photosynthesis
 b. engulfing bacteria
 c. digesting organic substrates
 d. parasitism

7. A hypha divided into compartments by cross walls is called
 a. nonseptate c. septate
 b. imperfect d. perfect

8. Algae generally contain some type of
 a. spore
 b. chlorophyll
 c. locomotor organelle
 d. toxin

9. Which algal group is most closely related to plants?
 a. diatoms
 b. Chlorophyta
 c. Euglenophyta
 d. dinoflagellates

10. Which characteristic(s) is/are not typical of protozoan cells?
 a. locomotor organelle c. spore
 b. cyst d. trophozoite

11. The protozoan trophozoite is the
 a. active feeding stage
 b. inactive dormant stage
 c. infective stage
 d. spore-forming stage

12. All mature sporozoa are
 a. parasitic
 b. nonmotile
 c. carried by an arthropod vector
 d. both a and b

13. Parasitic helminths reproduce with
 a. spores d. cysts
 b. eggs and sperm e. all of these
 c. mitosis

14. Mitochondria likely originated from
 a. archaea
 b. invaginations of the cell membrane
 c. rickettsias
 d. cyanobacteria

15. Human fungal infections involve and affect what areas of the human body?
 a. skin
 b. mucous membranes
 c. lungs
 d. all of these

16. Most helminth infections
 a. are localized to one site in the body
 b. spread through major systems of the body
 c. develop within the spleen
 d. develop within the liver

Multiple Matching. Select the description that best fits the word in the left column.

17. _____ diatom
18. _____ *Rhizopus*
19. _____ *Histoplasma*
20. _____ *Cryptococcus*
21. _____ euglenid
22. _____ dinoflagellate
23. _____ *Trichomonas*
24. _____ *Entamoeba*
25. _____ *Plasmodium*
26. _____ *Enterobius*

a. the cause of malaria
b. single-celled alga with silica in its cell wall
c. fungal cause of Ohio Valley fever
d. the cause of amebic dysentery
e. genus of black bread mold
f. helminth worm involved in pinworm infection
g. motile flagellated alga with an eyespot
h. a yeast that infects the lungs
i. flagellated protozoan genus that causes an STD
j. alga that causes red tides

Case Study Review

1. Which of these is/are an example(s) of neglected tropical protozoan diseases?
 a. hookworm d. a and b
 b. Chagas disease e. b and c
 c. leishmaniasis f. all of these

2. Which is a possible vector of a tropical eukaryotic parasite?
 a. contaminated drinking water c. biting fly
 b. spoiled food d. person with a cough

3. Provide some explanations for why the eukaryotic parasites are so widespread and successful.

Writing Challenge

For each question, compose a one- or two-paragraph answer that includes the factual information needed to completely address the question. Check Your Progress questions can also be used for writing-challenge exercises.

1. Describe the anatomy and functions of each of the major eukaryotic organelles.

2. Trace the synthesis of cell products, their processing, and their packaging through the organelle network.

3. a. What is the reproductive potential of molds in terms of spore production?
 b. How do mold spores differ from bacterial endospores?

4. a. Fill in the following summary table for defining, comparing, and contrasting eukaryotic cells.
 b. Briefly describe the manner of nutrition and body plan (unicellular, colonial, filamentous, or multicellular) for each group.
 c. Explain some ways that helminths differ from the protozoa and algae in structure and behavior.

Organelle/ Structure	Briefly Describe Functions in Cell	Commonly Present In (Check)		
		Fungi	Algae	Protozoa
Flagella				
Cilia				
Glycocalyx				
Cell wall				
Cell membrane				
Nucleus				
Mitochondria				
Chloroplasts				
Endoplasmic reticulum				
Ribosomes				
Cytoskeleton				
Lysosomes				
Microvilli				
Centrioles				

156 **Chapter 5** A Survey of Eukaryotic Cells and Microorganisms

 Concept Mapping

An Introduction to Concept Mapping found at http://www.mhhe.com/talaro9 provides guidance for working with concept maps.

1. Construct your own concept map using the following words as the *concepts*. Supply the linking words between each pair of concepts.

Golgi apparatus	ribosomes
chloroplasts	flagella
cytoplasm	nucleolus
endoplasmic reticulum	cell membrane

 Level II. Application, Analysis, Evaluation, and Synthesis

These problems go beyond just restating facts and require higher levels of understanding and an ability to interpret, problem solve, transfer knowledge to new situations, create models, and predict outcomes.

 Critical Thinking

Critical thinking is the ability to reason and solve problems using facts and concepts. These questions can be approached from a number of angles, and in most cases, they do not have a single correct answer.

1. Explain the ways that mitochondria resemble rickettsias and chloroplasts resemble cyanobacteria.

2. Give the common name of a eukaryotic microbe that is unicellular, walled, nonphotosynthetic, nonmotile, and bud-forming.

3. How are the eukaryotic ribosomes and cell membranes different from those of prokaryotes?

4. What general type of multicellular parasite is composed primarily of thin sacs of reproductive organs?

5. a. Name two parasites that are transmitted in the cyst form.
 b. How must a non-cyst-forming pathogenic protozoan be transmitted? Why?

6. Explain what factors could cause opportunistic mycoses to be a growing medical problem.

7. a. How are bacterial endospores and cysts of protozoa alike?
 b. How do they differ?

8. For what reasons would a eukaryotic cell evolve an endoplasmic reticulum and a Golgi apparatus?

9. Can you think of a simple test to determine if a child is suffering from pinworms? Hint: Clear adhesive tape is involved.

Visual Challenge

1. What term is used to describe a single species exhibiting both cell types shown below, and which types of organisms would most likely have this trait?

2. Label the major structures you can observe in the images in figure 5.16a, table 5.3A, B, and D, and table 5.6C.

www.mcgrawhillconnect.com
Enhance your study of this chapter with study tools and practice tests. Also ask your instructor about the resources available through ConnectPlus, including the media-rich eBook, interactive learning tools, and animations.

CHAPTER **6** An Introduction to Viruses

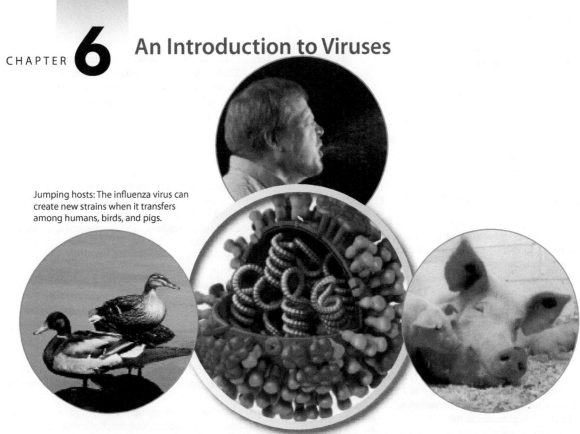

Jumping hosts: The influenza virus can create new strains when it transfers among humans, birds, and pigs.

A model of the influenza virus displays its hemagglutinin spikes (blue) and neuraminidase spikes (red). A cutaway gives a view of RNA strands (green).

 CASE STUDY Part 1 **The Mystery Influenza Virus**

In March 2009, the infectious disease monitoring system of Mexico began registering an increase in **influenza (flu)** cases. These reports caused concern because influenza cases would normally have been in decline by this time in the season, and **most** of the **cases** occurred in **healthy young adults,** rather than very young or old patients, as is the usual pattern.

By mid-April, nearly 1,000 Mexican cases had been reported, with around 70 deaths. Soon a few cases of this same type of flu cropped up in the United States, primarily in California and Texas. When the **Centers for Disease Control and Prevention (CDC)** received reports of these new cases, **virologists** immediately tested samples from American and Mexican patients to identify the **strain** of virus.

Major features used to identify the influenza virus are **protein molecules** on the surface of the virus called **receptors** or **spikes.** One of these receptors, called **hemagglutinin (H),** is essential for the virus to adhere to the cells of the respiratory tract. The other surface protein, **neuraminidase (N),** is an enzyme that breaks down mucus and helps the virus invade respiratory tissues. These receptors are genetically controlled and subject to frequent changes in structure. The spikes are assigned numbers to keep track of the several different forms, and from this practice comes the shorthand method of naming strains of virus.

> "Beginning with those first diagnoses, it took only six weeks for the influenza outbreak to explode into a pandemic."

In both groups of patients, investigators discovered identical influenza viruses that typed out to a strain known as **H1N1.** Because this virus strain had previously appeared in 1918 and 1976 and was associated with pigs, for a time, this outbreak was initially attributed to a **"swine flu virus."** But this influenza virus was unlike any that had appeared in the past. It had **genetic characteristics** of a swine virus, but it also carried some genes from human and bird viruses. To allay unfounded fears about acquiring this disease from swine, public health groups urged that it be given the more accurate title of **2009 H1N1 type A influenza** rather than swine flu. Determining the exact origin of this virus has proved difficult, and it may never be known. Viruses similar to it have circulated in the United States in the recent past, but this one also displayed characteristics of European and Asian swine influenza viruses. It now appears that this new H1N1 strain had undergone a **genetic mutation** that allowed animal-to-human transmission and human-to-human transmission.

▶ *How do the receptor spikes on viruses play a role in infection?*

▶ *How is it possible for the same influenza virus to be able to infect both swine and humans?*

To continue the Case Study, go to page 180. **157**

6.1 Overview of Viruses

 Expected Learning Outcomes

1. Indicate how viruses were discovered and characterized.
2. Describe the unique characteristics of viruses.
3. Discuss the origin and importance of viruses.

Early Searches for the Tiniest Microbes

The discovery of the light microscope made it possible to see first-hand the agents of many bacterial, fungal, and protozoan diseases. But the techniques for observing and cultivating these relatively large microorganisms were useless for viruses. For many years, the cause of viral infections such as smallpox and polio was unknown, even though it was clear that the diseases were transmitted from person to person. The French bacteriologist Louis Pasteur was certainly on the right track when he postulated that rabies was caused by a "living thing" smaller than bacteria, and in 1884, he was able to develop the first vaccine for rabies.

The first substantial revelations about the unique characteristics of viruses occurred in the 1890s. First, D. Ivanovski and M. Beijerinck showed that a disease in tobacco was caused by a virus (tobacco mosaic virus). In fact, it was Beijerinck who first proposed the term **virus** (L. poison) to denote this particular group of infectious agents. This discovery was followed by Friedrich Loeffler and Paul Frosch's isolation of the virus that causes foot-and-mouth disease in cattle. These early researchers found that when infectious fluids from host organisms were passed through porcelain filters designed to trap bacteria, the filtrate remained infectious even though they could not see the infectious agent with a microscope.

Over the succeeding decades, a remarkable picture of the physical, chemical, and biological nature of viruses began to take form. Years of experimentation were required to show that viruses were noncellular particles with a definite size, shape, and chemical composition. Specialized techniques were developed to culture them in the laboratory. In time, virology grew into a multifaceted discipline that promised to provide much information on disease, genetics, and even life itself (**6.1 Making Connections**).

The Position of Viruses in the Biological Spectrum

Viruses are a unique group of biological entities known to infect every type of cell, including bacteria, algae, fungi, protozoa, plants, and animals. Although the emphasis in this chapter is on animal viruses, much credit for our knowledge must be given to experiments with bacterial and plant viruses. The exceptional and curious nature of viruses prompts numerous questions, including:

1. How did viruses originate?
2. Are they organisms; that is, are they alive?
3. What are their distinctive biological characteristics?
4. How can particles so small, simple, and seemingly insignificant be capable of causing disease and death?
5. What is the connection between viruses and cancer?

In this chapter, we address these ideas and many others.

There is no universal agreement on how and when viruses originated. But there is little disagreement that they have been in existence for billions of years, probably ever since the early history of cells. One theory explains that viruses arose from loose strands of genetic material released by cells. These then developed a protective coating and a capacity to reenter a cell and use its machinery to reproduce. An alternate explanation for their origins suggests that they were once cells that have regressed to a highly parasitic existence inside other cells. Both of these viewpoints have some supportive evidence, and it is entirely possible that viruses have originated in more than one way.

In terms of numbers, viruses are considered the most abundant microbes on earth. To quote microbiologist Carl Zimmer, we live on "a planet of viruses." Based on a decade of research on the viral populations in the ocean, "virus hunters" now have evidence that there are hundreds of thousands of distinct virus types that have never been described. Many of them are parasites of bacteria, which are also abundant in most ecosystems. By one estimate, viruses outnumber bacteria by a factor of 10. Because viruses tend to interact with the genetic material of their host cells and can carry genes from one host cell to another (chapter 9), they have played an important part in the evolution of Bacteria, Archaea, and Eukarya.

Viruses are different from their host cells in size, structure, behavior, and physiology. They are a type of **obligate intracellular parasite** that cannot multiply unless it invades a specific host cell and instructs its genetic and metabolic machinery to make and release quantities of new viruses. Because of this characteristic, viruses are capable of causing serious damage and disease. Other unique properties of viruses are summarized in **table 6.1.**

The unusual structure and behavior of viruses have led to debates about their connection to the rest of the microbial world. One viewpoint holds that viruses are unable to exist independently from

TABLE 6.1 Properties of Viruses
• Obligate intracellular parasites of bacteria, protozoa, fungi, algae, plants, and animals
• Ultramicroscopic size, ranging from 20 nm up to 450 nm (diameter)
• Not cellular in nature; structure is very compact and economical.
• Do not independently fulfill the characteristics of life
• Inactive macromolecules outside the host cell and active only inside host cells
• Basic structure consists of protein shell (capsid) surrounding nucleic acid core.
• Nucleic acid of the viral genome is either DNA or RNA but not both.
• Nucleic acid can be double-stranded DNA, single-stranded DNA, single-stranded RNA, or double-stranded RNA.
• Molecules on virus surface impart high specificity for attachment to host cell.
• Multiply by taking control of host cell's genetic material and regulating the synthesis and assembly of new viruses
• Lack enzymes for most metabolic processes
• Lack machinery for synthesizing proteins

6.1 MAKING CONNECTIONS

An Alternate View of Viruses

Looking at this beautiful tulip, one would never guess that it derives part of its beauty from a viral infection. It contains tulip mosaic virus, which alters the development of the plant cells and causes varying patterns of colors in the petals. Aside from this, the virus does not immediately destroy the plants. Despite the reputation of viruses as destructive pathogens, there is another side to viruses—that of being benign and, in some cases, even beneficial.

Research in extreme habitats in Antarctica uncovered a surprisingly rich diversity of viruses inhabiting a frigid lake. When the genetic material of the samples was analyzed, it revealed over 10,000 unique viruses gathered from just a small area. Other studies of the ocean have documented the presence of 10 million viruses per milliliter of water—10 times the number of cellular microbes. This hints at the dominant role viruses have in the world's ecosystems, not only because they infect and can control populations of eukaryotic and prokaryotic cells, but because they appear to influence a number of biological activities, including photosynthesis and the cycling of nutrients.

Over the past several years, biomedical experts have been looking at viruses as vehicles to treat infections and disease. Vaccine experts have engineered new types of vaccines by combining a less harmful virus such as vaccinia or adenovirus with genetic material from a pathogen such as HIV and herpes simplex. This technique creates a vaccine that provides immunity but does not expose the person to the intact pathogen. Several of these types of vaccines are being tested.

The "harmless virus" approach is also being used to treat genetic diseases such as cystic fibrosis and sickle-cell anemia. With gene therapy, the normal gene is inserted into a virus vector, such as an adenovirus, and the patient is infected with this altered virus. It is hoped that the virus will introduce the needed gene into the cells and correct the defect. Dozens of experimental trials are underway to develop potential cures for diseases, with mixed success (look ahead to chapter 10).

An older therapy getting a second look involves use of bacteriophages to treat bacterial infections (phage therapy). The basis behind the therapy is that bacterial viruses can selectively attack and destroy their host bacteria without damaging human cells. Experiments with animals indicate that this method controls some infections as well as traditional drugs can. Potential applications include adding phage suspensions to skin grafts and to intravenous fluids to control infections.

The U.S. Department of Agriculture has recently approved bacteriophage treatments to prevent food infections. One type is designed to spray on livestock to reduce the incidence of pathogenic *Escherichia coli.* The other is intended for use on processed meats and poultry to control *Listeria monocytogenes,* another prominent food-borne pathogen.

Explain why bacterial viruses would be harmless to humans.
Answer available at http://www.mhhe.com/talaro9

the host cell, so they are not living things but are more akin to large, infectious molecules. Another viewpoint proposes that even though viruses do not exhibit most of the life processes of cells (look back at section 4.1), they can direct them and thus are certainly more than inert and lifeless molecules. Depending upon the circumstances, both views are defensible. This debate has greater philosophical than practical importance because viruses are agents of disease and must be dealt with through control, therapy, and prevention, whether we regard them as living or not: In keeping with their special position in the biological spectrum, it is best to describe viruses as *infectious particles* (rather than organisms) and as either *active* or *inactive* (rather than alive or dead).

 Check Your Progress SECTION 6.1

1. Describe 10 *unique* characteristics of viruses (can include structure, behavior, multiplication).
2. After consulting table 6.1 on page 158, what additional statements can you make about viruses, especially as compared with cells?
3. Explain what it means to be an obligate intracellular parasite.
4. What are some other ways to describe the sort of parasitism exhibited by viruses?

6.2 The General Structure of Viruses

Expected Learning Outcomes

4. Describe the general structure and size range of viruses.
5. Distinguish among types of capsids and nucleocapsids.
6. Describe envelopes and spikes, and discuss their origins.
7. Explain the functions of capsids, nucleocapsids, envelopes, and spikes.
8. Summarize the different viral groups based on their basic structure.

Size Range

As a group, viruses represent the smallest infectious agents (with some unusual exceptions to be discussed in section 6.8). Their size places them in the realm of the *ultramicroscopic*. This term means that most of them are so minute (< 0.2 μm) that an electron microscope is necessary to detect them or to examine their fine structure. They are dwarfed by their host cells: More than 2,000 bacterial viruses could fit into an average bacterial cell, and more than 50 million polioviruses could be accommodated by an average human cell. Animal viruses range in size from the small

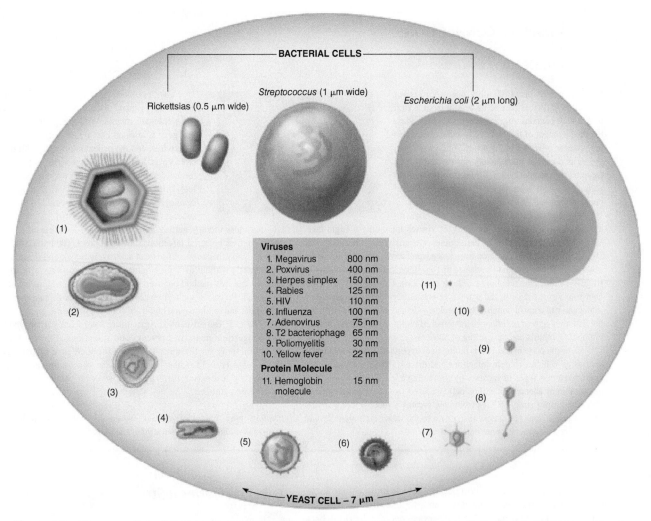

Figure 6.1 **Size comparison of viruses with a yeast cell colored blue (eukaryotic) and various bacteria (prokaryotic).** Viruses range from largest (1) to smallest (10). A molecule of a large protein (11) is included to indicate relative size of macromolecules.

parvoviruses[1] (around 20 nm in diameter) to megaviruses and pandoraviruses[2] that are as large as small bacteria (up to 1,000 nm in width) **(figure 6.1).** Some cylindrical viruses are relatively long (800 nm in length) but so narrow in diameter (15 nm) that their visibility is still limited without the high magnification and resolution of an electron microscope. Figure 6.1 compares the sizes of several viruses with prokaryotic and eukaryotic cells and molecules.

Viral architecture is most readily observed through special stains in combination with electron microscopy. Negative staining uses an opaque salt to outline the shape of the virus against a dark background and to enhance textural features on the viral surface. Internal details are revealed by positive staining of specific parts of the virus such as protein or nucleic acid. The *shadowcasting* tech-

nique showers a virus preparation with a dense metallic vapor directed from a certain angle. These techniques are featured in several figures throughout this chapter.

Monster Viruses

In chapter 4, we featured discoveries of unusual types of bacteria. Viruses are also known to have exceptional members. Probably the most outstanding examples are megaviruses **(figure 6.2)** and pandoraviruses. These are giants in the viral world, averaging about 500 to 1,000 nm in diameter, 20 to 50 times larger than an average virus and even larger than small bacteria such as rickettsias. The megaviruses were first discovered as parasites inside the cells of amoebas living in aquatic habitats. Pandoraviruses were isolated from sediments in the seafloor and also use amoebas as hosts. Both giant viruses lack cellular structure and ribosomes, metabolic enzymes, and fission-style division. They have a typical viral cycle, multiplying in the host cytoplasm in

1. DNA viruses that cause respiratory infections in humans.
2. Groups of large, complex viruses that are parasites inside cells of ocean-dwelling amoebas.

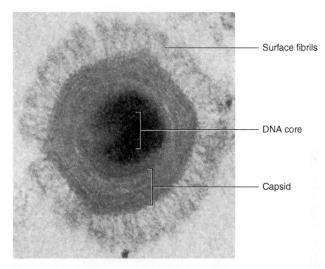

Figure 6.2 A monster virus—the megavirus. A TEM of one virus particle reveals its unique geometric shape, dark DNA core, and fine surface fibrils (4,500×). These viruses would be readily visible with an ordinary light microscope.

well-developed "virus factories." Although both are unusually large for viruses, the pandoraviruses have the largest capsids and genomes ever discovered, with 2,500 genes!

Where these unusual viruses fit on the "tree of life," if at all, is still the subject of debate. Some microbiologists suggest that they may belong to a separate evolutionary line of microbes that is different in origin from other viral groups. Another possibility is that these viruses are related to ancient forms that evolved into the first cells.

Viral Components: Capsids, Nucleic Acids, and Envelopes

It is important to realize that viruses bear no real resemblance to cells and that they lack any of the synthetic machinery found in even the simplest cells. Their molecular structure consists of regular, repeating molecules that give rise to their crystalline appearance. Indeed, many purified viruses can form large aggregates or crystals if subjected to special treatments **(figure 6.3).** The general plan of virus organization is very simple and compact. Viruses contain only those parts needed to invade and control a host cell: an external coating and a core containing one or more nucleic acid strands of either DNA or RNA. This pattern can be represented with a flowchart:

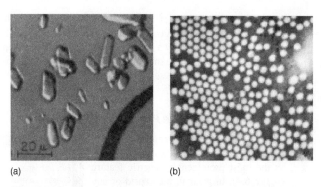

(a) (b)

Figure 6.3 The crystalline nature of viruses. (a) Light microscope magnification (1,200×) of purified poliovirus crystals. **(b)** Highly magnified (200,000×) negative stain of hundreds of polioviruses shows the tight geometric arrangements of particles.

All viruses have a protein **capsid,*** or shell, that surrounds the nucleic acid in the central core. Together, the capsid and the nucleic acid are referred to as the **nucleocapsid.** Viruses that consist of only a nucleocapsid are considered **naked viruses (figure 6.4a).** Members

* *capsid* (kap′-sid) L. *capsa*, box.

(a) Naked Nucleocapsid Virus

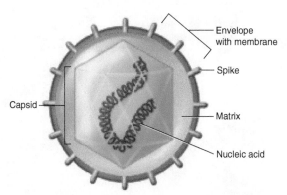

(b) Enveloped Virus

Figure 6.4 Generalized structure of viruses. (a) The simplest virus is a naked nucleocapsid consisting of a geometric capsid assembled around a nucleic acid strand or strands. **(b)** An enveloped virus is composed of a nucleocapsid surrounded by a flexible membrane called an envelope. The envelope usually has special receptor spikes inserted into its membrane.

of 13 of the 20 families of animal viruses are **enveloped,** that is, they possess an additional covering external to the capsid called an envelope, which is usually a modified piece of the host's cell membrane **(figure 6.4b).** As we shall see later, the enveloped viruses also differ from the naked viruses in the possible ways that they enter and leave a host cell.

The Viral Capsid: The Protective Outer Shell

When a virus particle is magnified several hundred thousand times, the capsid appears as the most prominent geometric feature (figure 6.4). In general, the capsid of any virus is constructed from a number of identical protein subunits called **capsomers.*** The capsomers can spontaneously self-assemble into the finished capsid. Depending on how the capsomers are shaped and arranged, this assembly results in two different types: helical and icosahedral.

> **Quick Search**
> Fun with viruses! Construct a virus capsid from instructions in "paper virus models" and look for images of a "bacteriophage balloon" on Google.

The simpler **helical capsids** have rod-shaped capsomers that bind together to form a series of hollow discs resembling a bracelet. During the formation of the nucleocapsid, these discs link together and form a continuous helix into which the nucleic acid strand is coiled **(figure 6.5).** In electron micrographs, the appearance of a helical capsid varies with the type of virus. The nucleocapsids of naked helical viruses are very rigid and tightly wound into a cylinder-shaped package **(figure 6.6a).** Several viruses that infect plants are of this type **(figure 6.6b).** Enveloped helical nucleocapsids are more flexible and tend to be arranged as a looser helix within the envelope **(figure 6.6c, d).** This type of capsid is found in several enveloped human viruses, including those of influenza, measles, and rabies.

* *capsomer* (kap'-soh-meer) L. *capsa,* box, and *mer,* part.

Figure 6.5 Assembly of helical nucleocapsids. (a) Capsomers assemble into hollow discs. **(b)** The nucleic acid is inserted into the center of the disc. **(c)** Elongation of the nucleocapsid progresses from both ends, as the nucleic acid is wound "within" the lengthening helix.

Several major virus families have capsids arranged in an **icosahedron***—a three-dimensional, 20-sided figure with 12 evenly spaced corners. The arrangements of the capsomers vary from one virus to another. The capsid of some viruses contains a

* *icosahedron* (eye"-koh-suh-hee'-drun) Gr. *eikosi,* twenty, and *hedra,* side. A type of polygon.

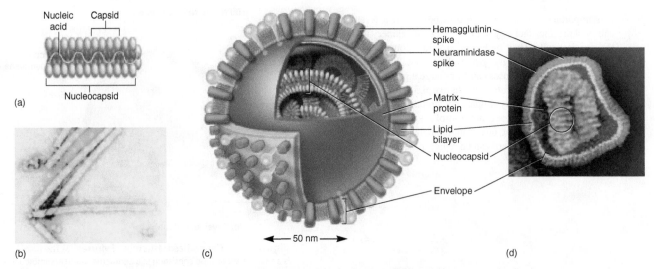

Figure 6.6 Typical variations of viruses with helical nucleocapsids. Naked helical virus (tobacco mosaic virus): (a) a schematic view and **(b)** a negative stain magnified 160,000×. Note the elongate cylindrical morphology. **Enveloped helical virus (influenza virus): (c)** a schematic view and **(d)** a colorized micrograph featuring a positive stain of the influenza virus (300,000×). This virus has a well-developed envelope with prominent spikes.

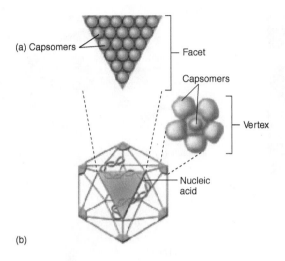

(a) Capsomers

Facet

Capsomers

Vertex

Nucleic acid

(b)

Capsomers

Vertex

Fiber

(c)

(d)

Figure 6.7 The structure and formation of an icosahedral virus (adenovirus is the model). (a) A facet or "face" of the capsid is composed of 21 identical capsomers arranged in a triangular shape. A vertex or "point" consists of five capsomers arranged with a single penton in the center. Other viruses can vary in the number, types, and arrangement of capsomers. **(b)** An assembled virus shows how the facets and vertices come together to form a shell around the nucleic acid. **(c)** A three-dimensional model (640,000×) of this virus shows fibers attached to the pentons. **(d)** A negative stain of this virus highlights its texture and fibers that have fallen off.

single type of capsomer, whereas others may contain several types of capsomers **(figure 6.7).** Although the capsids of all icosahedral viruses have this sort of symmetry, they can vary in the number of capsomers; for example, a poliovirus has 32 and an adenovirus has 242 capsomers. During assembly of the virus, the nucleic acid is packed into the center of this icosahedron, forming a nucleocapsid. Another factor that alters the appearance of icosahedral viruses is whether or not they have an outer envelope. Inspect **figure 6.8** to compare a rotavirus and its naked nucleocapsid with herpes simplex (cold sores) and its enveloped nucleocapsid.

The Viral Envelope

When **enveloped viruses** (mostly animal) are released from the host cell, they take with them a bit of its membrane system in the form of an envelope. Some viruses bud off the cell membrane; others leave via the nuclear envelope or the endoplasmic reticulum. Although the envelope is derived from the host, it is different because some or all of the regular membrane proteins are replaced with special viral proteins during the virus assembly process (see figure 6.11). Some proteins form a binding layer between the envelope and capsid of the virus, and glycoproteins (proteins bound to a carbohydrate) remain exposed on the outside of the envelope. These protruding molecules, called **spikes** or peplomers, are essential for the attachment of viruses to the

next host cell. Because the envelope is more supple than the capsid, enveloped viruses are pleomorphic and range from spherical to filamentous in shape.

Functions of the Viral Capsid/Envelope

The outermost covering of a virus is indispensable to viral function because it protects the nucleic acid from the effects of various enzymes and chemicals when the virus is outside the host cell. We see this in the capsids of enteric (intestinal) viruses such as polio and hepatitis A, which are resistant to the acid- and protein-digesting enzymes of the gastrointestinal tract. Capsids and envelopes are also responsible for helping to introduce the viral DNA or RNA into a suitable host cell, first by binding to the cell surface and then by assisting in penetration of the viral nucleic acid (discussed in later sections). In addition, parts of viral capsids and envelopes stimulate the immune system to produce antibodies that can neutralize viruses and protect the host's cells against future infections (see chapter 15).

Complex Viruses: Atypical Viruses

Two special groups of viruses, termed complex viruses **(figure 6.9),** are more intricate in structure than the helical, icosahedral, naked, or enveloped viruses just described. The **poxviruses** (including the

Figure 6.8 Two types of icosahedral viruses, highly magnified. (a) Left view: A negative stain of rotaviruses with unusual capsomers that look like spokes on a wheel (150,000×); right view is a three-dimensional model of this virus. **(b)** Herpes simplex virus, a type of enveloped icosahedral virus (300,000×).

Figure 6.9 Detailed structure of complex viruses.
(a) Section through the vaccinia virus, a poxvirus, shows its internal components. **(b)** Diagram of a T4 bacteriophage of *E. coli*, (280,000×). **(c)** Photomicrograph of a bacteriophage from cyanobacteria.

agent of smallpox) are very large DNA viruses that lack a typical capsid and are covered by a dense layer of lipoproteins and coarse fibrils on their outer surface. Some members of another group of very complex viruses, the **bacteriophages,*** have a polyhedral capsid head as well as a helical tail and fibers for attachment to the host cell. Their mode of multiplication is covered in section 6.5. **Figure 6.10** summarizes the primary morphological types found among the viruses.

Nucleic Acids: At the Core of a Virus

The sum total of the genetic information carried by an organism is known as its **genome.** So far, one biological constant is that the genome of all organisms is carried by and expressed through nucleic acids (DNA, RNA). Even viruses are no exception to this rule, but there is a significant difference. Unlike cells, which contain both DNA and RNA, **viruses contain either DNA or RNA** *but not both as the primary genetic material.* Because viruses must pack into a tiny space all of the genes necessary to instruct the host cell to make new viruses, the number of viral genes is usually quite small compared with that of a cell. It varies from nine genes in

* *bacteriophage* (bak-teer′-ee-oh-fayj″) From *bacteria,* and Gr. *phagein,* to eat. These viruses parasitize bacteria.

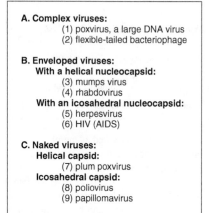

A. Complex Viruses

(1)

(2)

B. Enveloped Viruses

Helical Icosahedral

(3) (5)

(4) (6)

C. Nonenveloped Naked Viruses

Helical Icosahedral

(7) (8)

(9)

A. Complex viruses:
 (1) poxvirus, a large DNA virus
 (2) flexible-tailed bacteriophage

B. Enveloped viruses:
 With a helical nucleocapsid:
 (3) mumps virus
 (4) rhabdovirus
 With an icosahedral nucleocapsid:
 (5) herpesvirus
 (6) HIV (AIDS)

C. Naked viruses:
 Helical capsid:
 (7) plum poxvirus
 Icosahedral capsid:
 (8) poliovirus
 (9) papillomavirus

Figure 6.10 Basic types of viral morphology.

human immunodeficiency virus (HIV) to over 2,000 genes in pandoraviruses. By comparison, the bacterium *Escherichia coli* has approximately 4,000 genes, and a human cell has fewer than 21,000 genes. Having a larger genome allows cells to carry out the complex metabolic activity necessary for independent life. Viruses typically possess only the genes needed to invade host cells and redirect their synthetic machinery to make new viruses.

In chapter 2, you learned that DNA usually exists as a double-stranded molecule and that RNA is single-stranded. Although most viruses follow this same pattern, a few exhibit distinctive and exceptional forms. Notable examples are the parvoviruses, which contain single-stranded DNA, and reoviruses (a cause of respiratory and intestinal tract infections), which contain double-stranded RNA. In fact, viruses exhibit variety in how their RNA or DNA is

configured. DNA viruses can have single-stranded (ss) or double-stranded (ds) DNA; the dsDNA can be arranged linearly or in circles. RNA viruses can be double-stranded but are more often single-stranded. You will learn in chapter 9 that all proteins are made by "translating" the nucleic acid code on a single strand of RNA into an amino acid sequence. Single-stranded RNA genomes that are ready for immediate translation into proteins are called *positive-strand* RNA. RNA genomes that have to be converted into the proper form for translation are called *negative-strand* RNA.

RNA genomes may also be *segmented*, meaning that the individual genes exist in separate RNA molecules. The influenza virus (an orthomyxovirus) is an example of this form. An RNA virus with some unusual features is a *retrovirus*, one of the few virus types that converts its nucleic acid from RNA to DNA inside its host cell.

Whatever the virus type, these tiny strands of genetic material carry the blueprint for viral structure and functions. In a very real sense, viruses are genetic parasites because they cannot multiply until their nucleic acid has reached their haven inside the host cell. At the minimum, they must carry genes for synthesizing the viral capsid and genetic material, for regulating the actions of the host, and for packaging the mature virus.

Other Substances in the Virus Particle

In addition to the protein of the capsid, the proteins and lipids of envelopes, and the nucleic acid of the core, viruses can contain enzymes for specific operations within their host cell. They may come with preformed enzymes that are required for viral **replication.*** Examples include **polymerases*** that synthesize DNA and RNA and replicases that copy RNA. The human immunodeficiency virus (HIV) comes equipped with *reverse transcriptase* for synthesizing DNA from RNA. However, viruses completely lack the genes for synthesis of metabolic enzymes. As we shall see, this deficiency has little consequence, because viruses have adapted to assume total control over the cell's metabolic resources. Some viruses can actually carry away substances from their host cell. For instance, arenaviruses pack along host ribosomes, and retroviruses "borrow" the host's tRNA molecules.

6.3 How Viruses Are Classified and Named

 Expected Learning Outcomes

9. Explain the classification scheme used for viruses.
10. Indicate the characteristics used in identifying and naming viruses.

Although viruses are not classified as members of the domains discussed in chapter 1, they are diverse enough to require their own classification scheme to aid in their study and identification. In an informal and general way, we have already begun classifying viruses—as animal, plant, or bacterial viruses; enveloped or naked viruses; DNA or RNA viruses; and helical or icosahedral viruses. These introductory categories are certainly useful in organization and description, but the study of specific viruses requires a more standardized method of nomenclature. For many years, the animal viruses were classified mainly on the basis of their hosts and the kind of diseases they caused. Newer systems for naming viruses also take into account the actual nature of the virus particles themselves, with only partial emphasis on host and disease. The main criteria presently used to group viruses are structure, chemical composition, and similarities in genetic makeup, which indicate evolutionary relatedness.

The International Committee on the Taxonomy of Viruses lists 7 orders, 96 families, and 350 genera of viruses. Nomenclature of viruses follows these conventions: Virus families are italicized and given the suffix *-viridae,* and virus genera are likewise italicized and end in *-virus.*

Historically, some virologists had created an informal *species* naming system that mirrors the species names in higher organisms, using genus and species epithets such as *Measles morbillivirus.* The species category has created a lot of controversy within the virology community. Many scientists argue that nonorganisms such as viruses are too changeable and that fine distinctions used for deciding on species classifications will quickly disappear. Over the past decade, virologists have largely accepted the concept of viral species, defining them as consisting of members that have a number of properties in common but have some variations. In other words, a virus is placed in a species on the basis of a collection of properties such as host range, pathogenicity, and genetic makeup.

Because the use of standardized species names has not been widely accepted, the genus or common English vernacular names (for example, poliovirus and rabies virus) predominate in discussions of specific viruses in this text. **Table 6.2** illustrates a system of classification for important viruses and the diseases they cause. To-scale examples of each virus family are included.

Characteristics used for placement in a particular family include type of capsid, nucleic acid strand number, presence and type of envelope, overall viral size, and area of the host cell in which the virus multiplies. Some virus families are named for their microscopic appearance (shape and size). Examples include **rhabdoviruses,*** which have a bullet-shaped envelope, and **togaviruses,*** which have a cloaklike envelope. Anatomical or geographic areas have also been used in naming. For instance, **adenoviruses*** were first discovered in adenoids (one type of tonsil), and hantaviruses were originally isolated in the Korean Province of Hantaan. Viruses can also be named for their effects on the host. **Lentiviruses*** tend to cause slow, chronic infections. Acronyms made from blending several characteristics include **picornaviruses,*** which are tiny RNA viruses, and **hepadnaviruses** (for hepatitis and DNA).

Check Your Progress SECTIONS 6.2 AND 6.3

5. Characterize viruses according to size range. What does it mean to say that they are ultramicroscopic?
6. Describe the general structure of viruses.
7. What is the capsid, and what is its function; how are the two types of capsids constructed?
8. What is a nucleocapsid? Give examples of viruses with the two capsid types.
9. What is an enveloped virus, and how does the envelope arise? What are spikes, how are they formed, and what is their function?
10. What are bacteriophages, and what is unique about their structure?
11. How are the poxviruses different from other animal viruses?
12. Explain the characteristics used in viral classification and the nature of viral families.
13. How are generic and common names used?

replication (rep-lih-kay'-shun) L. *replicare,* to reply. To make an exact duplicate.
polymerase (pol-im'-ur-ace) An enzyme that synthesizes a large molecule from smaller subunits.

rhabdovirus (rab"-doh-vy'-rus) Gr. *rhabdo,* little rod.
togavirus (toh"-guh-vy'-rus) L. *toga,* covering or robe.
adenovirus (ad"-uh-noh-vy'-rus) G. *aden,* gland.
lentivirus (len"-tee-vy'-rus) Gr. *lente,* slow. HIV, the AIDS virus, belongs in this group.
picornavirus (py-kor"-nah-vy'-rus) Sp. *pico,* small, plus RNA.

TABLE 6.2 Important Human Virus Families, Genera, Common Names, and Types of Diseases

Nucleic Acid Type	Family	Genus of Virus	Common Name of Genus Members	Name of Disease
DNA Viruses				
Poxviridae Chordopoxvirinae *Herpesviridae*	*Poxviridae*	*Orthopoxvirus*	Variola and vaccinia	Smallpox, cowpox
	Herpesviridae	*Simplexvirus*	Herpes simplex 1 virus (HSV-1)	Fever blister, cold sores
			Herpes simplex 2 virus (HSV-2)	Genital herpes
		Varicellovirus	Varicella zoster virus (VZV)	Chickenpox, shingles
		Cytomegalovirus	Human cytomegalovirus (CMV)	CMV infections
Adenoviridae	*Adenoviridae*	*Mastadenovirus*	Human adenoviruses	Adenovirus infection
Papillomaviridae *Polyomaviridae*	*Papillomaviridae*	*Papillomavirus*	Human papillomavirus (HPV)	Several types of warts
	Polyomaviridae	*Polyomavirus*	JC virus (JCV)	Progressive multifocal leukoencephalopathy
Hepadnaviridae *Parvoviridae* Parvovirinae	*Hepadnaviridae*	*Hepadnavirus*	Hepatitis B virus (HBV or Dane particle)	Serum hepatitis
	Parvoviridae	*Erythrovirus*	Parvovirus B19	Erythema infectiosum
RNA Viruses				
Picornaviridae	*Picornaviridae*	*Enterovirus*	Poliovirus	Poliomyelitis
			Coxsackievirus	Hand-foot-mouth disease
Caliciviridae		*Hepatovirus*	Hepatitis A virus (HAV)	Short-term hepatitis
		Rhinovirus	Human rhinovirus	Common cold, bronchitis
Togaviridae	*Caliciviridae*	*Calicivirus*	Norwalk virus	Viral diarrhea, Norwalk virus syndrome
	Togaviridae	*Alphavirus*	Eastern equine encephalitis virus	Eastern equine encephalitis (EEE)
			Western equine encephalitis virus	Western equine encephalitis (WEE)
			Yellow fever virus	Yellow fever
			St. Louis encephalitis virus	St. Louis encephalitis
Flaviviridae	*Flaviviridae*	*Rubivirus*	Rubella virus	Rubella (German measles)
		Flavivirus	Dengue fever virus	Dengue fever
			West Nile fever virus	West Nile fever
Filoviridae *Bunyaviridae*	*Bunyaviridae*	*Bunyavirus*	Bunyamwera viruses	California encephalitis
		Hantavirus	Sin Nombre virus	Respiratory syndrome
		Phlebovirus	Rift Valley fever virus	Rift Valley fever
		Nairovirus	Crimean–Congo hemorrhagic fever (CCHF) virus	Crimean–Congo hemorrhagic fever
Reoviridae	*Filoviridae*	*Filovirus*	Ebola, Marburg virus	Ebola fever
	Reoviridae	*Coltivirus*	Colorado tick fever virus	Colorado tick fever
		Rotavirus	Human rotavirus	Rotavirus gastroenteritis
Orthomyxoviridae *Paramyxoviridae*	*Orthomyxoviridae*	*Influenza virus*	Influenza virus, type A (Asian, Hong Kong, and swine influenza viruses)	Influenza or "flu"
	Paramyxoviridae	*Paramyxovirus*	Parainfluenza virus	Parainfluenza
			Mumps virus	Mumps
		Morbillivirus	Measles virus	Measles (red)
		Pneumovirus	Respiratory syncytial virus (RSV)	Common cold syndrome

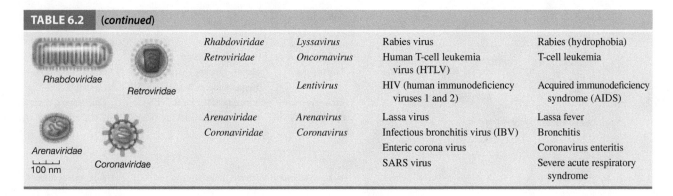

TABLE 6.2	(continued)				
Rhabdoviridae		*Rhabdoviridae*	*Lyssavirus*	Rabies virus	Rabies (hydrophobia)
	Retroviridae	*Retroviridae*	*Oncornavirus*	Human T-cell leukemia virus (HTLV)	T-cell leukemia
			Lentivirus	HIV (human immunodeficiency viruses 1 and 2)	Acquired immunodeficiency syndrome (AIDS)
Arenaviridae	*Coronaviridae*	*Arenaviridae*	*Arenavirus*	Lassa virus	Lassa fever
100 nm		*Coronaviridae*	*Coronavirus*	Infectious bronchitis virus (IBV)	Bronchitis
				Enteric corona virus	Coronavirus enteritis
				SARS virus	Severe acute respiratory syndrome

6.4 Modes of Viral Multiplication

 Expected Learning Outcomes

11. Describe the virus-host relationship.

12. Relate the stages in the multiplication cycle of animal viruses, and summarize what is happening in each stage.

13. Describe three ways that animal viruses enter into a host cell.

14. Define *replication* as it relates to viruses.

15. Explain two ways that animal viruses are released by a host cell.

16. Describe cytopathic effects of viruses and the possible results of persistent viral infections.

Viruses are closely associated with their hosts. In addition to providing the viral habitat, the host cell is absolutely necessary for viral multiplication, which is synonymous with infection. The way that viruses invade a host cell is an extraordinary biological phenomenon. Viruses have been aptly described as minute parasites that seize control of the synthetic and genetic machinery of cells. The nature of this cycle profoundly affects pathogenicity, transmission, the responses of the immune defenses, and human measures to control viral infections. From these perspectives, we cannot overemphasize the importance of a working knowledge of the relationship between viruses and their host cells.

Multiplication Cycles in Animal Viruses

The general phases in the life cycle of animal viruses are **adsorption,*** **penetration, synthesis, assembly,** and **release** from the host cell. Viruses vary in the exact mechanisms of these processes, but we will use a simple animal virus to illustrate the major events **(figure 6.11).** Other examples are given in chapter 9.

Adsorption and Host Range

Invasion begins when the virus encounters a susceptible host cell and adsorbs specifically to receptor sites on the cell membrane. The membrane receptors that viruses attach to are usually glycoproteins the cell requires for its normal function. For example, the rabies virus affixes

to receptors found on mammalian nerve cells, and the human immunodeficiency virus (HIV) attaches to the CD4 protein on certain white blood cells. The mode of attachment varies between the two general types of viruses. In enveloped forms such as influenza virus and HIV, glycoprotein spikes bind to the cell membrane receptors. Viruses with naked nucleocapsids (adenovirus, for example) use surface receptors on their capsids that adhere to cell membrane receptors **(figure 6.12).**

Because a virus can invade its host cell only through making an exact fit with a specific host molecule, the range of hosts it can infect in a natural setting is limited. This limitation, known as the **host range,** can vary from one virus to another. For example, hepatitis B infects only liver cells of humans; the poliovirus infects primarily intestinal and nerve cells of primates (humans, apes, and monkeys); and the rabies virus infects nerve cells of most mammals. Cells that lack compatible virus receptors are resistant to adsorption and invasion by that virus. This explains why, for example, human liver cells are not infected by the canine hepatitis virus and dog liver cells cannot host the human hepatitis A virus. It also explains why viruses usually have tissue specificities called **tropisms*** for certain cells in the body. The hepatitis B virus targets the liver, and the mumps virus targets salivary glands. Many viruses can be manipulated in the laboratory to infect cells that they do not infect naturally, thus making it possible to cultivate them.

> **Quick Search**
> Look up "Flu Attack! How a Virus Invades Your Body" on the internet.

Penetration/Uncoating of Animal Viruses

For an animal virus to successfully infect a cell, it must penetrate the cell membrane of the host cell and deliver the viral nucleic acid into the host cell's interior. How animal viruses do this varies with the type of virus and type of host cell, but most of them enter through some form of fusion or **endocytosis,** also known as **viropexis (figure 6.13).** In the case of **fusion,** the viral envelope fuses directly with the host cell membrane, so it can occur only in enveloped viruses **(figure 6.13*a*).** Following attachment of the virus to host cell receptors, the lipids within the adjacent membranes become rearranged so that the nucleocapsid can be translocated into the cytoplasm for the synthesis phase.

In the **endocytosis** version of penetration, the virus can be either enveloped **(figure 6.13*b*)** or naked **(figure 6.13*c*),** and it is

* *adsorption* (ad-sorp'-shun) L. ad, to, and *sorbere,* to suck. The attachment of one thing onto the surface of another.

* *tropism* (troh'-pizm) Gr. *trope,* a turn. Having a special affinity for an object or substance.

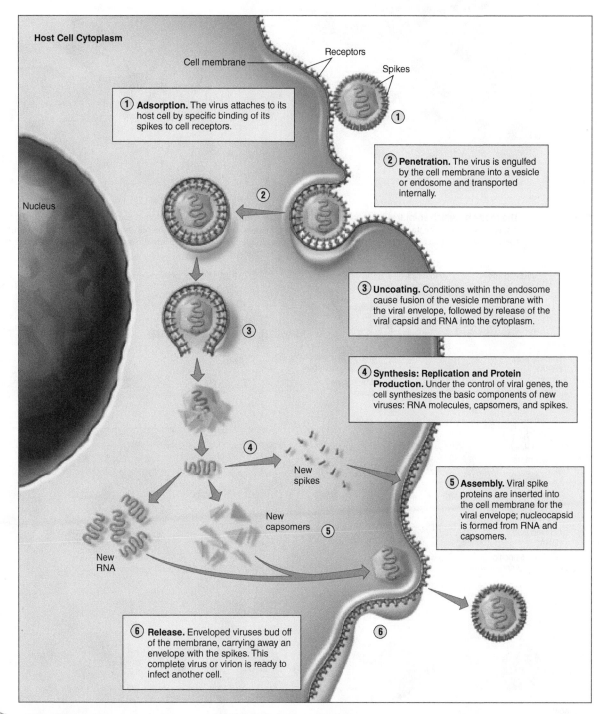

Host Cell Cytoplasm

Cell membrane — Receptors

Spikes

(1) **Adsorption.** The virus attaches to its host cell by specific binding of its spikes to cell receptors.

(2) **Penetration.** The virus is engulfed by the cell membrane into a vesicle or endosome and transported internally.

Nucleus

(3) **Uncoating.** Conditions within the endosome cause fusion of the vesicle membrane with the viral envelope, followed by release of the viral capsid and RNA into the cytoplasm.

(4) **Synthesis: Replication and Protein Production.** Under the control of viral genes, the cell synthesizes the basic components of new viruses: RNA molecules, capsomers, and spikes.

New spikes

New capsomers

(5) **Assembly.** Viral spike proteins are inserted into the cell membrane for the viral envelope; nucleocapsid is formed from RNA and capsomers.

New RNA

(6) **Release.** Enveloped viruses bud off of the membrane, carrying away an envelope with the spikes. This complete virus or virion is ready to infect another cell.

Process Figure 6.11 General features in the multiplication cycle of an enveloped animal virus. Using an RNA virus (rubella virus), the major events are outlined, although other viruses will vary in exact details of the cycle.

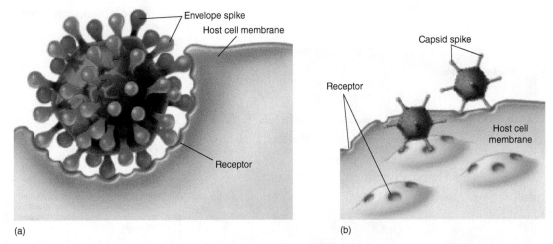

(a)

(b)

Figure 6.12 **The mode by which animal viruses adsorb to the host cell membrane. (a)** An enveloped coronavirus with prominent spikes. The configuration of the spike has a complementary fit for cell receptors. The process in which the virus lands on the cell and plugs into receptors is termed docking. **(b)** An adenovirus has a naked capsid that adheres to its host cell by nestling surface molecules on its capsid into the receptors on the host cell's membrane.

(c) Adhesion of virus to host receptors Engulfment into vesicle Viral RNA is released from vesicle

🜩 **Process Figure 6.13** **Modes of virus penetration.** Pictured in **(a)** is the process of fusion between the envelope of the virus and the host cell membrane, with release of the nucleocapsid into the cytoplasm. This is the mechanism for mumps and HIV viruses. Both **(b)** and **(c)** are examples of entry by endocytosis or engulfment, followed by uncoating. **(b)** In an enveloped virus such as herpesvirus, the entire virus is taken into a vesicle with subsequent release of the DNA. **(c)** A naked virus such as poliovirus is first taken into a vesicle and then releases its nucleic acid through a pore or rupture in the membrane.

Figure 6.14 Maturation and release of enveloped viruses.
(a) As parainfluenza virus is budded off the membrane, it simultaneously picks up an envelope and spikes. **(b)** AIDS viruses (HIV) leave their host T cell by budding off its surface.

engulfed entirely into a vesicle called an endosome after its initial attachment. Once inside the cell, the virus is **uncoated.** This means that the vesicle membrane becomes altered so that the viral nucleocapsid or nucleic acid can be released into the cytoplasm. In some viruses, the vesicle membrane fuses with the virus, and in other cases, the vesicle membrane develops openings for the virus to leave. There are numerous variations in the details of this process.

Synthesis: Replication and Protein Production

The synthetic and replicative phases of animal viruses are highly regulated and extremely complex at the molecular level. Free viral nucleic acid exerts control over the host's metabolism and synthetic machinery. How this control proceeds will vary, depending on whether the virus is a DNA or an RNA virus. In general, the DNA viruses (except poxviruses) enter the host cell's nucleus and are replicated and assembled there. RNA viruses are replicated and assembled in the cytoplasm, with some exceptions.

The details of animal virus replication are discussed in chapter 9. Here we provide a brief overview of the process, using an RNA virus as a model. Almost immediately upon entry, the viral nucleic acid

alters the genetic expression of the host and instructs it to synthesize the building blocks for new viruses. For example, it was recently shown that HIV depends on the expression of 250 human genes to complete its multiplication cycle. First, the RNA of the virus becomes a message for synthesizing viral proteins (translation). Most viruses with positive-strand RNA molecules already contain the correct message for translation into proteins. Viruses with negative-strand RNA molecules must first be converted into a positive-strand message. Some viruses come equipped with the necessary enzymes for synthesis of viral components; others utilize those of the host. During the final phase, the host's replication and synthesis machinery produces new RNA, proteins for the capsid, spikes, and viral enzymes.

Assembly of Animal Viruses: Host Cell as Factory

Toward the end of the cycle, mature virus particles are constructed from the growing pool of parts. In most instances, the capsid is first laid down as an empty shell that will serve as a receptacle for the nucleic acid strand. Electron micrographs taken during this time show cells with masses of viruses, often enclosed in packets (see figure 6.15*a*). One important event leading to the release of enveloped viruses is the insertion of viral spikes into the host's cell membrane so they can be picked up as the virus buds off with its envelope, as discussed.

Release of Mature Viruses

To complete the cycle, assembled viruses leave their host in one of two ways. Nonenveloped and complex viruses that reach maturation in the cell nucleus or cytoplasm are released through cell **lysis** or rupturing. Enveloped viruses are liberated by **budding** or **exocytosis**[3] from the membranes of the cytoplasm, nucleus, endoplasmic reticulum, or vesicles. During this process, the nucleocapsid binds to the membrane, which curves completely around it and forms a small pouch. Pinching off the pouch releases the virus with its envelope **(figure 6.14).** Budding of enveloped viruses causes them to be shed gradually, without the sudden destruction of the cell. Regardless of how the virus leaves, most active viral infections

3. For enveloped viruses, these terms are interchangeable. They mean the release of a virus from an animal cell by enclosing it in a portion of membrane derived from the cell.

are ultimately lethal to the cell because of accumulated damage. Lethal damages include a permanent shutdown of metabolism and genetic expression, destruction of cell membrane and organelles, toxicity of virus components, and release of lysosomes.

The length of a multiplication cycle, from adsorption to lysis, varies to some extent, but it is usually measured in hours. A simple virus such as poliovirus takes about 8 hours; parvovirus takes 16 to 18 hours; and more complex viruses, such as herpesviruses, require 72 hours or more.

A fully formed, extracellular virus particle that is virulent and able to establish infection in a host is called a **virion.*** The number of virions released by infected cells is variable, controlled by factors such as the size of the virus and the health of the host cell. About 3,000 to 4,000 virions are released from a single cell infected with poxviruses, whereas a poliovirus-infected cell can release over 100,000 virions. If even a small number of these virions happens to meet other susceptible cells and infect them, the potential for viral proliferation is immense.

Visible Damage to the Host Cell

The short- and long-term effects of viral infections on animal cells are well documented. **Cytopathic*** **effects** (CPEs) are defined as virus-induced damage to the cell that alters its microscopic appearance. Individual cells can become disoriented, undergo gross changes in shape or size, or develop intracellular changes **(figure 6.15a).** It is common to note **inclusion bodies,** or compacted masses of viruses or damaged cell organelles, in the nucleus and cytoplasm **(figure 6.15b).** Examination of cells and tissues for cytopathic effects has been a traditional tool for diagnosing viral infections that is usually supplemented with more specific serological and molecular methods (see chapter 17). **Table 6.3** summarizes some prominent cytopathic effects associated with specific viruses. One very common CPE is the fusion

* *virion* (vir′-ee-on) Gr. *iso*, poison.
* *cytopathic* (sy″-toh-path′-ik) Gr. *cyto*, cell, and *pathos*, disease.

CLINICAL CONNECTIONS

Persistent Viral Infections

As a general rule, a virus infection kills its host cell, but some cells escape destruction by harboring the virus in some form. These so-called **persistent infections** can last from a few weeks to years and even for the life of the host. Take for example the hepatitis B virus, which produces a chronic progressive infection of the liver that may lead to cirrhosis and cancer. Several viruses remain in a **latent state,** meaning that they remain inactive or nonproductive over long periods. Examples of this are herpes simplex viruses (cold sores and genital herpes) and herpes zoster virus (chickenpox and shingles). Both viruses go into latency in nerve cells and later emerge under the influence of various stimuli to cause recurrent symptoms.

Some animal viruses enter their host cell and permanently alter its genetic material, in many cases leading to cancer. These viruses are termed *oncogenic,* and their effect on the cell is called **transformation.** A startling feature of some of these viruses is that their nucleic acid becomes integrated into the host DNA. Transformed cells generally have an increased rate of growth, alterations in chromosomes, changes in the cell's surface molecules, and the capacity to divide for an indefinite period. Mammalian viruses involved in the development of tumors are called **oncoviruses.** Some of these are DNA viruses such as papillomavirus, which is associated with cervical cancer, and herpesviruses such as Epstein-Barr virus, which is a cofactor in Burkitt's lymphoma in genetically-predisposed individuals. These findings have spurred a great deal of speculation on the possible involvement of viruses in cancers whose cause is still unknown. Additional information on the connection between viruses and cancer is found in chapter 24.

Why would the integration of viral genes into a human chromosome cause cancer? *Answer available at http://www.mhhe.com/talaro9*

Multiple nuclei

Normal cell

Giant cell

(a)

Inclusion bodies

(b)

Figure 6.15 Cytopathic changes in cells and cell cultures infected by viruses. (a) Human epithelial cells (400×) infected by herpes simplex virus demonstrate multinucleate giant cells; inset with a cluster of viruses from an intranuclear inclusion (100,000×). **(b)** Fluorescent-stained human cells infected with cytomegalovirus. Note the inclusion bodies (1,000×) and the loss of cohesive junctions between cells.

TABLE 6.3	Cytopathic Changes in Selected Virus-Infected Animal Cells
Virus	**Response in Animal Cell**
Smallpox virus	Cells round up; inclusions appear in cytoplasm
Herpes simplex	Cells fuse to form multinucleated syncytia; nuclear inclusions (see figure 6.15)
Adenovirus	Clumping of cells; nuclear inclusions
Poliovirus	Cell lysis; no inclusions
Reovirus	Cell enlargement; vacuoles and inclusions in cytoplasm
Influenza virus	Cells round up; no inclusions
Rabies virus	No change in cell shape; cytoplasmic inclusions (Negri bodies)
Measles virus	Syncytia form (multinucleate)

of multiple host cells into single large cells containing multiple nuclei. These **syncytia** are a result of some viruses' ability to fuse membranes. One virus (respiratory syncytial virus) is even named for this effect.

 Check Your Progress SECTION 6.4

14. Write a narrative that describes the stages in the multiplication of an enveloped animal virus.
15. Describe some ways that animal viruses penetrate the host cell. What is uncoating?
16. Summarize the two major ways that animal viruses leave their host cells.
17. What is meant by the term *virion?*
18. Describe several cytopathic effects of viruses. What causes the appearance of the host cell, and how might it be used to diagnose viral infections?
19. Explain what it means for a virus to become persistent or latent, and how these events are important.
20. Briefly describe the effects of an oncogenic virus.

6.5 The Multiplication Cycle in Bacteriophages

 Expected Learning Outcomes

17. Describe the stages in the multiplication cycle of bacteriophages.
18. Explain what is meant by lysogeny, prophage, and lysogenic induction and conversion.
19. Compare the major stages in multiplication of animal viruses and bacteriophages.

For the sake of comparison, we now turn to multiplication in bacterial viruses—the bacteriophages. When Frederick Twort and Felix d'Herelle discovered these viruses in 1915, it first appeared that the bacterial host cells were being eaten by some unseen parasite; hence, the name bacteriophage was used.

So far as is known, all bacteria are parasitized by various specific viruses. Most bacteriophages (often shortened to *phage*) contain double-stranded DNA, though single-stranded DNA and RNA types exist as well. Bacteriophages are of great interest to medical microbiologists because they can make the bacteria they infect more virulent for humans.

Probably the most widely studied bacteriophages are those of the intestinal bacterium *Escherichia coli*—especially the T-even phages and the lambda phages. They are complex in structure, with an icosahedral capsid head containing DNA, a central tube (surrounded by a sheath), collar, base plate, tail pins, and fibers (see figure 6.9b). Momentarily setting aside a strictly scientific and objective tone, it is tempting to think of these extraordinary viruses as minute spacecrafts docking on an alien planet, ready to unload their genetic cargo.

Bacteriophages go through similar stages as the animal viruses described earlier **(figure 6.16).** First, they adsorb to host bacteria using specific receptors on the bacterial surface. Although the entire phage cannot enter the host cell, the nucleic acid is injected through a rigid tube the phage inserts through the bacterial membrane and wall **(figure 6.17).** The empty capsid remains attached to the cell surface. Entry of the nucleic acid stops host cell DNA replication and protein synthesis, and it soon prepares the cell machinery for viral replication and synthesis of viral proteins. As the host cell produces new phage parts, the parts spontaneously assemble into bacteriophages.

An average-size *Escherichia coli* cell can contain up to 200 new phage units at the end of this period. Eventually, the host cell becomes so packed with viruses that it undergoes **lysis** and splits open, thereby releasing the mature virions **(figure 6.18).** This process is hastened by viral enzymes produced late in the infection cycle that weaken the cell envelope. Upon release, the virulent phages can spread to other susceptible bacterial cells and begin a new cycle of infection.

Lysogeny: The Silent Virus Infection

The lethal effects of a virulent phage on the host cell present a dramatic view of virus-host interaction. However, not all bacteriophages go immediately into a lytic cycle. Depending upon the conditions in the bacterial host, some special DNA viruses, called **temperate* phages,** undergo adsorption and penetration into the bacterial host but are not replicated or released immediately. Instead, the viral DNA enters an inactive **prophage*** state, during which it is usually inserted into the bacterial chromosome. This viral DNA will be retained by the bacterial cell and copied during its normal cell division so that the cell's progeny will also have the phage DNA. This condition, in which the host chromosome carries bacteriophage DNA, is termed **lysogeny.*** Because viral particles are not produced, the bacterial cells carrying temperate phages do not lyse and they appear entirely normal. Later, in a process called **induction,** the prophage in a lysogenic cell will be activated and progress directly into viral replication and the lytic cycle. The lysogenic phase is depicted in the green section of figure 6.16. Lysogeny is a less deadly form of infection than the full lytic cycle and is thought to be an advancement that allows the virus to spread without killing the host.

* *temperate* (tem'-pur-ut) A reduction in intensity.
* *prophage* (pro'-fayj) L. *pro,* before, plus phage.
* *lysogeny* (ly-soj'-uhn-ee) The potential ability to produce phage.

The lysogenic state in bacteria.
The viral DNA molecule is inserted at specific sites on the bacterial chromosome. The viral DNA is duplicated along with the regular genome and can provide adaptive genes for the host bacterium.

Bacteriophage assembly line.
First the capsomers are synthesized by the host cell. A strand of viral nucleic acid is inserted during capsid formation. In final assembly, the prefabricated components fit together into whole parts and finally into the finished viruses.

Process Figure 6.16 Events in the multiplication cycle of lambda bacteriophages. The lytic cycle (1–7) involves full completion of viral infection through lysis and release of virions. Occasionally the virus enters a reversible state of lysogeny (left) and is incorporated into the host's genetic material.

Because of the intimate association between the genetic material of the virus and host, phages occasionally serve as transporters of bacterial genes from one bacterium to another and consequently can play a profound role in bacterial genetics. This phenomenon, called transduction, is one way that genes for toxin production and drug resistance are transferred between bacteria (see chapters 9 and 12).

Phages have profound effects on the infectiousness and virulence of pathogenic bacteria. Viral genomes often encode toxins, enzymes, and other factors that can alter the course and outcome of infections. When a bacterium acquires genes from its temperate phage, it is called **lysogenic conversion** (see figure 6.16). The phenomenon was first discovered in the 1950s in the pathogen that causes diphtheria, *Corynebacterium diphtheriae*. The diphtheria toxin responsible for the severe nature of the disease is a bacteriophage product. *C. diphtheriae* without the phage are less pathogenic. Other bacteria that are made virulent by their prophages are

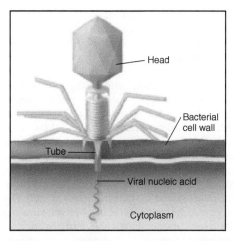

Figure 6.17 Penetration of a bacterial cell by a T-even bacteriophage. After adsorption, the phage plate becomes embedded in the cell wall, and the sheath contracts, pushing the tube through the cell wall and membrane and releasing the nucleic acid into the interior of the cell.

Figure 6.18 A weakened bacterial cell, crowded with viruses. The cell has ruptured and released numerous virions that can then attack nearby susceptible host cells. Note the empty heads of "spent" phages lined up around the ruptured wall.

Vibrio cholerae, the agent of cholera, and *Clostridium botulinum,* the cause of botulism.

The cycles of bacterial and animal viruses illustrate different patterns of viral multiplication, which are summarized in **table 6.4.**

 Check Your Progress SECTION 6.5

21. In simple terms, what does the virus nucleic acid do once it gets into the cell?

22. What processes are involved in bacteriophage assembly?

23. What is a prophage or temperate phage? What is lysogeny?

24. Compare and contrast the main phases in the lytic multiplication cycle in bacteriophages and animal viruses.

25. Why is penetration so different in the two groups?

TABLE 6.4	**Comparison of Bacteriophage and Animal Viral Multiplication**	
	Bacteriophage	**Animal Virus**
Adsorption	Precise attachment of special tail fibers to cell wall	Attachment of capsid or envelope to cell surface receptors
Penetration	Injection of nucleic acid through cell wall; no uncoating of nucleic acid	Whole virus is engulfed and uncoated, or virus surface fuses with cell membrane; nucleic acid is released.
Synthesis and Assembly	Occurs in cytoplasm Cessation of host synthesis Viral DNA or RNA replicated Viral components synthesized	Occurs in cytoplasm and nucleus Cessation of host synthesis Viral DNA or RNA replicated Viral components synthesized
Viral Persistence	Lysogeny	Latency, chronic infection, cancer
Release from Host Cell	Cell lyses when viral enzymes weaken it.	Some cells lyse; enveloped viruses bud off host cell membrane.
Cell Destruction	Immediate	Immediate or delayed

6.6 Techniques in Cultivating and Identifying Animal Viruses

 Expected Learning Outcomes

20. Describe the general purposes of cultivating viruses.

21. Compare the methods and uses of cell culture, bird embryos, and live animals in growing viruses.

One problem hampering early animal virologists was their inability to propagate specific viruses routinely in pure culture and in sufficient quantities for their studies. Virtually all of the pioneering attempts at cultivation had to be performed in an organism that was the usual host for the virus. But this method had its limitations. How could researchers have ever traced the stages of viral multiplication if they had been restricted to the natural host, especially in the case of human viruses? Fortunately, systems of cultivation with broader applications were developed, including **in vitro*** cell (or tissue) culture methods and **in vivo*** inoculation of laboratory-bred animals and embryonic bird tissues. Such use of substitute host

* *in vitro* (in vee'-troh) L. *vitros,* glass. Experiments performed in test tubes or other artificial environments.

* *in vivo* (in vee'-voh) L. *vivos,* life. Experiments performed in a living body.

systems permits greater control, uniformity, and wide-scale harvesting of viruses.

The primary purposes of viral cultivation are (1) to isolate and identify viruses in clinical specimens; (2) to prepare viruses for vaccines; and (3) to do detailed research on viral structure, multiplication cycles, genetics, and effects on host cells.

Although it is not the usual method of cultivating viruses, scientists at the State University of New York succeeded in using a cell-free extract to artificially create a virus that is virtually identical to natural poliovirus. They used DNA nucleotides bought "off the shelf" and put them together according to the published poliovirus sequence. They then added an enzyme that would transcribe the DNA sequence into the RNA genome used by poliovirus. They ended up with a virus that mimicked the structure, infectivity, and replication cycle of the poliovirus.

Using Cell (Tissue) Culture Techniques

The most important early discovery that led to easier cultivation of viruses in the laboratory was the development of a simple and effective way to grow populations of isolated animal cells in culture. These types of in vitro cultivation systems are termed **cell culture** or tissue culture. Although these terms are used interchangeably, cell culture is probably a more accurate description. This method makes it possible to propagate most viruses. Much of the virologist's work involves developing and maintaining these cultures. Animal cell cultures are grown in sterile chambers with special media that contain the correct nutrients required by animal cells to survive. The cultured cells grow in the form of a *monolayer*, a single, confluent sheet of cells that supports viral multiplication and permits close inspection of the culture for signs of infection (**figure 6.19**).

Cultures of animal cells usually exist in the primary or continuous form. *Primary cell cultures* are prepared by placing freshly isolated animal tissue in a growth medium. Embryonic, fetal, adult, and even cancerous tissues have served as sources of primary cultures. A primary culture retains several characteristics of the original tissue from which it was derived, but this original line generally has a limited existence. Eventually, it will die out or mutate into a line of cells that can grow by continuous subculture in fresh nutrient medium. One very clear advantage of cell culture is that a specific cell line can be available for viruses with a very narrow host range. Strictly human viruses can be propagated in one of several primary or continuous human cell lines, such as embryonic kidney cells, fibroblasts, bone marrow, and heart cells.

One way to detect the growth of a virus in culture is to observe degeneration and lysis of infected cells in a monolayer of a cell culture (**figure 16.19a**). The areas where virus-infected cells have been destroyed show up as clear, well-defined patches in the cell sheet called **plaques*** (**figure 6.19c**). Plaques are essentially the

* *plaque* (plak) Fr. *placke*, patch or spot.

(a)

(b)

(c)

100 μm

100 μm

Figure 6.19 Microscopic views of normal and infected cell cultures. **(a)** Cell culture plate infected with herpes simplex virus. Clear, round spaces are regions of infection (plaques) where the host cells have been destroyed by viruses. **(b)** Closeup of a normal, uninfected region of cultured cells. **(c)** Closeup of plaques, which consist of open spaces where cells have been disrupted by viral infection.

macroscopic manifestation of cytopathic effects (CPEs), discussed in section 6.4. This same technique is used to detect and count bacteriophages, because they also produce plaques when grown in soft agar cultures of their host cells. A plaque develops when the viruses released by an infected host cell radiate out to adjacent host cells. As new cells become infected, they die and release more viruses, and so on. As this process continues, the infection spreads gradu-

ally and symmetrically from the original point of infection, causing the macroscopic appearance of round, clear spaces that correspond to areas of lysed cells.

Using Bird Embryos

An embryo is an early developmental stage of animals marked by rapid differentiation of cells. Birds undergo their embryonic period within the closed protective case of an egg, which makes an incubating bird egg a nearly perfect system for viral propagation. It is an intact and self-supporting unit, complete with its own sterile environment and nourishment. Furthermore, it furnishes several embryonic tissues that readily support viral multiplication. Every year hundreds of millions of chicken embryos are inoculated to prepare influenza vaccines.

Chicken, duck, and turkey eggs are the most common choices for inoculation. The egg must be injected through the shell, necessitating rigorous sterile techniques to prevent contamination by bacteria and fungi from the air and the outer surface of the shell. The exact tissue inoculated is guided by the type of virus being cultivated and the goals of the experiment (**figure 6.20**).

Viruses multiplying in embryos may or may not cause effects visible to the naked eye. The signs of viral growth include death of the embryo, defects in embryonic development, and localized areas of damage in the membranes, resulting in discrete, opaque spots called pocks (a variant of *pox*). Embryonic fluids and tissues can be prepared for direct examination with an electron microscope. Certain viruses can also be detected by their ability to agglutinate red blood cells (form big clumps) or by their reaction with an antibody of known specificity that will affix to its corresponding virus, if it is present.

Using Live Animal Inoculation

Specially bred strains of white mice, rats, hamsters, guinea pigs, and rabbits are the usual choices for animal cultivation of viruses. Invertebrates or nonhuman primates are occasionally used as well. Because viruses can exhibit host specificity, certain animals can propagate a given virus more readily than others. Depending on the particular experiment, tests can be performed on adult, juvenile, or newborn animals. The animal is exposed to the virus by injection of a viral preparation or specimen into the brain, blood, muscle, body cavity, skin, or footpads.

(a)

Inoculation of amniotic cavity

Inoculation of embryo

Air sac

Inoculation of chorioallantoic membrane

Amnion

Shell

Allantoic cavity

Albumin

Inoculation of yolk sac

(b)

Figure 6.20 Cultivating animal viruses in a developing bird embryo. (a) A technician inoculates fertilized chicken eggs with viruses in the first stage of preparing vaccines. This process requires the highest levels of sterile and aseptic precautions. Influenza vaccine is prepared this way. **(b)** The shell is perforated using sterile techniques, and a virus preparation is injected into a site selected to grow the viruses. Targets include the allantoic cavity, a sac for embryonic waste removal; the amniotic cavity that cushions and protects the embryo; the chorioallantoic membrane, for embryonic gas exchange; the yolk sac, for the nourishment of the embryo; and the embryo itself.

6.7 Viral Infection, Detection, and Treatment

 Expected Learning Outcomes

22. Discuss the medical impact and importance of viruses.

23. Explain how animal viral infections are treated and detected.

The number of viral infections that occur on a worldwide basis is nearly impossible to measure accurately. Certainly, viruses are the most common cause of acute infections that do not result in hospitalization, especially when one considers widespread diseases

6.1 Secret World of Microbes
Seeking Your Inner Viruses

Would you be alarmed to be told that your cells carry around bits and pieces of fossil viruses? Well, we now know that they do. A fascinating aspect of the virus-host relationship is the extent to which viral genetic material becomes affixed to host chromosomes and is passed on, possibly even for millions of years. We know this from data obtained by the human genome project that sequenced all of the genetic codes on the 46 human chromosomes. While searching through the genome sequences, virologists began to find DNA they identified as viral in origin. So far they have found about 100,000 different fragments of viral DNA. In fact, over 8% of the DNA in human chromosomes comes from viruses!

These researchers are doing the work of molecular fossil hunters, locating and identifying these ancient viruses. Many of them are retroviruses that converted their RNA codes to DNA codes, inserted the DNA into a site in a host chromosome, and then became dormant and did not kill the cell. When this happened in an egg or sperm cell, the virus could be transmitted basically unchanged for hundreds of generations. One of the most tantalizing questions is what effect, if any, such retroviruses might have on modern humans. Some virologists contend that these virus genes would not have been maintained for thousands and even millions of years if they did not serve some function. Others argue that they are just genetic "garbage" that has accumulated over a long human history.

So far, we have only small glimpses of the possible roles of these viruses. One type of endogenous retrovirus has been shown to be intimately involved in forming the human placenta, leading microbiologists to conclude that some viruses have become an essential factor in evolution and development. Other retroviruses may be involved in diseases such as prostate cancer and chronic fatigue syndrome.

Does this virus make us look fat?

Evidence is mounting that certain viruses may contribute to human obesity. Several studies with animals revealed that chickens and mice infected with a human adenovirus (see figure) had larger fat deposits and were heavier than uninfected animals. Studies in humans show a similar association between infection with the strain of virus—called Ad-36—and an increase in adipose (fat) tissue. Although adenoviruses have usually been involved in respiratory and eye infections, they can also infect adipose cells. One of the possible explanations for this association suggests that a chronic infection with the virus allows its DNA to regulate cellular differentiation of stem cells into fat cells. This increase in fat cells adds adipose tissue, more fat production and storage, and greater body fat. In general, such an association does not prove causation, but it certainly warrants additional research.

Another finding is a human bornavirus that belongs to a family of animal viruses that are not retroviruses. Japanese scientists isolated this same virus from monkeys and apes as well, which allows them to fix a timeline for the age of the virus of about 40 million years. Bornaviruses are common among many animal groups, including ground squirrels, elephants, guinea pigs, and horses, where it causes a severe brain disease. Although we do not know what these agents do to humans, some researchers suggest they could be involved in psychoses such as schizophrenia. One thing is for sure: The discovery of this viral baggage will spur many years of research and provide greater understanding of the human genome and its tiny passengers.

Using information you have learned about viruses, explain how viruses could become a permanent component of an organism's genetic material. *Answer available at http://www.mhhe.com/talaro9*

such as colds, measles, chickenpox, influenza, herpes, and warts. If one also takes into account prominent viral infections found only in certain regions of the world (dengue fever, Rift Valley fever, and yellow fever), the total could easily exceed several billion cases each year. Although most viral infections do not result in death, some, such as rabies, HIV, and Ebola, have very high mortality rates, and others can lead to long-term debility (polio, hepatitis). Continuing research is focused on the connection of viruses to chronic afflictions of unknown cause, such as type I diabetes, multiple sclerosis, various cancers, and even conditions such as obesity **(6.1 Secret World of Microbes)**.

Because some viral diseases can be life threatening, it is essential to have a correct diagnosis as soon as possible. Obtaining the overall clinical picture of the disease (specific signs) is often the first step in diagnosis. This may be followed by identification of the virus in clinical specimens by means of rapid tests that detect the virus or signs of cytopathic changes in cells or tissues (see CMV herpesvirus, figure 6.15). Immunofluorescence techniques or direct examination with an electron microscope are often used for this (see figure 6.8). Samples can also be screened for the presence of indicator molecules (antigens) from the virus itself. A standard procedure for many viruses is the polymerase chain reaction (PCR), which can detect and amplify even minute amounts of viral DNA or RNA in a sample. In certain infections, definitive diagnosis requires cell culture, embryos, or animals, but this method can be time-consuming and slow to give results. Screening tests can detect specific antibodies that indicate signs of virus infection in a patient's blood. This is the main test for HIV infection (see figure 17.16). Additional details of viral diagnosis are provided in chapter 17.

The nature of viruses has at times been a major impediment to effective therapy. Because viruses are not bacteria, antibiotics aimed at bacterial infections do not work. While there are increasing

numbers of antiviral drugs, most of them block virus replication by targeting the function of host cells. This can cause severe side effects. Antiviral drugs are designed to target one of the steps in the viral life cycle you learned about earlier in this chapter. Azidothymidine (AZT), a drug used to treat AIDS, targets the nucleic acid synthesis stage. A newer class of HIV drugs, the protease inhibitors, disrupts the final assembly phase of the viral life cycle. Another compound that shows some potential for treating and preventing viral infections is a naturally occurring human cell product called *interferon* (see chapters 12 and 14). Vaccines that stimulate immunity are an extremely valuable tool but are available for only a limited number of viral diseases (see chapter 15).

> **Quick Search**
> Find "Mad Cow Disease 101" on YouTube for a short overview of the condition.

 Check Your Progress SECTIONS 6.6 AND 6.7

26. Describe the three main techniques for cultivating viruses.
27. What are the advantages of using cell culture and what are the disadvantages?
28. What are cell lines and monolayers, and how are plaques formed?
29. What are the primary problems in treating viral infections with drugs?

6.8 Prions and Other Nonviral Infectious Particles

 Expected Learning Outcomes

24. Describe the properties of nonviral infectious particles.
25. Discuss the importance of prions and viroids and the diseases they cause.

Prions are a group of noncellular infectious agents that are not viruses and really belong in a category all by themselves. The term *prion* is derived from the words **pr**oteinaceous **in**fectious particle to suggest its primary structure—that of a naked protein molecule. They are quite remarkable in being the only biologically active agent that lacks any sort of nucleic acid (DNA or RNA). Up until their discovery about 30 years ago, it was considered impossible that an agent lacking genetic material could ever be infectious or transmissible.

The diseases associated with prions are known as **transmissible spongiform encephalopathies (TSEs).** This description recognizes that the diseases are spread from host to host by direct contact, contaminated food, or other means. It also refers to the effects of the agent on nervous tissue, which develops a spongelike appearance due to loss of nerve and glial cells (see figure 25.28b). Another pathological effect observed in these diseases is the buildup of tiny protein fibrils in the brain tissue (**figures 6.21a and 6.21b).** Several forms of prion diseases are known in mammals, including scrapie in sheep,

(a)

Prion protein fibers

(b)

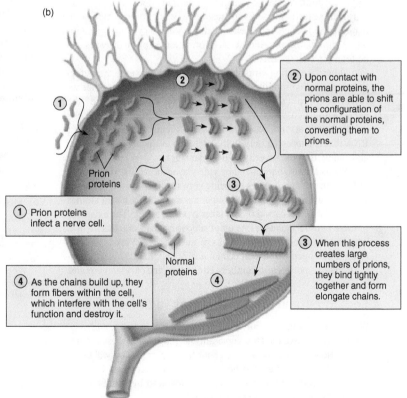

① Prion proteins infect a nerve cell.

② Upon contact with normal proteins, the prions are able to shift the configuration of the normal proteins, converting them to prions.

③ When this process creates large numbers of prions, they bind tightly together and form elongate chains.

④ As the chains build up, they form fibers within the cell, which interfere with the cell's function and destroy it.

Prion proteins

Normal proteins

 Process Figure 6.21 **The appearance and mechanisms of prion-based diseases.** (a) A magnified view of nerve cells infected with prion protein. Red areas indicate places in the cytoplasm where the prion fibers have deposited. (b) A diagram of a nerve cell to outline the stages in the conversion of normal cell proteins into prions and the formation of prion fibers.

bovine spongiform encephalopathy (mad cow disease) in cattle, and wasting disease in elk, deer, and mink. These diseases have a long latent period (usually several years) before the first symptoms of brain degeneration appear. The animals lose coordination, have difficulty moving, and eventually progress to collapse and death.

Humans are host to similar chronic diseases, including *Creutzfeldt-Jakob Disease* (CJD), kuru, fatal familial insomnia, and others. In all of these conditions, the brain progressively deteriorates and the patient loses motor coordination, along with sensory and cognitive abilities. There is no treatment and most cases so far have been fatal. In the 1990s, a different variant of CJD that appeared in Europe was traced to people eating meat from cows infected with the bovine form of encephalopathy. Several hundred people developed the disease and a majority of them have since died. This was the first indicator that prions of animals could cause infections in humans. It sparked a crisis in the beef industry and strict controls on imported beef. Although only three cases of human disease have occurred in the United States, infected cattle have been reported.

The medical importance of these novel infectious agents has led to a great deal of research into how they function. Researchers have discovered that prion or prionlike proteins are very common in the cell membranes of plants, yeasts, and animals. One widely accepted theory suggests that the prion protein is an abnormal version of a normal protein. When the prion comes in contact with a normal protein, it can induce spontaneous abnormal folding in the normal protein. Ultimately, the buildup of these converted proteins damages and kills the cell (figure 6.21*b*).

Another serious issue with prions is their extreme resistance. They are not destroyed by disinfectants, radiation, and the usual sterilization techniques. Even treatments with extreme high temperatures and concentrated chemicals are not always reliable methods to eliminate them. Additional information on prion diseases can be found in chapter 25.

Other fascinating viruslike agents in human disease are defective forms called satellite viruses that actually depend on other viruses for replication. Two remarkable examples are the adeno-associated virus (AAV), which can replicate only in cells infected with adenovirus, and the delta agent, a naked strand of RNA that is expressed only in the presence of the hepatitis B virus and can worsen the severity of liver damage.

Plants are also parasitized by viruslike agents called **viroids** that differ from ordinary viruses by being very small (about one-tenth the size of an average virus) and being composed of only naked strands of RNA, lacking a capsid or any other type of coating. The existence of these unusual agents is one bit of supportive evidence that viruses may have evolved from naked bits of nucleic acid. Viroids are significant pathogens in several economically important plants, including tomatoes, potatoes, cucumbers, citrus trees, and chrysanthemums.

Looking Ahead at the Chapters To Come

We have completed our survey of prokaryotes, eukaryotes, and viruses and have described the significant characteristics of these three groups. Now that we know more about these microbes, we will use chapters 7, 8, and 9 to explore how they maintain themselves, beginning with microbial nutrition (chapter 7) followed by metabolism (chapter 8), and ending with genetics (chapter 9).

 Check Your Progress SECTION 6.8

30. What is the principal effect of the prion agent of Creutzfeldt-Jakob disease?
31. Explain how prions and viroids are different from viruses.

 CASE STUDY Part 2

Beginning with those first diagnoses, it took only 6 weeks for the influenza outbreak to explode into a pandemic. New cases quickly appeared in Canada, Central and South America, Europe, Asia, and eventually in more than 200 countries. The CDC's estimates from April to November 2009 suggested that the United States alone accounted for 50 million cases and close to 10,000 deaths. Deaths were particularly high among young children and pregnant women whose treatment had been delayed. Fortunately, the disease experienced by most people was milder than the usual seasonal flu, and it cleared up with few complications. The common symptoms are fever, muscle aches, and problems with breathing and coughing that clear up in 1 or 2 weeks. The most serious complication is pneumonia. One group that seemed to be less susceptible to H1N1 influenza virus were members of the population 60 years or older.

Influenza viruses come in about 144 different subtypes and circulate within many vertebrate groups. As long as the viruses lack the correct spikes for a given host, they cannot jump hosts. But influenza viruses are also notorious for altering the shapes of their spikes so that they can invade more than one host. This has happened several times with bird (avian) flu virus and swine flu viruses. One possible circumstance is when a single animal becomes infected with strains of viruses from two different hosts. The recombination of genes from these viruses can give rise to new viruses with spikes that fit all of the hosts. What evidently happened with the 2009 H1N1 strain is that a small change in a spike was just enough to allow the virus to infect humans.

■ What would cause a local infection to spread into a pandemic so rapidly?

■ Why would some people be more resistant to the virus?

To conclude this Case Study, go to Perspectives on the Connect website.

See chapter 25 for additional details on influenza and track the latest information on flu outbreaks at www.cdc.gov/flu/.

 Chapter Summary with Key Terms

6.1 Overview of Viruses
A. Viruses, being much smaller than bacteria, fungi, and protozoa, had to be indirectly studied until the 20th century, when they were finally seen with an electron microscope.
B. Scientists don't agree about whether viruses are living or not. They are **obligate intracellular parasites.**

6.2 The General Structure of Viruses
A. Viruses are infectious particles and not cells; lack organelles and locomotion of any kind; are large, complex molecules; and can be crystalline in form. A virus particle is composed of a nucleic acid core (DNA or RNA, not both) surrounded by a geometric protein shell, or **capsid;** the combination is called a **nucleocapsid;** a capsid is **helical** or **icosahedral** in configuration; many are covered by a membranous **envelope** containing viral protein **spikes.** Complex viruses have additional external and internal structures.
B. *Shapes/Sizes:* Icosahedral, helical, spherical, and cylindrical shaped. Smallest infectious forms range from the largest poxvirus (0.45 mm or 450 nm) to the smallest viruses (0.02 mm or 20 nm).
C. *Nutritional and Other Requirements:* Lack enzymes for processing food or generating energy; are tied entirely to the host cell for all needs (obligate intracellular parasites).
D. Viruses are known to parasitize all types of cells, including bacteria, algae, fungi, protozoa, animals, and plants. Each viral type is limited in its host range to a single species or group, mostly due to specificity of adsorption of virus to specific host receptors.

6.3 How Viruses Are Classified and Named
A. The two major types of viruses are *DNA* and *RNA viruses*. These are further subdivided into families, depending on shape and size of capsid, presence or absence of an envelope, whether double- or single-stranded nucleic acid, antigenic similarities, and host cell.
B. Viruses are classified into orders, families, and genera. These groupings are based on virus structure, chemical composition, and genetic makeup.

6.4 Modes of Viral Multiplication
A. *Multiplication Cycle: Animal Cells*
1. The life cycle steps of an animal virus are **adsorption, penetration, synthesis** and **assembly,** and **release** from the host cell. A fully infective virus is a **virion.**

2. Some animal viruses cause chronic and **persistent infections.**
3. Viruses that alter host genetic material may cause *oncogenic* effects.

6.5 The Multiplication Cycle in Bacteriophages
A. Bacteriophages are viruses that attack bacteria. They penetrate by injecting their nucleic acid and are released as virulent phages upon **lysis** of the cell.
B. Some viruses go into a latent, or **lysogenic,** phase in which they integrate into the DNA of the host cell and later may be active and produce a lytic infection.

6.6 Techniques in Cultivating and Identifying Animal Viruses
A. The need for an intracellular habitat makes it necessary to grow viruses in living cells, either in isolated cultures of host cells (**cell culture**), in bird embryos, or in the intact host animal.
B. *Identification:* Viruses are identified by means of cytopathic effects (CPE) in host cells, direct examination of viruses or their components in samples, genetic analysis to detect virus nucleic acid, and growing viruses in culture.

6.7 Viral Infection, Detection, and Treatment
A. *Medical:* Viruses attach to specific target hosts or cells. They cause a variety of infectious diseases, ranging from mild respiratory illnesses (common cold) to destructive and potentially fatal conditions (rabies, AIDS). Some viruses can cause birth defects and cancer in humans and other animals.
B. *Research:* Viruses have become an invaluable tool for studying basic genetic principles. Current research is focused on the connection of viruses to afflictions of unknown causes, such as type I diabetes and multiple sclerosis.
C. Viral infections are detected by direct examination of specimens, genetic tests, testing patients' blood, and characteristic symptoms. Some viral infections can be treated with drugs that block viral replication.

6.8 Prions and Other Nonviral Infectious Particles
A. Spongiform encephalopathies are chronic persistent neurological diseases caused by **prions.**
B. Prions are infectious agents composed of a protein that can alter the structure of nerve cells.
C. Examples of neurological diseases include "mad cow disease" and Creutzfeldt-Jakob disease.
D. Other noncellular infectious agents include satellite viruses and **viroids.**

Level I. Knowledge and Comprehension

These questions require a working knowledge of the concepts in the chapter and the ability to recall and understand the information you have studied.

(?) Multiple-Choice Questions

Select the correct answer from the answers provided. For questions with blanks, choose the combination of answers that most accurately completes the statement.

1. A virus is a tiny infectious
 a. cell c. particle
 b. living thing d. nucleic acid

2. Viruses are known to infect
 a. plants c. fungi
 b. bacteria d. all organisms

3. The capsid is composed of protein subunits called
 a. spikes c. virions
 b. protomers d. capsomers

4. The envelope of an animal virus is derived from the _____ of its host cell.
 a. cell wall c. glycocalyx
 b. membrane d. receptors

5. The nucleic acid of a virus is
 a. DNA only
 b. RNA only
 c. both DNA and RNA
 d. either DNA or RNA

6. The general steps in a viral multiplication cycle are
 a. adsorption, penetration, synthesis, assembly, and release
 b. endocytosis, replication, assembly, and budding
 c. adsorption, duplication, assembly, and lysis
 d. endocytosis, penetration, replication, maturation, and exocytosis

7. A prophage is a/an _____ stage in the cycle of _____.
 a. latent, bacterial viruses
 b. infective, RNA viruses
 c. early, poxviruses
 d. late, enveloped viruses

8. The nucleic acid of animal viruses enters the host cell through
 a. injection
 b. fusion
 c. endocytosis
 d. b and c

9. In general, RNA viruses multiply in the cell _____, and DNA viruses multiply in the cell _____.
 a. nucleus, cytoplasm
 b. cytoplasm, nucleus
 c. vesicles, ribosomes
 d. endoplasmic reticulum, nucleolus

10. Enveloped viruses carry surface receptors called
 a. buds c. fibers
 b. spikes d. sheaths

11. Viruses that persist in the cell and cause recurrent disease are considered
 a. oncogenic c. latent
 b. cytopathic d. resistant

12. Viruses cannot be cultivated in
 a. cell culture
 b. bird embryos
 c. live mammals
 d. blood agar

13. Clear patches in cell cultures that indicate sites of virus infection are called
 a. plaques
 b. pocks
 c. colonies
 d. prions

14. Which of these is *not* a general pattern of virus morphology?
 a. enveloped, helical
 b. naked, icosahedral
 c. enveloped, icosahedral
 d. complex, helical

15. Which of these is true of prions?
 a. They are small RNA viruses.
 b. They replicate in the nucleus.
 c. They lack protein.
 d. They cause death of brain cells.

(🗀) Case Study Review

1. Which receptor of the influenza virus is most involved in binding to the respiratory cells?
 a. neuraminidase spikes c. the viral capsid
 b. hemagglutinin spikes d. the viral envelope

2. What features of the new H1N1 influenza classified it as a pandemic?
 a. It was transmitted from pigs to humans.
 b. It was transmitted from Mexico to the United States.

 c. It was readily transmitted from human to human.
 d. It was spread from the Americas to Europe.
 e. both c and d

3. Outline the factors that caused the pandemic H1N1 influenza virus to spread so rapidly.

 Writing Challenge

For each question, compose a one- or two-paragraph answer that includes the factual information needed to completely address the question. Check Your Progress questions can also be used for writing-challenge exercises.

1. a. What characteristics of viruses could be used to describe them as life forms?
 b. What makes them more similar to lifeless molecules?

2. HIV attacks only specific types of human cells, such as certain white blood cells and nerve cells. Can you explain why a virus can enter some types of human cells but not others?

3. a. Since viruses lack metabolic enzymes, how can they synthesize necessary components?
 b. Name some enzymes that viruses may have for invading and completing their cycles.

4. a. What dictates the host range of animal viruses?
 b. How is the influenza virus different in its host range from most other viruses?

 Concept Mapping

An Introduction to Concept Mapping found at http://www.mhhe.com/talaro9 provides guidance for working with concept maps.

1. Supply your own linking words or phrases in this concept map, and provide the missing concepts in the empty boxes.

Level II. Application, Analysis, Evaluation, and Synthesis

These problems go beyond just restating facts and require higher levels of understanding and an ability to interpret, problem solve, transfer knowledge to new situations, create models, and predict outcomes.

Critical Thinking

Critical thinking is the ability to reason and solve problems using facts and concepts. These questions can be approached from a number of angles, and in most cases, they do not have a single correct answer.

1. Comment on the possible origin of viruses. Is it not curious that the human cell welcomes a virus in and hospitably removes its coat as if it were an old acquaintance?

2. a. If viruses that normally form envelopes were prevented from budding, would they still be infectious? Why or why not?
 b. If only the RNA of an influenza virus were injected into a cell by itself, could it cause a lytic infection?

3. The end result of most viral infections is death of the host cell.
 a. If this is the case, how can we account for such differences in the damage that viruses do? (Compare the effects of the cold virus with those of the rabies virus.)
 b. Describe the adaptations of viruses that do not immediately kill the host cell and explain what their functions may be.

4. a. Given that DNA viruses can actually be carried in the DNA of the host cell's chromosomes, comment on what this phenomenon means in terms of inheritance in the offspring.
 b. Discuss the connection between viruses and cancers, giving possible mechanisms for viruses that cause cancer.

5. a. If you were involved in developing an antiviral drug, what would be some important considerations? (Can a drug "kill" a virus?)
 b. How could multiplication be blocked?

6. Is there such a thing as a "good virus"? Explain why or why not. Consider both bacteriophages and viruses of eukaryotic organisms.

7. Discuss some advantages and disadvantages of bacteriophage therapy in treating bacterial infections.

8. a. Consult table 6.2, page 167, right-hand column to determine which viral diseases you have had and which ones you have been vaccinated against.
 b. Which viruses would more likely be possible oncoviruses and why would this be the case?

9. Circle the viral infections on this list: cholera, rabies, plague, cold sores, whooping cough, tetanus, genital warts, gonorrhea, mumps, Rocky Mountain spotted fever, syphilis, rubella, rat bite fever.

Visual Challenge

1. Label the parts of viruses in figures 6.7*d*, 6.9*c*, and 6.10.

2. How would you describe the kind of capsid found on this virus from figure 6.2? In what ways is this virus different from other viruses?

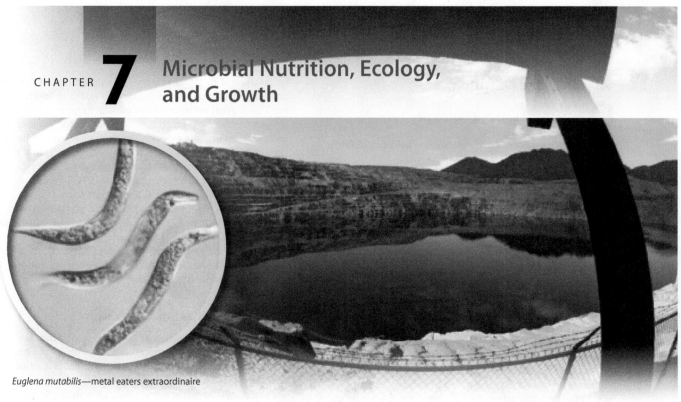

Euglena mutabilis—metal eaters extraordinaire

The Berkeley Pit—a murky brown soup of toxic chemicals

 CASE STUDY Part 1 **Life Will Find a Way**

Carved into a hillside near Butte, Montana, lies the **Berkeley Pit,** an industrial body of water that stretches about 1 mile across and contains a volume of close to 40 billion gallons. This site was formerly an open pit **copper mine** abandoned in 1982 and left to fill up with water seeping out of the local **aquifer.** At the bottom of the pit lay a massive deposit of **mining waste** that was like an accident waiting to happen.

A gradual buildup over 30 years has transformed the pit into a lake-size cauldron of **concentrated chemicals** so **toxic** that it quickly kills any animals or plants that came in contact with it. Substances found in abundance are **lead, cadmium, iron, copper, arsenic,** and sulfides. Chemical reactions caused the pit to become **10,000 times** more **acidic** than normal fresh water. There is serious concern that water from the pit will **contaminate** local groundwater and river drainages, creating one of the greatest **ecological disasters** on record. The federal **Environmental Protection Agency** designated it as a major superfund cleanup site. So far, the only actions taken have been to divert the drainage water, treat it, and remove some of the **heavy metals.**

"In spite of the hostile conditions that were seemingly deadly, the water turned out to be teeming with microscopic life."

In 2018 the EPA will begin a more comprehensive cleanup program to protect the watershed in the area.

When a team of curious scientists from nearby Montana Tech University began examining samples of the water under a microscope, they were startled at what they found. In spite of the **hostile conditions** that were seemingly deadly, the water turned out to be teeming with **microscopic life.** It included an array of very hardy eukaryotes and prokaryotes—a rich **community of microorganisms**—that had established a foothold in this toxic soup. Rather than being doomed to death, these robust **colonists** had **survived, grown,** and **spread** into available **habitats** in a relatively short time.

▶ *What types of microbes would one expect to be living in such polluted water?*

▶ *Suggest some possible ways that microbes survive and even thrive under such conditions.*

To continue the Case Study, go to page 213.

7.1 Microbial Nutrition

 Expected Learning Outcomes

1. Describe the major environmental factors to which microbes must adapt for survival.
2. Define nutrition and nutrients and their subcategories based on need and quantity.
3. Differentiate between organic and inorganic nutrients.
4. Discuss the origins, types, and functions of bioelements and nutrients.

There are millions of habitats on earth, of both natural and human origin. In these settings, microorganisms are exposed to a tremendous variety of conditions that affect their survival. Environmental factors with the greatest impact on microorganisms are nutrient and energy sources, temperature, gas content, water, salt, pH, radiation, and other organisms **(figure 7.1)**. Microbes survive in their habitats through the process of gradual adjustment of anatomy and physiology, a process called **adaptation.** * It is this adaptability that allows microbes to inhabit all parts of the biosphere. The process that selects for favorable adaptations is also a major force behind the evolution of species. With these concepts as a theme for the chapter, we take a closer look at how microbes interact with their environment, how they transport materials, and how they grow.

Nutrition is a process by which chemical substances called **nutrients** are acquired from the environment and used in cellular activities such as metabolism and growth. With respect to nutrition, microbes are not really so different from humans. Bacteria living deep in a swamp on a diet of inorganic sulfur or protozoa digesting wood in a termite's intestine seem to show radical adaptations, but even these organisms require a constant influx of certain substances from their habitat.

In general, all living things have an absolute need for the bioelements, traditionally listed as carbon, hydrogen, oxygen, phosphorus, potassium, nitrogen, sulfur, calcium, iron, sodium, chlorine, magnesium, and certain other elements.[1] Beyond these basic requirements, microbes have significant differences in the source, chemical form, and amount of the elements they use. Any substance, whether an element or compound, that must be provided to an organism is called an **essential nutrient.** Once absorbed, nutrients are processed and transformed into the chemicals of the cell.

Two categories of essential nutrients are **macronutrients** and **micronutrients.** Macronutrients are required in relatively large quantities and play principal roles in cell structure and metabolism. Examples of macronutrients are compounds such as sugars and amino acids that contain carbon, hydrogen, and oxygen. Micronutrients, or **trace elements,** such as manganese, zinc, and nickel are present in much smaller amounts and are involved in enzyme function and maintenance of protein structure. What constitutes a micronutrient can vary from one microbe to another and often must

be determined in the laboratory. This determination is made by deliberately omitting the substance in question from a growth medium to see if the microbe can grow in its absence.

Another way to categorize nutrients is according to their carbon content. Most **organic** nutrients are molecules that contain a basic framework of carbon and hydrogen. Natural organic molecules are nearly always the products of living things. They range from the simplest organic molecule, methane (CH_4), to large polymers (carbohydrates, lipids, proteins, and nucleic acids).

In contrast, an **inorganic** nutrient is composed of an element or elements other than carbon and hydrogen. The natural reservoirs of many inorganic compounds are mineral deposits in the soil, bodies of water, and the atmosphere. Examples include metals and their salts (magnesium sulfate, ferric nitrate, sodium phosphate), gases (oxygen, carbon dioxide), and water.

Chemical Analysis of Cell Contents

To gain insight into a cell's nutritional makeup, it can be useful to analyze its chemical composition. The following list is a brief summary of some nutritional patterns in the intestinal bacterium *Escherichia coli.* Some nutrients are absorbed in a ready-to-use form, and others must be synthesized by the cell from simple compounds:

- Water content is the highest of all components (70%).
- About 97% of the dry cell weight is composed of organic compounds.
- Proteins are the most prevalent organic compound.
- About 96% of the cell is composed of six elements (represented by CHONPS).
- Chemical elements are needed in the overall scheme of cell growth, but most of them are available to the cell as compounds and not as pure elements.
- A cell as "simple" as *E. coli* contains on the order of 5,000 different compounds, yet it needs to absorb only a few types of nutrients to synthesize this great diversity. These include $(NH_4)_2SO_4$, $FeCl_2$, NaCl, trace elements, glucose, KH_2PO_4, $MgSO_4$, $CaHPO_4$, and water.

Escherichia coli

Forms, Sources, and Functions of Essential Nutrients

The elements that comprise nutrients ultimately exist in an environmental inorganic reservoir of some type. These reservoirs serve not only as a source of these elements but can be replenished by the activities of organisms. Thus, elements cycle in a pattern from an inorganic form in an environmental reservoir to an organic form in organisms. Organisms may, in turn, serve as a continuing source of that element for other organisms. Eventually, the element is recycled to the inorganic form, usually by the actions of microorganisms. All in all, a tremendous variety of microorganisms are involved in processing the elements. From a larger perspective, the overall cycle of life on this planet depends

* *adaptation* L. *adaptare*, to fit. Changes in structure and function that improve an organism's survival in a given environment.

1. See critical thinking question 1. b for a useful mnemonic device to recall the essential elements.

Figure 7.1 Environmental conditions that influence microbial adaptations. The earth's habitats provide a constant supply of energy, nutrients, and gases; maintain a certain pH and temperature; and establish communities of interactive organisms.

upon the combined action of several interacting nutritional schemes, each performing a necessary step. In fact, as we shall see in chapter 26, the framework of microbial nutrition underlies the nutrient cycles of all life on earth.

The source of nutrients is extremely varied: Microbes such as photosynthetic bacteria obtain their nutrients entirely in inorganic form from the environment. Others require a combination of organic and inorganic nutrients. For example, parasites that invade and live on the human body derive all essential nutrients from host tissues, tissue fluids, secretions, and wastes.

Refer to **table 7.1** to see an overview of the major bioelements, compounds, their sources, and their importance to microorganisms.

Carbon-Based Nutritional Types

The element carbon is so key to the structure and metabolism of all life forms that the source of carbon defines two basic nutritional groups:

- A **heterotroph*** is an organism that must obtain its carbon in an organic form. Because organic carbon usually originates from organisms, heterotrophs are nutritionally dependent on other life forms. Among the common organic molecules that can satisfy this requirement are proteins, carbohydrates, lipids, and nucleic acids. In most cases, these nutrients provide several

* *heterotroph* (het′-uhr-oh-trohf) Gr. *hetero,* other, and *troph,* to feed.

TABLE 7.1	Sources and Biological Functions of Essential Elements and Nutrients	
Element/Nutrient Forms Found in Nature	Sources/Reservoirs of Compounds	Significance to Cells
Carbon CO_2 (carbon dioxide) gas CO_3^{2-} (carbonate) Organic compounds	Air (0.036%*) Sediments/soils Living things	CO_2 is produced by respiration and used in photosynthesis; CO_3^{2-} is found in cell walls and skeletons; organic compounds are essential to the structure and function of all organisms and viruses.
Nitrogen N_2 gas NO_3^- (nitrate) NO_2^- (nitrite) NH_3 (ammonium) Organic nitrogen (proteins, nucleic acids)	Air (79%*) Soil and water Soil and water Soil and water Organisms	Nitrogen gas is available only to certain microbes that fix it into other inorganic nitrogen compounds—nitrates, nitrites, and ammonium— the primary sources of nitrogen for algae, plants, and the majority of bacteria; animals and protozoa require organic nitrogen; all organisms use NH_3 to synthesize amino acids and nucleic acids.
Oxygen O_2 gas Oxides H_2O	Air (20%*), a major product of photosynthesis Soil	Oxygen gas is necessary for the metabolism of nutrients by aerobes. Oxygen is a significant element in organic compounds and inorganic compounds (see water, sulfates, phosphates, nitrates, carbon dioxide).
Hydrogen H_2 gas H_2O H_2S (hydrogen sulfide) CH_4 (methane) Organic compounds	Waters, swamps soil, volcanoes, vents, organisms	Water is the most abundant compound in cells and a solvent for metabolic reactions; H_2, H_2S, and CH_4 gases are produced and used by bacteria and archaea; H^+ ions are the basis for transfers of cellular energy and help maintain the pH of cells.
Phosphorus PO_4^{3-} (phosphate)	Rocks, mineral deposits Soil	Phosphate, a key component of DNA and RNA, is critical to the genetic makeup of cells and viruses; also found in ATP and NAD, where it takes part in numerous metabolic reactions; its presence in phospholipids provides stability to cell membranes.
Sulfur S SO_4^{2-} (sulfate) SH (sulfhydryl)	Mineral deposits, volcanic sediments Soil	Elemental sulfur is oxidized by some bacteria as an energy source; sulfur is found in vitamin B1; sulfhydryl groups are part of certain amino acids, where they form disulfide bonds that shape and stabilize proteins.
Potassium K^+	Mineral deposits, ocean water, soil	Plays a role in protein synthesis and membrane transport
Sodium Na^+	Same as potassium	Major participant in membrane actions; maintains osmotic pressure in cells
Calcium Ca^+	Oceanic sediments, rocks, and soil	A component of protozoan shells (as $CaCO_3$); stabilizes cell walls; adds resistance to bacterial endospores
Magnesium Mg^{2+}	Geologic sediments, rocks, and soil	A central atom in the chlorophyll molecule; required for function of membranes, ribosomes, and some enzymes
Chloride Cl^-	Ocean water, salt lakes	May function in membrane transport; required by obligate halophiles to regulate osmotic pressure
Zinc Zn^{2+}	Rocks, soil	An enzyme cofactor; regulates eukaryotic genetics
Iron Fe^{2+}	Rocks, soil	Essential element for the structure of respiratory proteins (cytochromes)
Micronutrients: copper, cobalt, nickel, molybdenum, manganese, iodine	Geologic sediments, soil	Required in tiny amounts to serve as cofactors in specialized enzyme systems of some microbes but not all

*As a portion of the earth's atmosphere.

other elements as well. Some organic nutrients already exist in a form that is simple enough for absorption (for example, monosaccharides and amino acids), but many larger molecules must be digested by the cell before absorption. Not all heterotrophs can use the same organic carbon sources. Some are restricted to a few substrates, whereas others (certain *Pseudomonas* bacteria, for example) are so versatile that they can metabolize hundreds of different substrates.

• An **autotroph*** is an organism that uses inorganic CO_2 as its carbon source. Because autotrophs have the special capacity to convert CO_2 into organic compounds, they are not nutritionally dependent on other living things. We later enlarge on the topic of nutritional types based on carbon and energy sources.

* *autotroph* (aw'-toh-trohf) Gr. *auto,* self, and *troph,* to feed.

Carbon Source Versus Carbon Function

It may be helpful to clear up any confusion about the *extracellular source* of carbon as opposed to the *intracellular function* of carbon compounds. Although a distinction is made between the type of carbon compound cells absorb as nutrients (inorganic or organic), the majority of carbon compounds involved in the normal structure and metabolism of all cells are organic. So, even microbes that use carbon dioxide as their primary source of carbon will convert this CO_2 into organic compounds once it gets into the cell.

Growth Factors: Essential Organic Nutrients

Many fastidious bacteria lack the genetic and metabolic mechanisms to synthesize every organic compound they need for survival. An organic compound such as an amino acid, nitrogenous base, or vitamin that cannot be synthesized by an organism and must be provided as a nutrient is a **growth factor.** For example, all cells require 20 different amino acids for proper assembly of proteins, but many cells cannot synthesize all of them. Those that must be obtained from food are called essential amino acids. A notable example of the need for growth factors occurs in *Haemophilus influenzae*, a bacterium that causes meningitis and respiratory infections in humans. It can grow only when hemin (factor X), NAD^+ (factor V), thiamine and pantothenic acid (vitamins), uracil, and cysteine are provided by another organism or a growth medium.

 Check Your Progress SECTION 7.1

1. Summarize the main environmental factors that microbes encounter and their basic characteristics.
2. Differentiate between micronutrients, macronutrients, and essential nutrients.
3. List the general functions of the essential bioelements in the cell.
4. Define growth factors and metallic ions with examples, and explain their functions in cells.

7.2 Classification of Nutritional Types

 Expected Learning Outcomes

5. Describe the main categories of nutritional types among organisms.
6. Distinguish different types of autotrophs and their energy sources.
7. Distinguish different types of heterotrophs and their energy sources.

The earth's limitless habitats and microbial adaptations are matched by an elaborate menu of microbial nutritional schemes. Fortunately, most organisms show consistent trends and can be described by a few general categories (**table 7.2**) and a few selected terms (**7.1 Making Connections**).

The main determinants of a microbe's nutritional type are its sources of carbon and energy. We saw earlier that microbes can be defined according to their carbon sources as autotrophs or heterotrophs. Another system classifies them according to their energy source as **phototrophs** or **chemotrophs.** Microbes that photosyn-

TABLE 7.2	Nutritional Categories of Microbes by Energy and Carbon Source	
Category/ Carbon Source	**Energy Source**	**Example**
Autotroph/CO_2	**Nonliving Environment**	
Photoautotroph	Sunlight	Photosynthetic organisms, such as algae, plants, cyanobacteria
Chemoautotroph	Simple inorganic chemicals	Only certain bacteria and archaea, such as methanogens and deep-sea vent bacteria
Heterotroph/ Organic	**Other Organisms or Sunlight**	
Chemoheterotroph	Metabolic conversion of the nutrients from other organisms	Protozoa, fungi, many bacteria, animals
1. Saprobe	Metabolize the organic matter from dead organisms	Fungi, bacteria, some protozoa (decomposers)
2. Symbiotic microbes	Obtain organic matter from living organisms	Parasites, commensals, mutualistic microbes
Photoheterotroph	Sunlight or organic matter	Purple and green photosynthetic bacteria

thesize are phototrophs, and those that gain energy from chemical compounds are chemotrophs. The terms for carbon and energy source are often merged into a single word for convenience (as in table 7.2). The categories described here are meant to describe only the major nutritional groups and do not include unusual exceptions.

Autotrophs and Their Energy Sources

Autotrophs derive energy from one of two possible nonliving sources: sunlight and chemical reactions involving simple chemicals.

Photoautotrophs and Photosynthesis **Photoautotrophs** are photosynthetic; that is, they capture the energy of light rays and transform it into chemical energy that can be used in cell metabolism. In general, photosynthesis relies on special pigments to collect the light and uses the energy to convert CO_2 into simple organic compounds. There are variations in the mechanisms of photosynthesis.

Oxygenic (oxygen-producing) photosynthesis can be summed up by the equation:

$$CO_2 + H_2O \xrightarrow[\text{by chlorophyll}]{\text{Sunlight absorbed}} (CH_2O)_n + O_2$$

in which $(CH_2O)_n$ is shorthand for a carbohydrate. This type of photosynthesis occurs in plants, algae, and cyanobacteria and uses

7.1 MAKING CONNECTIONS

A Guide to Terminology

Much of the vocabulary for describing microbial adaptations is based on some common root words. These are combined in various ways that assist in discussing the types of nutritional or ecological adaptations, as shown in the list below.

Modifier terms are also used to specify the nature of an organism's adaptations. **Obligate** or **strict** means being confined to a narrow niche or habitat, such as an obligate thermophile that requires high temperatures to grow. By contrast, **facultative*** means not being so restricted but adapting to a wider range of environmental conditions. A facultative halophile can grow with or without high-salt concentration. **Tolerance** is another term that can be used to describe the capacity to survive a range of conditions.

Using this guide, define obligate halophile, facultative psychrophile, and aerotolerant anaerobe. *Answer available at http://www.mhhe. com/talaro9*

* *facultative* (fak'-uhl-tay-tiv) Gr. *facult,* capability or skill, and *tatos,* most.

Root	Meaning	Example of Use
troph-	Food, nourishment	Trophozoite—the feeding stage of protozoa
-phile	To love	Extremophile—an organism that has adapted to ("loves") extreme environments
-obe	To live	Microbe—to "live small"
hetero-	Other	Heterotroph—an organism that requires nutrients from other organisms
auto-	Self	Autotroph—an organism that "feeds by itself"
photo-	Light	Phototroph—an organism that uses light as an energy source
chemo-	Chemical	Chemotroph—an organism that uses chemicals rather than light for energy
sapro-	Rotten	Saprobe—an organism that lives on dead organic matter
halo-	Salt	Halophile—an organism that can grow in high-salt environments
thermo-	Heat	Thermophile—an organism that grows at high temperatures
psychro-	Cold	Psychrophile—an organism that grows at cold temperatures
aero-	Air (O_2)	Aerobe—an organism that uses oxygen in metabolism

chlorophyll as the primary pigment. Carbohydrates formed by the reaction can be used by the cell to synthesize other cell components. This topic is covered in more depth in chapter 8. Since these organisms are the primary producers in most ecosystems, they constitute the basis of food chains by providing nutrition for heterotrophs. This type of photosynthesis is also responsible for maintaining the level of oxygen gas in the atmosphere that is so vital to life.

The other form of photosynthesis is termed *anoxygenic* (no oxygen produced). It may be summarized by the equation:

$$CO_2 + H_2S \xrightarrow[\text{by bacteriochlorophyll}]{\text{Sunlight absorbed}} (CH_2O)_n + S^0 + H_2O$$

Note that this type of photosynthesis is different in several respects. It uses a unique pigment, bacteriochlorophyll; its hydrogen source is hydrogen sulfide gas; and it gives off elemental sulfur as one product. The reactions all occur in the absence of oxygen as well. Common groups of photosynthetic bacteria are the purple and green sulfur bacteria that live in various aquatic habitats, often in mixtures with other photosynthetic microbes (see figure 4.32).

Chemoautotrophy—A Radical Existence Compared to common, familiar organisms, **chemoautotrophs** have adapted to the most stringent nutritional strategy on earth. All chemoautotrophs are bacteria or archaea that survive totally on inorganic substances such as minerals and gases. They require neither light nor organic nutrients in any form, and they derive energy in diverse and some-

times surprising ways. In very simple terms, they remove electrons from inorganic substrates such as hydrogen gas, hydrogen sulfide, sulfur, or iron and combine them with other inorganic substances such as carbon dioxide, oxygen, and hydrogen. These reactions release simple organic molecules and a modest amount of energy to drive the synthetic processes of the cell. **Figure 7.2a** provides an example of an unusual bacterium that inhabits hot springs in New Zealand. Chemoautotrophs play an important part in recycling inorganic nutrients and elements. For an example of chemoautotrophy and its importance to deep-sea communities, see 7.1 Secret World of Microbes.

The Methanogen World Methanogens* are a unique type of chemoautotroph widely distributed in the earth's habitats. All known methanogens are archaea, and many of them are found in extreme habitats, ranging from hot springs and vents to the deepest, coldest parts of the ocean. **(figure 7.2b).** Others are common in soil, swamps, and even the intestines of humans and other animals.

Their metabolism is adapted to producing methane gas (CH_4 or "swamp gas") by reducing carbon dioxide, using hydrogen gas under anaerobic conditions, summarized as:

$$4H_2 + CO_2 \rightarrow CH_4 + 2H_2O$$

* *methanogen* (meth-an"oh-gen') From *methane,* a colorless, odorless gas, and *gennan,* to produce.

(a)

(b)

Figure 7.2 **Examples of chemotrophy.** (a) *Venenivibrio*, an extremophilic bacterium that lives in acidic hot springs and derives energy by combining hydrogen gas with oxygen to form water and hydrogen peroxide. (b) *Methanocaldococcus jannaschii* is an archaeon and methanogen that inhabits hot vents in the seafloor. It also metabolizes hydrogen gas but its product is methane gas (180,000✕).

Researchers sampling deep underneath the seafloor have uncovered massive deposits of methanogens. The immensity of this community has led one group of scientists to estimate that it comprises nearly one-third of all life on the planet! Evidence points to its extreme age: It has been embedded in the earth's crust for billions of years. Placed under tremendous pressures, the methane it releases becomes frozen into crystals. Some of it serves as a nutrient source for other extreme archaea, and some of it escapes into the ocean. From this position, it may be a significant factor in the development of the earth's climate and atmosphere. Some microbial ecologists suggest that future rises in sea temperature could increase the melting of these methane deposits. Because methane is an important "greenhouse gas," this process could contribute considerably to ongoing global warming.

Heterotrophs and Their Energy Sources

The majority of heterotrophic microorganisms are **chemoorganotrophs** that derive both carbon and energy from organic compounds. Processing these organic molecules by respiration or fermentation releases energy in the form of ATP. We will explore these topics in greater depth in chapter 8. An example of chemoheterotrophy is *aerobic respiration,* the principal energy-yielding pathway in animals, most protozoa and fungi, and aerobic bacteria. It can be simply represented by the equation:

$$\text{Glucose } [C_6H_{12}O_6] + 6O_2 \rightarrow 6CO_2 + 6H_2O + \text{Energy(ATP)}$$

Note that this reaction is complementary to photosynthesis. Here, glucose and oxygen are reactants and carbon dioxide is given off. Indeed, the earth's balance of both energy and metabolic gases greatly depends on this relationship. Chemoheterotrophic microbes are all similar in requiring an organic carbon source, but they differ in how they obtain it. This category includes a wide variety of organisms that feed on other organisms: animals, protozoa, fungi, and many types of bacteria. Examples of varied nutritional patterns include grazers, scavengers, and predators, but the dominant chemoheterotrophic microorganisms fit the description of saprobes or symbionts. **Saprobes**[2] are free-living microbes that feed primarily on organic detritis released by dead organisms, and **symbionts*** derive their organic nutrients from the bodies of living organisms. These categories are not absolute, in that some saprobes can adapt to living organisms, and some symbionts can obtain nutrients from a nonliving source. Because many of these nutritional patterns are also ecological in nature, they will be given fuller coverage in section 7.5. In this section, we introduce saprobes and parasites as they relate to nutrition.

Saprobic Microorganisms The primary niche of saprobes is as decomposers of plant litter, animal matter, and dead microbes. If not for the work of decomposers, the earth would gradually fill up with organic material and the nutrients it contains would not be recycled. Most saprobes, notably bacteria and fungi, have a rigid cell wall and cannot engulf large particles of food. To compensate, they release enzymes to the extracellular environment and digest the food particles into smaller molecules that can be transported into the cell **(figure 7.3)**.

Many saprobes exist strictly on dead organic matter in environmental reservoirs such as soil and water, and are unable to adapt to the body of a live host. This group includes free-living protozoa, most fungi, and a variety of bacteria. Apparently, there are fewer of these microbes than was once thought, and many supposedly nonpathogenic saprobes can adapt to and invade a susceptible host. When a saprobe does infect a host, it is considered a *facultative parasite.* Because such an infection usually occurs when the host is compromised, the microbe is said to be an *opportunistic pathogen.* For example, although its natural habitat is soil and water, *Pseudomonas aeruginosa* frequently causes infections in patients when it is carried into the hospital environment.

2. Synonyms are *saprotroph* and *saprophyte.* We prefer to use the terms *saprobe* and *saprotroph* because they are more consistent with other terminology.

* *symbiont* An organism that lives in association with another organism, from the term symbiosis (sim″-bye-oh′-sis) Gr, *syn*, together, and *bios*, to live. Literally, living together.

(a) Cell wall acts as a barrier.

Organic debris

(b) Enzymes are transported outside the wall.

Enzymes

(c) Enzymes hydrolyze the bonds on nutrients.

(d) Smaller molecules are transported across the
wall and cell membrane into the cytoplasm.

**Figure 7.3 Extracellular digestion in a saprobe with a cell wall
(bacterium or fungus).** **(a)** A walled cell is inflexible and cannot engulf
large pieces of organic debris. **(b)** In response to a usable substrate, the cell
synthesizes enzymes that are transported across the wall into the
extracellular environment. **(c)** The enzymes hydrolyze the bonds in the
debris molecules. **(d)** Digestion produces molecules small enough to be
transported into the cytoplasm.

Parasitic Microorganisms Most human infections are caused
by heterotrophic microorganisms, but those having the greatest
adverse impact on human health are **parasites.** By definition, a
parasite is a microbe that invades the body of a host, uses it as a
habitat and source of nutrients and, in the process, harms the host
to some degree. Such parasitic microbes that grow inside sterile
tissues, cause damage, and even death are also termed **pathogens.**
Parasites range from viruses to helminth worms, and they can live
on the body (ectoparasites), in the organs and tissues (endopara-
sites), or even within cells (intracellular parasites, the most ex-
treme type). The more successful parasites generally have no fatal

effects and may eventually evolve to a less harmful relationship
with their host (see section 7.5).

Obligate parasites (for example, the leprosy bacillus and the
syphilis spirochete) are so dependent that they are unable to grow
outside of a living host. Less strict parasites such as the gonococcus
and pneumococcus can be cultured artificially if provided with the
correct nutrients and environmental conditions.

 Check Your Progress SECTION 7.2

5. Compare autotrophs and heterotrophs with respect to the form of
 carbon-based nutrients they require.
6. Describe the nutritional strategy of two types of chemoautotrophs
 described in the chapter.
7. Contrast chemoautotrophs and chemoheterotrophs as to carbon
 and energy sources and other unique strategies they may have.
8. What are the main differences between saprobes and parasites?

7.3 Transport: Movement of Substances Across the Cell Membrane

 Expected Learning Outcomes

8. Describe the basic factors in diffusion and passive transport systems.
9. Define *osmosis* and describe varying osmotic conditions.
10. Analyze adaptations microbes make in response to osmosis.
11. Describe the features of active transport and differentiate among
 its mechanisms.

A microorganism's habitat provides necessary substances—some
abundant, others scarce—that must still be taken into the cell. For
survival, cells must transport waste materials out of the cell (and into
the environment). Whatever the direction, transport occurs across the
cell membrane, the structure specialized for this role. This is true
even in organisms with cell walls (bacteria, algae, and fungi), because
the cell wall is usually only a partial, nonselective barrier. In this sec-
tion, we discuss some important physical forces in cell transport.

Diffusion and Molecular Motion

All atoms and molecules, regardless of being in a solid, liquid, or gas,
are in continuous movement. As the temperature increases, the
molecular movement becomes faster due to an increase in kinetic en-
ergy. In any solution, including cytoplasm, these moving molecules
cannot travel very far without having collisions with other molecules
and, therefore, will bounce off each other like millions of pool balls
every second (**figure 7.4**). As a result of each collision, the directions
of the colliding molecules are altered and the direction of any one
molecule is unpredictable and considered random. An example would
be a situation in which molecules of a substance are more concen-
trated in one area than another. Just by random thermal movement, the
molecules will become dispersed away from an area of higher con-
centration to an area of lower concentration. In time, this will evenly
distribute the molecules in the solution. This net movement of mole-
cules down their concentration gradient by random thermal motion is

How Molecules Diffuse in Aqueous Solutions

Figure 7.4 Diffusion of molecules in aqueous solutions. A high concentration of sugar exists in the cube at the bottom of the liquid. An imaginary molecular view of this area shows that sugar molecules are in a constant state of motion. Those at the edge of the cube diffuse from the concentrated area into more dilute regions. As diffusion continues, the sugar will spread evenly throughout the aqueous phase, and eventually there will be no gradient. At that point, the system is said to be in equilibrium.

known as **diffusion.** It can be demonstrated by a variety of simple observations. A drop of perfume released into one part of a room is soon smelled in another part, or a lump of sugar in a cup of tea spreads through the whole cup without stirring (figure 7.4).

Diffusion is a driving force in cell activities, but its effects are greatly controlled by membranes. Two special cases are osmosis and facilitated diffusion. Both processes are considered a type of **passive transport.** This means that the cell does not expend extra energy for them to function. The inherent energy of the molecules moving down a gradient does the work of transport.

The Diffusion of Water: Osmosis

Diffusion of water through a selectively permeable membrane, a process called **osmosis,*** is a physical phenomenon that is easily demonstrated in the laboratory with nonliving materials. Simple experiments provide a model of how cells deal with various solute concentrations in aqueous solutions **(figure 7.5).** In an osmotic system, the membrane is *selectively,* or *differentially, permeable,* having passageways that allow free diffusion of water but can block certain dissolved molecules. When this type of membrane is placed between solutions of

* *osmosis* (oz-moh′-sis) Gr. *osmos,* impulsion, and *osis,* a process.

differing concentrations where the solute cannot pass across (protein, for example), then under the laws of diffusion, water will diffuse at a faster rate from the side that has more water to the side that has less water. As long as the concentrations of the solutions differ, one side will experience a net loss of water and the other a net gain of water until equilibrium is reached and the rate of diffusion is equalized.

Osmosis in living systems is similar to the model shown in figure 7.5. Living membranes generally block the entrance and exit of larger molecules and permit free diffusion of water. Because most cells contain and are surrounded by some sort of aqueous solution, osmosis can have far-reaching effects on cellular activities and survival. Depending on the water content of a cell as compared with its environment, a cell can gain or lose water, or it may remain unaffected. Terms that we use for describing these conditions are *isotonic, hypotonic,* and *hypertonic*[3] **(figure 7.6).**

Under **isotonic*** conditions, the environment is equal in solute concentration to the cell's internal environment; and because diffusion of water proceeds at the same rate in both directions, there is no net change in cell volume. Isotonic solutions are generally the most stable environments for cells, because they are already in an osmotic steady state with the cell. Parasites living in host tissues are most likely to be living in isotonic habitats.

Under **hypotonic*** conditions, the solute concentration of the external environment is lower than that of the cell's internal environment. Pure water provides the most hypotonic environment for cells because it has no solute. Because the net direction of osmosis is from the hypotonic solution into the cell, cells without walls swell and can burst when exposed to this condition.

Slight hypotonicity is tolerated quite well by most bacteria because of their rigid cell walls. The light flow of water into the cell keeps the cell membrane fully extended and the cytoplasm full. This is the optimum condition for the many processes occurring in and on the membrane.

A cell in a **hypertonic*** environment is exposed to a solution with higher solute concentration than its cytoplasm. Because hypertonicity will force water to diffuse out of a cell, it is said to create high *osmotic pressure* or potential. In cells with a wall, water loss causes shrinkage of the protoplast away from the wall, a condition called **plasmolysis.*** Although the whole cell does not collapse, this event can still damage and even kill many kinds of cells. The effect on cells lacking a wall is to shrink down and usually to collapse (figure 7.6). The growth-limiting effect of hypertonic solutions on microbes is the principle behind using concentrated salt and sugar solutions as preservatives for food, such as in salted hams and fish.

Adaptations to Osmotic Variations in the Environment

Let us now see how specific microbes have adapted osmotically to their environments. In general, isotonic conditions pose little stress on cells, so survival depends on counteracting the adverse effects of hypertonic and hypotonic environments.

3. It will help you to recall these osmotic conditions if you remember that the prefixes *iso-, hypo-,* and *hyper-* refer to the environment *outside* of the cell.

* *isotonic* (eye-soh-tahn′-ik) Gr. *iso,* same, and *tonos,* tension.
* *hypotonic* (hy-poh-tahn′-ik) Gr. *hypo,* under, and *tonos,* tension.
* *hypertonic* (hy-pur-tahn′-ik) Gr. *hyper,* above, and *tonos,* tension.
* *plasmolysis* (plaz′-moh-ly′-sis)

(a) Inset shows a close-up of the osmotic process. The gradient goes from the outer container (higher concentration of H_2O) to the sac (lower concentration of H_2O). Some water will diffuse the opposite direction but the net gradient favors osmosis into the sac.

(b) As the H_2O diffuses into the sac, the volume increases and forces the excess solution into the tube, which will rise continually.

(c) Even as the solution becomes diluted, there will still be osmosis into the sac. Equilibrium will not occur because the solutions can never become equal. (Why?)

Figure 7.5 Model system to demonstrate osmosis. Here we have a solution enclosed in a membranous sac and attached to a hollow tube. The membrane is permeable to water (solvent) but not to solute. The sac is immersed in a container of pure water and observed over time.

An alga and an amoeba living in fresh pond water are examples of cells that live in constantly hypotonic conditions. The rate of water diffusing across the cell membrane into the cytoplasm is rapid and constant, and the cells would die without a way to adapt. As with bacteria, the majority of algae have a cell wall that protects them from bursting even as the cytoplasmic membrane becomes **turgid*** from pressure. The amoeba has no cell wall to protect it, so it must expend energy to deal with the influx of water. This is accomplished with a water, or contractile, vacuole that siphons excess water out of the cell like a tiny pump.

A microbe living in a high-salt environment (hypertonic) has the opposite problem and must either restrict its loss of water to the environment or increase the salinity of its internal environment. Halobacteria living in the Great Salt Lake and the Dead Sea actually absorb salt to make their cells isotonic with the environment; thus, they have a physiological need for a high-salt concentration in their habitats (see halophiles on page 202).

The Movement of Solutes Across Membranes

Simple diffusion works well for movement of small nonpolar molecules such as oxygen or lipid soluble molecules that readily pass through membranes. But many substances that cells require are polar and ionic chemicals with greatly reduced permeability. Simple diffusion alone would be unable to transport these substances. One way that cells have adapted to this limitation involves a process called **facilitated diffusion (figure 7.7).** This passive transport mechanism utilizes a carrier protein in the membrane that will bind a specific substance. This binding changes the conformation of the carrier proteins in a way that facilitates movement of the substance across the membrane. Once the substance is transported, the carrier protein resumes its original shape and is ready to transport again. These carrier proteins exhibit **specificity,** which means that they bind and transport only a single type of molecule. For example, a carrier protein that transports sodium will not bind glucose. A second characteristic exhibited by facilitated diffusion is *saturation.* The rate of transport of a substance is limited by the number of binding sites on the transport proteins. As the substance's concentration increases, so does the rate of transport until the concentration of the transported substance causes all of the transporters' binding sites to be occupied. Then the rate of transport reaches a steady state and cannot move faster despite further increases in the substance's concentration.

Other examples of passive protein carriers found in a wide variety of cells are aquaporins, also known as water channels. These openings in the membrane facilitate passive transport of water molecules following an existing osmotic gradient. They appear to be involved in regulating volume and osmotic pressure.

* *turgid* (ter'-jid) A condition of being swollen or congested.

Cells with cell walls

Isotonic Solution	Hypotonic Solution	Hypertonic Solution

Cell wall

Cell membrane

Cell membrane

Water concentration is equal inside and outside the cell, thus rates of diffusion are equal in both directions.

Net diffusion of water is into the cell; this swells the protoplast and pushes it tightly against the wall. Wall usually prevents cell from bursting.

Water diffuses out of the cell and shrinks the cell membrane away from the cell wall; process is known as **plasmolysis.**

Cells lacking walls

Cell membrane

Early

Late (osmolysis)

Early

Late

Rates of diffusion are equal in both directions.

Diffusion of water into the cell causes it to swell, and may burst it if no mechanism exists to remove the water.

Water diffusing out of the cell causes it to shrink and become distorted.

 Direction of net water movement.

Figure 7.6 **Cell responses to solutions of differing osmotic content.**

Active Transport: Bringing in Molecules Against a Gradient

Free-living microbes exist under relatively nutrient-starved conditions and cannot rely completely on slow and rather inefficient passive transport mechanisms. To ensure a constant supply of nutrients and other required substances, microbes must capture those that are in low concentrations and actively transport them into the cell. Cells must likewise transport substances in the reverse direction to the external environment. Some microbes have such efficient active transport systems that an essential nutrient can be found in intracellular concentrations that are hundreds of times greater than the habitat.

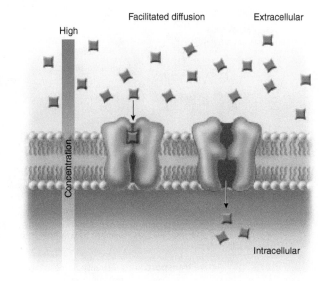

Facilitated diffusion

Extracellular

High

Concentration

Intracellular

Figure 7.7 **Facilitated diffusion.** Facilitated diffusion involves the attachment of a molecule to a specific protein carrier. Bonding of the molecule causes a conformational change in the protein that facilitates the molecule's passage across the membrane (left view). The membrane protein releases the molecule into the cell interior (right view). The cell does not have to expend energy for transport.

Features inherent in **active transport** systems are:

1. the transport of nutrients against the diffusion gradient or in the same direction as the natural gradient but at a rate faster than by diffusion alone,
2. the presence of specific membrane proteins (permeases and pumps; **figure 7.8a**), and

3. the expenditure of additional cellular energy in the form of ATP-driven uptake. Examples of substances transported actively are monosaccharides, amino acids, organic acids, phosphates, and metal ions.

Carrier-mediated active transport functions with specific membrane proteins that bind both ATP and the molecules to be

(a) **Carrier-mediated active transport.** (1) Membrane-bound transporter proteins (permeases) interact with nearby solute binding proteins that carry essential solutes (sodium, iron, sugars). (2) Once a binding protein attaches to a specific site, an ATP is activated and generates energy to pump the solute into the cell's interior through a special channel in the permease.

(b) **In group translocation,** (1) a specific molecule is actively captured, but on its passage through the membrane protein carrier (2) it is chemically altered or activated for use in the cell. By coupling transport with synthesis, the cell conserves energy.

(c) **Endocytosis.** With phagocytosis, solid particles are engulfed by flexible cell extensions or pseudopods (1,000X). (5) With pinocytosis, fluids and/or dissoved substances are enclosed in vesicles by very fine protrusions called microvilli (3,000X). Oil droplets fuse with the membrane and are released directly into (1-4) the cell.

Figure 7.8 **Active transport.** In active transport mechanisms, energy is expended (ATP) to transport the molecule across the cell membrane.

TABLE 7.3	Summary of Transport Processes in Cells				
General Process	**Nature of Transport**	**Examples**	**Description**	**Qualities**	
Passive early	Energy expenditure by the cell is not required. Substances exist in a gradient and move from areas of higher concentration toward areas of lower concentration in the gradient.	Diffusion osmosis	A fundamental property of atoms and molecules that exist in a state of random motion	Nonspecific Brownian movement Movement of small uncharged molecules across membranes	
		Facilitated diffusion	Molecule binds to a carrier protein in membrane and is carried across to other side.	Molecule specific; transports both ways Transports sugars, amino acids, water	
Active	Energy expenditure is required. Molecules need not exist in a gradient. Rate of transport is increased. Transport may occur against a concentration gradient.	Carrier-mediated active transport	Atoms or molecules are pumped into or out of the cell by specialized receptors; driven by ATP or other high-energy molecules	Transports simple sugars, amino acids, inorganic ions (Na^+, K^+)	
		Group translocation	Molecule is moved across membrane and simultaneously converted to a metabolically useful substance.	Alternate system for transporting nutrients (sugars, amino acids)	
		Bulk transport	Mass transport of large particles, cells, and liquids by engulfment and vesicle formation	Process is endocytosis; examples are phagocytosis and pinocytosis	

transported. Release of energy from ATP drives the movement of the molecule through the protein carrier. This can occur in either direction. Some bacteria transport certain sugars, amino acids, vitamins, and phosphate into the cell by this mechanism. Other bacteria can actively pump drugs out of the cell, thereby providing them resistance to the drugs. Other active transport pumps can rapidly carry ions such as K^+, Na^+, and H^+ across the membrane.

Another type of active transport, **group translocation,** couples the transport of a nutrient with its conversion to a substance that is immediately useful inside the cell (**figure 7.8b**). This method is used by certain bacteria to transport sugars (glucose, fructose) while simultaneously adding phosphate molecules that activate them in preparation for a metabolic cycle.

Endocytosis: Eating and Drinking by Cells

Some cells can transport large molecules, particles, liquids, or even other cells across the cell membrane. Because the cell usually expends energy to carry out this movement, it is also a form of active transport. The substances transported do not pass physically through the membrane but are carried into the cell by **endocytosis.** First the cell encloses the substance in its membrane, simultaneously forming a vacuole and engulfing it (**figure 7.8c**). Amoebas and certain white blood cells ingest whole cells or large solid matter by a type of endocytosis called **phagocytosis.** Liquids, such as oils or molecules in solution, enter the cell through **pinocytosis.** The mechanisms for transport of molecules into cells are summarized in **table 7.3.**

Check Your Progress SECTION 7.3

9. Compare and contrast passive and active forms of transport, using examples of what is being transported and the requirements for each.

10. How are phagocytosis and pinocytosis similar? How are they different?

11. Explain the differences between facilitated diffusion and group translocation.

12. Compare the effects of isotonic, hypotonic, and hypertonic solutions on an amoeba and on a bacterial cell. If a cell lives in a hypotonic environment, what will occur if it is placed in a hypertonic one? Answer for the opposite case as well.

7.4 Environmental Factors That Influence Microbes

Expected Learning Outcomes

12. Differentiate between habitat and niche.

13. Describe the range of temperatures a microbe can function within.

14. Explain the adaptive temperature groups with examples of microbes that exist in them.

15. List the major gases and describe microbial requirements for these gases.

16. Outline the adaptations of microbial groups to variations in pH.

17. Identify microbial adaptations to osmotic pressure.

7.1 Secret World of Microbes
Life in the Extremes

Any extreme habitat—whether hot, cold, salty, acidic, alkaline, high pressure, arid, oxygen-free, or toxic—is likely to harbor microorganisms with special adaptations to these conditions. Although in most instances the inhabitants are archaea and bacteria, certain fungi, protozoans, algae, and even viruses are also capable of living in severe habitats. Microbiologists have termed such remarkable organisms **extremophiles.**

Extreme Temperatures

Some of the most extreme habitats are hot springs, geysers, volcanoes, and ocean vents, all of which support flourishing microbial populations. Temperatures in these regions range from 50°C (122°F) to well above the boiling point of water, with some ocean vents even approaching 350°C (662°F). Many heat-adapted microbes are ancient archaea whose genetics and metabolism are extremely modified for this mode of existence. A unique ecosystem based on hydrogen sulfide–oxidizing bacteria exists in the hydrothermal vents lying along deep oceanic ridges. Other denizens of hot volcanic waters are unusual invertebrates such as the Pompeii worm that frequents rocky hideouts around sea vents measuring 80°C (176°F) (see photo a). Their survival is greatly dependent on symbiotic bacteria that form an insulated coat on the worm's surface.

A large part of the earth exists at cold temperatures. Microbes settle and grow throughout the Arctic and Antarctic and in the deepest parts of the ocean in near-freezing temperatures. Several species of algae and fungi thrive on the surfaces of snow and glacier ice (see figure 7.10). More surprising still is that some bacteria and algae flourish in the sea ice of Antarctica. Although the ice appears to be completely solid, it is honeycombed by various-size pores and tunnels filled with a solution that is

−20°C (−4°F). These frigid microhabitats harbor a microcosm of planktonic bacteria, algae, and predators that feed on them.

High Salt, Acidity, and Alkalinity

The growth of most microbial cells is inhibited by high amounts of salt; for this reason, salt is a common food preservative. But there are many salt lovers, including rich communities of bacteria and algae living in oceans, salt lakes, and inland seas, some of which are saturated with salt (30%). Microbiologists recently discovered salt pockets that supported archaea living in water 100 times more concentrated than seawater.

"Conan the Bacterium"

A tiny gram-positive coccus, *Deinococcus radiodurans*, (see photo b), has been called "Conan the bacterium" because of its capacity to survive extreme drying and very high levels of radiation. This bacterium is widespread in many habitats, but its resistance to radiation sets it apart from every other organism ever known. The DNA and proteins of most organisms are very sensitive to gamma rays and other high-energy radiation, which is why radiation is so damaging to cells. But we now know its secret. *Deinococcus* carries around several copies of its genome, making it easily replaceable, and it contains radiation-resistant enzymes that help it rapidly repair DNA damage. This microbe is being studied for its potential in bioremediation of radioactive waste and as a model organism for Mars studies.

Brave "Old" World

When samples of ancient Antarctic ice (several million years old) were brought into the lab, they yielded up living bacteria. Some of the oldest

Microbes are exposed to a wide variety of environmental factors that affect growth and survival. Microbial ecology focuses on ways that microorganisms deal with or adapt to such factors as heat, cold, gases, acid, radiation, osmotic and hydrostatic pressures, and even other microbes. Adaptation involves a complex adjustment in biochemistry or genetics that enables long-term survival and growth. The term biologists use to describe the totality of adaptations organisms make to their habitats is **niche.*** For most microbes, environmental factors fundamentally affect the function of metabolic enzymes. Thus, survival is largely a matter of whether the enzyme systems of microorganisms can continue to function even in a changing environment. Read **7.1 Secret World of Microbes** to discover the broad range of conditions that support microbial life.

Adaptations to Temperature

Microbial cells cannot control their temperature and therefore assume the ambient temperature of their natural habitats. To survive, they must adapt to whatever temperature variations are encountered in their habitat. The range of temperatures for microbial growth can be ex-

pressed as three **cardinal temperatures.** The **minimum temperature** is the lowest temperature that permits a microbe's continued growth and metabolism; below this temperature, its activities are inhibited. The **maximum temperature** is the highest temperature at which growth and metabolism can proceed. If the temperature rises slightly above maximum, growth will stop. If it continues to rise beyond that point, the enzymes and nucleic acids will eventually become permanently inactivated—a condition known as denaturation—and the cell will die. This is why heat works so well as an agent in microbial control. The **optimum temperature** covers a small range, intermediate between the minimum and maximum, which promotes the fastest rate of growth and metabolism. Only rarely is the optimum a single point.

Depending on their natural habitats, some microbes have a narrow cardinal range, others a broad one. Some strict parasites will not grow if the temperature varies more than a few degrees below or above the host's body temperature. For instance, rhinoviruses (one cause of the common cold) multiply successfully only in tissues that are slightly below normal body temperature (33°C to 35°C or 91°F to 95°F). Other microbes are not so limited. Strains of *Staphylococcus aureus* grow within the range of 6°C to 46°C (43°F to 114°F), and the intestinal bacterium *Enterococcus faecalis* grows within the range of 0°C to 44°C (32°F to 112°F).

* *niche* (nitch) Fr. *nichier,* to nest.

isolates were unusual, very slow-growing forms, but others were similar to modern bacteria.

Another weird, ancient ultraextremophile was discovered 3 kilometers down in an African gold mine. The bacterium *Desulforudis* is the only occupant of this totally dark, anaerobic, hot, alkaline habitat, and it derives its energy from the radioactive decay of uranium. This is the first organism on earth known to have established its own ecosystem and to sustain itself without the contributions of other organisms.

Numerous species have carved a niche for themselves in the deepest layers of mud, swamps, and oceans, where oxygen gas and sunlight cannot penetrate. The predominant living things in the deepest part of the oceans (10,000 m or below) are pressure- and cold-loving microorganisms. Even

parched zones in sand dunes and deserts harbor a hardy brand of microbes; and thriving bacterial populations can be found in petroleum, coal, and mineral deposits containing copper, zinc, gold, and uranium. Microbes that can adapt and survive under such lethal conditions are called toxophiles.

As a rule, a microbe that has adapted to an extreme habitat will die if placed in a moderate one. And, except for rare cases, none of the organisms living in these extremes is a pathogen because the human body is a rather hostile habitat for them.

Provide some examples of extreme habitats created by human technologies that would support microbes. *Answer available at http:// www.mhhe.com/talaro9*

(a) The hottest animal on earth is this Pompeii worm wearing a coat of symbiotic bacteria (fine filaments) to protect against the heat. **(b)** A fluorescent micrograph of *Deinococcus radiodurans*, showing its packet arrangement, cell walls (red), and chromosomes (green).

Another way to express temperature adaptation is to describe whether an organism grows optimally in a cold, moderate, or hot temperature range. The terms used for these ecological groups are *psychrophile, mesophile,* and *thermophile* (**figure 7.9**).

A **psychrophile*** is a microorganism (bacterium, archaea, fungus, or alga) with an optimum temperature below 15°C (59°F) but generally can grow at 0°C (32°F). It is obligate with respect to cold and generally cannot grow above 20°C (68°F). Laboratory work with true psychrophiles can be a real challenge. Inoculations have to be done in a cold room because ordinary room temperature can be lethal to these organisms. Unlike most laboratory cultures, storage in the refrigerator incubates rather than inhibits them. As one might predict, true psychrophiles are not capable of surviving in the human body and do not cause infections. Instead, they populate some of the coldest places on earth, including

Figure 7.9 Ecological groups by temperature of adaptation. Psychrophiles can grow at or near 0°C and have an optimum below 15°C. As a group, mesophiles can grow between 10°C and 50°C, but their optima usually fall between 20°C and 40°C. One type of mesophile termed a psychrotroph is capable of growth at temperatures below 20°C. Generally speaking, thermophiles require temperatures above 45°C and grow optimally between this temperature and 80°C. Extreme thermophiles are bacteria and archaea with optima above 80°C. Note that the extremes of the ranges can overlap to an extent.

* *psychrophile* (sy'-kroh-fyl) Gr. *psychros,* cold, and *philos,* to love.

(a) (b)

Figure 7.10 **Red snow. (a)** The surface of an Alaskan glacier provides a perfect habitat for psychrophilic photosynthetic organisms such as *Chlamydomonas nivalis.* **(b)** Microscopic views of this snow alga, actually classified as a "green" alga although a red pigment dominates at this stage of its life cycle (600×).

snowfields (**figure 7.10),** polar ice, and the deep ocean. Recently, bacteria were isolated from an undersea lake in Antarctica that were living at −15°C (5°F). True psychrophiles must be distinguished from *psychrotrophs* or *facultative psychrophiles* that grow slowly in cold but have an optimum temperature above 20°C (68°F). Psychrotrophs such as *Staphylococcus aureus* and *Listeria monocytogenes* are a concern because they can grow in refrigerated food and cause food-borne illness.

The majority of medically significant microorganisms are **mesophiles,*** organisms that grow at intermediate temperatures. Although an individual species can grow between the extremes of 10°C and 50°C (50°F and 122°F), the optimum growth temperatures (optima) of most mesophiles fall into the range of 20°C to 40°C (68°F to 104°F). Organisms in this group inhabit animals and plants as well as soil and water in temperate, subtropical, and tropical regions. Most human pathogens have optima somewhere between 30°C and 40°C (human body temperature is 37°C or 98°F). *Thermoduric* microbes, which can survive short exposure to high temperatures but are normally mesophiles, are common contaminants of heated or pasteurized foods (see chapter 11). Examples include heat-resistant cysts such as *Giardia* or sporeformers such as *Bacillus* and *Clostridium.*

A **thermophile*** is a microbe that grows optimally at temperatures greater than 45°C (113°F). Such heat-loving microbes live in soil and water associated with volcanic activity, in compost piles, and in habitats directly exposed to the sun. Thermophiles generally range in growth temperatures from 45°C to 80°C (113°F to 176°F). Most eukaryotic forms cannot survive above 60°C (140°F), but a few bacteria and archaea, called **hyperthermophiles,** grow at between 80°C and 121°C (250°F, currently thought to be the highest temperature limit endured by enzymes and cell structures). Strict thermophiles are so heat tolerant that researchers may use a heat-sterilizing device to isolate them in culture.

Currently, there is intense interest in thermal microorganisms on the part of biotechnology companies. One of the most profitable discoveries so far was a strict thermophile *Thermus aquaticus,* which produces an enzyme that can make copies of DNA even at high temperatures. This enzyme—Taq polymerase—is now an essential component of the polymerase chain reaction or PCR, a process used in many areas of medicine, forensics, and biotechnology (see chapter 10).

Gas Requirements

The atmospheric gases that most influence microbial growth are oxygen (O_2) and carbon dioxide (CO_2). Oxygen comprises about 20% of the atmosphere and CO_2 about 0.03%. Oxygen gas has a great impact on microbial adaptation. It is an important respiratory gas, and it is also a powerful oxidizing agent that exists in many toxic forms. In general, microbes fall into one of three categories: those that use oxygen and can detoxify it; those that can neither use oxygen nor detoxify it; and those that do not use oxygen but can detoxify it.

How Microbes Process Oxygen

As oxygen gas enters into cellular reactions, it can be transformed into several toxic products. Singlet oxygen (1O_2) is an extremely reactive molecule produced by both living and nonliving processes. Notably, it is one of the substances produced by phagocytes to kill invading bacteria (see chapter 14). The buildup of singlet oxygen and the oxidation of membrane lipids and other molecules can damage and destroy a cell. The highly reactive superoxide ion (O_2^-), peroxide (H_2O_2), and hydroxyl radicals (OH) are other destructive metabolic by-products of oxygen. To survive these toxic oxygen products, many microorganisms have developed enzymes capable of scavenging and neutralizing these chemicals. The complete conversion of superoxide ion into harmless oxygen involves a two-step process and at least two enzymes:

Step 1. $$2O_2^- + 2H^+ \xrightarrow{\text{Superoxide dismutase}} H_2O_2 \text{ (hydrogen peroxide)} + O_2$$

Step 2. $$2H_2O_2 \xrightarrow{\text{Catalase}} 2H_2O + O_2$$

In this series of reactions essential for aerobic organisms, the superoxide ion is first converted to hydrogen peroxide and normal oxygen by the action of an enzyme called superoxide dismutase. Because hydrogen peroxide is also toxic to cells (it is used as a disinfectant and antiseptic), it must be degraded by an enzyme—either catalase or peroxidase—into water and oxygen. If a microbe is not capable of dealing with toxic oxygen by these or similar mechanisms, it will be restricted to habitats free of oxygen.

With respect to oxygen requirements, several general categories are recognized. An **aerobe*** (aerobic organism) can use gaseous oxygen in its metabolism and possesses the enzymes needed to process toxic oxygen products. An organism that cannot grow without oxygen is an **obligate aerobe.** Most fungi and protozoa, as well as many bacteria (genera *Micrococcus* and *Bacillus*), have strict requirements for oxygen in their metabolism.

A **facultative anaerobe** is an aerobe that does not require oxygen for its metabolism and is capable of growth in the absence of it. This

* *mesophiles* (mez′-oh-fylz) Gr. *mesos,* middle.
* *thermophile* (thur′-moh-fyl) Gr. *therme,* heat.

* *aerobe* (air′-ohb) Although the prefix means air, it is used in the sense of oxygen.

type of organism metabolizes by aerobic respiration when oxygen is present, but in its absence, it adopts an anaerobic mode of metabolism such as fermentation. Facultative anaerobes usually possess catalase and superoxide dismutase. A number of bacterial pathogens fall into this group. This includes gram-negative intestinal bacteria and staphylococci. A **microaerophile*** does not grow at normal atmospheric concentrations of oxygen but requires a small amount of it (1%–15%) in metabolism. Most organisms in this category live in a habitat such as soil, water, or the human body that provides small amounts of oxygen but is not directly exposed to the atmosphere.

A true **anaerobe** (anaerobic microorganism) lacks the metabolic enzyme systems for using oxygen gas in respiration. Because **strict,** or **obligate, anaerobes** also lack the enzymes for processing toxic oxygen, they cannot tolerate any free oxygen in the immediate environment and will die if exposed to it. Strict anaerobes live in highly reduced habitats, such as deep muds, lakes, oceans, and soil.

Determining the oxygen requirements of a microbe from a biochemical standpoint can be a very time-consuming process. An initial clarification comes from cultures made with reducing media that contain an oxygen-removing chemical such as thioglycollate. The location of growth in a tube of fluid thioglycollate medium is a fair indicator of an organism's adaptation to oxygen use **(figure 7.11).** Growing strictly anaerobic bacteria usually requires special media, methods of incubation, and handling chambers that exclude oxygen. **Figure 7.12** shows special systems for handling and growing anaerobes.

Even though human cells use oxygen, and oxygen is found in the blood and tissues, some body sites present anaerobic pockets or microhabitats where colonization or infection can occur. Dental caries are partly due to the complex actions of aerobic and anaerobic bacteria in plaque. Most gingival infections consist of similar mixtures of oral bacteria that have invaded damaged gum tissues. Another common site for anaerobic infections is the large intestine, a relatively oxygen-free habitat that harbors a rich assortment of strictly anaerobic bacteria. Anaerobic infections can occur following abdominal surgery and traumatic injuries (gas gangrene and tetanus).

Aerotolerant anaerobes do not utilize oxygen gas but can survive and grow in its presence. These anaerobes are not harmed by oxygen, and some of them possess alternate mechanisms for breaking down peroxide and superoxide. For instance, lactobacilli, which are common residents of the intestine, inactivate these compounds with manganese ions.

Although microbes require some carbon dioxide in their metabolism, **capnophiles** grow best at higher CO_2 tensions (3%–10%) than are normally present in the atmosphere (0.033%). This becomes important in the initial isolation of some pathogens from

* *microaerophile* (myk″-roh-air′-oh-fyl)

(a)

(b)

Figure 7.12 Culturing techniques for anaerobes. (a) An anaerobic environmental chamber is equipped with ports for handling strict anaerobes without exposing them to air. It also has provisions for incubation and inspection in a completely O_2-free system. **(b)** A small anaerobic or CO_2 incubator system.

Figure 7.11 Use of thioglycollate broth to demonstrate oxygen requirements. Thioglycollate is a reducing medium that can establish a gradation in oxygen content. Oxygen concentration is highest at the top of the tube and absent in the deeper regions. When a series of tubes is inoculated with bacteria that differ in O_2 requirements, the relative position of growth provides some indication of their adaptations to oxygen use. Tube 1 (far left): aerobic (*Pseudomonas aeruginosa*); Tube 2: facultative (*Staphylococcus aureus*); Tube 3: facultative (*Escherichia coli*); Tube 4: obligate anaerobe (*Clostridium butyricum*).

clinical specimens, notably *Neisseria* (gonorrhea, meningitis), *Brucella* (undulant fever), and *Streptococcus pneumoniae*. Incubation is carried out in a CO_2 incubator that provides the correct range of CO_2 (**figure 7.12b**). Keep in mind that CO_2 is an essential nutrient for autotrophs, which use it to synthesize organic compounds.

Effects of pH

Microbial growth and survival are also influenced by the pH of the habitat. The pH was defined in chapter 2 as the degree of acidity or alkalinity of a solution. It is expressed by the pH scale, a series of numbers ranging from 0 to 14, pH 7 being neither acidic nor alkaline. As the pH value decreases toward 0, the acidity increases, and as the pH increases toward 14, the alkalinity increases. The majority of organisms live or grow in habitats between pH 6 and pH 8 because strong acids and bases can be highly damaging to enzymes and other cellular substances.

Although most microorganisms living in soil, fresh water, or the bodies of plants and animals are **neutrophiles,** living within the range of pH 5.5 to 8, some can manage exposure to pH extremes. Highly acidic or alkaline habitats such as acidic bogs and streams or alkaline soils and ponds can provide numerous habitats for specialized microbial communities. Obligate **acidophiles** include *Euglena mutabilis* (featured in Case Study 7), an alga that grows in acid pools between 0 and 1.0 pH, and *Thermoplasma,* an archaea that lives in hot coal piles at a pH of 1 to 2, and will lyse if exposed to pH 7. A few species of algae, archaea, and bacteria can actually survive at a pH near that of concentrated hydrochloric acid near a pH of 0. Not only do they require such a low pH for growth but particular bacteria actually help maintain the low pH by releasing strong acid. Because many molds and yeasts tolerate moderate acidity, they are the most common spoilage agents of pickled foods.

Alkalinophiles live in hot pools and soils that contain high levels of basic minerals. Probably the upward limit of tolerance is shown by proteobacteria in California's Mono Lake that have adapted to pH 12. Bacteria that decompose urine create alkaline conditions, because ammonium (NH_4^+) can be produced when urea (a component of urine) is digested. Metabolism of urea is one way that *Proteus* spp. can neutralize the acidity of the urine to colonize and infect the urinary system.

Osmotic Pressure

Although most microbes exist under hypotonic or isotonic conditions, a few, called osmophiles, live in habitats with a high solute concentration. One common type of osmophile requires high concentrations of salt; these organisms are called **halophiles.***

Obligate *halophiles* such as *Halobacterium* and *Halococcus* inhabit salt lakes, ponds, and other hypersaline habitats. They grow optimally in solutions of 25% NaCl but require at least 9% NaCl (combined with other salts) for growth. These archaea have significant modifications in their cell walls and membranes, and will lyse in hypotonic habitats.

Some microbes adapt to wide concentrations in solutes. These are called **osmotolerant.** Such organisms are remarkably resistant

* *halophiles* (hay'-loh-fylz)

to salt, even though they do not normally reside in high-salt environments. For example, *Staphylococcus aureus* can grow on NaCl media ranging from 0.1% up to 20%. Although it is common to use high concentrations of salt and sugar to preserve food (jellies, syrups, and brines), many bacteria and fungi actually thrive under these conditions and are common spoilage agents. A particularly hardy sugar-loving or *saccharophilic* yeast withstands the high sugar concentration of honey and candy.

Miscellaneous Environmental Factors

Descent into the ocean depths subjects organisms to increasing hydrostatic pressure. Deep-sea microbes called **barophiles** exist under pressures many times that of the atmosphere. Marine biologists sampling deep-sea trenches 7 miles below the surface isolated unusual eukaryotes called foraminifera that were being exposed to pressures 1,100 times normal. These microbes are so strictly adapted to high pressures that they will rupture when exposed to normal atmospheric pressure.

Because of the high water content of cytoplasm, all cells require water from their environment to sustain growth and metabolism. Water is the solvent for cell chemicals, and it is needed for enzyme function and digestion of macromolecules. A certain amount of water on the external surface of the cell is required for the diffusion of nutrients and wastes. Even in apparently dry habitats, such as sand or dry soil, the particles retain a thin layer of water usable by microorganisms. Only dormant, dehydrated cell stages (for example, spores and cysts) tolerate extreme drying because of the inactivity of their enzymes.

 Check Your Progress SECTION 7.4

13. Why are most pathogens mesophilic?
14. What are the ecological roles of psychrophiles and thermophiles?
15. Explain what it means to be an obligate intracellular parasite. Name three groups of obligate intracellular parasites.
16. Where in the body are anaerobic habitats apt to be found?
17. Where do superoxide ions and hydrogen peroxide originate? What are their toxic effects?

7.5 Ecological Associations Among Microorganisms

 Expected Learning Outcomes

18. Discuss the range of associations among microorganisms and their basic qualities.
19. Explain what occurs in symbiosis and coevolution.
20. Differentiate among mutual, commensal, and parasitic associations, providing examples.
21. Explain syntrophy and amensalism, using examples.
22. Describe interactions between humans and their microbiota.

Two major unifying themes of this chapter are microbial adaptiveness and ubiquity. The presence of microbes in most natural settings and their interactions with other organisms in these settings

7.2 Secret World of Microbes
A Mutual Attraction

A tremendous variety of mutualistic symbioses occur in nature. These associations gradually coevolve as participating members come to require some substance or habitat that the other members provide. In many cases, they are so interdependent that they will not survive outside of this association.

Protozoan cells often receive growth factors from symbiotic bacteria and algae that are mutually nurtured by the protozoan cell. One peculiar ciliate propels itself by affixing symbiotic bacteria to its cell membrane to act as "oars." Other ciliates and amoebas harbor specialized bacteria or algae inside their cells to provide nutrients.

Mutualism Between Microbes and Animals

Microorganisms carry on mutual symbiotic relationships with animals as diverse as sponges, worms, and mammals. Complex, multipartner mutualism is especially striking in termites, which harbor 250 or more specialized microbes inside their gut. The termite's role is simply to gnaw off pieces of wood, but it cannot digest the wood. Endosymbiotic protozoans and bacteria do the final work of breaking down the wood particles, and all mutualists share in the nutrients provided (see figure).

Bacteria and protozoa are essential in the operation of the rumen (a complex, four-chambered stomach) of cud-chewing mammals. These mammals produce no enzymes of their own to break down the cellulose that is a major part of their diet, but the microbial population harbored in their rumens does. The complex food materials are digested through several stages, during which time the animal regurgitates and chews the partially digested plant matter (the cud) and occasionally burps methane produced by the microbial symbionts.

Thermal Vent Communities

Another fascinating relationship has been found in the deep hydrothermal vents in the seafloor, where geologic forces spread the crustal plates and release superheated fluid (over 350°C or 662°F) and gas. These vents are a focus of tremendous biological and geologic activity. The source of energy in this community is not the sun, because the vents are too deep for light to penetrate (2,600 m). Instead, this ecosystem is based on a massive chemoautotrophic bacterial population that oxidizes the abundant hydrogen sulfide (H_2S) gas given off by the volcanic activity there. As the bottom of the food web, these bacteria serve as the primary producers of nutrients that service a broad spectrum of specialized animals. One example, the tube worm *Riftia* has become so specialized that it has lost its gastrointestinal tract and feeds solely from its bacterial symbionts.

> **Quick Search**
> Find "Hydrothermal Vents" or "Black Smokers" on YouTube to watch videos of these ecosystems.

Describe some of the ecological benefits of mutualism. *Answer available at http://www.mhhe.com/talaro9*

Left: A termite displayed alongside its gut. Middle, right: Some gut microbes involved in wood digestion are protozoa (blue) and spirochete bacteria.

has produced an abundance of specialized adaptations and niches of incredible diversity. If we go by the constant discoveries of new organisms and new associations, it is likely that every possible combination and example of microbial association probably exists somewhere on earth. When it comes to organizing coverage of microbial interactions, we are faced with a broad continuum, ranging from organisms living together in a totally dependent existence to free-living microbes that interact in loose and temporary unions.

Probably the best-described and best-understood interactions are **symbioses,**[4]* defined as close associations between organisms that are advantageous to at least one of the members. Recall that the members of symbiotic relationships are termed symbionts. Symbioses can be obligatory or nonobligatory, involve animals, plants, and other microbes, and can include complex multipartner interactions. Some symbionts live internally (endosymbionts), whereas others are affixed to the outside surfaces of their partners (ectosymbionts). **Figure 7.13** provides an overview of the major categories of symbiosis with examples.

The most intimate and interdependent type of symbiosis is **mutualism,** a term that implies all members share in the benefits of the relationship. Many mutualistic associations have developed over hundreds of millions and even billions of years of shared evolution, a process termed **coevolution.** Coevolving symbionts remain in very close contact and must evolve together to sustain

4. Although it is sometimes misused as a synonym for mutualism, be aware that the term does not refer only to mutually beneficial associations, as parasitism is also a form of symbiosis.

Figure 7.13 **Part 1—Symbiosis: A shared existence.** These relationships vary in the degree of interaction and its outcome.

Obligate Mutualism Organisms are so intimately associated that they require each other to survive. Root nodules **(a1)** have nitrogen-fixing endosymbiotic bacteria that supply the plant with usable nitrogen and provide a nurturing habitat for the bacteria **(a2 inset)**. Jellyfish **(b1)** and corals rely on endosymbiotic algae called dinoflagellates **(b2 inset)** for survival.

(a1) Root nodules on a legume; **(a2)** *Bradyhizobium* bacteria inside a nodule (3,000×)

(b1) A *Casseopeia* jellyfish gets its color and nutrition from **(b2)** dinoflagellates (400×).

Nonobligate Mutualism Organisms interact at the cellular level for mutual benefit, but they can be separated and live apart. The protozoan in **(c)** engulfs the algae but absorbs the nutrients they release and shelters them. **(d)** The plant supplies nutrients to the fungus and the fungus protects the plants against drying and insects.

(c) The ciliophoran *Euplotes* (800×) harbors unicellular green algae.

(d) Fungal hyphae (blue filaments—500×) growing in close contact with the cells of a grass leaf.

Commensalism The members have an unequal relationship. One partner is favored by the association and the other is not harmed or helped. **(e)** Tiny colonies of *Haemophilus* absorb required growth factors given off by *Staphylococcus*. **(f1 and 2)** Human commensals associated with the epidermis make a living off flakes and excretions, generally with neutral effects.

(e) Satellite *Haemophilus* colonies clustered around *Staphylococcus* (white line of growth).

(f1) *Demodex* mite lives in or around human hair follicles. (100×) and **(f2)** *Micrococcus luteus* bacteria lives on the skin surface (2,000×)

Parasitism A microbe invades the sterile regions of a host and occupies its tissues and cells, causing some degree of damage. **(g)** All viruses are parasites that invade cells and take over their function. **(h)** Malaria shows multilevel parasitism. Mosquitoes **(h1)** are blood-sucking ectoparasites of humans that carry their own parasites **(h2)** that can also infect humans.

(g) Sin Nombre hantavirus, a human pathogen carried in the waste of mice (5,000×).

(h1) The malaria vector, a female *Anopheles* mosquito; **(h2)** malaria parasites (*Plasmodium,* 1,000×) from blood

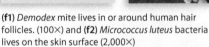

Figure 7.13 **Part 2—Additional microbial adaptations.**

Syntrophy Microbes sharing a habitat feed off substances released by other organisms. **(i)** *Azotobacter* releases NH₄ that feeds *Cellulomonas*, and *Cellulomonas* degrades cellulose that feeds *Azotobacter*. **(j)** A dust mite lives in human settings and feeds off dead skin flakes.

(i) Cycle of cross-feeding in two soil bacteria

(j) *Dermatophagoides* mite (100×)

Amensalism One member of an association produces a substance that harms or kills another. **(k)** Ants have complex symbiotic relationships that involve mutualism and amensalism with fungi and bacteria. **(l1 and l2)** In the amensal phase of their ecology, the ants cultivate actinomycetes to protect their habitat from microbial pests.

(k) Leaf cutting ants gathering food for a fungus garden that is their source of food.

Zone with no growth where antibiotic inhibits undesirable fungus

Actinomycete colony that produces antibiotic

(l1) Antibiosis by an actinomycete against a pathogenic fungus; **(l2)** micrograph of actinomycete (800×)

themselves. Any changes in partner A exert a selective pressure on partner B to adapt to these changes, and vice versa. These adaptations occur at the genetic level, and in some cases, genes are exchanged between the partners. Over very long periods, the mutualists can become completely interdependent. We see this in *Buchnera* endosymbionts of certain aphids. These bacteria provide the aphid with needed amino acids and the aphid provides them a protective habitat. The bacteria are now so obligate that they have lost a large part of their genome and cannot survive outside the aphid. The aphids too have come to require the bacteria for survival. Be reminded that endosymbiotic bacteria are thought to have given rise to the mitochondria and chloroplasts of eukaryotic cells. Other well-studied examples of obligate mutualism can be found in termites, corals, root nodules, tube worms, and ants (**figure 7.13** *a*1, 2, *b*1, 2 and 7.2 Secret World of Microbes).

The nondependent forms of mutualism are sometimes referred to as **cooperation.** Organisms gain mutual benefit from their association, but they can survive independently outside of the partnership. In many cases, such cooperative relationships are coevolving to greater dependency. One example is the protozoan *Euplotes,* which harbors endosymbiotic algae in its cells (**figure 7.13***c*). Both members can survive apart from their mutualistic habit but have a well-developed affinity for each other.

Other examples include fungi that grow within plant tissues and protect the plant from drought and insects while being harbored

and fed (**figure 7.13***d*). Hot vent Pompeii worms harbor ectosymbiotic filamentous bacteria on their surfaces to protect against high temperatures and toxic metals (**7.2 Secret World of Microbes**).

Another common symbiotic relationship is **commensalism.*** Commensal organisms live in close contact, but only one partner benefits, while the other receives neither benefit nor harm from the union. The members of the association are called **commensals.** One form of commensalism observed in cultured microbes is termed the "satellite phenomenon," in which one species releases various growth factors that are required by a nearby species to grow. The feeder microbe grows around its partner as tiny colonies, while the passive partner is not harmed or helped (**figure 7.13***e*). Many of the microbes that occupy a niche on the human body are considered commensals. They make a living by feeding off dead skin and secretions, but do not usually cause harm (**figure 7.13***f*1, 2). The ongoing microbiome studies will no doubt find that many human residents are actually mutualists that contribute to human health.

The last type of symbiotic interrelationship is **parasitism,** first introduced in section 7.2. This is the one type of symbiosis that is primarily beneficial to the parasite and harmful to the host. Parasitism is widespread throughout nature. All organisms host parasites, and even some viruses have recently been found to harbor their own viral parasites! Many parasitic relationships also

* *commensalism* (kuh-men′-sul-izm) L. *com,* together, and *mensa,* table.

undergo coevolution, and complete dependency of the parasite for the host is rather common.

There are various degrees of parasitism. The most extreme form is **obligate intracellular parasitism,** which means the microbe spends all or most of its life cycle inside the host cell, from which it derives essential nutrients and other types of support. Viruses are genetic and metabolic parasites (**figure 7.13g**); *Rickettsia* and *Chlamydia* bacteria are energy parasites; and apicomplexan protozoans like *Plasmodium* (cause of malaria) are hemoglobin parasites (**figure 7.13h1, 2).** The kinds of harm that parasites do to their hosts varies from superficial damage (ringworm on the skin from a fungal infection) to death (rabies virus). It is reasonable to think that most parasites modulate the damage they do and can even coevolve into a commensal or mutualistic existence as the host develops tolerance.

Additional interactions can be important factors in the ecology and adaptations of organisms. One of these, **syntrophy,** or **cross-feeding,** is communal feeding of organisms sharing a habitat In essence, products given off by one organism are usable by another (**figure 7.13i).** The organisms involved do not require this relationship for survival but they generally benefit from it. Many syntrophic associations occur in aquatic habitats and soils within biofilms and are related to nutrient and bioelement recycling. A simple example involves a pair of free-living soil bacteria that share their metabolic products cyclically (**figure 7.13j).** *Cellulomonas* uses its enzymes to digest plant cellulose into glucose, but it cannot fix nitrogen. *Azotobacter* fixes nitrogen gas from the air and releases ammonium, but it does not digest cellulose. The glucose is a source of carbon for *Azotobacter,* and the ammonium supplies *Cellulomonas* with usable nitrogen. Even more complex interactions occur in the cycling of elements such as sulfur, phosphorus, and nitrogen (look ahead to chapter 26).

Amensalism is an action of one microbe that causes an adverse effect in another microbe. It usually involves antagonism or competition of some type and occurs in a community where microbes are sharing space and nutrient sources. Some microbes effectively compete by using up a vital nutrient to grow faster and dominate the habitat. Other microbes may release specific inhibitory chemicals into the surrounding environment. This is the description of **antibiosis**—the release of natural chemicals or antibiotics—that inhibit or kill microbes (look ahead to chapter 12). Many fungi and bacteria are adapted to this survival strategy. An intriguing example can be found in the complex symbiosis of certain ants. These ants have been shown to cultivate specialized gardens of fungi as a source of food. To protect the fungi from other microbes, the ants also cultivate species of filamentous bacteria called actinomycetes that produce antibiotics. The ants spread the chemical in their gardens to protect the fungi from invasion by parasites. **Figure 7.13k, l** features some aspects of this relationship.

Biofilms—A Microbial Conversation

Among the most common and prolific associations of microbes are **biofilms,** first described in 4.1 Making Connections. Biofilms result when organisms attach to a substrate by some form of extracellular matrix that binds them together in complex organized layers. Biofilms

* *syntrophy* (sin'-trof-ee) Gr, *sym*, together, and *troph,* to feed.
* *amensalism* (ae-men'-sul-izm) Gr, *a,* not, and L. *mensa,* table.

CLINICAL CONNECTIONS

Our Microbial Passengers

Microbial interrelationships obviously affect humans in many ways, but those having the most impact are microbes that naturally live on the body and parasites that attack the body. The normal residents, called **microbiota,** are so abundant that, cell-for-cell, they outnumber us by 10 times.* From this standpoint, one could argue that we are more microbial than human. Obviously, a community of microbes this large is bound to have enormous effects on our physiology, immunity, and genetics.

Resident microbes come from nearly all groups and include viruses, archaea, bacteria, fungi, and protozoa that have adapted to specialized niches throughout our surfaces. Certainly some are commensals that make a living on the body without harm or benefit, but a greater number are probably mutualistic, providing some form of nutrition or protection. For example, lactobacilli growing in the vagina maintain an acidic pH that can protect the female reproductive tract from infections (see figure), and other species are involved in digestive processes and the function of the intestine. The mutualist *Bacteroides thetaiotaomicron* processes complex food molecules and even regulates the expression of the human genome. The stabilizing effects of bacteria on the intestinal environment are the basis behind probiotic supplements and foods. Results of hundreds of new studies are rapidly accumulating information on the complex interrelationships we have with our microbiota (look ahead to chapter 13).

Most of the time our 10^{14} microbial passengers do more good than harm, but if they are displaced from their niche or are allowed to enter the sterile tissues, they become opportunistic pathogens and can cause infections. Microbes living in biofilms can create mixed infections, meaning that several microbes acting together invade the tissues and cause damage. This is the pattern in dental caries, periodontal disease, and gas gangrene.

Stained vaginal smear reveals a large pink epithelial cell harboring gram- positive rods of *Lactobacillus,* an important member of the normal microbiota that helps protect against infection.

Explain the role of broad-spectrum antibiotics in disrupting the microbial symbionts of humans and the possible problems this can cause. *Answer available at http://www.mhhe.com/talaro9*

*On average, humans are made up of 10^{13} cells and 10^{14} microbes, even though the microbes together weigh only about 2 to 5 pounds.

are so prevalent that they dominate the structure of most natural environments on earth. This tendency of microbes to form biofilm communities is an ancient and effective adaptive strategy. Not only would biofilms favor microbial persistence in habitats, but they would also offer greater access to life-sustaining conditions. In a sense, these living networks operate as "superorganisms" that influence such microbial activities as adaptation to a particular habitat, content of soil and water, nutrient cycling, and the course of infections.

It is generally accepted that the individual cells in the bodies of multicellular organisms such as animals and plants have the capacity to produce, receive, and react to chemical signals such as hormones made by other cells. For many years, biologists regarded most single-celled microbes as simple individuals without comparable properties, other than to cling together in colonies. But these assumptions have turned out to be incorrect. It is now evident that microbes show a well-developed capacity to communicate and cooperate in the formation and function of biofilms. This is especially true of bacteria, although fungi and other microorganisms can participate in these activities.

One idea to explain the development and behavior of biofilms is termed **quorum sensing.** This process occurs in several stages, including self-monitoring of cell density, secretion of chemical signals, and genetic activation **(figure 7.14).** Early in biofilm formation, free-floating or swimming microbes—often described as **planktonic**—are attracted to a surface and come to rest or settle down. Settling stimulates the cells to secrete a slimy or adhesive matrix, usually made of polysaccharide, that binds them to the substrate. Once attached, cells begin to release **inducer* molecules** that accumulate as the cell population grows. By this means, they can monitor the size of their own population. In time, a critical number of cells, termed a **quorum,*** accumulates and this ensures that there will be sufficient quantities of inducer molecules. These inducer molecules enter biofilm cells and stimulate specific genes on their chromosomes to begin expression.

The nature of this expression varies, but generally it allows the biofilm to react as a unit. For example, by coordinating the expression of genes that code for proteins, the biofilm can simultaneously produce large quantities of a digestive enzyme or toxin. This regulation of expression accounts for several observations made about microbial activities. For instance, it explains how saprobic microbes in soil and water rapidly break down complex substrates and how some pathogens release their toxins into the tissues simultaneously.

The effect of quorum sensing has also given greater insight into how pathogens invade their hosts and produce large quantities of substances that damage host defenses. It has been well studied in a number of pathogenic bacteria. Infections by *Pseudomonas* give rise to tenacious lung biofilms in some types of pneumonia. *Staphylococcus aureus* commonly forms biofilms on inanimate medical

> **Quick Search**
> Find out more about "How Biofilms Form" and "Quorum Sensing" on YouTube.

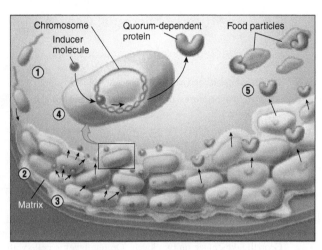

① Free-swimming cells lose their motility and settle down onto a surface or substrate.

② Cells synthesize an adhesive matrix that holds them tightly to the substrate.

③ When biofilm grows to a certain density (quorum), the cells release inducer molecules that can coordinate a response.

④ Enlargement of one cell to show genetic induction. Inducer molecule stimulates expression of a particular gene and synthesis of a protein product, such as an enzyme.

⑤ Cells secrete their enzymes in unison to digest food particles.

Process Figure 7.14 **Stages in biofilm formation, quorum sensing, induction and expression, shown in progression from left to right.**

devices and in wounds. *Streptococcus* species are the initial colonists on teeth surfaces leading to dental plaque (see figure 21.30).

Although the best-studied biofilms involve just a single type of microorganism, most biofilms observed in nature are polymicrobial. In fact, many symbiotic and cooperative relationships are based on complex communication patterns among coexisting organisms. As each organism in the biofilm carries out its specific niche, signaling among the members sustains the overall partnership. Biofilms are known to be a rich ground for genetic transfers among neighboring cells that involve conjugation and transformation (see chapter 9). As our knowledge of biofilm patterns grows, it will likely lead to greater understanding of their involvement in infections and their contributions to disinfectant and drug resistance (see chapter 12).

Check Your Progress SECTION 7.5

18. Explain the process of coevolution and how it influences the development of microorganisms.

19. Define *symbiosis* and differentiate among mutualism, commensalism, syntrophy, parasitism, and amensalism, using examples.

20. Outline quorum sensing by using a flow diagram to organize the stages.

21. Relate several advantages to communication within a biofilm.

* *inducer* (in-doos´-ur) L. *inducere,* to lead. Something that brings about or causes an effect.
* *quorum* (kwor´-uhm) L. *qui,* who. Indicates the minimum number of group members necessary to conduct business.

7.6 The Study of Microbial Growth

 Expected Learning Outcomes

23. Define *growth* and explain the process of binary fission.

24. Describe the process of population growth and how it is measured.

25. Explain the stages in the population growth curve and its practical importance.

26. Relate the techniques and tools used to detect and count cells in culture.

When microbes are provided with nutrients and the required environmental factors, they become metabolically active and grow. Growth takes place on two levels. On one level, a cell synthesizes new cell components and increases its size; on the other level, the number of cells in the population increases. This capacity for multiplication, increasing the size of the population by cell division, has tremendous importance in microbial control, infectious disease, and biotechnology. In the following sections, we focus primarily on the characteristics of bacterial growth that are generally representative of single-celled microorganisms.

The Basis of Population Growth: Binary Fission and the Bacterial Cell Cycle

The division of a bacterial cell occurs mainly through **binary,** or **transverse, fission.**[5] The term *binary* means that one cell becomes two, and *transverse* refers to the division plane forming across the width of the cell. During the bacterial cell division cycle, the parent cell enlarges, duplicates its chromosome, and forms a central transverse septum that divides the cell into two daughter cells. This process is repeated at intervals by each new daughter cell in turn; and with each successive round of division, the population increases. The stages in this continuous process are shown in greater detail in **figures 7.15** and **7.16.**

> **Quick Search**
> Search the internet for the video " A nice introduction to bacterial growth."

The Rate of Population Growth

The time required for a complete fission cycle—from parent cell to two new daughter cells—is called the **generation,** or **doubling,**

5. Research with bacteria that are not culturable indicates that not all cells divide this way. Some bud and others divide by multiple fission.

① **A parent cell at the beginning of the cell cycle**
What cannot be seen is the synthesis and activity gearing up for cell division.

② **Chromosome replication and cell enlargement**
The parent cell duplicates the chromosome and synthesizes new structures that enlarge the cell in preparation for the daughter cells.

③ **Chromosome division and septation**
The chromosomes affix to the cytoskeleton and are separated into the forming cells. The cell lays down a septum that begins to wall off the new cells. Other components (ribosomes) are equally distributed to the developing cells.

④ **Completion of cell compartments**
The septum is synthesized completely through the center, and the cell membrane patches itself so that there are two separate cell chambers.

⑤ **End of cell division cycle**
Daughter cells are now independent units. Some species will separate completely as shown here, while others will remain attached, forming chains or pairs, for example.

▨ Cell wall　▨ Cell membrane　◯ Chromosome 1　◯ Chromosome 2　▨ Cytoskeleton　• Ribosomes

Process Figure 7.15　**Stages in the bacterial cell cycle and binary fission of a rod-shaped bacterium.**

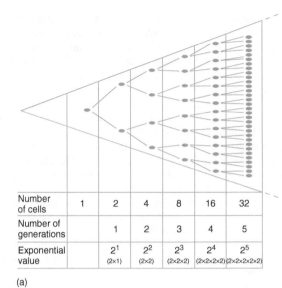

Number of cells	1	2	4	8	16	32
Number of generations		1	2	3	4	5
Exponential value		2^1 (2×1)	2^2 (2×2)	2^3 (2×2×2)	2^4 (2×2×2×2)	2^5 (2×2×2×2×2)

(a)

Figure 7.16 The mathematics of population growth. (a) Starting with a single cell, if each product of reproduction goes on to divide by binary fission, the population doubles with each new cell division or generation. This process can be represented by logarithms (2 raised to an exponent) or by simple numbers. **(b)** Plotting the logarithm of the cells produces a straight line indicative of exponential growth, whereas plotting the cell numbers arithmetically gives a curved slope.
*Note that the left scale is logarithmic, and the right scale is arithmetic.

time. The term *generation* has a similar meaning as it does in humans. It is the period between an individual's birth and the time of producing offspring. In bacteria, each new fission cycle or generation increases the population by a factor of 2, or doubles it. Thus, the initial parent stage consists of 1 cell, the first generation consists of 2 cells, the second 4, the third 8, then 16, 32, 64, and so on. As long as the environment remains favorable, this doubling effect can continue at a constant rate. With the passing of each generation, the population will double, over and over again.

The length of the generation time is a measure of the growth rate of an organism. Compared with the growth rates of most other living things, bacteria are notoriously rapid. The average generation time is 30 to 60 minutes under optimum conditions. The shortest generation times average 5 to 10 minutes, and longer generation times require days. For example, *Mycobacterium leprae,* the cause of Hansen's disease, has a generation time of 10 to 30 days—as long as some animals. Most pathogens have relatively short doubling times. *Salmonella enteritidis* and *Staphylococcus aureus,* bacteria that cause food-borne illness, double in 20 to 30 minutes, which explains why leaving food at room temperature even for a short period has caused many a person to be suddenly stricken with an attack of food-borne disease. In a few hours, a population of these bacteria can easily grow from a small number of cells to several million.

Figure 7.16 shows some quantitative characteristics of growth: (1) The cell population size can be represented by the number 2 with an exponent (2^1, 2^2, 2^3, 2^4); (2) the exponent increases by one in each generation; and (3) the number of the exponent also gives the number of the generation. This growth pattern is termed **exponential.** Because these populations often contain very large numbers of cells, it is useful to express them by means of exponents or logarithms (see "Exponents" found at http://www.mhhe.com/talaro9). The data from a growing bacterial population are graphed by plotting the number of cells as a function of time. The cell number can be represented logarithmi-

cally or arithmetically. Plotting the logarithm number over time provides a straight line indicative of exponential growth. Plotting the data arithmetically gives a constantly curved slope. In general, logarithmic graphs are preferred because an accurate cell number is easier to read, especially during early growth phases.

Predicting the number of cells that will arise during a long growth period (yielding millions of cells) is based on a relatively simple concept. One could use the method of addition $2 + 2 = 4$; $4 + 4 = 8$; $8 + 8 = 16$; $16 + 16 = 32$, and so on, or a method of multiplication (for example, $2^5 = 2 \times 2 \times 2 \times 2 \times 2$), but it is easy to see that for 20 or 30 generations, this calculation could be very tedious. An easier way to calculate the size of a population over time is to use an equation such as:

$$N_f = (N_i)2^n$$

In this equation, N_f is the total number of cells in the population at some point in the growth phase, N_i is the starting number, the exponent n denotes the generation number, and 2^n represents the number of cells in that generation. If we know any two of the values, the other values can be calculated. Let us use the example of *Staphylococcus aureus* to calculate how many cells (N_f) will be present in an egg salad sandwich after it sits in a warm car for 4 hours. We will assume that N_i is 10 (number of cells deposited in the sandwich while it was being prepared). To derive n, we need to divide 4 hours (240 minutes) by the generation time (we will use 20 minutes). This calculation comes out to 12, so 2^n is equal to 2^{12}. Using a calculator or table,[6] we find that 2^{12} is 4,096.

Final number (N_f) = 10 × 4,096
 = 40,960 bacterial cells in the sandwich

This same equation, with modifications, is used to determine the generation time, a more complex calculation that requires

6. See "Exponents" found at http://www.mhhe.com/talaro9 for a table with powers of 2.

knowing the number of cells at the beginning and end of a growth period. Such data are obtained through actual testing by a method discussed in the following section.

Determinants of Population Growth

In reality, a population of bacteria does not maintain its potential growth rate and does not double endlessly, because in most systems numerous factors prevent the cells from continuously dividing at their maximum rate. Quantitative laboratory studies indicate that a population typically displays a predictable pattern, or **growth curve,** over time. The method traditionally used to observe the population growth pattern is a viable count technique, in which the live cells in a culture are sampled, grown, and counted during a growth period, as described in the next section.

The Viable Plate Count: Batch Culture Method

A growing population is established by inoculating a flask containing a known quantity of sterile liquid medium with a few cells of a pure culture. The flask is incubated at that bacterium's optimum temperature and timed. The population size at any point in the growth cycle is quantified by removing a tiny measured sample of the culture from the growth chamber and plating it out on a solid medium to develop isolated colonies. This procedure is repeated at evenly spaced intervals (i.e., every hour for 24 hours) (**figure 7.17**).

Evaluating the samples involves a common and important principle in microbiology: One colony on the plate represents one cell or colony-forming unit (CFU) from the original sample. Because the CFU of some bacteria is actually composed of several cells (consider the clustered arrangement of *Staphylococcus,* for instance), using a colony count can underestimate the exact population size to an extent. This is not a serious problem because, in such bacteria, the CFU is the smallest unit of colony formation and dispersal. Multiplication of the number of colonies in a single sample by the container's volume gives a fair estimate of the total population size (number of cells) at any given point. The growth curve is determined by graphing the number for each sample in sequence for the whole incubation period (see figure 7.18).

Because of the scarcity of cells in the early stages of growth, some samples can give a zero reading even if there are viable cells in the culture. The sampling itself can remove enough viable cells to alter the tabulations, but since the purpose is to compare relative trends in growth, these factors do not significantly change the overall pattern.

Stages in the Normal Growth Curve

The system of batch culturing just described is *closed,* meaning that nutrients and space are finite and there is no mechanism for the removal of waste products. Data from an entire growth period of 3 to 4 days typically produce a curve with a series of phases termed the lag phase, the exponential growth (log) phase, the stationary phase, and the death phase (**figure 7.18**).

Flask inoculated
Samples taken at equally spaced intervals (0.1 ml)

	60 min	120 min	180 min	240 min	300 min	360 min	420 min	480 min	540 min	600 min
500 ml 0.1 ml										
Sample is diluted in liquid agar medium and poured or spread over surface of solidified medium										
Plates are incubated, colonies are counted	None									
Number of colonies (CFU) per 0.1 ml	<1*	2	4	7	13	23	45	80	135	230
Total estimated cell population in flask	<5,000	10,000	20,000	35,000	65,000	115,000	225,000	400,000	675,000	1,150,000

*The culture is probably in lag period with no new cells added.

Figure 7.17 The general steps in a viable plate count. 1. Place a few cells into a sterile liquid medium. **2.** Incubate this culture over a period of several hours. **3.** Sample the broth at regular intervals during incubation. **4.** Plate each sample onto solid media. **5.** Count the number of colonies present after incubation.

Figure 7.18 The growth curve in a bacterial culture. On this graph, the number of viable cells expressed as a logarithm (log) is plotted against time. See text for discussion of the various phases. Note that with a generation time of 30 minutes, the population has risen from 10 (10^1) cells to 1,000,000,000 (10^9) cells in only 16 hours. Even though they are not counted, dead cells are indicated to show stages in the cycle where death affects the appearance of the curve.

The **lag phase** is an early "flat" period on the graph when the population appears not to be growing or is growing at less than the exponential rate. Growth lags primarily because

1. the newly inoculated cells require a period of adjustment, enlargement, and synthesis of DNA, enzymes, and ribosomes;
2. the binary fission cycle has not reached its maximum rate; and
3. the population of cells is so sparse or dilute that the sampling misses them.

The length of the lag period varies from one population to another, depending on the condition of the microbes and medium. It is important to note that even though the population of cells is not increasing (growing), individual cells are metabolically active as they synthesize new components and prepare to divide.

The cells reach the maximum rate of cell division during the **exponential growth (logarithmic or log) phase,** a period during which the curve increases geometrically. This phase will continue as long as cells have adequate nutrients and the environment is favorable. During this phase, the population fulfills its potential generation time, and growth is balanced and genetically coordinated.

At the **stationary growth phase,** the population reaches a size limit in which cells divide more slowly or stop dividing entirely and may have died. The curve levels off because the rate of cell inhibition or death balances out the rate of multiplication. The number of viable cells has reached maximum and remains relatively constant during this period. The decline in the growth rate is caused by several factors. A common reason is the depletion of nutrients and oxygen. Another is that the increased cell density often causes an accumulation of organic acids and other toxic biochemicals.

As the limiting factors intensify, the population now shows a decline, seen as a downward slope on the curve. This stage has been called the **death phase,** but what is actually happening is more complex. Some cells go into dormancy and remain viable but do not grow. Some cells enter a starvation mode that helps them resist the lack of nutrients and other factors. Depending upon the species,

some microbes could remain in these states for long periods. It is also apparent that many cells go through a programmed cell death and lyse during this phase. Under these conditions, it is possible for persistent members of the culture to survive by using the nutrients released by the dead cells.

Practical Importance of the Growth Curve The tendency for populations to exhibit phases of rapid growth, slow growth, and death has important implications in microbial control, infection, food microbiology, and culture technology. Antimicrobial agents such as heat and disinfectants rapidly accelerate the death phase in all populations, but microbes in the exponential growth phase are more vulnerable to these agents than are those that have entered the stationary phase. In general, actively growing cells are more vulnerable to conditions that disrupt cell metabolism and binary fission.

Growth patterns in microorganisms can account for the stages of infection (see chapter 13). A person shedding bacteria in the early and middle stages of an infection is more likely to spread it to others than is a person in the late stages. The course of an infection is also influenced by the relatively faster rate of multiplication of the microbe, which can overwhelm the slower growth rate of the host's own cellular defenses.

Understanding the stages of cell growth is crucial for work with cultures. Sometimes a culture that has reached the stationary phase is incubated under the mistaken impression that enough nutrients are present for the culture to continue to multiply. In most cases, it is unwise to incubate a culture beyond the stationary phase, because doing so will reduce the number of active cells and the culture could die out completely. It is also preferable to do stains (an exception is the spore stain) and motility tests on young cultures, because the cells will show their natural size and correct reaction, and motile cells will have functioning flagella.

For certain research or industrial applications, closed-batch culturing with its four phases is inefficient. The alternative is an automatic growth chamber called the **chemostat,** or continuous culture

(a) (b) (1) (2)

Figure 7.19 Turbidity measurements as indicators of population density and amount of growth. (a) Holding a broth to the light is a practical method of checking for gross differences in cloudiness (turbidity). The broth on the left is transparent, indicating little or no growth; the broth on the right is cloudy and opaque, indicating heavy growth. (b) The eye is not sensitive enough to pick up fine degrees in turbidity; more sensitive measurements can be made with a spectrophotometer. A culture placed into the machine is exposed to a beam of light. A detector picks up the amount of light transmitted through the tube and registers this on a screen as absorbance. In (b1), very little light is being scattered and the absorbance reads low, indicating few cells are present. In (b2), more light is scattered, and the absorbance reads higher, indicating significant numbers of cells and growth.

system. This device can admit a steady stream of new nutrients and siphon off used media and old bacterial cells, thereby stabilizing the growth rate and cell number. The chemostat is very similar to industrial fermentors used to produce vitamins and antibiotics. It has the advantage of maintaining the culture in a biochemically active state and preventing it from entering the death phase.

Other Methods of Analyzing Population Growth

Microbiologists have developed several alternative ways of analyzing bacterial growth qualitatively and quantitatively. One of the simplest methods for estimating the size of a population is through turbidometry. This technique relies on the simple observation that a tube of clear nutrient solution becomes cloudy, or **turbid,** as microbes grow in it. In general, a greater turbidity indicates a higher microbial count. Differences in turbidity can be measured by means of sensitive instruments such as a spectrophotometer. It measures the ability of cells to scatter light as it passes through a liquid culture, a phenomenon called absorbance. The higher the absorbance measurement, the more growth or cell mass there is in the culture, and vice versa **(figure 7.19b).**

Quantifying and Analyzing Cultures

Turbidity readings are useful for evaluating relative amounts of growth, but if a more quantitative evaluation is required, the viable colony count or some other enumeration (counting) procedure is necessary. The **direct,** or **total, cell count** involves counting the number of cells in a sample microscopically **(figure 7.20).** This technique, very similar to that used in blood cell counts, employs a special microscope slide (cytometer) calibrated to accept a tiny sample that is spread over a premeasured grid. The cell count from a cytometer can be used to estimate the total number of cells in a larger sample (for instance, of milk or water). One inherent inaccuracy in this method as well as in spectrophotometry is that no distinction can be made between dead and live cells, both of which are

Figure 7.20 Direct microscopic count of bacteria. A small sample is placed on the grid under a cover glass. Individual cells, both living and dead, are counted. This number can be used to calculate the total count of a sample.

included in the count. Additional procedures that can assay the microbial content of water are the most probable number (MPN) and membrane filtration techniques. These are discussed in chapter 26.

Counting can be automated by sensitive devices such as the *Coulter counter,* which electronically scans a culture as it passes through a tiny pipette. As each cell flows by, it is detected and registered on an electronic sensor. A **flow cytometer** is a device that works on a similar principle. It is widely used for counting, sorting, sizing, and identifying cells in suspension **(figure 7.21a).** For most applications, the cells to be analyzed have to be stained with different fluorescent dyes. They are streamed one at a time through a flow chamber and illuminated by a laser that causes each one to fluoresce in a specific color. As each color signal is detected, it is compiled in graph form **(figure 7.21b).** Final separation is accomplished by magnets that pull the cells into collection chambers according to their charge. Some of the more common applications include blood cell counts and blood cell separation and identification; analysis of cancer cells; and differentiation of gram-negative and gram-positive bacteria. Even live and dead cells can be differentiated with this method.

Although flow cytometry can be used to count bacteria in natural samples without the need for culturing them, it still requires

(a)

(b)

Figure 7.21 Design and functions of a flow cytometer. (a) The main body of the device is a sheath and flow chamber, which holds fluid and cells. As the labeled cells pass through it, they are lasered and detected by the color they emit. The cells are then diverted into collection chambers. **(b)** A graphic readout analyzes the pattern of cells detected. The result here reveals live and dead bacterial cells stained with red and green fluorescent colors. Each dot on the graph represents one bacterial cell. To see an animation of this process go to http://www.helmholtz-muenchen.de/imi/zs/e-prinzip.html.

fluorescent labeling of the cells, which is not always possible. In this event, there are newer DNA-based techniques (for instance, real-time PCR) that can detect and differentiate microbes that have not been isolated, cultured, or identified.

Check Your Progress SECTION 7.6

22. What is microbial growth? Explain the stages in the bacterial cell cycle and binary fission.
23. Why is growth called exponential? What causes the pattern of the growth curve?
24. Contrast two different methods of detecting and counting microbial populations, and discuss their advantages and disadvantages.
25. Explain the relationship between colony counts and colony-forming units. Why can one use the number of colonies as an index of population size?

CASE STUDY Part 2

To understand how extremophiles survive such severe conditions, you should consider that such habitats are not extreme to the microbes—they are extreme only from a human perspective. Most microbial ancestors have been exposed to these environments for billions of years. The Berkeley Pit provides vivid insight into the process of adaptation and evolution. Only those microbes that can express traits for tolerating and growing in such conditions will survive to reproduce. Thus, the environment has selected those microbes with hidden genetic capabilities for handling the toxic heavy metals, acidity, and other extremes, and they establish the nature of the community that develops there.

The unique ecology of the pit has provided numerous subjects for research. The Montana scientists scrutinized samples in the lab and discovered around 130 different species of microbes, many of them never before identified. The dominant microbes appear to be algae. In their role as photosynthesizers, the algae provide nutritional support for heterotrophs such as fungi and protozoans.

The researchers determined that some of these algae not only thrive in the presence of high levels of metals, but they also can remove them from solution. These observations quickly pointed to some possible applications for future cleanup of the pit. One line of research is exploring the effects of stimulating massive overgrowth of algae to speed bioremediation of the pit and lessen the threat to the watershed in the area.

■ In what other ways would the algae impact the ecology of the pit?

■ What is involved in the process of bioremediation?

To conclude this Case Study, go to Perspectives on the Connect website.

Go to www.pitwatch.com to learn more about this topic.

Chapter Summary with Key Terms

7.1 Microbial Nutrition
Environmental factors that have the greatest impact on microbes are nutrients, temperature, pH, amount of available water, atmospheric gases, light, pressure, and other organisms. **Nutrition** consists of taking in chemical substances (nutrients) and assimilating and extracting energy from them.
 A. Substances required for survival are **essential nutrients**— usually containing the elements (C, H, N, O, P, S, Na, Cl, K, Ca, Fe, Mg). Essential nutrients are considered **macronutrients** (required in larger amounts) or **micronutrients** (trace elements required in smaller amounts—Zn, Mn, Cu). Nutrients are classed as either **inorganic** or **organic.**
 B. A **growth factor** is an organic nutrient (amino acid and vitamin) that cannot be synthesized and must be provided.

7.2 Classification of Nutritional Types
 A. An **autotroph** depends on carbon dioxide for its carbon needs. An autotroph that derives energy from light is a **photoautotroph;** one that extracts energy from inorganic substances is a **chemoautotroph. Methanogens** are chemoautotrophs that produce methane.
 B. A **heterotroph or chemoorganotroph** acquires carbon from organic molecules originating from the bodies of dead or living organisms. A **saprobe** is a decomposer that feeds primarily upon dead organic matter, and a **parasite** feeds from a live host and usually causes harm. Parasites that cause damage or death are called **pathogens.**

7.3 Transport: Movement of Substances Across the Cell Membrane
 A. A microbial cell must take in nutrients from its surroundings by transporting them across the cell membrane.
 B. Passive transport involves the natural movement of substances down a concentration gradient and requires no additional energy (**diffusion**). A form of passive transport that can move specific substances is **facilitated diffusion.**
 C. **Osmosis** is diffusion of water through a selectively permeable membrane.
 D. Osmotic changes that affect cells are **hypotonic** solutions, which contain less solute than the cell, and **hypertonic** solutions, which contain more solute than the cell. **Isotonic** solutions have the same solute concentration as the inside of the cell. A **halophile** thrives in hypertonic surroundings, and an **obligate halophile** requires a salt concentration of at least 15% but grows optimally in 25%.
 E. In **active transport,** substances are taken into the cell by a process that consumes energy. In **group translocation,** molecules are altered during transport.
 F. **Phagocytosis** and **pinocytosis** are forms of active transport in which bulk quantities of solid and fluid material are taken into the cell.

7.4 Environmental Factors That Influence Microbes
Every organism adapts to a particular habitat and niche.
 A. *Temperature:* An organism exhibits **optimum, minimum,** and **maximum temperatures.** Organisms that cannot grow above 20°C but thrive below 15°C and continue to grow even at 0°C are known as **psychrophiles. Mesophiles** grow from 10°C to 50°C, having temperature optima from 20°C to 40°C. The growth range of **thermophiles** is 45°C to 80°C. Extreme thermophiles may grow to temperatures of 250°C.
 B. *Oxygen Requirements:* The ecological need for free oxygen (O_2) is based on whether a cell can handle toxic by-products such as superoxide and peroxide.
 1. **Aerobes** grow in normal atmospheric oxygen and have enzymes to handle toxic oxygen by-products. An aerobic organism capable of living without oxygen if necessary is a **facultative anaerobe.** An aerobe that requires a small amount of oxygen but does not grow under anaerobic conditions is a **microaerophile.**
 2. **Strict (obligate) anaerobes** do not use free oxygen and cannot produce enzymes to dismantle reactive oxides. They are actually damaged or killed by oxygen. An aerotolerant anaerobe cannot use oxygen for respiration yet is not injured by it.
 C. *Effects of pH:* Acidity and alkalinity affect the activity and integrity of enzymes and the structural components of a cell. Optimum pH for most microbes ranges from 6 to 8. **Acidophiles** prefer a pH below 7, **alkalinophiles** prefer a pH above 7, and **neutrophiles** grow best around pH 7.
 D. *Other Environmental Factors:* Radiation and barometric pressure affect microbial growth. A **barophile** is adapted to life under high pressure (bottom dwellers in the ocean, for example).

7.5 Ecological Associations Among Microorganisms
 A. *Microbial Interactions:* Microbes coexist in varied relationships in nature.
 1. Types of **symbiosis** are **mutualism,** a reciprocal, obligatory, and beneficial relationship between two organisms, and **commensalism,** an organism receiving benefits from another without harming the other organism in the relationship. **Parasitism** occurs between a host and an infectious agent; the host is harmed in the interaction.
 2. **Syntrophism** is a beneficial but not obligatory coexistence in which organisms cross-feed. **Amensalism** entails competition, inhibition, and injury directed against an opposing organism. A special case is antibiotic production.
 3. **Quorum sensing** is an interaction among members of a biofilm that results in a coordinated reaction, such as secretion of **inducer molecules** and enzymes. By behaving as a unit, the biofilm remains stable and organized. It can occupy and exploit a wide variety of habitats.

7.6 The Study of Microbial Growth
 A. During the bacterial cell cycle, the parent cell splits to form a pair of daughter cells by means of **binary,** or **transverse, fission.**
 B. It involves replication of the chromosome and the equal division of other cell components.
 C. The duration of each division is called the **generation,** or **doubling, time.** A population theoretically doubles with each generation, so the growth rate is **exponential,** and each cycle increases in geometric progression.
 D. A **growth curve** is a graphic representation of a closed population over time, using an estimate of live cells called a viable count. The initial flat period of the curve is called the **lag phase,** followed by the **exponential growth phase,** in

which viable cells increase in logarithmic progression. Adverse environmental conditions create a plateau, or **stationary growth phase.** In the **death phase,** nutrient depletion and waste buildup cause increased cell death.

E. Cell numbers can be counted by a viable plate count, microscope counting chamber, Coulter counter, or, **flow cytometer.** Cell growth can also be determined by turbidometry and a total cell count.

Level I. Knowledge and Comprehension

These questions require a working knowledge of the concepts in the chapter and the ability to recall and understand the information you have studied.

? Multiple-Choice Questions

Select the correct answer from the answers provided. For questions with blanks, choose the combination of answers that most accurately completes the statement.

1. An organic nutrient essential to an organism's metabolism that cannot be synthesized itself is termed a/an
 a. trace element c. growth factor
 b. micronutrient d. mineral

2. The source of the necessary elements of life is
 a. an inorganic environmental reservoir
 b. the sun
 c. rocks
 d. the air

3. An organism that can synthesize all its required organic components from CO_2 using energy from the sun is a
 a. photoautotroph c. chemoautotroph
 b. photoheterotroph d. chemoheterotroph

4. An obligate halophile requires high
 a. pH c. salt
 b. temperature d. pressure

5. Chemoautotrophs can survive on _____ alone.
 a. minerals c. minerals and CO_2
 b. CO_2 d. methane

6. Which of the following substances are required by *all* organisms?
 a. organic nutrients c. growth factors
 b. inorganic nutrients d. oxygen gas

7. A pathogen would most accurately be described as a
 a. parasite c. saprobe
 b. commensal d. symbiont

8. Which of the following is true of passive transport?
 a. it requires a gradient c. it includes endocytosis
 b. it uses the cell wall d. it only moves water

9. A cell exposed to a hypertonic environment will _____ by osmosis.
 a. gain water c. neither gain nor lose water
 b. lose water d. burst

10. Active transport of a substance across a membrane requires
 a. a gradient c. water
 b. the expenditure of ATP d. diffusion

11. Psychrophiles would be expected to grow
 a. in hot springs c. at refrigeration temperatures
 b. on the human body d. at low pH

12. Which of the following is *not* involved in quorum sensing?
 a. accumulation of inducer molecules
 b. a certain level of biofilm density
 c. self-monitoring
 d. release of genetic material

13. Superoxide ion is toxic to strict anaerobes because they lack
 a. catalase c. dismutase
 b. peroxidase d. oxidase

14. The time required for a cell to undergo binary fission is called the
 a. exponential growth rate c. generation time
 b. growth curve d. lag period

15. In a viable plate count, each _____ represents a _____ from the sample population.
 a. cell, colony c. hour, generation
 b. colony, cell d. cell, generation

16. The stage in population growth with the highest rate of cell division is the
 a. stationary phase c. exponential phase
 b. lag phase d. enlargement phase

📖 Case Study Review

1. Which group are the dominant microorganisms in the Berkeley Pit?
 a. archaea c. algae
 b. bacteria d. protozoa

2. How can the microbes in the Berkeley Pit detoxify the water?
 a. By removing heavy metals. d. a and b
 b. By neutralizing the acidity. e. a, b, and c
 c. By recycling elements.

3. Using the Guide to Terminology, develop terms to describe several adaptations microbes have made to conditions in the Berkeley Pit.

✎ Writing Challenge

For each question (except 7), compose a one- or two-paragraph answer that includes the factual information needed to completely address the question. Check Your Progress questions can also be used for writing-challenge exercises.

1. Look at the following diagrams and predict in which direction osmosis will take place. Use arrows to show the net direction of osmosis. Is one of these microbes a halophile? Which one?

2. Describe the basic metabolism of methanogens.

3. Discuss extreme environments and types of extremophiles that live there.

4. Differentiate between mutualism and syntrophy with examples.

5. a. What biochemical events in quorum sensing ensure that a biofilm can function as a unit?
 b. Explain how biofilm self-monitoring would favor infections.

6. Explain what is happening to the population at points A, B, C, and D in the following diagram.

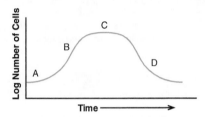

7. Fill in the following table:

	Source of Carbon	Usual Source of Energy	Example
Photoautotroph			
Photoheterotroph			
Chemoautotroph			
Chemoheterotroph			
Saprobe			
Parasite			

🌐 Concept Mapping

An Introduction to Concept Mapping found at http://www.mhhe.com/talaro9 provides guidance for working with concept maps.

1. Supply your own lines (linkers) and linking words or phrases in this concept map, and provide the missing concept in the empty box.

Level II. Application, Analysis, Evaluation, and Synthesis

These problems go beyond just restating facts and require higher levels of understanding and an ability to interpret, problem solve, transfer knowledge to new situations, create models, and predict outcomes.

 Critical Thinking

Critical thinking is the ability to reason and solve problems using facts and concepts. These questions can be approached from a number of angles, and in most cases, they do not have a single correct answer.

1. a. Is there a microbe that could grow on a medium that contains only the following compounds dissolved in water: $CaCO_3$, $MgNO_3$, $FeCl_2$, $ZnSO_4$, and glucose? Defend your answer.

 b. A useful mnemonic device for keeping track of major elements required by most organisms is: **C HOPKINS Ca Fe, Na Cl Mg**ood. Read aloud, it becomes, See Hopkin's Cafe, NaCl (salt) M good! What does each letter stand for?

2. Describe how one might determine the nutrient requirements of a microbe from Mars. If, after exhausting various nutrient schemes, it still does not grow, what other factors might one take into account?

3. Patients with ketoacidosis associated with diabetes are especially susceptible to fungal infections. Propose why this might be the case.

4. a. Explain how osmotic pressure and pH are used in preserving foods.

 b. What effects do they have on microbes?

5. Provide some suggestions for treating anaerobic infections by manipulating the gas content.

6. Could anaerobes and aerobes coexist in the same habitat? Why or why not?

7. a. If an egg salad sandwich sitting in a warm car for 4 hours develops 40,960 bacterial cells, how many more cells would result with just one more hour of incubation? Use the same criteria that were stated in the sample problem on page 209.

 b. With 10 additional hours of incubation?

 c. What do your answers tell you about using clean techniques in food preparation and storage (other than aesthetic considerations)?

8. The noted microbial ecologist Martin W. Beijerinck has stated: "Everything is everywhere, the environment selects." Use this concept to explain what ultimately determines whether a microorganism can live in a certain habitat.

9. Describe the similarities and differences between a mutualistic endosymbiont and a parasitic endosymbiont.

Visual Challenge

1. Place appropriate points on the axes and draw separate graphs that fit a psychrotroph and an obligate thermophile.

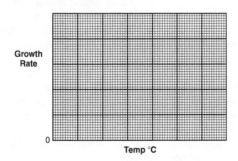

Growth Rate

0

Temp °C

2. Enter points on the axes and graph the probable results for the Berkeley Pit algae *Euglena mutabilis* and the fastidious pathogen *Haemophilus influenzae*.

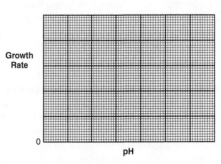

Growth Rate

0

pH

CHAPTER **8** # An Introduction to Microbial Metabolism
The Chemical Crossroads of Life

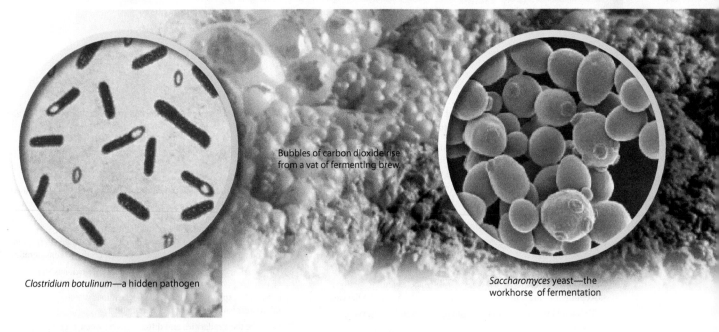

Bubbles of carbon dioxide rise from a vat of fermenting brew.

Clostridium botulinum—a hidden pathogen

Saccharomyces yeast—the workhorse of fermentation

 CASE STUDY Part 1 Brewing Up a Batch of Bad Wine

This Case Study provides insight into the practical importance of microbial biochemistry. It brings together elements of **fermentation** and **alcohol formation** and introduces us to the concept of **anaerobic respiration** by a microbe that synthesizes a **toxin** with deadly potential. To help understand the circumstances of this Case Study, we will revisit several concepts from chapter 7, including **nutrition,** temperature, pH, and **metabolism** in the absence of oxygen gas.

In October 2011, an inmate at Utah State Prison was brought to the infirmary with **vision** and **swallowing difficulties, muscular weakness,** and **vomiting.** The man was hospitalized for medical evaluation. When he admitted to having recently consumed an illegal, **prison-made wine,** his doctors believed they were dealing with a case of **food poisoning.** A number of other inmates were interviewed about drinking this substance, and 12 of them confessed that they had also consumed it about **30 hours** earlier. When some of these prisoners started having similar symptoms, medical personnel concluded that the wine was probably the source of the attack and hospitalized the other sick inmates. Specimens from the **wine, stool, stomach,** and **bloodstream** were sent for analysis. Final results were delayed because specialized testing done by the Centers for Disease Control and Prevention takes several days.

Preparation of the illicit homemade wine called "pruno" is rather common in prisons. This alcohol is usually made from a mixture

> "Pruno tastes so putrid that even hardened prisoners gulp it down while holding their noses."

of crushed fruit, juice, water, a source of sugar, and a **starter culture** from an older brew. The preparation is placed in **sealed, airtight** plastic containers and **incubated** in warm tap water for several days. These conditions foster **anaerobic growth** and alcoholic fermentation, which will bring final alcohol levels as high as 15%. The liquid portion is strained off and consumed. According to one inmate's description: "Pruno tastes so putrid that even hardened prisoners gulp it down while holding their noses." Unfortunately, their desire for alcohol overcomes the beverage's foul qualities.

Investigators continued to trace the possible events that led to this outbreak. Examination of the materials used to brew the wine yielded bits of a baked **potato,** which is a departure from the usual "recipe." One of the inmates admitted that he had stored the potato in a **sealed container** for several days before using it. Other batches of pruno that had been made at the same time did not contain potato and did not cause illness.

▶ *What substances and conditions are required for fermentation, and what are its usual products?*

▶ *What signs, if any, might have indicated that the prison brew was tainted and why?*

To continue the Case Study, go to page 250.

8.1 The Metabolism of Microbes

 Expected Learning Outcomes

1. Define *metabolism* and differentiate its two types.
2. Describe the basic functions of enzymes in cells.
3. Outline the outstanding characteristics of enzymes.
4. Explain how enzymes lower the energy required for a reaction to occur.
5. Discuss enzyme structure and interactions between enzymes and substrates.
6. Describe the types of enzyme functions and methods of naming them.
7. Summarize key features of enzyme regulation.

Metabolism, from the Greek term *metaballein,* meaning change, pertains to all chemical and physical workings of cells. It is a very useful term that can be used to designate almost any physiological process. Although metabolism entails thousands of different reactions, most of them can be placed into one of two general categories. In the case of **catabolism,** larger molecules are degraded or broken down into smaller molecules, usually with the release of energy. In the case of **anabolism,** also called biosynthesis, larger molecules are built from smaller ones, which results in the formation of cell structures. It is usually driven by energy derived from catabolism. Even though they have opposite effects, these two forms of metabolism are tightly linked and highly complementary. As we will see, the result of them working together is that all metabolism is coordinated for the cell to carry out essential life functions (**figure 8.1**). The major metabolic functions in cells and the sections of the chapter that cover them are listed here:

1. Enzymes serve as catalysts for both catabolic and anabolic activities. Because of their importance in all areas of microbiology, the remainder of section 8.1 is devoted to characteristics of enzymes.
2. Cells acquire energy from an external source (outside the cell) such as nutrients or the sun. This idea was first discussed in chapter 7 and continues in sections 8.2 and 8.6.
3. Cells extract the energy and transfer it to a high-energy molecule, adenosine triphosphate (ATP), a universal compound for managing energy. This is accomplished by several different types of catabolic pathways, covered in sections 8.3 and 8.4.
4. Cells use ATP to power anabolic processes. Simple building blocks are bonded into larger molecules and cell structures, thereby creating greater complexity through the input of this energy. Anabolic pathways are covered in section 8.5.

We suggest you review relevant sections in chapter 2 covering organic molecules and biochemistry.

Enzymes: Catalyzing the Chemical Reactions of Life

A microbial cell could be viewed as a microscopic factory, complete with basic building materials, a source of energy, and a genetic "blueprint" for running its extensive network of metabolic reactions. But the chemical reactions of life would never proceed without a special class of proteins called **enzymes.** Enzymes are a remarkable example of **catalysts,** chemicals that increase the rate of a chemical reaction without becoming part of the products or being consumed in the reaction. Do not make the mistake of thinking that an enzyme creates a reaction. Because of the free energy inherent in molecules, a reaction could occur spontaneously at some point even without an enzyme but at a very slow rate. A study of the enzyme urease shows that it increases the rate of the breakdown of urea by a factor of

Figure 8.1 Simplified model of metabolism. Cellular reactions fall into two major categories. Catabolism involves the breakdown of complex organic molecules to extract energy and form simpler end products. Anabolism uses the energy to synthesize necessary macromolecules and cell structures from simple precursors, increasing chemical complexity. The two systems interact in a continuous cycle that maintains the metabolic balance inside cells.

8.1 MAKING CONNECTIONS

Enzymes as Biochemical Levers

An analogy will allow us to envision the relationship of enzymes to the energy of activation. A large boulder sitting precariously on a cliff's edge contains a great deal of potential energy, but it will not fall to the ground and release this energy unless something disturbs it. It might eventually be disturbed spontaneously as the cliff erodes below it, but that could take a very long time. Moving it with a crowbar (to overcome the resistance of the boulder's weight) will cause it to tumble down freely by its own momentum. If we relate this analogy to chemicals, the reactants are the boulder on the cliff, the activation energy is the energy needed to move the boulder, the enzyme is the crowbar, and the product is the boulder at the bottom of the cliff. Like the crowbar, an enzyme permits a reaction to occur rapidly by getting over the energy "hump." Although this analogy concretely illustrates the concept of the energy of activation, it is imperfect in that the enzyme, unlike the person with the crowbar, does not actually add any energy to the system.

This phenomenon can be represented by plotting the energy of the reaction against the direction of the reaction. The curve of reaction is shown in the accompanying graph. Reactants must overcome the energy of activation (E_{act}) for the reaction to proceed. When a catalyst is present, it lowers the E_{act}. It does this by providing the reactants with an alternate pathway, requiring less energy, by which they can progress to the final state. Note that the products reach the same final energy state with or without an enzyme.

What is the actual physical process performed by the enzyme that speeds up a reaction? *Answer available at http://www.mhhe.com/talaro9*

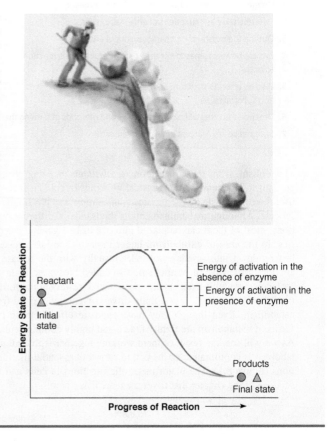

100 trillion as compared to an uncatalyzed reaction. Because most uncatalyzed metabolic reactions do not occur fast enough to sustain cell processes, enzymes are indispensable to life. Other major characteristics of enzymes are summarized in **table 8.1.**

How Do Enzymes Work?

We have said that an enzyme speeds up the rate of a metabolic reaction, but just how does it do this? During a chemical reaction, reactants are converted to products by bond formation or breakage. A certain amount of energy is required to initiate every such reaction, which limits its rate. This resistance to a reaction, which must be overcome for a reaction to proceed, is measurable and is called the **energy of activation** or activation energy (**8.1 Making Connections**). In the laboratory, overcoming this initial resistance can be achieved by

- increasing thermal energy (heating) to increase molecular velocity,
- increasing the concentration of reactants to increase the rate of molecular collisions, or
- adding a catalyst.

TABLE 8.1	Checklist of Enzyme Characteristics

- Composed mostly of protein; may require nonprotein cofactors
- Act as organic catalysts to speed up the rate of cellular reactions
- Lower the activation energy required for a chemical reaction to proceed (see 8.1 Making Connections)
- Enable metabolic reactions to proceed at a speed compatible with life
- Have unique characteristics such as shape, specificity, and function
- Provide an active site for target molecules called substrates
- Are much larger in size than their substrates
- Associate closely with substrates but do not become integrated into the reaction products
- Are not used up or permanently changed by the reaction
- Can be recycled and function in extremely low concentrations
- Are greatly affected by temperature and pH
- Can be regulated by feedback and genetic mechanisms

8.2 MAKING CONNECTIONS

A Different Kind of Catalyst

The molecular reactions of cells are still an active and rich source of discovery, and new findings come along on a regular basis that break older "rules" and adjust our understanding. Originally, proteins were considered the only biological molecules that act as catalysts. Then biologists found a novel type of RNA they termed **ribozymes.** Ribozymes appear to be rather common, with around 500 having been identified in all types of cells and some viruses. They display some of the properties of protein catalysts, such as having a specific active site and interacting with a substrate. But these molecules are remarkable because their substrates are other molecules of RNA. Ribozymes are thought to be remnants of the earliest molecules on earth that could have served as both catalysts and genetic material. In natural systems, ribozymes are involved in self-splicing or cutting of RNA molecules during processing of the genetic code, and even ribosomes function as ribozymes during protein synthesis (see chapter 9). Further research has shown that ribozymes can be designed to handle other kinds of activities, such as inhibiting gene expression. Several companies have developed and are testing ribozyme-based therapies for treating cancer and HIV infection.

Propose some effects that ribozymes have on microorganisms that would make them suitable for therapy. *Answer available at http://www.mhhe.com/talaro9*

A ribozyme (here a "hairpin loop" type) can clip RNA and remove sections of it.

In most living systems, the first two alternatives are not feasible, because elevating the temperature is potentially harmful, and higher concentrations of reactants are not practical. This leaves only the action of catalysts, and enzymes fill this need efficiently and potently.

At the molecular level, an enzyme promotes a reaction by serving as a physical site upon which the reactant molecules, called **substrates,** can be positioned for various interactions. The enzyme is much larger in size than its substrate, and it presents a uniquely shaped pocket that fits only that particular substrate. Although an enzyme binds to the substrate and participates directly in changes to the substrate, it does not become a part of the products, is not used up by the reaction, and can function over and over again. Enzyme speed, defined as the number of substrate molecules converted per enzyme per second, is well documented. Speeds range from several million for catalase to a thousand for lactate dehydrogenase. A key to understanding the roles of enzymes in metabolism is their structure.

Quick Search
Locate a video on "How Stuff Works— Enzyme Catalysts" to observe a quick animation of the reactions of enzymes.

Enzyme Structure

Enzymes are composed largely of protein molecules, although certain types of RNA can function as nonenzyme catalysts (**8.2 Making Connections**). Enzymes can be classified as simple or

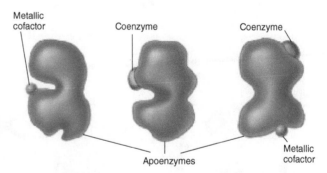

Figure 8.2 Conjugated enzyme structure. All examples have an apoenzyme (polypeptide or protein) component and one or more cofactors.

conjugated. Simple enzymes consist of protein alone, whereas conjugated enzymes (**figure 8.2**) contain protein and nonprotein molecules. A conjugated enzyme, sometimes referred to as a **holoenzyme,** is a combination of a protein, now called the **apoenzyme,** and one or more **cofactors (table 8.2).** Cofactors are either organic molecules, called **coenzymes,** or inorganic elements (metal ions) that many enzymes require to become functional. In some enzymes, the cofactor is loosely associated with the apoenzyme by noncovalent bonds; in others, it is linked by covalent bonds.

Apoenzymes: Specificity and the Active Site

Apoenzymes range in size from small polypeptides with about 100 amino acids and a molecular weight of 12,000 to large polypeptide conglomerates with thousands of amino acids and a molecular weight of over 1 million. Like all proteins, an apoenzyme exhibits levels of molecular complexity called the primary, secondary, tertiary, and, in larger enzymes, quaternary organization (**figure 8.3**). As we saw in chapter 2 (see figure 2.22), the first three levels of structure arise when a single polypeptide chain undergoes an automatic folding process and achieves stability by forming disulfide and other types of bonds. Folding causes the surface of the apoenzyme to acquire three-dimensional features that result in the enzyme's specificity for substrates. The actual pocket where the substrate binds is called the **active site**, or **catalytic site**, and there can be from one to several such sites (figure 8.3). Because each type of enzyme has a different primary structure (type and sequence of amino acids), this gives rise to variations in folding and unique active sites.

Enzyme-Substrate Interactions

For a reaction to take place, a temporary **enzyme-substrate** union must occur at the active site. There are several explanations for the way this happens (**figure 8.4**). The

(a) As the polypeptide forms intrachain bonds and folds, it assumes a three-dimensional (tertiary) state that displays an active site (AS).

(b) Because each unique polypeptide folds differently, each apoenzyme will have a differently shaped active site.

(c) More complex enzymes have a quaternary structure consisting of more than one polypeptide. New active sites may be formed by the junction of polypeptides.

Levels of Structure

Primary Secondary Tertiary

AS

Quaternary AS

AS

Figure 8.3 **How the active site and specificity of the apoenzyme arise.** Review figure 2.22 for details of this process.

Substrate (S)

Products

Enzyme (E)

Does not fit

ES complex

E

(a) (b) (c)

S

E E E

(d)

Figure 8.4 **Enzyme-substrate reactions. (a)** When the enzyme and substrate come together, the substrate (S) must show the correct fit and position with respect to the enzyme (E). **(b)** When the ES complex is formed, it enters a transition state. During this temporary but tight interlocking union, the enzyme participates directly in breaking or making bonds. **(c)** Once the reaction is complete, the enzyme releases the products. **(d)** The induced-fit model proposes that the enzyme recognizes its substrate and adapts slightly to it so that the final binding is even more precise.

TABLE 8.2	Selected Enzymes, Catalytic Actions, and Cofactors	
Enzyme	**Action**	**Metallic Cofactor Required**
Catalase	Breaks down hydrogen peroxide	Iron (Fe)
Oxidase	Adds electrons to oxygen	Iron, copper (Cu)
Hexokinase	Transfers phosphate to glucose	Magnesium (Mg)
Urease	Splits urea into an ammonium ion	Nickel (Ni)
Nitrate reductase	Reduces nitrate to nitrite	Molybdenum (Mo)
DNA polymerase	Synthesis of DNA	Zinc (Zn) and Mg
Botulinum toxin	Hydrolyzes protein needed for vesicle transport	Zinc

specificity is often described as a "lock-and-key" fit in which the substrate is inserted into the active site's pocket. This is a useful analogy, but an enzyme is not a rigid lock mechanism. It is likely that the enzyme actually helps the substrate move into the active site through slight changes in its shape. This is called an *induced fit* (**figure 8.4d**). The bonds formed between the substrate and enzyme are weak and, of necessity, easily reversible. Once the enzyme-substrate complex has formed, appropriate reactions occur on the substrate, often with the aid of a cofactor, and a product is formed and released. The enzyme can then attach to another substrate molecule and repeat this action.

Cofactors: Supporting the Work of Enzymes

In chapter 7, you learned that microorganisms require specific metal ions called trace elements and certain organic growth factors. In many cases, the need for these substances arises from their roles as **cofactors.** The **metallic cofactors,** including iron, copper, magnesium, manganese, zinc, cobalt, selenium, and many others, participate in precise functions between the enzyme and its substrate. In general, metals activate enzymes, help bring the active site and substrate close together, and participate directly in chemical reactions with the enzyme-substrate complex.

Coenzymes are organic cofactors that work in conjunction with the apoenzyme to perform a necessary alteration of a substrate. The general function of a coenzyme is to remove a chemical group from one substrate molecule and add it to another substrate, thereby serving as a temporary carrier of this group (**figure 8.5**). The specific activities of coenzymes are many and varied. In section 8.3, we shall see that coenzymes carry and transfer hydrogen atoms, electrons, carbon dioxide, and amino groups. One of the most common components of coenzymes are **vitamins,** which explains why vitamins are important to nutrition and may be required as growth factors for living things. Vitamin deficiencies prevent the complete holoenzyme from forming. Consequently, both the

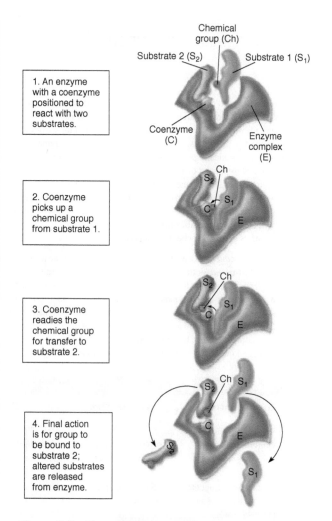

1. An enzyme with a coenzyme positioned to react with two substrates.

2. Coenzyme picks up a chemical group from substrate 1.

3. Coenzyme readies the chemical group for transfer to substrate 2.

4. Final action is for group to be bound to substrate 2; altered substrates are released from enzyme.

Figure 8.5 The carrier functions of coenzymes. Many enzymes use coenzymes to transfer chemical groups from one substrate to another.

chemical reaction and the structure or function dependent upon that reaction are compromised.

Classification of Enzyme Functions

Enzymes are classified and named according to characteristics such as site of action, type of action, and substrate (**8.3 Making Connections**).

Location and Regularity of Enzyme Action

Enzymes perform their tasks either inside or outside of the cell in which they were produced. After initial synthesis in the cell, **exoenzymes** are transported extracellularly, where they break down large food molecules or harmful chemicals (see discussion of hydrolysis reactions). Examples of exoenzymes are cellulase, amylase, and penicillinase. By contrast, **endoenzymes** are retained intracellularly and function there (**figure 8.6**). Most enzymes of the metabolic pathways are of this variety.

8.3 MAKING CONNECTIONS

The Enzyme Name Game

Most metabolic reactions require a separate and unique enzyme. Up to the present time, researchers have discovered and named over 5,000 of them. Given the complex chemistry of the cell and the extraordinary diversity of living things, many more enzymes probably remain to be discovered. A standardized system of nomenclature and classification was developed to prevent discrepancies.

In general, an enzyme name is composed of two parts: a prefix or stem word derived from a certain characteristic—usually the substrate acted upon or the type of reaction catalyzed, or both—followed by the ending *-ase.*

The system classifies the enzyme in one of these six classes, on the basis of its general biochemical action:

1. *Oxidoreductases* transfer electrons from one substrate to another, and *dehydrogenases* transfer a hydrogen from one compound to another.
2. *Transferases* transfer functional groups from one substrate to another.
3. *Hydrolases* cleave bonds on molecules with the addition of water.
4. *Lyases* add groups to or remove groups from double-bonded substrates.
5. *Isomerases* change a substrate into its isomeric form. An **isomer** is a compound that has the same molecular formula as another compound but differs in arrangement of the atoms.

6. *Synthases* are enzymes that catalyze the formation of large molecules; for example, fatty acid synthase makes one component of triglycerides.

Each enzyme is also assigned a technical name that indicates the specific reaction it catalyses. These names are useful for biochemists but are often too lengthy for routine use. More often, a common name is derived from some notable feature such as the substrate or enzyme action. For example, *hydrogen peroxide oxidoreductase* is more commonly known as *catalase*. With this system, an enzyme that digests a carbohydrate substrate is a *carbohydrase;* a specific carbohydrase, *amylase*, acts on starch (amylose is a major component of starch). An enzyme that hydrolyzes peptide bonds of a protein is a *proteinase, protease,* or *peptidase*, depending on the size of the protein substrate. Some fats and other lipids are digested by *lipases*. DNA is hydrolyzed by *deoxyribonuclease,* generally shortened to *DNase*, and a *polymerase* synthesizes DNA or RNA. Other examples of enzymes are presented in **table 8.A**. (See also table 8.2.)

Give the common names for enzymes that digest collagen, that make ATP, and that clot blood. *Answer available at http://www.mhhe.com/talaro9*

TABLE 8.A	A Sampling of Enzymes, Their Substrates, and Their Reactions			
Common Name	**Systematic Name**	**Enzyme Class**	**Substrate**	**Action**
Lactase	β-D-galactosidase	Hydrolase	Lactose	Breaks lactose down into glucose and galactose
Penicillinase	Beta-lactamase	Hydrolase	Penicillin	Hydrolyzes beta-lactam ring
DNA polymerase	DNA nucleotidyl-transferase	Synthase	DNA nucleosides	Synthesizes a strand of DNA using the complementary strand as a model
Lactate dehydrogenase	Same as common name	Oxidoreductase	Pyruvic acid	Catalyzes the conversion of pyruvic acid to lactic acid
Oxidase	Cytochrome oxidase	Oxidoreductase	Molecular oxygen	Catalyzes the reduction (addition of electrons and hydrogen) to O_2

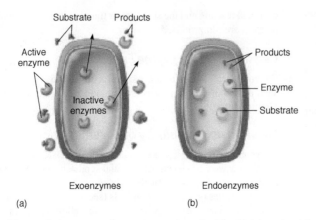

Figure 8.6 Types of enzymes, as described by their location of action. (a) Exoenzymes are transported outside the cell to become active. **(b)** Endoenzymes remain in the cell and function there.

In terms of their presence in the cell, enzymes are not all produced in equal amounts or at equal rates. Some, called **constitutive enzymes (figure 8.7a),** are always present and in relatively constant amounts, regardless of the amount of substrate. The enzymes involved in utilizing glucose, for example, are very important in metabolism and thus are constitutive. Other enzymes are **regulated enzymes (figure 8.7b),** the production of which is either turned on (induced) or turned off (repressed) in response to changes in concentration of the substrate or product. The level of inducible and repressible enzymes is controlled by the degree to which the genes for these proteins are expressed, as discussed in chapter 9.

Synthesis and Hydrolysis Reactions A growing cell is in a constant state of synthesis. Such anabolic reactions require enzymes (synthases) to form covalent bonds between smaller substrate molecules. Also known as **condensation (dehydration) reactions,** synthesis reactions release one water molecule for each bond made

(figure 8.8a). Catabolic reactions involving energy transactions are equally active in a growing cell and require their own set of enzymes. For example, digestion of large substrates requires enzymes to break them down into smaller molecules so they can be used. Because the breaking of bonds usually requires the input of water, digestion is also termed a **hydrolysis* reaction (figure 8.8b).**

> * *hydrolysis* (hy-drol′-uh-sis) Gr. *hydro*, water, and *lysis*, setting free.

CLINICAL CONNECTIONS

The Role of Microbial Enzymes in Disease

Many pathogens secrete unique exoenzymes that help them avoid host defenses or promote their multiplication in tissues. Because these enzymes contribute to pathogenicity, they are referred to as virulence factors, or toxins in some cases (look ahead to chapter 13). *Streptococcus pyogenes* (a cause of throat and skin infections) produces a streptokinase that stimulates the digestion of blood clots and apparently assists in invasion of wounds. Another exoenzyme from this bacterium is called streptolysin.[1] In mammalian hosts, streptolysin damages blood cells and tissues. It is also responsible for lysing red blood cells used in blood agar media, and this trait is used for identifying the bacteria growing in culture (see figure 3.17).

Pseudomonas aeruginosa, a respiratory and skin pathogen, produces elastase and collagenase, which digest elastin and collagen, two proteins found in connective tissue. These increase the severity of certain lung and burn infections. Members of the genus *Clostridium* secrete toxins with significant pathological effects. Many of these toxins—for example, botulinum and tetanus toxins—have an enzymatic component that causes the symptoms of the diseases. Both of them prevent cell vesicles containing neurotransmitters from releasing their contents and thus block nerve transmission to muscles. The result in botulism is loss of muscle tone (flaccid paralysis); in tetanus it is sustained muscle tone (rigid paralysis). *Clostridium perfringens*, an agent of gas gangrene, synthesizes lecithinase C, a lipase that profoundly damages cell membranes and accounts for the tissue death associated with this disease. Other medically important enzymes of microbes do not target tissues. Some, such as the beta-lactamases, act on portions of some penicillin and cephalosporin antibiotics and inactivate them. This makes the bacteria drug resistant and protected from the effects of the drugs.

Even though viruses lack most features of metabolism, a few of them can express genes for enzymes. How would you describe the actions of the following viral enzymes: neuraminidase, reverse transcriptase, and integrase? *Answer available at http://www.mhhe.com/talaro9*

1. Even though most enzyme names end in *-ase* (see 8.3 Making Connections), not all do.

The Sensitivity of Enzymes to Environmental Conditions

The activity of an enzyme is highly influenced by the cell's environment. In general, enzymes operate only under the natural temperature, pH, and osmotic pressure of an organism's habitat. When enzymes are subjected to changes in these normal conditions, they tend to be chemically unstable, or **labile.** Low temperatures inhibit catalysis, and high temperatures denature the apoenzyme.

Figure 8.7 Constitutive and regulated enzymes. (a) Constitutive enzymes are present in constant amounts in a cell. The addition of more substrate does not increase the numbers of these enzymes. **(b)** The concentration of some regulated enzymes in a cell increases or decreases in response to substrate levels.

Denaturation is a process by which the bonds that collectively maintain the native shape of the apoenzyme are disrupted. This loss causes extreme distortion of the enzyme's shape and prevents the substrate from attaching to the active site (look ahead to chapter 11). Such nonfunctional enzymes block metabolic reactions and thereby can lead to cell death. Low or high pH and certain chemicals (heavy metals, alcohol) are also denaturing agents.

Regulation of Enzymatic Activity and Metabolic Pathways

Metabolic pathways proceed in a systematic, highly regulated manner that maximizes the use of available nutrients and energy. The cell responds to environmental conditions by adopting those

Glycosidic bond

(a) **Condensation Reaction.** Forming a glycosidic bond between two glucose molecules to generate maltose requires the removal of a water molecule.

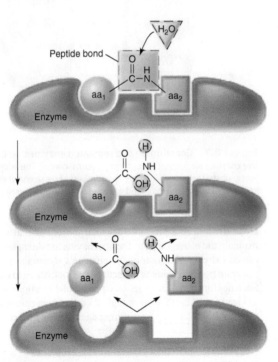

(b) **Hydrolysis Reaction.** Breaking a peptide bond between two amino acids requires a water molecule that adds OH to one amino acid and H to the other.

Figure 8.8 Examples of enzyme-catalyzed synthesis and hydrolysis reactions.

metabolic reactions that most favor growth and survival. Because enzymes are critical to these reactions, the regulation of metabolism is largely the regulation of enzymes by an elaborate system of checks and balances. Let us take a look at some general features of metabolic pathways.

Patterns of Metabolic Pathways

Metabolic reactions rarely consist of a single action or step. More often, they occur in a multistep series or pathway, with each step catalyzed by an enzyme. An individual reaction is shown in various ways, depending on the purpose at hand (**figure 8.9**). The product of one reaction is often the reactant (substrate) for the next, forming a linear chain of reactions. Many pathways have branches that provide alternate methods for nutrient processing. Others take a cyclic form, in which the starting molecule is regenerated to initiate another turn of the cycle. Pathways generally do not stand alone; they are interconnected and merge at many sites.

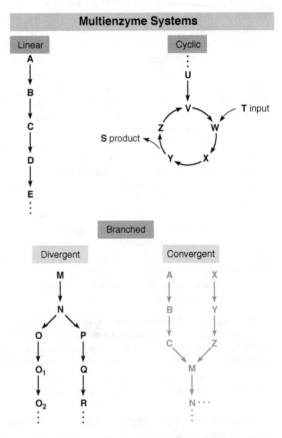

Figure 8.9 Patterns of metabolic pathways. In general, metabolic pathways consist of a linked series of individual chemical reactions that produce intermediary metabolites and lead to a final product. These pathways occur in several patterns, including linear, cyclic, and branched. Anabolic pathways involved in biosynthesis result in a more complex molecule, each step adding on a functional group, whereas catabolic pathways involve the dismantling of molecules and can generate energy. Virtually every reaction in a series involves a specific enzyme.

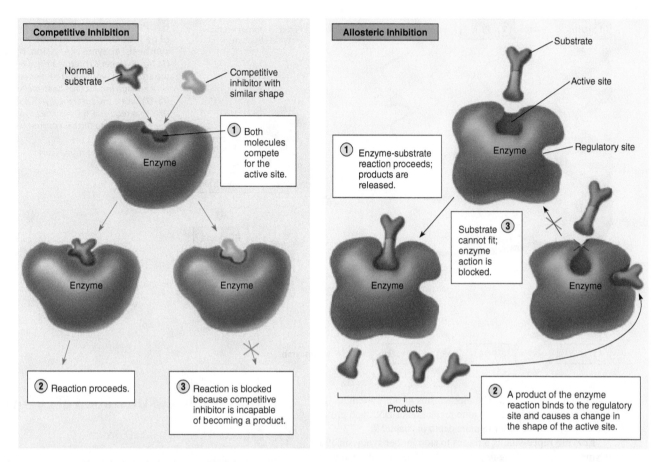

Figure 8.10 **Examples of two common modes of competitive inhibition that regulate enzyme action.** For a quick animation of these mechanisms, go to "Cellular Metabolism, Pathways, & Feedback" on YouTube.

Every pathway has one or more enzyme pacemakers that set the rate of a pathway's progression. Regulation of pacemaker enzymes proceeds on two fundamental levels. Either the enzyme itself is directly inhibited or activated, or the amount of the enzyme in the system is altered (decreased or increased). When factors affect the enzyme directly, the system can be finely controlled or "tuned." When regulation is at the genetic level (enzyme synthesis), control is slower and less sensitive.

Direct Controls on the Action of Enzymes

The bacterial cell has many ways of directly influencing the activity of its enzymes. It can inhibit enzyme activity by supplying a molecule that resembles the enzyme's normal substrate. The "mimic" can then occupy the enzyme's active site, preventing the actual substrate from binding there. Because the mimic cannot actually be acted on by the enzyme and a product is not released, the enzyme is effectively shut down. This is one example of **competitive inhibition,** because the mimic is competing with the substrate for the binding site (**figure 8.10**). In chapter 12, you will see that some antibiotics have the same strategy of competing with enzymatic active sites to shut down metabolic processes.

Another form of competitive inhibition can occur with special types of enzymes that have two binding sites: the active site and another area called the **regulatory** or **allosteric* site** (figure 8.10). The action of these enzymes is controlled by the binding of molecules other than the substrate in the regulatory site. Often the regulatory molecule is the product of the enzymatic reaction itself. This provides a negative feedback mechanism that can slow down enzymatic activity once a certain concentration of product is produced.

Non-competitive inhibition is a third mechanism that does not involve an inhibitor molecule competing with substrate for the active site or disable the active site. This type of inhibitor binds to the enzyme-substrate complex and prevents the enzyme from completing its action on the substrate.

Controls on Enzyme Synthesis

Controlling enzymes by controlling their synthesis is another effective mechanism. Because enzymes do not last indefinitely, they eventually degrade and must be replaced. This cycle works into the scheme of the cell, where replacement of enzymes can be regulated

* *allosteric* (al-oh-stair'-ik) Gr. *allos*, other, and *steros*, solid. Literally, "another space."

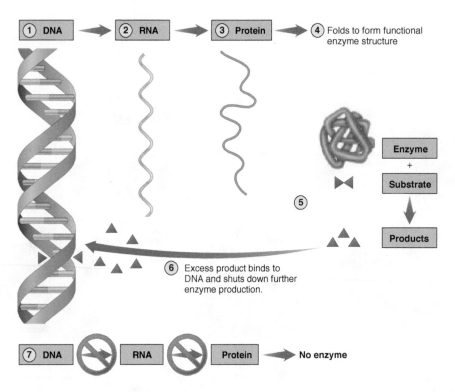

(1) DNA → **(2)** RNA → **(3)** Protein → **(4)** Folds to form functional enzyme structure

Enzyme
+
Substrate
↓
Products

(5)

(6) Excess product binds to DNA and shuts down further enzyme production.

(7) DNA ⊘ RNA ⊘ Protein → **No enzyme**

Process Figure 8.11 **One type of genetic control of enzyme synthesis: enzyme repression.** (1), (2), (3), (4), (5) Genetic controls are active and the enzyme is synthesized continuously until enough product has been made. (6)–(7) Excess product reacts with a site on DNA that regulates the enzyme's synthesis, thereby inhibiting further enzyme production.

according to cell demand. The mechanisms of this system are genetic in nature; that is, they require regulation of DNA and protein synthesis, a topic we cover in more depth in chapter 9.

Enzyme repression is a means to stop further synthesis of an enzyme somewhere along its pathway. As the level of the end product from a given enzymatic reaction has built to excess, the genetic apparatus responsible for replacing these enzymes is automatically suppressed (**figure 8.11**). The response time is longer than for feedback inhibition, but its effects are more enduring.

A response that resembles the inverse of enzyme repression is **enzyme induction.** In this process, enzymes appear (are induced) only when suitable substrates are present; that is, the synthesis of enzyme is induced by its substrate. This response enables the organism to adapt to a variety of nutrients, and it also prevents a microbe from wasting energy by making enzymes for which substrates are lacking.

✅ *Check Your Progress* SECTION 8.1

1. Differentiate between catabolism and anabolism using examples.
2. Describe 10 important biochemical properties of enzymes.
3. Describe the chemistry of enzymes, and explain how the apoenzyme forms.
4. Show diagrammatically the interaction of holoenzyme and its substrate and general products that can be formed from a reaction.
5. Differentiate among the chemical composition and functions of various cofactors. Provide examples of each type.
6. Summarize the direct and indirect controls that regulate enzymes.

8.2 The Pursuit and Utilization of Energy

💡 Expected Learning Outcomes

8. Relate the diverse sources of energy and the cellular management of energy.
9. Describe biological oxidation-reduction and energy transfer.
10. Discuss the structure, basic formation, and roles of ATP in cells.

Energy is defined as the capacity to do work or to cause change. In order to carry out the work of an array of metabolic processes, cells require constant input and expenditure of some form of usable energy. Energy commonly exists in these forms:

- thermal (heat) energy from molecular motion,
- radiant (wave) energy from visible light or other rays,
- electrical energy from a flow of electrons,
- mechanical energy from a physical change in position,
- atomic energy from reactions in the nucleus of an atom, and
- chemical energy present in the bonds of molecules.

Cells are far too fragile to rely in any constant way on thermal or atomic energy for cell transactions. Except for certain chemoautotrophic bacteria, the ultimate source of energy is the sun, but only phototrophs can tap this source directly. This capacity of photosynthesis to convert solar energy into chemical energy provides both a nutritional and an energy basis for all heterotrophic living things. We cover this essential form of metabolism in section 8.6. For the most part, only chemical energy and reactions can fuel cellular energetics of nonphotosynthetic organisms.

In this section, we further explore the role of energy as it is related to the use of nutrients, redox carriers, and the generation of ATP.

Cell Energetics

Cells manage energy in the form of chemical reactions that change molecules. This often involves activities such as the making or breaking of bonds and the transfer of electrons. Not all cellular reactions have the same relation to energy. Some release energy and others require it to proceed. For example, a reaction with this equation:

$$X + Y \xrightarrow{\text{Enzyme}} Z + \text{Energy}$$

releases energy as it goes forward. This type of reaction is termed **exergonic.*** Energy of this type is considered free: it is available for doing cellular work. Energy transactions such as the following:

$$\text{Energy} + A + B \xrightarrow{\text{Enzyme}} C$$

are called **endergonic*** because they are driven forward with the addition of energy.

Summaries of metabolism might make it seem that cells "create" energy from nutrients, but they do not. What they actually do is extract chemical energy already present in nutrient fuels and apply that energy toward useful work in the cell, much like a gasoline engine releases energy as it burns fuel. The engine does not actually produce energy, but it converts the potential energy of the fuel to the free energy of work.

The basis for cell energetics lies in the chemical bonds, electron transfers, and special pathways along with their enzymes. During exergonic reactions, electrons are pulled out of atoms, thereby releasing their inherent energy. These electrons are picked up by special carriers and transferred through a series of reactions until they reach a final electron acceptor. As we will see in section 8.3, the production of ATP is intimately tied to this process. As ATP is formed, it is used to support endergonic reactions such as synthesis. These reactions are balanced and cyclic, so that ATP is constantly being made, used, regenerated, and so on. The actual process of electron transfer is a type of redox reaction that was first described in chapter 2. Let us revisit this topic and see how it is involved in metabolism.

Biological Oxidation and Reduction: Electron and Energy Transfer

Many chemical substances readily donate or receive electrons and participate in oxidation (the loss of electrons) or reduction (the gain of electrons). The compound that loses the electrons is **oxidized,** and the compound that receives the electrons is **reduced.** Such oxidation-reduction or **redox reactions** are common in cells and indispensable to energy transactions (look back at figure 2.9). Such

reactions always occur in pairs, with an electron donor and an electron acceptor, which constitute a *conjugate pair,* or *redox pair.* The reaction can be represented as follows:

Electron donor + Electron acceptor ⟷ Electron donor + Electron acceptor
 •e⁻ •e⁻
Reduced Oxidized Oxidized Reduced

Redox reactions in cells often involve not only electrons but also hydrogen atoms which donate them. Recall that a hydrogen atom consists of a single proton and a single electron. Hydrogen readily gives up its single electron to positively charged molecules, leaving a hydrogen ion or proton (H^+). For simplicity's sake, our discussions will emphasize the process of electron transfer. But keep in mind that many pathways also require the hydrogen ions (protons) generated by oxidation-reduction to carry out essential functions in the metabolic pathways.

One example of a typical redox reaction is seen in this overall equation associated with aerobic respiration:

$$C_6H_{12}O_6 + 6O_2 \rightarrow 6CO_2 + 6H_2O + \text{Energy}$$

(Oxidation / Reduction)
Glucose

Note that the electron donor is hydrogen and the electron acceptor is oxygen. The electrons are transported and energy is released through a stepwise series of reactions, covered in section 8.3.

For it to be useful, the energy is ultimately captured through **phosphorylation,** a process that adds an inorganic phosphate P_i to adenosine diphosphate, converting it to ATP:

$$ADP + P_i + \text{Energy} \leftrightarrows ATP$$

Several different types of carriers exist for handling and transporting electrons and protons until they can be transferred to a final electron acceptor. Such redox reactions are a constant supplier of electrons for the final "processing plant" operating in cells—the electron transport system (look ahead to figure 8.16).

Managing Electrons in Metabolism

We learned in chapter 2 that electrons are highly reactive, negatively charged particles, and that they are transferred or shared between atoms during bond formation. These electrons do not bounce around randomly in cells. Generally, they are captured and transported by some form of carrier molecule.

Much of the work of electron capture and transport in metabolic pathways falls to molecules with increased affinity for electrons. They readily accept electrons from one substrate and donate them to another substrate. The most common of these carriers is the coenzyme **nicotinamide adenine dinucleotide (NAD^+)(figure 8.12).** Other related carriers are FAD (flavin adenine dinucleotide), coenzyme A, and the compounds of the respiratory chain, all discussed in section 8.3.

NAD^+ reduces 2 hydrogen atoms and carries 2 electrons away from this reaction, represented as NADH. The electrons are carried in the nicotinamide ring, where they can be accessed during other electron transfers (figure 8.12).

At some point, the electrons will be received by a final electron acceptor, which in aerobic metabolism is molecular oxygen. An

* *exergonic* (ex-er-gon'-ik) Gr. *exo,* without, and *ergon,* work. In general, catabolic reactions are exergonic.
* *endergonic* (en-der-gon'-ik) Gr. *endo,* within, and *ergon,* work. Anabolic reactions tend to be endergonic.

important part of this carrier system is that every transfer of electrons from NADH to another carrier molecule automatically makes NAD$^+$ available for the redox cycle once again (see example in figure below).

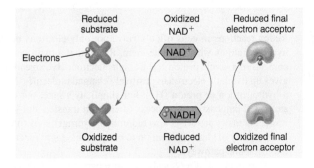

Adenosine Triphosphate: Metabolic Money

ATP has been described as metabolic currency because it can be earned, spent, and exchanged. You can gain some appreciation for the enormous need for ATP if you consider that even one tiny cell of *Escherichia coli* consumes around 2.5 million ATP molecules per second

for synthesis alone! As a temporary energy repository, ATP provides a connection between energy-yielding catabolism and all other cellular activities that require energy. Some clues to its energy-storing properties lie in its unique molecular structure.

The Molecular Structure of ATP ATP is a three-part molecule consisting of a nitrogen base (adenine) linked to a 5-carbon sugar (ribose), with a chain of three phosphate groups bonded to the ribose (**figure 8.13**). The type, arrangement, and especially the proximity of atoms in ATP combine to form a compatible but unstable high-energy molecule. The high energy of ATP originates in the orientation of the phosphate groups, which are relatively bulky and carry negative charges. The proximity of these repelling electrostatic charges imposes a strain that is most acute on the bonds between the last two phosphate groups. When the strain on the phosphate bonds is released by removal of the terminal phosphates, free energy is released.

Breaking the bonds between the second and third phosphates of ATP yields adenosine diphosphate (ADP), which can then be converted to adenosine monophosphate (AMP). It is worthwhile noting how economically a cell manages its pool of adenosine nucleotides. AMP derivatives help form the backbone of RNA and are also a major component of certain coenzymes (NAD$^+$, FAD, and coenzyme A).

The Metabolic Roles of ATP ATP is at the center of a cell's energy cycle, regardless of whether it is a heterotroph using respiration, a photosynthetic organism, or a chemoautotroph. Expenditure

Figure 8.12 Structure of NAD$^+$ and its carrier function.
(a) The coenzyme NAD$^+$ contains the vitamin nicotinamide (niacin) bound to two ribose phosphates and an adenine. (b) The site of reduction is at the nicotinamide ring portion (box), which carries 2 electrons, one at the ring nitrogen and the other on a hydrogen bound to a ring carbon.

— Bond that releases
 energy when broken

Figure 8.13 Two views of adenosine triphosphate (ATP).
A structural model of ATP and its related components ADP and AMP. Note that the last two phosphate bonds release energy when they are cleaved.

of ATP powers nearly all processes that are part of cellular work. This energy cycle can be depicted as shown here:

Respiration
Fermentation
Photosynthesis
Chemoautotrophy

ADP + P$_i$

ATP

Chemical work
Transport work
Mechanical work

In many instances, the energy released from the high energy bond in ATP activates individual subunits before they are enzymatically bonded during synthesis. ATP is also used to prepare a molecule for catabolism such as the phosphorylation of a 6-carbon sugar during the early stages of glycolysis (**figure 8.14**).

Because ATP needs to be constantly replenished, reactions are constantly continuing in the reverse order. ADPs are situated to react immediately with inorganic phosphate and a high-energy source. The energy for these high-energy phosphate bonds comes from catabolic pathways where substrates or electron carriers are harvesting energy.

Most ATPs in aerobic organisms are formed during **oxidative phosphorylation,** a series of reactions involving electron transport and an enzyme (ATP synthase) that can trap energy and store it in ATP (look ahead to figure 8.20). Some ATP molecules are formed through **substrate-level phosphorylation,** a process that all cells carry out, regardless of their metabolic type. In this mode of phosphorylation, ATP is formed by transfer of a phosphate group from a

Phosphorylated
substrate

+ ADP

Enzyme

Substrate

+ ATP

Figure 8.15 ATP formation by substrate-level phosphorylation. The substrate has been bound to a phosphate, creating a bond with high potential energy. Transfer of the high-energy phosphate to ADP gives rise to ATP and returns the substrate to its original form.

high-energy compound (substrate) directly to ADP (**figure 8.15**; see also figure 8.17, step 6).

Photosynthetic organisms have a system of **photophosphorylation,** in which the ATP is formed through a form of sunlight-driven electron transport discussed in more detail in section 8.6.

Check Your Progress SECTION 8.2

7. Explain how oxidation of a substrate proceeds without oxygen.

8. Refer to the redox equation on page 229 for glucose, and name which substance is reduced, which is oxidized, the oxidizing agent, and the reducing agent.

9. In the following redox pairs, which compound is reduced and which is oxidized?
 a. NAD$^+$ and NADH
 b. FADH$_2$ and FAD
 c. NO$_3^-$ and NO$_2^-$

10. a. Describe the roles played by ATP and NAD$^+$ in metabolism.
 b. What particular features of their structure lend them to these functions?

11. Name the major ways that substrate-level phosphorylation is different from oxidative phosphorylation.

12. What is meant by the concept of the "final electron acceptor"?

8.3 Pathways of Bioenergetics

Expected Learning Outcomes

11. Relate the main points of bioenergetics and energy strategies in microorganisms.

12. Describe the main catabolic pathways and where they occur in aerobic respiration.

13. Define *glycolysis* and explain its input and output, its basic steps, and how it is linked to the Krebs cycle and oxidative phosphorylation.

14. Explain the basic steps in the Krebs cycle, its input and output, and how it is linked to oxidative phosphorylation.

15. Describe the components of the respiratory chain and their functions.

16. Explain the chemiosmotic mechanism of ATP formation, its relationship to electron transport, and the final step in electron transfer.

17. Summarize the results of aerobic respiration.

18. Define and describe some reactions of anaerobic respiration.

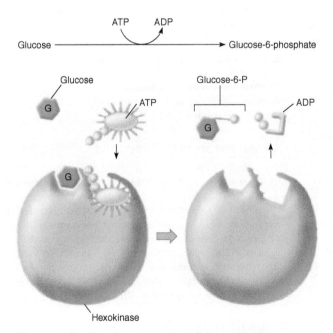

Glucose

ATP ADP

Glucose-6-phosphate

Glucose

ATP

Glucose-6-P

ADP

G

G

G

Hexokinase

Figure 8.14 The phosphorylation of glucose by ATP. The first step in catabolizing glucose is the addition of a phosphate from ATP by an enzyme called hexokinase. This use of high-energy phosphate as an activator is a recurring feature of many metabolic pathways.

One of the scientific community's greatest achievements was deciphering the biochemical pathways of cells. Initial work with bacteria and yeasts, followed by studies with animal and plant cells, clearly demonstrated metabolic similarities and strongly supported the presence of metabolic patterns that are universal. **Bioenergetics** is a study of the mechanisms of cellular energy release, including catabolic and anabolic routes. Although these pathways are interconnected and interdependent, anabolic pathways are not simply reversals of catabolic ones. At first glance, it may seem more economical to use identical pathways, but having different enzymes and divided pathways allows anabolism and catabolism to proceed simultaneously without interference.

In the following sections, we focus our discussion on the most common catabolic pathways that illustrate general principles of other pathways as well.

Catabolism: An Overview of Nutrient Breakdown and Energy Release

For chemoheterotrophs, the primary catabolism of fuels (such as glucose) that release energy proceeds through a series of three coupled pathways:

1. **glycolysis,*** also called the Embden-Meyerhof-Parnas (EMP) pathway;[2]
2. the **Krebs cycle,** also known as the citric acid or tricarboxylic acid cycle TCA;[2] and
3. the **respiratory chain** (electron transport and oxidative phosphorylation).

Each segment of the pathway is responsible for a specific set of actions on various products of glucose. The major interconnections of these pathways in aerobic respiration are represented in **figure 8.16,** and their reactions are summarized in **table 8.3.** In the following sections, we observe each of these pathways in greater detail.

Energy Strategies in Microorganisms

In chapter 7, we gained insight into the metabolic diversity of microbes. There are numerous strategies used by microbes to derive energy and synthesize cell components. Because microbial metabolism is so varied, we have chosen to cover elements of the most common types of metabolism, based on the three basic catabolic pathways. In previous discussions, microorganisms were categorized according to their requirement for oxygen gas, and this requirement is related directly to their mechanisms of energy release. As we shall see, **aerobic respiration** is a series of reactions (glycolysis, Krebs cycle, and the respiratory chain) that converts glucose to CO_2, produces H_2O, and generates energy **(figure 8.16a).** It relies on molecular oxygen (O_2) as the final acceptor for electrons and hydrogens, and releases a relatively large amount of ATP.

Aerobic respiration is characteristic of many bacteria, fungi, protozoa, and animals, and it is the system we emphasize here.

Facultative and aerotolerant anaerobes may use only glycolysis or similar pathways to incompletely oxidize or **ferment** glucose. In this case, oxygen is not required, organic compounds are the final electron acceptors, and a relatively small amount of ATP is synthesized **(figure 8.16c).**

Some anaerobic microorganisms metabolize by means of **anaerobic respiration.** This system may involve the same three pathways as aerobic respiration, but it does not use molecular oxygen as the final electron acceptor **(figure 8.16b).** Instead, it uses other oxidized ions such as NO_3^-, SO_4^{2-}, or CO_2 for the final electron acceptor. Aspects of fermentation and anaerobic respiration are covered later in this section.

Aerobic Respiration

Aerobic respiration is a series of enzyme-catalyzed reactions in which electrons are transferred from fuel molecules such as glucose to oxygen as a final electron acceptor. This pathway is the principal energy-yielding scheme for aerobic heterotrophs, and it provides both ATP and metabolic intermediates for many other pathways in the cell, including those of protein, lipid, and carbohydrate synthesis (see figure 8.25).

Aerobic respiration in microorganisms can be summarized by an equation:

$$\text{Glucose (C}_6\text{H}_{12}\text{O}_6) + 6\text{O}_2 + 38 \text{ ADP} + 38\text{P}_i \rightarrow 6\text{CO}_2 + 6\text{H}_2\text{O} + 38 \text{ ATP}$$

The seeming simplicity of the equation for aerobic respiration conceals its complexity. Fortunately, we do not have to present all of the details to address some important concepts concerning its reactants and products, as follows:

1. the steps in the oxidation of glucose,
2. the involvement of coenzyme carriers and the final electron acceptor,
3. where and how ATP originates,
4. where carbon dioxide originates, and
5. where oxygen is required.

Glucose: The Starting Compound

Carbohydrates such as glucose are good fuels because these compounds are readily oxidized; that is, they are superior electron donors. The electrons they donate can be used in energy transfers. The end products of these organic compounds are energy-rich ATP and energy-poor carbon dioxide and water. Polysaccharides (starch, glycogen) and disaccharides (maltose, lactose) are stored sources of glucose for the respiratory pathways. Although we use glucose as the main starting compound, other hexoses (fructose, galactose) and fatty acid subunits can enter the pathways of aerobic respiration as well, as we will see in section 8.5.

Glycolysis: The Starting Lineup

The process called glycolysis (EMP) is a pathway that converts glucose through several steps into pyruvic acid. Depending on the organism and the conditions, it may be only the first phase of respiration, or

* *glycolysis* (gly-kol′-ih-sis) Gr. *glykys,* sweet, and *lysis,* to split.

2. The EMP pathway is named for the biochemists who first outlined its steps. Krebs is in honor of Sir Hans Krebs who, with F. A. Lipmann, delineated this pathway, an achievement for which they won the Nobel Prize in Physiology or Medicine in 1953. TCA refers to the involvement of several organic acids containing three carboxylic acid groups, citric acid being the first tricarboxylic acid formed.

Figure 8.16 **Side-by-side comparison of the stages, reactions, and major products of pathways for aerobic respiration, anaerobic respiration, and fermentation.** Note that all begin with glycolysis but vary in use of other pathways, electron acceptors, and ATP yield.

TABLE 8.3	Metabolic Strategies Among Heterotrophic Microorganisms Growing on Glucose			
Scheme	Pathways Involved	Final Electron Acceptor	Products	Primary Pathway Found In
Aerobic respiration	Glycolysis, Krebs cycle, electron transport	O_2	ATP, CO_2, H_2O	Aerobes; facultative anaerobes
Anaerobic metabolism				
Fermentative	Glycolysis	Organic molecules	ATP, CO_2, ethanol, lactic acid*	Facultative, aerotolerant, strict anaerobes
Respiration	Glycolysis, Krebs cycle, electron transport	Various inorganic ions $(NO_3^-, SO_4^{2-}, CO_3^{3-})$	CO_2, ATP, organic acids, H_2S, CH_4, N_2	Anaerobes; some facultatives and aerotolerants

*The products of microbial fermentations are extremely varied and include organic acids, alcohols, and gases.

it may serve as the primary metabolic pathway for fermentative microbes. Glycolysis provides a way to synthesize a small amount of ATP in the presence or absence of oxygen, to release NADH, and to generate pyruvic acid, an essential intermediary metabolite.

Steps in the Glycolytic Pathway Glycolysis proceeds along nine linear steps. The first portion of glycolysis involves activation of glucose, which is followed by oxidation reactions of the glucose fragments, the synthesis of ATP, and the formation of pyruvic acid. **Although each step of metabolism is catalyzed by a specific enzyme, we will mention only certain key ones.** The following outline lists the principal steps of glycolysis. To see an overview of glycolysis, go to **figure 8.17.** Detailed illustrations appear in **Appendix A.**

1. **Glucose** is phosphorylated by an **ATP** to produce glucose-6-phosphate. This is a way of "priming" the system and keeping the glucose inside the cell.
2. Glucose-6-phosphate is converted to its isomer, fructose-6-phosphate.
3. Another **ATP** is spent in phosphorylating the first carbon of fructose-6-phosphate, which yields fructose-1,6-diphosphate.

Up to this point, no energy has been released, no oxidation-reduction has occurred, and, in fact, 2 ATPs have been used and the molecules remain in the 6-carbon state.

4. Fructose-1,6-diphosphate is split into two 3-carbon fragments: glyceraldehyde-3-phosphate (G-3-P) and dihydroxyacetone phosphate (DHAP). These molecules are isomers, and DHAP is converted to G-3-P, which is the more reactive form for the following reactions.

The effect of the splitting of fructose diphosphate is to double every subsequent reaction, because where there was once a single molecule, there are now two to be fed into the remaining pathways.

5. Each molecule of glyceraldehyde-3-phosphate becomes involved in the single oxidation-reduction reaction of glycolysis. This sets the scene for ATP synthesis. The **NAD$^+$** coenzyme complex picks up hydrogens from G-3-P, forming **NADH.** This step is accompanied by the addition of an inorganic phosphate (PO_4^{3-}) to form an unstable bond on the third carbon of the G-3-P substrate. The product of these reactions is diphosphoglyceric acid (DPGA).
6. One of the high-energy phosphates of diphosphoglyceric acid is donated to ADP via **substrate-level phosphorylation** resulting in a molecule of **ATP.** The other product of this reaction is 3-phosphoglyceric acid (3-PGA).
7, 8. During this phase, the 3-phosphoglyceric acid is converted to 2-phosphoglyceric acid (2-PGA) through the shift of a phosphate from the third to the second carbon. Then, the removal of a water molecule from 2-phosphoglyceric acid converts it to phosphoenolpyruvic acid (PEPA). The result gives rise to a high-energy phosphate bond.
9. In the final reaction of glycolysis, phosphoenolpyruvic acid gives up its high-energy phosphate to form a second ATP, again via **substrate-level phosphorylation.** This reaction also produces **pyruvic acid** (pyruvate), a compound with many roles in metabolism.

The reactions of glycolysis thus give rise to two pyruvic acids per glucose. The two substrate-level phosphorylations produce a total of **4 ATPs.** However, 2 ATPs were expended for steps 1 and 3, so the net number of ATPs available to the cell from these reactions is **2.**

In aerobic organisms, the NADH formed during step 5 is shuttled to the electron transport system, where the final electron acceptor will be oxygen, and additional ATPs will be generated per NADH. In organisms that ferment glucose, the NADH will be oxidized back to NAD$^+$, and the electron acceptor will be an organic compound (see figure 8.16b).

Pyruvic Acid—A Central Metabolite

Pyruvic acid occupies an important position in several pathways, and different organisms handle it in different ways **(figure 8.18).** In strictly aerobic organisms and some anaerobes, pyruvic acid is channeled into the Krebs cycle for processing and energy release. Facultative anaerobes can adopt a fermentative metabolism, in which pyruvic acid is further reduced into acids or other products.

The Preparation of Pyruvic Acid for the Krebs Cycle

The oxidation of glucose by glycolysis yields a comparatively small amount of energy. Pyruvic acid is still energy-rich, containing a number of extractable electrons to power ATP synthesis, and this will be achieved through the work of the second and third phases of aerobic respiration, during which pyruvic acid is converted to CO_2 and H_2O. In the following section, we examine the second phase—the Krebs cycle—that takes place in the mitochondrial matrix in eukaryotes and in the cytoplasm of bacteria.

To connect the glycolysis pathway to the Krebs cycle, the pyruvic acid is first converted to a starting compound for that cycle **(figure 8.19,** tan oval at top). This step brings in an enzyme complex and coenzyme A to participate in the oxidation of pyruvic acid, the reduction of NAD$^+$ to NADH, and the decarboxylation of pyruvic acid to a 2-carbon acetyl group accompanied by release of carbon dioxide. The acetyl group remains attached to coenzyme A, forming **acetyl coenzyme A** (acetyl CoA) that feeds into the Krebs cycle. Pyruvate dehydrogenase, the enzyme complex that makes this reaction possible, is huge. In *E. coli*, it contains four vitamins and has a molecular weight of 6 million—larger than a ribosome!

Artist's concept of pyruvate dehydrogenase

The NADH produced in the formation of acetyl CoA will be shuttled into electron transport and used to generate ATP via oxidative phosphorylation in the third phase of aerobic respiration.

Keep in mind that all reactions during these subsequent phases happen twice for each glucose because of the two pyruvates that are released during glycolysis.

The Krebs Cycle—A Carbon and Energy Wheel

As you learned earlier, a cyclic pathway is one in which the starting compound is regenerated at the end of the cycle so it will be ready to go around again. The Krebs cycle has eight steps, beginning with

These steps take place in the cytoplasm of both prokaryotic and eukaryotic cells.

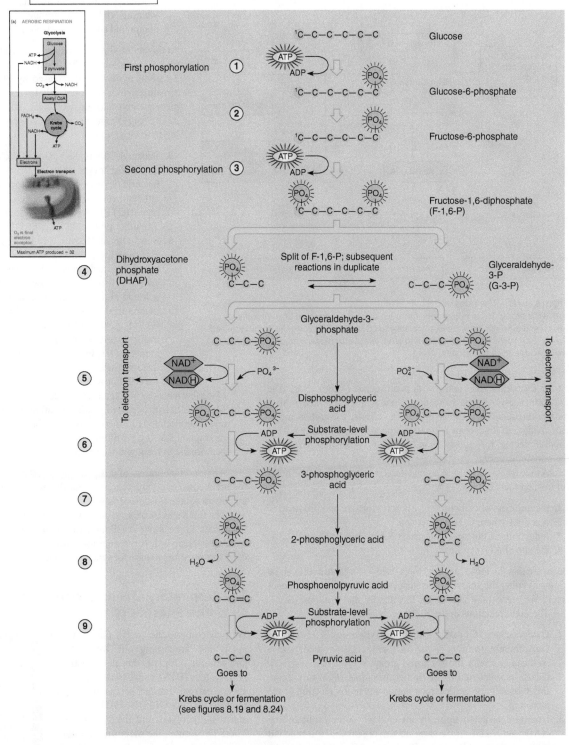

Process Figure 8.17 Summary of the steps in glycolysis. The primary reaction steps are described in the accompanying text. These reactions all take place in the cytoplasm, regardless of the cell type. Inset in upper corner has a gold box to show the position of this pathway in the scheme of aerobic respiration. A detailed analysis of specific chemical structures and reactions can be found in Appendix A.

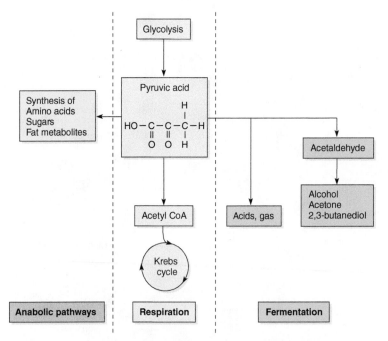

Figure 8.18 The fates of pyruvic acid (pyruvate). This metabolite is an important hub in the processing of nutrients by microbes. It may be fermented anaerobically to several end products or oxidized completely to CO_2 and H_2O through the Krebs cycle and the electron transport system. It can also serve as a source of raw material for synthesizing amino acids and carbohydrates.

citrate formation and ending with oxaloacetate (figure 8.19). The 2-carbon acetyl groups from coenzyme A are combined with a 4-carbon oxaloacetate molecule to form citrate, a 6-carbon molecule. Although this seems a cumbersome way to dismantle such a small molecule, it is necessary in biological systems for extracting the remaining energy from the acetyl fragment.

As we take a single spin around the Krebs cycle, it will be helpful to keep track of

1. the numbers of carbons (#C) of each substrate and product,
2. reactions where CO_2 is generated,
3. reductions of the electron carriers NAD^+ and FAD, and
4. the site of ATP synthesis.

Be aware that the terms and structures used for organic acids can be shown as either the acid form (oxaloacetic acid) or its salt (oxaloacetate). We present the salt form in this text for the most part.

The eight reactions in the Krebs cycle are:

1. Oxaloacetate (4C) reacts with the acetyl group (2C) on acetyl CoA, thereby forming citrate (6C) and releasing coenzyme A so it can join with another acetyl group.
2. Citrate is converted to its isomer, isocitrate (6C), to prepare this substrate for the decarboxylation and redox reaction of the next step.
3. Isocitrate is acted upon by an enzyme complex including NAD^+ or NADP (depending on the organism) in a reaction that generates NADH or NADPH, splits off a carbon dioxide, and leaves α-ketoglutarate (5C).

4. Alpha-ketoglutarate serves as a substrate for the final decarboxylation reaction and yet another redox reaction, involving coenzyme A-SH and yielding NADH. The product is the high-energy compound succinyl CoA (4C).

At this point, the cycle has completed the formation of 3 CO_2 molecules that balance out each original 3-carbon pyruvic acid released by glycolysis. The remaining steps serve not only to regenerate the oxaloacetate and start the cycle again but also to extract more energy from the intermediate compounds leading to oxaloacetate.

5. Succinyl CoA is the source of the one substrate level phosphorylation in the Krebs cycle. In most bacteria, it proceeds with the formation of ATP, although eukaryotes produce guanosine triphosphate (GTP), an equivalent source of energy. The other product at this step is succinate (4C).
6. Succinate undergoes a redox reaction, but in this case, the electron and H^+ acceptor is flavin adenine dinucleotide (FAD). The enzyme that catalyzes this reaction, succinyl dehydrogenase, is found in the bacterial cell membrane and mitochondrial crista of eukaryotic cells. The $FADH_2$ generated directly enters the electron transport system but at a different carrier site than NADH. Fumarate (4C) is the product of this reaction.
7. The addition of water to fumarate results in malate (4C). This is one of the few reactions in respiration that directly incorporates water.
8. Malate is dehydrogenated (with formation of a final NADH), and oxaloacetate is formed. This step brings the cycle back to its original starting position, where the oxaloacetate molecule is available to react with acetyl coenzyme A.

An important feature of this pathway is that acetyl groups from the breakdown of certain fats can enter the pathway and be used as an energy source (discussed in section 8.5).

The full Krebs cycle is not present in all cells, and it may not function under all metabolic conditions. But even in cells with alternate metabolic schemes, it is essential for generating small organic molecules that microbes require for synthesis (look ahead to figure 8.25).

The Respiratory Chain: Electron Transport and Oxidative Phosphorylation

We now come to the energy chain, which is the final "processing mill" for electrons and protons. Overall, the electron transport system (ETS) consists of a chain of special carriers that receive electrons from reduced carriers (NADH, $FADH_2$) generated by glycolysis and the Krebs cycle. The ETS shuttles the electrons through a series of redox transfers (**figure 8.20**). The flow of electrons down this chain is highly

Quick Search
Observe this process in action at "Cellular Respiration: The Electron Transport Chain" on YouTube.

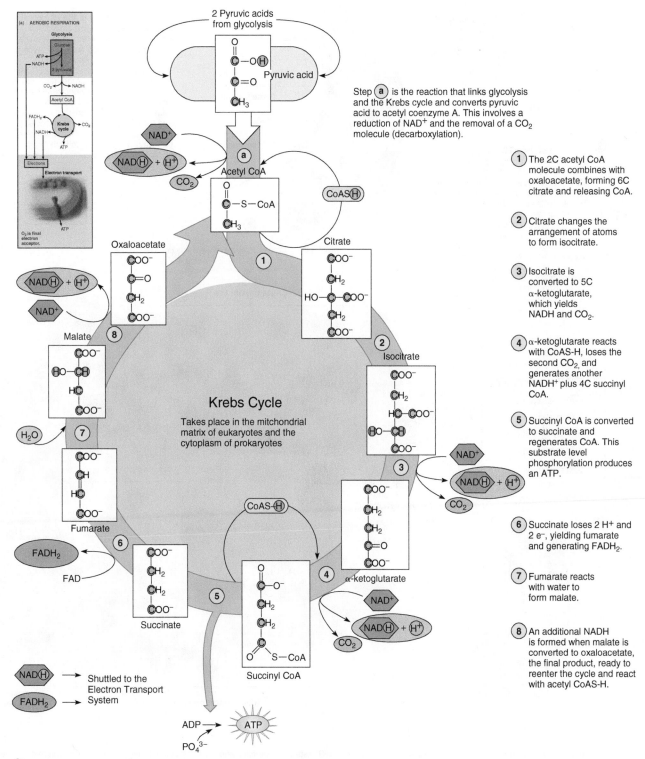

Step **a** is the reaction that links glycolysis and the Krebs cycle and converts pyruvic acid to acetyl coenzyme A. This involves a reduction of NAD^+ and the removal of a CO_2 molecule (decarboxylation).

1. The 2C acetyl CoA molecule combines with oxaloacetate, forming 6C citrate and releasing CoA.

2. Citrate changes the arrangement of atoms to form isocitrate.

3. Isocitrate is converted to 5C α-ketoglutarate, which yields NADH and CO_2.

4. α-ketoglutarate reacts with CoAS-H, loses the second CO_2, and generates another $NADH^+$ plus 4C succinyl CoA.

5. Succinyl CoA is converted to succinate and regenerates CoA. This substrate level phosphorylation produces an ATP.

6. Succinate loses 2 H^+ and 2 e^-, yielding fumarate and generating $FADH_2$.

7. Fumarate reacts with water to form malate.

8. An additional NADH is formed when malate is converted to oxaloacetate, the final product, ready to reenter the cycle and react with acetyl CoAS-H.

Krebs Cycle

Takes place in the mitchondrial matrix of eukaryotes and the cytoplasm of prokaryotes

NAD(H) → Shuttled to the Electron Transport System
$FADH_2$ →

Process Figure 8.19 The reactions of a single turn of the Krebs cycle. Each glucose will produce two spins of this pathway. Note that this is an enlarged, more detailed view of the middle phase depicted in figure 8.16a (inset).

Cutaway view of a mitochondrion

Outer membrane
Inner membrane
Matrix
Intermembrane space
Cristae
ATP synthases

① The mitochondrion is the site of electron transport and oxidative phosphorylation in eukaryotic cells. Its double membrane feature creates two separate compartments: the intermembrane space (brown) between the outer and inner membranes and the matrix (yellow) entirely enclosed by the inner membrane folded into cristae (blue). The electron transport proteins and the ATP synthases are stationed throughout the cristae. From here, the pathways have access to both matrix and intermembrane compartments.

② Close up of the ETS. NAD dehydrogenase accepts electrons from NADH and transfers them to CoQ. Electrons removed from $FADH_2$ by the FeS complex are also transferred to CoQ. These electrons are passed through the remaining carriers: the cytochrome b/c_1 complex, cytochrome c, and cytochrome a/a_3. At cytochrome a/a_3, 2 electrons combine with 2 protons (H^+) and an oxygen atom to form H_2O. Electron transport is coupled with the pumping of protons across the crista membrane into the intermembrane space by three of the carrier complexes. This process forms the basis of chemiosmosis.

Closeup shows relative positions of cristae, compartments, ETS, and ATP synthase.

I		NADH dehydrogenase (N)
II		FeS proteins (F)
		Coenzyme Q
III		Cytochrome b
		Cytochrome c_1
		Cytochrome c
IV		Cytochrome a
		Cytochrome a_3

(a) (b)

+ Charged − Charged

③ (a) Proton transport by the ETS into the intermembrane space (IMS) sets up a chemical and charge gradient between the IMS and the matrix called the proton motive force. **(b)** ATP synthase. The gradient creates an electrical potential for capturing the free energy of electron movement to drive ATP synthesis. As protons (H^+) diffuse from the intermembrane space through the F_0 portion of the ATP synthase into the matrix, the F_1 portion rotates, pulls in ADP and P_i, and releases ATP. This is an exergonic reaction that requires 3 protons for each ATP.

Figure 8.20 Electron transport, oxidative phosphorylation, the proton motive force, chemiosmosis, and ATP synthesis in the mitochondrion.

energetic and ultimately drives the synthesis of ATP. The step that finalizes the transport process is the acceptance of electrons and hydrogen ions by oxygen, with the production of water.

Some variability exists from one organism to another, but the principal compounds that carry out these complex reactions are NADH dehydrogenase, iron-sulfide complexes (FeS), coenzyme Q (**ubiquinone**),* and several **cytochromes**.* The cytochromes contain a tightly bound metal atom at their center that is actively involved in accepting electrons and donating them to the next carrier in the series. The highly compartmentalized structure of the respiratory chain is an important factor in its function. Note in figure 8.20 that the electron transport carriers and enzymes are associated in complexes in the inner mitochondrial membranes in eukaryotes. The cell membrane is the equivalent structure for housing them in bacteria (see figure 8.21).

The Carriers of Electron Transport: The Energy Cascade in the Mitochondria

The principal questions about the electron transport system are: How are the electrons passed from one carrier to another in the series? How is this progression coupled to ATP synthesis? and, Where and how is oxygen utilized? Although the biochemical details of this process are complicated, the basic reactions consist of a number of redox reactions now familiar to us. In general, the carrier compounds and their associated enzymes are arranged in linear sequence and are reduced and oxidized while shuttling the electrons along to their final acceptor (**figure 8.20, part 2**).

The electron carrier complexes and associated molecules present in aerobic organisms are as follows:

1. **Complex I** consists of a huge multienzyme cluster termed NADH dehydrogenase (reductase), which receives the NADH from glycolysis and the Krebs cycle.
2. **Complex II** is made up of a series of iron-sulfur (FeS) proteins effective in electron transfer from $FADH_2$ produced in the sixth step of the Krebs cycle.
3. **Coenzyme Q,** or **ubiquinone,** is a mobile carrier not embedded in the membrane that can pick up electrons from both complexes I and II and donate them to complex III.
4. **Complex III** is comprised of cytochromes b and c_1, which deliver electrons to cytochrome c.
5. **Cytochrome c** is another mobile carrier that shuttles electrons between complexes III and IV.
6. **Complex IV** catalyzes the reaction between electrons, H^+, and oxygen, yielding H_2O and completing the electron transfer process.

In addition to the roles outlined here, complexes I, III, and IV have the additional function of pumping protons from the matrix into the intermembrane space to establish a charge gradient (discussed under the next heading). With each redox exchange, the energy level of the reactants is lessened. This free energy is captured and used by **ATP synthase** complexes stationed in the cristae in close association with the ETS carriers. Each NADH that enters electron transport can potentially give rise to a maximum of 3 ATPs. Because $FADH_2$ from the Krebs cycle enters the cycle after complex I, its reactions result in a maximum yield of about 2 ATPs. This coupling of ATP synthesis to electron transport is termed **oxidative phosphorylation.**

The Formation of ATP and Chemiosmosis What biochemical processes are involved in coupling electron transport to the production of ATP? According to a widely accepted concept called **chemiosmosis,** during electron transport, some of the carriers actively transport protons across the cristae membrane and into the intermembrane compartment of the mitochondrion. This process sets up a concentration gradient of hydrogen ions called the **proton motive force (PMF)**. The PMF consists of a difference in charge between the intermembrane compartment $(+)$ and the matrix compartment $(-)$ (**figure 8.20, part 3**).

Separating the charge has an effect similar to a battery, which can temporarily store potential energy. This charge will be maintained by the impermeability of the cristae membranes to protons. The only site where protons can diffuse into the matrix compartment is at the ATP synthase complex, which sets the stage for ATP synthesis.

ATP synthase is one of the most remarkable enzymes in the molecular world. Its structure includes two motors, an ion pump, and an enzyme that can capture energy and store it as ATP. These synthases are located throughout the membranes of the cristae in high numbers (one estimate is around 10,000 per mitochondrion). Each ATP synthase complex consists of two large units, F_0 and F_1 (**figure 8.20, part 3**). The F_0 portion is embedded in the membrane and can rotate like a motor to pull in protons. As protons flow through the F_0 portion by diffusion, the F_1 compartments pull in ADP and P_i. Rotation induces a change in the three-dimensional structure of ATP synthase. This adjustment creates a high-energy bond between ADP and P_i. The ATP that forms is released into the matrix, where it will serve as a constant supply for cellular reactions (figure 8.20, part 3). The enzyme is then rotated back to the start position and will continue the process.

An important issue is just how the ATP is delivered out of the mitochondrion and into the cytoplasm for use in cell synthesis and other activities. The mitochondrial membranes are impregnated with a number of specialized active transporters called ATP-ADP translocases that constantly transport ATP out of and ADP into the mitochondrion.

Bacterial ATP synthesis occurs by means of this same overall process. However, bacteria have the ETS stationed in the cell membrane, and the direction of the proton movement is from the cytoplasm to the periplasmic space between the membrane and cell wall. Bacteria may also show variations in the number and types of electron carriers (**figure 8.21**). As we will see, these differences will affect the amount of ATP produced. In both cell types, the chemiosmotic theory has been supported by tests showing that oxidative phosphorylation is blocked if the mitochondrial or bacterial cell membranes are disrupted.

* *ubiquinone* (yoo-bik′-wih-nohn) L. *ubique,* everywhere. A type of chemical, similar to vitamin K, that is very common in cells.
* *cytochrome* (sy′-toh-krohm) Gr. *cyto,* cell, and *kroma,* color. Cytochromes are pigmented, iron-containing molecules similar to hemoglobin.

Figure 8.21 Chemiosmosis in bacteria. Enlarged view of bacterial cell envelope to show the relationship of electron transport and ATP synthesis. Bacteria have the ETS carriers and ATP synthase stationed in the cell membrane. As the ETS shuttles electrons delivered by NADH and FADH$_2$, some of the ETS carriers also transport protons into the periplasmic space, which sets up a gradient just as it occurs in mitochondria. Bacteria will vary in the exact nature of the carriers in the ETS.

The Terminal Step of Electron Transport

The terminal step, during which oxygen accepts the electrons, is catalyzed by cytochrome a/a_3, also called cytochrome oxidase. This large enzyme complex is specifically adapted to receive electrons from cytochrome c, pick up hydrogen ions from the solution, and react with oxygen to form a molecule of water (figure 8.20, part 3). This reaction, though in actuality more complex, is summarized as follows:

$$2H^+ + 2e^- + \tfrac{1}{2}O_2 \rightarrow H_2O$$

Most eukaryotic aerobes have a fully functioning cytochrome system, but bacteria exhibit wide-ranging variations in this part of the system. Some species lack one or more of the redox steps; others have several alternative electron transport schemes. Because many bacteria lack cytochrome oxidase, this variation can be used to differentiate among certain genera of bacteria. An oxidase detection test can be used to help identify members of the genera *Neisseria* and *Pseudomonas* and some species of *Bacillus*. Another variation in the cytochrome system is evident in certain bacteria (*Klebsiella, Enterobacter*) that can grow even in the presence of cyanide because they lack cytochrome oxidase. Cyanide will cause rapid death in humans and other eukaryotes because it blocks cytochrome oxidase, thereby completely terminating aerobic respiration, but it is harmless to these bacteria.

A potential side reaction of the respiratory chain in aerobic organisms is the incomplete reduction of oxygen to superoxide ion (O_2^-) and hydrogen peroxide (H_2O_2). As mentioned in chapter 7, these toxic oxygen products can be very damaging to cells. Aerobes have neutralizing enzymes to deal with these products, including *superoxide dismutase* and *catalase*. One exception is the genus *Streptococcus,* which can grow well in oxygen yet lacks both cytochromes and catalase. The tolerance of these organisms to oxygen can be explained by the neutralizing effects of a special peroxidase. The lack of cytochromes, catalase, and peroxidases in strict anaerobes as a rule limits their ability to process free oxygen and contributes to its toxic effects on them.

Summary of Aerobic Respiration

Reviewing the summary equation for respiration on page 232, we are now in a position to estimate the theoretical total of ATP molecules arising from a single glucose molecule through a combination of substrate-level phosphorylation and oxidation of NADH and FADH$_2$:

- There are 3 substrate-level reactions that give rise directly to ATP—2 in glycolysis and 1 in the Krebs cycle. Because these are happening **twice** for each event, they provide **6 ATPs** overall.
- There are **5 NADHs**—1 from glycolysis, 1 from pyruvic acid oxidation, and 3 from the Krebs cycle. Each NADH could potentially power the synthesis of 3 ATPs, yielding $5 \times 3 = 15$ ATPs. Again, this happens **twice for each glucose** and could generate **30 ATPs.**
- There is a single reaction in the Krebs cycle that yields FADH$_2$, which can power synthesis of 2 ATPs, and multiplied by 2 provides **4 ATPs.**
- The theoretical total for ATP synthesis could be $6 + 30 + 4 = 40$; however, because the first and second reactions of glycolysis use up 2 ATPs, the **final net number** is **38 ATPs.**

We emphasize that these totals are theoretical because the yields for NADH and FADH$_2$ are lower when the actual conditions in cells are taken into account. It is likely that oxidation of each NADH$^+$ provides closer to 2.5 ATPs and oxidation of FADH$_2$, about 1.75 ATPs. This will decrease the practical total to around **32 ATPs.** Another reason this total will be reduced for eukaryotic cells is that they must use active transport (and ATP) to carry the NADH from glycolysis into the mitochondrial cristae, bringing the total down to **30 ATPs** per glucose. Most prokaryotic cells probably produce even less ATP because they lack one or more of the carriers in the electron transport system or do not generate as much NADH. **Figure 8.22** charts the course of these calculations as they occur in the three phases of aerobic respiration.

No summary would be complete without considering three other key participants:

- Six carbon dioxide molecules are generated by reactions just prior to and during the Krebs cycle. These represent all of the carbons and oxygens from the original glucose molecule.

Pathways and Products

Net Output Summary**

Glycolysis	2 ATPs
	2 NADHs
	2 Pyruvic acids
Transition step	2 NADHs
	2 CO₂s
Krebs Cycle	4 CO₂s
	6 NADHs
	2 ATPs
	2 FADH₂s
Electron transport and Oxidative Phosphorylation	34 ATPs
	6 H₂Os

*These compounds are processed by the electron transport system.

**This net figure accounts for total ATPs minus the 2 used in glycolysis and the doubling of the products after the split into 2 3C compounds in glycolysis.

Figure 8.22 Summary of aerobic metabolism products and ATP yields. Compare this figure with the original equation on page 232.

- Six oxygen molecules are consumed during the final transfer of electrons and hydrogens to cytochrome oxidase a_3.
- Six water molecules are produced in electron transport and 2 in glycolysis, but because 2 are used in the Krebs cycle, this leaves a net number of 6.

Anaerobic Respiration

Some bacteria have evolved an anaerobic respiratory system that functions like the aerobic cytochrome system except that it utilizes oxygen-containing ions rather than free oxygen as the final electron acceptor. Of these, the nitrate (NO_3^-) and nitrite (NO_2^-) reduction systems are best known. The reaction in species such as *E. coli* is represented as follows:

$$\overset{\text{Nitrate reductase}}{NO_3^- + NADH + H^+ \longrightarrow NO_2^- + H_2O + NAD^+}$$

The enzyme nitrate reductase catalyzes the removal of oxygen from nitrate, leaving nitrite and water as products. This reac-

tion is the basis for a physiological test used in identifying certain bacteria.

Some species of *Pseudomonas* and *Bacillus* possess enzymes that can further reduce nitrite to nitric oxide (NO), nitrous oxide (N_2O), and even nitrogen gas (N_2). This process, called **denitrification,** is a very important step in recycling nitrogen in the biosphere. Other oxygen-containing nutrients reduced anaerobically by various bacteria are carbonates and sulfates.

Most obligate anaerobes use the NADH they generate during glycolysis and the Krebs cycle to reduce some compound other than O_2 but still use the oxidative phosphorylation pathway. Methanogens (described in chapter 7) reduce CO_2 or CO_3^- (carbonate) to CH_4 (methane gas), and certain sulfate bacteria reduce SO_4^{2-} to S (sulfide) or hydrogen sulfide gas (H_2S). Some use metals or organic compounds as the final electron acceptor. These microbes live in subterranean habitats such as swamps and deep oceanic vents that are devoid of O_2 gas.

 ## *Check Your Progress* SECTION 8.3

13. Describe the basic energy strategies of microbes and the catabolic pathways they use.
14. Compare and contrast the location of glycolysis, Krebs cycle, and electron transport in prokaryotic and eukaryotic cells.
15. Outline the basic steps in glycolysis, indicating where ATP is used and given off.
16. Where does NADH originate, and what is its fate in an aerobe?
17. What is the fate of NADH in a fermentative organism?
18. Why does the total of ATPs generated differ between bacteria and many eukaryotes?
19. Summarize the chemiosmotic theory of ATP formation.
20. How many ATPs could *theoretically* be formed from a glucose molecule carried through aerobic respiration, and how many are *probably* formed?
21. Name the sources of oxygen in bacteria that use anaerobic respiration.
22. What are the final electron acceptors in aerobic, anaerobic, and fermentative metabolism?
23. Describe the reaction between electrons, H^+, and oxygen at the final step of electron transport.

8.4 The Importance of Fermentation

Expected Learning Outcomes

19. Explain what is meant by the term fermentation and how it is used by natural biological systems and biotechnology.

20. Describe some of the processes of fermentation and the products that result.

Of all the results of pyruvate metabolism, probably the most varied is fermentation. Technically speaking, **fermentation*** is a

* *fermentation* (fur-men-tay'-shun) L. *fervere*, to boil, or *fermentatum*, leaven or yeast.

process that involves (1) the incomplete oxidation of glucose or other carbohydrates in the absence of oxygen, (2) the oxidation of NADH to NAD^+, which is essential to keeping glycolysis going, (3) the use of organic compounds as the terminal electron acceptors, and (4) the release of a small amount of ATP.

Over time, the term *fermentation* has acquired several looser meanings. Originally, Pasteur called the microbial action of yeast during wine production *ferments,* and to this day, biochemists use the term in reference to the production of ethyl alcohol by yeasts acting on glucose and other carbohydrates. Fermentation is traditionally what bacteriologists call the formation of acid, gas, and other products by the action of various bacteria on pyruvic acid. Industrial processes that produce chemicals on a massive scale through the actions of microbes are also called fermentations. Each of these usages is acceptable for one application or another.

It may seem that fermentation yielding only meager amounts of energy (2 ATPs maximum per glucose) would slow down growth. And yet the process is a common metabolic strategy among bacteria. What actually happens is that many bacteria can grow as fast as they would in the presence of oxygen. This rapid growth is made possible by an increase in the rate of glycolysis. From another standpoint, fermentation permits survival and growth in the absence of molecular oxygen and allows colonization of anaerobic environments. It also enables microorganisms with a versatile metabolism to adapt to variations in the availability of oxygen. For these facultative microbes, fermentation provides a means to function even when oxygen levels are too low for aerobic respiration or a suitable terminal electron acceptor is unavailable. An additional advantage of fermentation is that it generates a number of intermediates that can be used in anabolic pathways and shared with other nearby microbes.

Bacteria that digest cellulose in the rumens of cattle are largely fermentative. After initially hydrolyzing cellulose to glucose, they ferment the glucose to organic acids, which are then absorbed as the bovine's principal energy source. Even human muscle cells can undergo a form of fermentation that permits short periods of activity after the oxygen supply in the muscle has been exhausted. Muscle cells convert pyruvic acid into lactic acid, which allows anaerobic production of ATP to proceed for a time. But this cannot go on indefinitely, and after a few minutes, the accumulated lactic acid causes muscle fatigue.

Products of Fermentation in Microorganisms

Alcoholic beverages (wine, beer, whiskey) are perhaps the most prominent among fermentation products; others are solvents (acetone, butanol), organic acids (lactic, acetic), dairy products, and many other foods. Derivatives of proteins, nucleic acids, and other organic compounds are fermented to produce vitamins, antibiotics, and even hormones such as hydrocortisone.

Fermentation products can be grouped into two general categories: alcoholic fermentation products and acidic fermentation products **(figure 8.23)**. **Alcoholic fermentation** occurs in yeast or bacterial species that have metabolic pathways for converting pyruvic acid to ethanol. This process involves a decarboxylation of pyruvic acid to acetaldehyde, followed by a

Figure 8.23 The fermentation systems that produce acid and alcohol. In both cases, the final electron acceptor is an organic compound. In yeasts, pyruvic acid is decarboxylated to acetaldehyde, and the NADH given off in the glycolytic pathway reduces acetaldehyde to ethyl alcohol. In homolactic fermentative bacteria, pyruvic acid is reduced by NADH to lactic acid. Both systems regenerate NAD^+ to feed back into glycolysis or other cycles.

reduction of the acetaldehyde to ethanol. In oxidizing the NADH formed during glycolysis, NAD^+ is regenerated, thereby allowing the glycolytic pathway to continue. These processes are crucial in the production of beer and wine, though the actual techniques for arriving at the desired amount of ethanol and the prevention of unwanted side reactions are important tricks of the brewer's trade **(8.4 Making Connections)**. Note that the products of alcoholic fermentation include both ethanol *and* CO_2, a gas that accounts for the bubbles in champagne and beer and the rising of bread dough.

Alcohols other than ethanol can be produced during bacterial fermentation pathways. Certain clostridia produce butanol and isopropanol through a complex series of reactions. Although this process was once an important source of alcohols for industrial use, it has been largely replaced by a nonmicrobial petroleum process.

The pathways of **acidic fermentation** are extremely varied. Lactic acid bacteria ferment pyruvate in the same way that humans do—by reducing it to lactic acid. If the product of this fermentation is mainly lactic acid, as in certain species of *Streptococcus* and *Lactobacillus*, it is termed *homolactic*. The souring of milk is due largely to the production of this acid by bacteria. When glucose is fermented to a mixture of lactic acid, acetic acid, and carbon dioxide, as is the case with *Leuconostoc* and

8.4 MAKING CONNECTIONS

Pasteur and the Wine-to-Vinegar Connection

The microbiology of alcoholic fermentation was greatly clarified by Louis Pasteur after French winemakers hired him to uncover the causes of periodic spoilage in wines. Especially troublesome was the conversion of wine to vinegar and the resultant sour flavor. Up to that time, wine formation had been considered strictly a chemical process. After extensively studying beer making and wine grapes, Pasteur concluded that wine, both fine and not so fine, was the result of microbial action on the juices of the grape and that wine "disease" was caused by contaminating organisms that produced undesirable products such as acid. Although he did not know it at the time, the bacterial contaminants responsible for the acidity of the spoiled wines were likely to be *Acetobacter* or *Gluconobacter* introduced by the grapes, air, or wine-making apparatus. These common gram-negative genera further oxidized ethanol to acetic acid and are presently used in commercial vinegar production. The following formula shows how this is accomplished:

An analysis of wine shows that in addition to water and ethyl alcohol, it contains thousands of other chemical compounds (see "Wine chemistry" on Wikipedia). What does this tell you about the metabolism of yeasts during alcoholic fermentation? *Answer available at http://www.mhhe.com/talaro9*

$$ \underset{\text{Ethanol}}{H-\overset{\overset{\displaystyle H}{|}}{\underset{\underset{\displaystyle H}{|}}{C}}-\overset{\overset{\displaystyle H}{|}}{\underset{\underset{\displaystyle H}{|}}{C}}-OH} \xrightarrow{O_2} \underset{\text{Acetic acid}}{H-\overset{\overset{\displaystyle H}{|}}{\underset{\underset{\displaystyle H}{|}}{C}}-C\overset{\displaystyle O}{\underset{\displaystyle OH}{}} } + 2H_2O $$

Pasteur's far-reaching solution to the problem is still with us today—mild heating, or *pasteurization,* of the grape juice to destroy the contaminants, followed by inoculation of the juice with a pure yeast culture. The topic of pasteurization is explored further in chapter 11.

other species of *Lactobacillus,* the process is termed *heterolactic fermentation.*

Many members of the family Enterobacteriaceae (*Escherichia, Shigella,* and *Salmonella*) possess enzyme systems for converting pyruvic acid to several acids simultaneously **(figure 8.24). Mixed acid fermentation** produces a combination of acetic, lactic, succinic, and formic acids, and it lowers the pH of a medium to about 4.0. *Propionibacterium* produces primarily propionic acid, which gives the characteristic flavor to Swiss cheese while fermentation gas (CO_2) produces the holes. Some members also further decompose formic acid completely to carbon dioxide and hydrogen gases. Because enteric bacteria commonly occupy the intestine, this

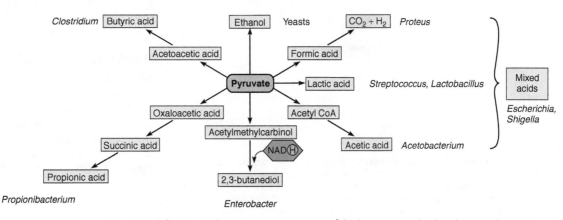

Figure 8.24 **Miscellaneous products of pyruvate fermentation and some of the bacteria involved in their production.**

fermentative activity accounts for the accumulation of some types of gas—primarily CO_2 and H_2—in the intestine. Some bacteria reduce the organic acids and produce the neutral end product 2,3-butanediol. Several of these end products are the basis of biochemical tests discussed in chapters 17 and 20.

We have provided only a brief survey of fermentation products, but it is worth noting that microbes can be harnessed to synthesize a variety of other substances by varying the raw materials provided them. In fact, so broad is the meaning of the word *fermentation* that the large-scale industrial syntheses by microorganisms are not technically fermentations and often utilize entirely different mechanisms from those described here. They even occur aerobically, particularly in antibiotic, hormone, vitamin, and amino acid production, but they still produce a useful biological product.

 Check Your Progress SECTION 8.4

24. What adaptive advantages does a fermentative metabolism confer on a microbe?
25. Describe three patterns of fermentation typical of microbes.

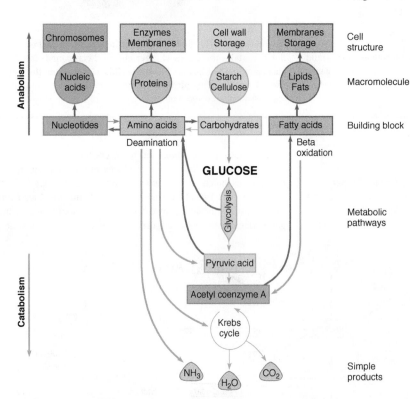

Figure 8.25 An amphibolic view of metabolism. Intermediate compounds such as pyruvic acid and acetyl coenzyme A serve multiple functions. With comparatively small modifications, these compounds can be converted into other compounds and enter a different pathway. Note that catabolism of glucose (center) furnishes numerous intermediates for anabolic pathways that synthesize amino acids, fats, nucleic acids, and carbohydrates. These building blocks can serve in further synthesis of larger molecules to construct various cell components.

8.5 Biosynthesis and the Crossing Pathways of Metabolism

 Expected Learning Outcomes

21. Explain how cells perform anabolic functions and what is involved in amphibolism.
22. Identify several pathways where molecules can be redirected or converted into useful cell products.
23. Briefly describe several mechanisms in biosynthesis of macromolecules.

Our discussion now turns from catabolism and energy extraction to anabolic functions and biosynthesis. In this section, we present aspects of intermediary metabolism, including amphibolic pathways, the synthesis of simple molecules, and the synthesis of macromolecules.

The Frugality of the Cell—Waste Not, Want Not

It must be obvious by now that cells have mechanisms for careful management of carbon compounds. Rather than being dead ends, most catabolic pathways contain strategic molecular intermediates (metabolites) that can be diverted into anabolic pathways. In this way, a given molecule can serve multiple purposes, and the maximum benefit can be derived from all nutrients and metabolites of the cell pool. The property of a system to integrate catabolic and anabolic pathways to improve cell efficiency is termed **amphibolism.***

At this point in the chapter, you can appreciate a more complex view of metabolism than that presented at the beginning figure 8.1. **Figure 8.25** demonstrates the amphibolic nature of intermediary metabolism. The pathways of glucose catabolism are an especially rich "metabolic marketplace." The principal sites of amphibolic interaction occur during glycolysis (glyceraldehyde-3-phosphate and pyruvic acid) and the Krebs cycle (acetyl coenzyme A and various organic acids).

Amphibolic Sources of Cellular Building Blocks

Glyceraldehyde-3-phosphate can be diverted away from glycolysis and converted into precursors for amino acid, carbohydrate, and triglyceride (fat) synthesis. (A precursor molecule is one that gives rise to a different compound.) Earlier, we noted the numerous

* *amphibolism* (am-fee-bol'-izm) Gr. *amphi*, two-sided, and *bole*, a throw.

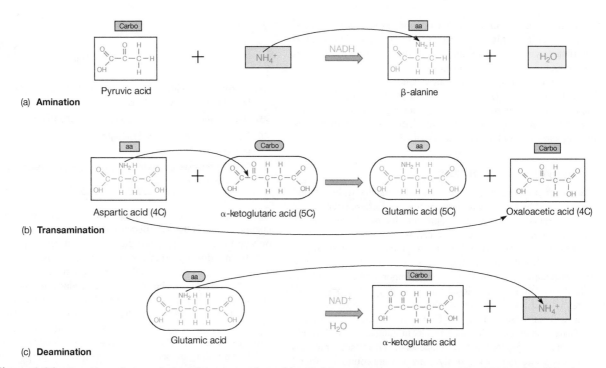

Figure 8.26 Reactions that produce and convert amino acids. All of the reactions require energy as ATP or NADH and specialized enzymes. **(a)** Through amination (the addition of an ammonium molecule [amino group]), a carbohydrate can be converted to an amino acid. **(b)** Through transamination (transfer of an amino group from an amino acid to a carbohydrate), metabolic intermediates can be converted to amino acids that are in low supply. **(c)** Through deamination (removal of an amino group), an amino acid can be converted to a useful intermediate of carbohydrate catabolism. This is how proteins are used to derive energy. Ammonium is one waste product. Note that carbohydrate structures are in brown and amino acids are in blue.

directions that pyruvic acid catabolism can take. In terms of synthesis, pyruvate also plays a pivotal role in providing intermediates for amino acids. In the event of an inadequate glucose supply, pyruvate serves as the starting point in glucose synthesis from various metabolic intermediates, a process called **gluconeogenesis.***

The acetyl group that starts the Krebs cycle is another extremely versatile metabolite that can be fed into a number of synthetic pathways. This 2-carbon fragment can be converted as a single unit into one of several amino acids, or a number of these fragments can be condensed into hydrocarbon chains that are important building blocks for fatty acid and lipid synthesis. Note that the reverse is also true: Fats can be degraded to acetyl and thereby enter the Krebs cycle via acetyl coenzyme A. This aerobic process, called **beta oxidation,** releases significant energy. Oxidation of a 6-carbon fatty acid with glycerol potentially yields 50 ATPs, compared with 38 for a 6-carbon sugar.

Two carbohydrate metabolites from the Krebs cycle are oxaloacetic acid and α-ketoglutaric acid—essential intermediates in the synthesis of certain amino acids. This occurs through **amination,** the addition of an amino group to a carbon skeleton **(figure 8.26a).** A certain core group of amino acids can then be used to synthesize others. Amino acids and carbohydrates can be interchanged through **transamination** as well **(figure 8.26b).**

Pathways that synthesize the nitrogen bases (purines, pyrimidines), which are components of DNA and RNA, originate in amino acids and so can be dependent on intermediates from the Krebs cycle as well. Because the coenzymes NAD^+, NADP, FAD, and others contain purines and pyrimidines similar to the nucleic acids, their synthetic pathways are also dependent on amino acids. During times of carbohydrate deprivation, organisms can likewise convert amino acids to intermediates of the Krebs cycle by **deamination** (removal of an amino group) and thereby derive energy from proteins. Deamination results in the formation of nitrogen waste products such as ammonium ions or urea **(figure 8.26c).**

Formation of Macromolecules

Monosaccharides, amino acids, fatty acids, nitrogen bases, and vitamins—the building blocks that make up the various macromolecules and organelles of the cell—come from two possible sources. They can enter the cell from the outside as nutrients, or they can be synthesized through various cellular pathways. The degree to which an organism can synthesize its own building blocks (simple molecules) is determined by its genetic makeup, a factor that varies tremendously from group to group. In chapter 7, you learned that autotrophs require only CO_2 as a carbon source, a few minerals to synthesize all cell substances, and no organic nutrients. Some heterotrophic organisms (*E. coli,* yeasts) are so metabolically complete that they can synthesize all cellular

* *gluconeogenesis* (gloo″-koh-nee″-oh-gen′-uh-sis) Literally, the formation of "new" glucose.

substances from minerals and one organic carbon source such as glucose. Compare this with a strict parasite lacking or having lost significant synthetic capabilities and having to obtain most essential nutrient molecules from its host.

Whatever their source, once these building blocks are added to the metabolic pool, they are available for synthesis of polymers by the cell. The details of synthesis vary among the types of macromolecules, but all of them involve the formation of bonds by specialized enzymes and the expenditure of ATP.

Carbohydrate Biosynthesis

The role of glucose in bioenergetics is so crucial that its biosynthesis is ensured by several alternative pathways. Certain structures in the cell depend on an adequate supply of glucose as well. It is the major component of the cellulose cell walls of some eukaryotes and of certain storage granules (starch, glycogen). One of the intermediaries in glycolysis, glucose-6-P, is used to form glycogen. Monosaccharides other than glucose are important in the synthesis of bacterial cell walls. Peptidoglycan contains a linked polymer of muramic acid and glucosamine. Fructose-6-P from glycolysis is used to form these two sugars. Carbohydrates (deoxyribose, ribose) are also essential building blocks in nucleic acids. Polysaccharides are the predominant components of cell surface structures such as capsules and the glycocalyx, and they are commonly found in slime layers (dextran). Remember that most polymerization reactions occur via loss of a water molecule (see figure 2.16) and the input of energy.

Assembly of the Cell

The component parts of a bacterial cell are being synthesized on a continuous basis, and catabolism is also taking place, as long as nutrients are present and the cell is in a nondormant state. When anabolism produces sufficient macromolecules, and when DNA replication produces duplicate copies of the cell's genetic material, the cell undergoes binary fission. The two new cells will need twice as many ribosomes, twice as many enzymes, and so on. The cell has created these during the initial anabolic phases we have described. Before cell division, the membrane(s) and the cell wall will have increased in size to create a cell that is almost twice as big as a "newborn" cell. Once synthesized, the phospholipid bilayer components of the membranes assemble themselves spontaneously, but proteins and other components must be added to the membranes. Growth of the cell wall, accomplished by the addition and coupling of sugars and peptides, requires energy input. The catabolic processes provide constant energy for these complex building reactions.

 Check Your Progress SECTION 8.5

26. What is meant by amphibolism, and what are its most important functions?
27. Identify major ways that amino acids are processed.
28. Which macromolecules are synthesized by specialized anabolic pathways?

8.6 Photosynthesis: The Earth's Lifeline

 Expected Learning Outcomes

24. Outline the general reactions of photosynthesis and the importance it holds for the energetics of life.
25. Describe the pigment systems and how they function.
26. Describe the main events in the light-dependent reactions and the products that result.
27. Describe the main events in the light-independent reactions and the products that result.

As mentioned earlier, the ultimate source of most of the chemical energy in cells is the sun. Because this source is directly available only to the cells of photosynthesizers, most organisms are either directly or indirectly dependent on photosynthesis, except for a few chemoautotrophs that derive their energy and nutrients solely from inorganic substrates. The other major products of photosynthesis are organic carbon compounds, which are produced from carbon dioxide through a process called carbon fixation. On land, green plants are the primary photosynthesizers; and in aquatic ecosystems, where 80% to 90% of all photosynthesis occurs, this role is filled by algae, cyanobacteria, and green sulfur, purple sulfur, and purple nonsulfur bacteria.

The summary equation for the main reactants and products of photosynthesis is

$$6CO_2 + 6H_2O \xrightarrow{\text{Light and pigment}} \underset{\text{Glucose}}{C_6H_{12}O_6} + 6O_2\uparrow$$

The anatomy of photosynthetic cells is adapted to trapping sunlight, and their physiology effectively uses this solar energy to produce high-energy glucose from low-energy CO_2 and water. Photosynthetic organisms achieve this remarkable feat through a series of reactions involving light, pigment, CO_2, and water, which is used as a source for electrons.

Photosynthesis proceeds in two phases: the **light-dependent reactions,** which proceed only in the presence of sunlight, and the **light-independent reactions,** which do not require direct exposure to light, but do require products of the light-dependent reactions in order to proceed **(figure 8.27).**

Solar energy is delivered in discrete energy packets called **photons** (also called quanta) that travel as waves. The wavelengths of light operating in photosynthesis occur in the visible spectrum between 400 nanometers (violet) and 700 nanometers (red) and above. As this light strikes photosynthetic pigments, some wavelengths are absorbed, some pass through, and some are reflected. The activity that has the greatest impact on photosynthesis is the absorbance of light by photosynthetic pigments. These include the **chlorophylls,** which are green; **carotenoids,** which are yellow, orange, or red; and **phycobilins,** which are red or blue-green.[3] By far the most important of these pigments are the chlorophylls, which contain a *photocenter* that consists of a magnesium atom held in the center of a

3. The color of the pigment corresponds to the wavelength of light it reflects.

membranes of compartments called **grana** (singular, granum) in chloroplasts (**figure 8.28, part 1**) and in thylakoid layers of the cell membranes of cyanobacteria (see figure 4.28c). These systems exist as two separate complexes called **photosystem I (PS700)** and **photosystem II (PS680)**[4] (**figure 8.28, part 4).**

Both systems contain chlorophyll, but their chlorophylls are sensitive to different wavelengths: PS I absorbs longer wavelengths (above 680 nm) and PS II absorbs shorter wavelengths (680 nm and below), which efficiently covers the range of light to which phototrophs are exposed. Both photosystems are stationed in **antennae**—clusters of about 300 molecules of chlorophyll located in the thylakoid membranes. Antennae absorb light and convey it to **reaction centers,** where the light-dependent reactions take place (figure 8.28, part 4).

The chloroplast is composed of separate compartments similar to mitochondria. One compartment—the **stroma**—is the region surrounding the thylakoids, and the other one is a space inside the thylakoids called the **lumen** (figure 8.28, part 4.).

Overview of the Light-Dependent Reactions and Photophosphorylation

The thylakoids are specially situated to bring together all components of the light-dependent reactions. Most of these components are embedded in the thylakoid membranes and are accessible from both the lumen and the stroma. They include chlorophyll molecules and their photosystems (PS II and PS I)[5]; an oxygen-evolving complex; electron transport systems—consisting of a mobile electron carrier plastoquinone (PQ); cytochrome b_f complex; plastocyanin (PC), a second mobile electron carrier; ferredoxin (Fd) with nicotinamide adenine dinucleotide phosphate ($NADP^+$) reductase (FNR); and ATP synthase. Several of the systems and their actions are very similar to those we previously examined in mitochondria.

The light-dependent pathway proceeds as follows:

PS II Reactions

1. When light strikes the magnesium in PS II, an electron becomes excited (is raised to a higher energy level) and is released by PS II to the first electron transport system.
2. An oxygen-evolving complex associated with PS II splits two water molecules into 4 electrons, 4 protons (H^+), and oxygen. Because it occurs in the presence of light, this step is termed **photolysis,** and it results in **the first major product** of the light-dependent reactions—the **O_2 gas** required by all aerobic organisms, including even most photosynthesizers. In addition, the electrons released by photolysis return the PS II complex to a ground state so it is again ready to respond to light. Another important effect of photolysis is the release of protons into the lumen, which contributes to the chemiosmotic proton gradient so essential to ATP synthesis.

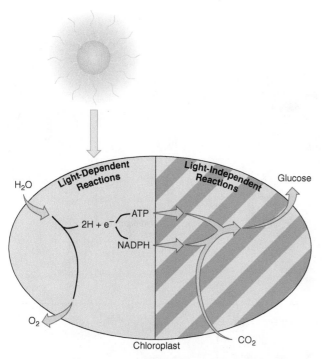

H_2O

Light-Dependent Reactions

Light-Independent Reactions

Glucose

$2H + e^-$

ATP

NADPH

O_2

CO_2

Chloroplast

Figure 8.27 Overview of photosynthesis. The general reactions of photosynthesis, divided into two phases called light-dependent reactions and light-independent reactions. The light-dependent reactions involve two major events: (1) the trapping of light with a photosensitive pigment, such as chlorophyll, and converting the light energy into chemical energy in the form of ATP and NADPH; and (2) the splitting of water molecules with the release of oxygen gas. The light-independent reactions utilize ATP and NADPH produced during the light-dependent reactions to fix CO_2 into organic compounds such as glucose.

complex ringed molecule called a *porphyrin* (**figure 8.28, part 3**). As we will see, the chlorophyll molecule harvests the energy of photons and converts it to electron (chemical) energy. Accessory photosynthetic pigments such as carotenes trap light energy and shuttle it to chlorophyll, thereby functioning like antennae. These light-dependent reactions are responsible for **photophosphorylation,** the channeling of energy extracted from light to make high-energy bonds of ATP. This sets the scene for the light-independent reactions, which use both ATP and NADPH for synthesis. During this phase, carbon atoms from CO_2 are fixed to the carbon backbones of organic molecules.

The detailed biochemistry of photosynthesis is beyond the scope of this text, but we will provide an overview of the general process as it occurs in green plants, algae and cyanobacteria. It is worth noting that many of the basic activities are biochemically similar to certain pathways of aerobic metabolism.

Light-Dependent Reactions

The systems that carry the photosynthetic pigments are also the sites for the light-dependent reactions. They occur in the **thylakoid**

4. The numbers refer to the wavelength of light to which each system is most sensitive.
5. These numbers signify the order in which they were discovered, not the order of reactivity.

🔁 **Process Figure 8.28 The location and participants in the light-dependent reactions of a chloroplast. (1)** A cell of the algae, *Chlamydomonas*, with a single chloroplast—a cutaway view to show the internal structure of stroma and grana. **(2)** A granum consists of a stack of hollow membrane-bound discs called thylakoids, which house the chlorophylls **(3)**, arranged in arrays (antennae) for capturing light. **(4)** The chlorophylls exist in separate systems called PS II and PS I, embedded in the thylakoid membrane. Other players in the process are an electron transport chain, an oxygen-evolving complex, a final electron acceptor ($NADP^+$), and ATP synthase. The text covers the main mechanisms of this process.

Quick Search

Search the internet for videos referencing: "Photosynthesis Light Reactions."

Electron Transport

1. The electron given off by PS II is picked up by the first compound of the electron transport chain—PQ—which moves it to the cytochrome b_f complex. From here, it is transported to plastocyanin and to the PS I complex.
2. An event coupled to electron transport is the delivery of protons (H^+) from the stroma side to the lumen side by the actions of the cytochrome b_f complex, which helps maintain the electrochemical gradient between the stroma and lumen.

PS I Reactions

1. When PS I is excited by light, it also releases an electron that will be transported through a different series of carriers. It also receives the electrons from PS II carried by plastocyanin.
2. These electrons are shuttled to the final electron acceptors, ferredoxin and the FNR complex. The function of the FNR is to transfer 2 electrons (and 2 protons) to $NADP^+$, converting it to **NADPH.** This is the **second major product** of the light-dependent reactions, one which provides reducing power for the light-independent reactions.

ATP Synthase and Photophosphorylation ATP synthase complexes are distributed throughout the thylakoid membranes. They have the same structure as those of mitochondria and they, too, capture the free energy inherent in the proton motive force to synthesize ATP. As protons flow through the F_0 portion of the synthase from the lumen to the stroma, the F_1 component pulls in ADP and P_i, releasing ATP, the **third major product** of the light reactions. You may notice that the energy-associated molecules (NADPH and ATP) are released in the stroma, which situates them for immediate use in the light-independent reactions covered in the next section.

Light-Independent Reactions

The anabolic reactions of photosynthesis occur in the stroma of a chloroplast or the cytoplasm of cyanobacteria. These reactions use energy produced by the light phase to synthesize glucose by means of the Calvin cycle (**figure 8.29**).

The cycle begins at the point where CO_2 is combined with a 5-carbon acceptor molecule with two terminal phosphates called

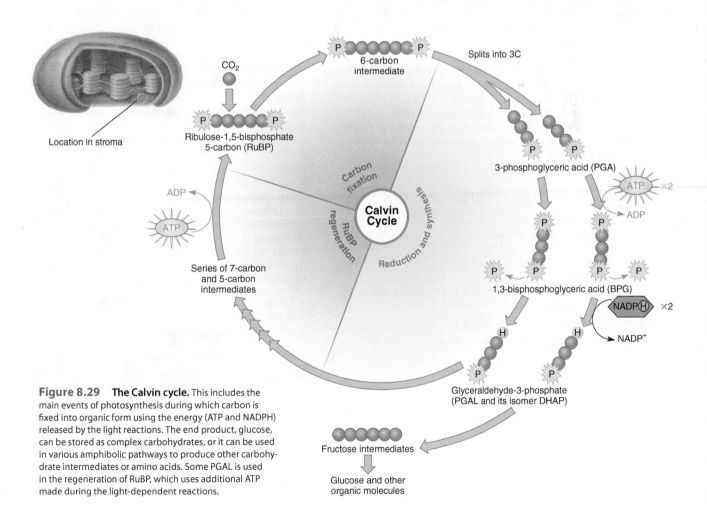

Figure 8.29 The Calvin cycle. This includes the main events of photosynthesis during which carbon is fixed into organic form using the energy (ATP and NADPH) released by the light reactions. The end product, glucose, can be stored as complex carbohydrates, or it can be used in various amphibolic pathways to produce other carbohydrate intermediates or amino acids. Some PGAL is used in the regeneration of RuBP, which uses additional ATP made during the light-dependent reactions.

ribulose-1,5-bisphosphate (**RuBP**). This process, called **carbon fixation,** generates a 6-carbon intermediate compound that immediately splits into two 3-carbon molecules of 3-phosphoglyceric acid (PGA). The subsequent steps use ATP and NADPH generated by the photosystems to form high-energy intermediates. First, 2 ATPs are expended to add a second phosphate to 3-PGA, producing two molecules of 1,3-bisphosphoglyceric acid (BPG). This is followed by NADPH contributing its electrons to BPG with the removal of one high-energy phosphate. These events give rise to two glyceraldehyde-3-phosphate (G3P). This molecule and its isomer dihydroxyacetone phosphate (DHAP) are key compounds in hexose synthesis leading to fructose and glucose. Some of the G3P is conveyed to the remainder of the cycle, where it participates in the regeneration of RuBP. This involves numerous steps not depicted in figure 8.29. You may notice that this pathway is very similar to glycolysis, except that it runs in reverse (see figure 8.17).

Other Mechanisms of Photosynthesis

The **oxygenic,** or oxygen-releasing, photosynthesis that occurs in plants, algae, and cyanobacteria is the dominant type on the earth. Other photosynthesizers such as green and purple sulfur bacteria possess bacteriochlorophyll, which is more versatile in capturing light. They have only a cyclic photosystem I, which routes the electrons from the photocenter to the electron carriers and back to the photosystem again. This pathway generates a relatively small amount of ATP, and it may not produce NADPH. As photolithotrophs, these bacteria use H_2, H_2S, or elemental sulfur rather than H_2O as a source of electrons and reducing power. As a consequence, they are **anoxygenic** (non-oxygen-producing), and many are strict anaerobes.

 Check Your Progress SECTION 8.6

29. Indicate whether each of the following is produced during the light-independent or light-dependent reactions of photosynthesis: O_2, ATP, NADPH, and glucose.
30. During which reactions are water and CO_2 consumed, and what is the outcome?
31. What are the functions of chlorophyll and the photosystems?
32. What are the fates of the ATP and NADH?
33. Compare oxygenic with nonoxygenic photosynthesis.

 CASE STUDY Part 2

Results of the tests were positive for the bacterium *Clostridium botulinum** type A, as well as its toxin, botulinum.* This finding, along with the symptoms, clearly confirmed the cases as botulism. Although the pathogen is quite sensitive to acid, the addition of water and other pH-neutral substances to the fruit-potato mixture probably maintained a low enough acid content to allow germination of *Clostridium* endospores and growth of its vegetative cells.

Botulinum neurotoxin is a complex protein molecule described as an AB toxin that consists of two functional parts (look ahead to chapter 13). It is transported in the bloodstream and carried to motor neurons in the muscles. One part of the toxin molecule (A) attaches to the membrane of the nerve cell

Molecule of botulinum toxin

and is transferred into the interior of the cell along with an enzyme component (B). B is a protease that hydrolyzes key secretory proteins, thereby blocking the release of a neurotransmitter (acetylcholine) from secretory vesicles. This blockade prevents the muscle from receiving a chemical stimulus necessary for contraction. The result is the paralysis of many large muscles, including those of the jaw, skeleton, eyes, neck, and diaphragm.

All together, eight prisoners developed botulism, several with severe morbidity and breathing problems. The only effective treatment for botulism is antitoxin, a serum which contains antibodies that attach to the toxin and inactivate it. To be most effective, it must be given early on. Four inmates required prolonged hospitalization and continued to have residual neurological and muscular symptoms for several months, but there were no fatalities. In the past, botulism was often a death sentence because it caused respiratory failure, but modern medical care and use of mechanical ventilation have greatly improved survival. This toxin, also available as Botox, is currently used in therapy for a wide variety of muscular disorders and, of course, for temporary elimination of wrinkles.

- Why must the antitoxin be administered in the earliest phases of botulism?

- How could the inmates have prevented making such a toxic brew?

To conclude this Case Study, go to Perspectives on the Connect website.

See chapter 19 for complete coverage of botulism.

* *Clostridium botulinum* (klawss-trih'-dee-um bawt"-yoo-ly'-num) Gr. *kloster*, spindle, and *idion*, of a shape; L. *botulus*, sausage, and *ismus*, the result of.
* *botulinum* This toxin is one of the most potent chemical compounds on earth.

 Chapter Summary with Key Terms

8.1 The Metabolism of Microbes
 A. *Metabolism*
 1. Metabolism is the sum of cellular chemical and physical activities; it involves chemical changes to reactants and the release of products using well-established pathways.
 2. Metabolism is a complementary process consisting of **anabolism,** synthetic reactions that convert small molecules into large molecules, and **catabolism,** in which large molecules are degraded. Together, they generate thousands of intermediate molecular states, called metabolites, which are regulated at many levels.
 B. *Enzymes: Metabolic Catalysts*
 1. Metabolism is made possible by organic **catalysts,** or **enzymes,** that speed up reactions by lowering the **energy of activation.** Enzymes are not consumed and can be reused. Each enzyme acts specifically upon its matching molecule or **substrate.**
 2. *Enzyme Structure:* A conjugated enzyme consists of a protein component called the **apoenzyme** and one or more activators called **cofactors.**
 3. *Enzyme Specificity:* Substrate attachment occurs in the special pocket called the **active,** or **catalytic, site.** In order to fit, a substrate must conform to the active site of the enzyme. This three-dimensional state is determined by the shape of the apoenzyme, making enzymes **substrate-specific.**
 4. *Cofactors:* Metallic cofactors impart greater reactivity to the enzyme-substrate complex. **Coenzymes** such as **NAD$^+$** (nicotinamide adenine dinucleotide) are transfer agents that pass functional groups from one substrate to another. Coenzymes usually contain **vitamins.**
 5. *Enzyme Classification:* Enzyme names often consist of a prefix derived from the type of reaction or the substrate and the ending *-ase.*
 6. *Microbial Enzymes and Disease:* Many pathogens secrete enzymes or toxins, which are referred to as virulence factors, that enable them to avoid host defenses.
 7. *Types of Enzyme Function:* The release of water that comes with formation of new covalent bonds is a **condensation** reaction. **Hydrolysis** reactions involve addition of water to break bonds. Functional groups may be added, removed, or traded in many reactions. Coupled **redox reactions** transfer electrons and protons (H$^+$) from one substrate to another.
 8. *Enzyme Sensitivity:* Enzymes are **labile** (unstable) and function only within narrow operating ranges of temperature, osmotic pressure, and pH; extreme conditions can cause **denaturation.** Enzymes are frequently the targets for physical and chemical agents used in control.
 C. *Regulation of Enzymatic Activity*
 Regulatory controls can act on enzymes directly or on the process that gives rise to the enzymes.
 1. A substance that resembles the normal substrate and can occupy the same active site is said to exert **competitive inhibition.**
 2. **Allosteric inhibition** occurs when a substance binds to a regulatory site and prevents substrate binding.
 3. **Noncompetitive inhibition** occurs when the regulator molecule binds the enzyme-substrate complex and keeps a product from being formed.

 3. The mechanisms of **enzyme repression** and **enzyme induction** exert control at the genetic level by controlling the synthesis of key enzymes.

8.2 The Pursuit and Utilization of Energy
 A. *Cell Energetics*
 Energy is the capacity of a system to perform work. It is consumed in **endergonic reactions** and is released in **exergonic reactions.**
 B. *A Closer Look at Biological Oxidation and Reduction*
 1. Extracting energy requires a series of electron carriers arrayed in a downhill redox chain between electron donors and electron acceptors.
 2. NAD$^+$ is the primary carrier of electrons from one pathway to another.
 3. In **substrate-level** and **oxidative phosphorylation,** energy is transferred to high-energy compounds such as ATP.

8.3 Pathways of Bioenergetics
 A. *Pathways in Aerobic Respiration.*
 These use oxygen as a final electron acceptor and glucose as the electron and energy source. The three pathways involved are glycolysis, the Krebs cycle, and electron transport.
 1. **Glycolysis** is a pathway that degrades glucose to **pyruvic acid** without requiring oxygen.
 2. Pyruvic acid is an important key molecule in several pathways.
 B. *Fate of Pyruvic Acid in Krebs Cycle and Electron Transport*
 1. Pyruvic acid is completely metabolized via the **Krebs cycle** and its associated electron transport chain.
 2. Acetyl coenzyme A is the initial product of pyruvic acid processing that undergoes further oxidation and decarboxylation in the Krebs cycle and generates ATP, CO$_2$, and H$_2$O.
 3. The respiratory chain carries electrons that support final energy extraction.
 4. The chemiosmotic theory and **proton motive force** are conceptual models that explain the origin and maintenance of electropotential gradients across a membrane that leads to ATP synthesis by **ATP synthase.**
 5. The final electron acceptor in aerobic respiration is oxygen. In **anaerobic respiration,** compounds such as sulfate, nitrate, or nitrite serve this function. Bacteria serve as important agents in the nitrogen cycle (**denitrification**).
 6. The phosphogluconate pathway is an alternative anaerobic pathway.

8.4 The Importance of Fermentation
 A. **Fermentation** is based on the glycolysis pathway in which both the electron donor and final electron acceptors are organic compounds. It is an essential source of NAD$^+$ required for electron transport.
 B. Fermentation enables anaerobic and facultative microbes to survive in environments devoid of oxygen. Production of alcohol, vinegar, and certain industrial solvents relies upon fermentation.

8.5 Biosynthesis and the Crossing Pathways of Metabolism
 A. *Amphibolism*
 The ability of a cell or system to integrate catabolic and anabolic pathways to improve efficiency is called **amphibolism.**

252 **Chapter 8** An Introduction to Microbial Metabolism

B. *Anabolism: Formation of Macromolecules*
Macromolecules, such as proteins, carbohydrates, and nucleic acids, are made of building blocks from two possible sources: from outside the cell (preformed) or via synthesis in one of the anabolic pathways.

C. *Versatility of Glycolysis and Krebs Cycle*
Glycolysis and the Krebs cycle are central pathways that link catabolic and anabolic pathways, allowing cells to break down different classes of molecules in order to synthesize compounds required by the cell.
1. Metabolites of these pathways double as building blocks and sources of energy. Intermediates such as pyruvic acid are convertible into amino acids through **amination.** Amino acids can be **deaminated** and used as a source of glucose and other carbohydrates (**gluconeogenesis**).
2. Two-carbon acetyl molecules from pyruvate **decarboxylation** can be used in fatty acid synthesis.

8.6 Photosynthesis: The Earth's Lifeline
Photosynthesis takes place in two stages—**light-dependent** and **light-independent reactions.**

A. During the light-dependent reactions, **photons** of solar energy are absorbed by **chlorophyll** and other pigments in **thylakoid** membranes of **chloroplast grana** in eukaryotes and the cell membrane in cyanobacteria. Light energy is captured by two photosystems (**PS II** and **PS I**), and water is split by **photolysis.** This releases oxygen gas. The light energy harvested by photosystems becomes the chemical energy of electrons; electron transport energy is stored in NADPH and ATP; ATP is formed through **photophosphorylation** and chemiosmosis. Light energy is used to synthesize ATP and NADPH.

B. The **Calvin cycle** (light-independent) occurs in the **stroma** of chloroplasts and uses ATP to **fix** carbon dioxide to a carrier molecule, ribulose-1,5-bisphosphate, and convert it to glucose in a multistep process.

C. The type of photosynthesis commonly found in plants, algae, and cyanobacteria is called **oxygenic** because it liberates molecular oxygen as a by-product of the light-dependent reactions. **Anoxygenic** photosynthesis occurs in photolithotrophs, which do not produce oxygen.

Level I. Knowledge and Comprehension

These questions require a working knowledge of the concepts in the chapter and the ability to recall and understand the information you have studied.

 Multiple-Choice Questions

Select the correct answer from the answers provided. For questions with blanks, choose the combination of answers that most accurately completes the statement.

1. _____ is another term for biosynthesis.
 a. Catabolism c. Metabolism
 b. Anabolism d. Catalyst

2. Catabolism is a form of metabolism in which _____ molecules are converted into _____ molecules.
 a. large, small c. amino acid, protein
 b. small, large d. food, storage

3. An enzyme _____ the activation energy required for a chemical reaction.
 a. increases c. lowers
 b. converts d. catalyzes

4. An enzyme
 a. becomes part of the final products
 b. is nonspecific for substrate
 c. is consumed by the reaction
 d. is heat and pH labile

5. An apoenzyme is where the _____ is located.
 a. cofactor c. redox reaction
 b. coenzyme d. active site

6. Many coenzymes are
 a. metals c. proteins
 b. vitamins d. substrates

7. To digest cellulose in its environment, a fungus produces a/an
 a. endoenzyme c. catalase
 b. exoenzyme d. polymerase

8. Energy in biological systems is primarily
 a. electrical c. radiant
 b. chemical d. mechanical

9. Energy is carried from catabolic to anabolic reactions in the form of _____.
 a. ADP c. coenzymes
 b. high-energy ATP bonds d. inorganic phosphate

10. Exergonic reactions
 a. release potential energy c. form bonds
 b. consume energy d. occur only outside the cell

11. A reduced compound is
 a. NAD^+ c. NADH
 b. FAD d. ADP

12. Most oxidation reactions in microbial bioenergetics involve the
 a. removal of electrons and hydrogens
 b. addition of electrons and hydrogens
 c. addition of oxygen
 d. removal of oxygen

13. A product or products of glycolysis is/are
 a. ATP c. CO_2
 b. pyruvic acid d. both a and b

14. Fermentation of a glucose molecule has the potential to produce a net number of _____ ATPs.
 a. 4 c. 38
 b. 2 d. 32

15. Complete oxidation of glucose in aerobic respiration by a eukaryote could potentially yield a net maximum output of _____ ATPs.
 a. 40
 b. 30
 c. 38
 d. 2

16. The compound that enters the Krebs cycle is
 a. citric acid
 b. oxaloacetic acid
 c. pyruvic acid
 d. acetyl coenzyme A

17. The $FADH_2$ formed during the Krebs cycle enters the electron transport system at which site?
 a. NADH dehydrogenase
 b. complex II
 c. complex IV
 d. ATP synthase

18. The proton motive force is the result of
 a. ATP synthase transporting protons during ATP synthesis
 b. an electron gradient between the matrix and the intermembrane space of a mitochondrion
 c. a proton gradient between the matrix and intermembrane space of a mitochondrion
 d. a buildup of negatively charged ions

19. Photosynthetic organisms convert the energy of _____ into chemical energy.
 a. electrons
 b. protons
 c. photons
 d. hydrogen atoms

20. The Calvin cycle operates during which part of photosynthesis?
 a. only the light-dependent phase
 b. only in the dark
 c. the light-independent phase
 d. only during photosystem I

21. The oxygen produced by photosynthesis comes from:
 a. CO_2
 b. NO_3
 c. H_2O
 d. glucose

22. **Multiple Matching.** Match the process a, b, or c with the metabolic events in the list.
 a. glycolysis
 b. Krebs cycle
 c. electron transport/oxidative phosphorylation
 _____ H^+ and e^- are delivered to O_2 as the final acceptor.
 _____ Pyruvic acid is formed.
 _____ ATP is formed.
 _____ H_2O is produced.
 _____ CO_2 is formed.
 _____ Fructose diphosphate is split into two 3-carbon fragments.
 _____ NADH is oxidized.
 _____ ATP synthase is active.

 Case Study Review

1. What is the most likely source of the botulism bacteria that grew in the prison wine?
 a. fruit
 b. air
 c. potato
 d. sugar

2. Could other inmates develop botulism from being in contact with the ill prisoners?
 a. Yes, it can be spread in body fluids.
 b. No, a person must ingest the toxin.
 c. Yes, it can be carried by inanimate objects.
 d. No, *C. botulinum* bacteria cannot grow in human tissue.

3. Describe the conditions of nutrition, pH, temperature, oxygen, and life cycle that made it possible for both the yeast and *Clostridium* to grow and synthesize their products in the pruno mixture.

 Writing Challenge

For each question, compose a one- or two-paragraph answer that includes the factual information needed to completely address the question. Check Your Progress questions can also be used for writing-challenge exercises.

1. Discuss the relationship of
 a. anabolism to catabolism
 b. ATP to ADP
 c. glycolysis to fermentation
 d. electron transport to oxidative phosphorylation

2. Give the general name of the enzyme that
 a. converts citrate to isocitrate
 b. reduces pyruvic acid to lactic acid
 c. reduces nitrate to nitrite

3. What is unique about the actions of ATP synthase?

4. Compare the general equation for aerobic metabolism (page 232) with the summary of aerobic metabolism (figure 8.22), verify the final totals of reactants and products, and indicate where they occur in the pathways.

5. Describe four requirements required for fermentation to take place.

6. Is fermentation catabolic or anabolic? Explain your choice.

7. What would be the expected pHs of the matrix and intermembrane space of the mitochondrion? What about the stroma and thylakoid lumen of the chloroplast? Explain your answer.

8. Explain the similarities and differences between anaerobic respiration and fermentation.

254 **Chapter 8** An Introduction to Microbial Metabolism

 Concept Mapping

An Introduction to Concept Mapping found at http://www.mhhe.com/talaro9 provides guidance for working with concept maps.

1. Supply your own linking words or phrases in this concept map, and provide the missing concepts in the empty box.

Level II. Application, Analysis, Evaluation, and Synthesis

These problems go beyond just restating facts and require higher levels of understanding and an ability to interpret, problem solve, transfer knowledge to new situations, create models, and predict outcomes.

 Critical Thinking

Critical thinking is the ability to reason and solve problems using facts and concepts. These questions can be approached from a number of angles, and in most cases, they do not have a single correct answer.

1. Use the following graph to diagram the energetics of a chemical reaction, with and without an enzyme. Be sure to position reactants and products at appropriate points and to indicate the stages in the reaction and the energy levels.

2. Explain what is meant by the "biochemical circle of life" that exists between phototrophs and heterotrophs.

3. Explain how it is possible for certain microbes to survive and grow in the presence of cyanide, which would kill many other organisms.

4. Suggest the advantages of having metabolic pathways staged in specific membrane or organelle locations rather than being free in the cytoplasm.

5. Two steps in glycolysis are catalyzed by allosteric enzymes. These are: (1) step 2, catabolized by phosphoglucoisomerase, and (2) step 9, catabolized by pyruvate kinase. Suggest what metabolic products might regulate these enzymes. How might one place these regulators in figure 8.17?

6. Why would the Krebs cycle require oxygen?

7. Beer production requires an early period of rapid aerobic metabolism of glucose by yeast. Given that anaerobic conditions are necessary to produce alcohol, can you explain why this step is necessary?

8. Where in the mitochondrion and chloroplast do the ATP molecules collect after being made by ATP synthases, and what is the advantage of this?

9. Explain the relationship between enzyme sensitivity and the adaptations microbes make to their environments.

10. a. Where are botulism spores normally found?
　　b. Why wouldn't antibiotics work as therapy for botulism?

Visual Challenge

1. From **chapter 7, figure 7.12.** Describe the likely metabolic strategies of the microbes growing in tubes 1 through 4. Specify the pathways, final electron acceptor, and end products.

2. Look at the two figure parts (a) and (b) from figure 8.8, and explain what processes are depicted and what the results of the reactions will be.

(a)

(b)

CHAPTER **9** # An Introduction to Microbial Genetics

Plasmid—a circular snippet of DNA carrying genetic treasures.

Acinetobacter—tiny nonmotile gram-negative bacilli, coming to a hospital in your neighborhood?

A mating "dance" between cells connected by conjugation pili.

 CASE STUDY Part 1 At War with an Emerging Pathogen

A 55-year-old woman recovering from a **lung transplant** surgery developed a case of **pneumonia** from a ventilator she needed for breathing. The bacteria isolated from her lungs were identified as ***Acinetobacter baumannii,*** a widespread resident of soil and water that has found its way into hospitals and long-term care facilities. Tests showed that all of the drugs available to treat the infection were ineffective against the pathogen—except for **colistin.** Early on, the drug appeared to be curing the infection, but after a few days, it returned and the patient died of respiratory failure. Cultures taken late in the case detected a **new strain** of the infectious agent that had developed **resistance** to all known drugs, including colistin.

During the same period, several other patients in the ICU developed drug-resistant *A. baumannii* infections. This sudden outbreak of **nosocomial infections** spurred an investigation by an infection control nurse, who took samples from multiple locations and cultured them. The **bacteria** were **isolated** from **nearly every possible source,** including medical devices, patient skin samples, bedding, hospital workers, the air, and room surfaces.

> "Over time, so many soldiers suffered battlefield-related infections by this ubiquitous pathogen that it was given the nickname 'Iraqnobacter.'"

But problems with *A. baumannii* were not restricted to North America. A continent away in Iraq and Afghanistan, this same microbe became one of the most **fearsome pathogens** to infect soldiers with **battle injuries.** In one case, a 55-year-old man sustained a grenade injury while transporting soldiers. Shrapnel penetrated his thigh and fractured the femur. When X rays revealed the presence of an **infection** in his broken bone, he was transported to a trauma hospital. Cultures of the **wound** isolated a **gram-negative coccobacillus** identified as *Acinetobacter baumannii.* Testing indicated that it was **resistant to all drugs** except for a new type of drug called **tigecycline.** After a several weeks' course of tigecycline, the infection was resolved and the patient was released. Over time, so many soldiers suffered battlefield-related infections by this ubiquitous pathogen that it was given the nickname "Iraqnobacter."

▶ *What are the probable origins of the pathogen, and what is meant by the term nosocomial?*

▶ *What does drug resistance mean from a genetic standpoint?*

To continue the Case Study, go to page 288.

9.1　Introduction to Genetics and Genes: Unlocking the Secrets of Heredity

 Expected Learning Outcomes

1. Define *heredity, genetics, genome, gene, phenotype,* and *genotype.*
2. Discuss the basic nature of genetic material in eukaryotes, prokaryotes, and viruses.
3. Explain how DNA is organized and packaged.
4. Describe the chemical structure of DNA and its significance.
5. List the nitrogen bases and explain their bonding patterns.
6. Describe the process of DNA replication as it occurs in prokaryotic cells.

Genetics is the science that studies the inheritance of biological characteristics by living things. This subject, also known as heredity, is a wide-ranging science that examines:

- the transmission of biological properties (traits) from parent to offspring,
- the expression and variation of those traits,
- the structure and function of the genetic material, and
- how this material changes or evolves.

The study of genetics takes place on several levels **(figure 9.1).** Organismal genetics observes the transmission and expression of genetic factors in the whole organism or cell; chromosomal genetics examines the characteristics and actions of chromosomes; and molecular genetics deals with the biochemistry of gene function. All of these levels provide insight into microbial structure, physiology, evolution, and pathogenicity. It should also be noted that the study of microbial genetics will emphasize universal themes in the genetics of all organisms, and it will increase appreciation for the astounding advances in genetic engineering covered in chapter 10.

The Nature of the Genetic Material

Deoxyribonucleic acid or **DNA** is the central molecule of genetics, so it is essential that you develop a working knowledge of its characteristics to understand a broad range of genetic principles. With this in mind, we will use the first section of this chapter to lay some groundwork on DNA organization, structure, and duplication. This will be followed by coverage of related concepts such as RNA and protein synthesis, genetic control, mutations, and genetic transfers in the remaining five sections.

The Levels of Structure and Function of the Genome

The **genome** is the sum total of genetic material carried within a cell. Although most of the genome exists in the form of chromosomes, genetic material can appear in nonchromosomal sites as well **(figure 9.2).** For example, bacteria and some fungi contain tiny extra pieces of DNA **(plasmids),** and the mitochondria and chloroplasts of eukaryotes are equipped with their own functional chromosomes. Genomes of cells are composed exclusively of DNA, but viruses contain either DNA or RNA as the principal genetic material. Although the specific genome of an individual organism is unique, the general pattern of nucleic acid structure and function is similar among all organisms and viruses.

In general, a **chromosome** is a discrete cellular structure composed of a neatly packaged DNA molecule. The chromosomes of eukaryotes and bacterial cells differ in several respects. The structure of eukaryotic chromosomes consists of a DNA molecule tightly wound around histone proteins, whereas a bacterial chromosome is condensed and secured into a packet by means of a different type of protein. Eukaryotic chromosomes are located in the nucleus; they vary in number from a few to hundreds; they can occur in pairs (diploid) or singles (haploid); and they are linear in format. In contrast, most bacteria have a single, circular chromosome, although some have multiple chromosomes and a few have linear chromosomes.

All chromosomes contain a series of basic informational "packets" called genes. A **gene** can be defined from more than one perspective. In classical genetics, the term refers to the fundamental

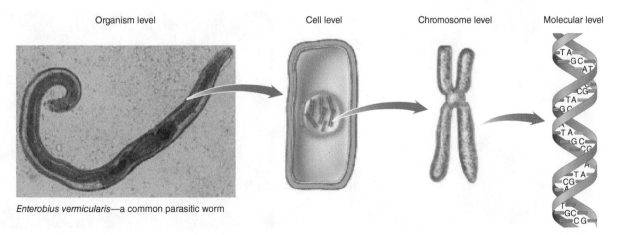

Organism level　　　Cell level　　　Chromosome level　　　Molecular level

Enterobius vermicularis—a common parasitic worm

Figure 9.1　Levels of genetic study. Genetic processes can be observed at the levels of organism, cell, chromosome, and DNA sequence (molecular level). Although levels shown here are for a eukaryotic organism they would follow a similar pattern in prokaryotes.

unit of heredity responsible for a given trait in an organism. In the molecular and biochemical sense, it is a portion of the chromosome that provides information for a given cell function. More specifically still, it is a specific segment of DNA that contains the necessary codes to make a **protein** or RNA molecule. This last definition of a gene is emphasized in this chapter.

Genes fall into three basic categories: *structural genes* that code for proteins, genes that code for RNA, and *regulatory genes* that control gene expression. The sum of all of these types of genes constitutes an organism's distinctive genetic makeup, or **genotype.*** The expression of the genotype creates traits (certain structures or functions) referred to as the **phenotype.*** For example a person inherits a combination of genes (genotype) that gives a certain eye color or height (phenotype), a bacterium inherits genes that direct the formation of a flagellum or the ability to metabolize a certain substrate, and a virus has genes that dictate its capsid structure. All organisms contain more genes in their genotypes than are being seen as a phenotype at any given time. In other words, the phenotype can change depending on which genes are "turned on" or expressed.

The Size and Packaging of Genomes

Genomes vary greatly in size. Viruses have anywhere from a few to over a thousand genes; the bacterium *Escherichia coli* has a single chromosome containing 4,288 genes, and a human cell packs about five times that many into 46 chromosomes. The chromosome of *E. coli* would measure about 1 mm if unwound and stretched out linearly, and yet this fits within a cell that measures just over 1 μm across, making the stretched-out DNA 1,000 times longer than the cell (**figure 9.3**). Still, the bacterial chromosome takes up only about one-third to one-half of the cell's volume. Likewise, if the sum of all DNA contained in the 46 human chromosomes were unraveled and laid end to end, it would measure about 6 feet. How can such elongated genomes fit into the minuscule volume of a cell and, in the case of eukaryotes, into an even smaller compartment, the nucleus? The answer lies in the complex coiling of the DNA chain.

The Packaging of DNA

Packing the mass of DNA into the cell involves compacting the DNA molecule by means of supercoils or superhelices. In the simpler system of prokaryotes, the circular chromosome is packaged by the action of a special enzyme called a **topoisomerase** (specifically, DNA

* *genotype* (jee′-noh-typ) Gr. *gennan*, to produce, and *typos*, type.
* *phenotype* (fee′-noh-typ) Gr. *phainein*, to show. The physical manifestation of gene expression.

Cells

Eukaryotic (composite)

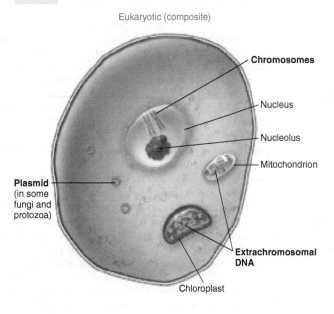

- Chromosomes
- Nucleus
- Nucleolus
- Mitochondrion
- Plasmid (in some fungi and protozoa)
- Extrachromosomal DNA
- Chloroplast

Prokaryotic

Chromosome Plasmids

Viruses

DNA RNA

Figure 9.2 The general location and forms of the genome in two cell types and selected viruses (not to scale).

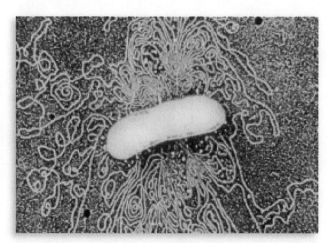

Figure 9.3 A disrupted *Escherichia coli* cell has spewed out its chromosome in a single, uncoiled DNA strand.

gyrase). This enzyme coils the chromosome into a tight bundle by introducing a reversible series of twists into the DNA molecule.

The system in eukaryotes is more complex, with three or more levels of coiling. First, the DNA molecule of a chromosome, which is linear, is wound twice around the histone proteins, creating a chain of **nucleosomes.** The nucleosomes fold in a spiral formation upon one another. An even greater supercoiling occurs when this spiral arrangement further twists on its radius into a giant spiral with loops radiating from the outside. This extreme degree of compactness is what makes the eukaryotic chromosome visible during mitosis **(figure 9.A).**

The condensation of DNA and protein into chromatin was once thought to function mainly as a way for such a long molecule to fit into a cell. However, new research has shown that the coiling of DNA also serves to make certain segments of the genetic program either more or less available to the cell. This is a major control on the expression of many traits, especially in eukaryotes. Having an additional regulatory function creates an entirely new set of information to guide phenotypic expression. The realization that the phenotype of a cell is due to more than just the order of nucleotides in the DNA has led to a rethinking of some of the most basic aspects of genetics (see 9.2 Making Connections, page 273).

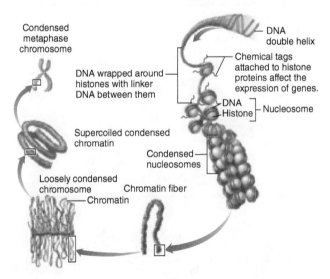

Figure 9.A Eukaryotic DNA interacts with a variety of proteins and small molecules. This relationship modulates the expression of many genes while at the same time allowing for the ordered condensation of DNA into a compact molecule.

The Structure of DNA: A Double Helix with Its Own Language

To analyze the structure of DNA at the molecular level, imagine being able to magnify a small piece of a gene about 5 million times. What you would see is one of the great marvels of life. The pieces of this molecular puzzle were finally worked out by James Watson and Francis Crick in 1953 **(9.1 Making Connections, page 261).** They determined that DNA is a giant molecule with two strands forming a double helix. Extensive evidence shows that the general structure of DNA is universal, except in some viruses that contain single-stranded DNA.

The basic unit of DNA structure is a **nucleotide,** composed of **phosphate, deoxyribose sugar,** and a **nitrogen base,** as shown in this simplified model **(figure 9.B):**

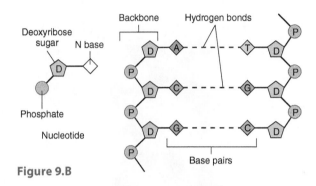

Figure 9.B

Figure 9.4 lays out the structure of DNA going from general (*a,b,c*) to specific (*d*). To make the sugar-phosphate backbone of the molecule, each deoxyribose sugar bonds covalently in a repeating pattern with two phosphates. One of the bonds is to the number $5'$ (read "five prime") carbon on deoxyribose, and the other is to the $3'$ carbon. This pattern will format the direction of the strands, which run opposite to each other, as shown in **figure 9.4d** and discussed next.

The nitrogen bases, **purines** and **pyrimidines,** attach by covalent bonds at the $1'$ position of the sugar **(figure 9.4c,d).** By spanning the center of the molecule and pairing with appropriate complementary bases from the opposite strand, a double-stranded helix is formed. The **paired bases** are held together by hydrogen bonds, which can be readily disrupted, allowing the molecule to be "unzipped" into its complementary strands. This feature is of great importance in gaining access to the information encoded in the nitrogen base sequence. Pairing of purines and pyrimidines is not random; it is dictated by the structure of the bases and how they align to form hydrogen bonds. Thus, in DNA, the purine **adenine** (A) pairs with the pyrimidine **thymine** (T), and the purine **guanine** (G) pairs with the pyrimidine **cytosine** (C). Note that adenine forms two hydrogen bonds with thymine, and cytosine forms three hydrogen bonds with guanine. This difference will influence a number of DNA functions. Evidence also indicates that the bases are attracted to each other in this pattern because each has a complementary three-dimensional shape that fits together with its pair. Although the base-pairing partners generally do not vary, the sequence of base pairs along the DNA molecule can assume any order, resulting in an infinite number of possible nucleotide sequences. One significant finding that has emerged from sequencing chromosomal DNA is how extremely long it can be for a single molecule. An average bacterial chromosome consists of 5 million to 6 million nucleotides; the 46 chromosomes (diploid) of humans total about 6.4 billion nucleotides.

Other important considerations of DNA structure concern the nature of the double helix itself. As indicated previously, one side of the helix runs in the opposite direction of the other, in what is called an *antiparallel arrangement.* Using the order of the bond between the carbon on deoxyribose and the phosphates, we see that one helix runs from the $5'$ to $3'$ direction and the other runs from the $3'$ to $5'$ direction **(figure 9.4d).** This characteristic is a significant

factor in DNA synthesis, transcription, and translation. Although the DNA is constructed somewhat like a twisted ladder, it is not symmetrical. The curvature of the helix and the stepwise stacking of the nitrogen bases produce two different-size surface features, the major and minor grooves **(figure 9.5).**

DNA Replication: Preserving the Code and Passing It On

For a species to survive, it must reproduce. In bacteria, this involves division of the cell by means of binary fission or budding, but it also involves the accurate duplication and separation of the genetic material into each daughter cell to ensure normal function.

It is the sequence of bases along the length of DNA that constitutes its "language." For this language to be preserved for hundreds of generations, the codes it contains will need to be duplicated with high fidelity. This process of duplication is called **DNA replication.** In the following example, we will show replication in bacteria, but with some exceptions, it also applies to the process as it works in eukaryotes and some viruses. Recall from chapter 7 that early in binary fission, the metabolic machinery of a bacterium is programmed to initiate the duplication of the chromosome. Despite its

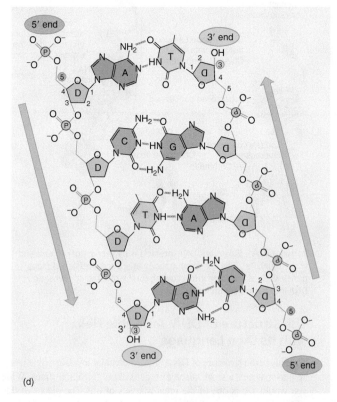

Figure 9.4 **Levels of DNA structure. (a)** A space-filling model of DNA shows its basic configuration as a double helix of sugar-phosphate backbones holding the nitrogen bases between them. **(b)** The twisted ladder model depicts how the complementary nitrogen bases (bars) pair with each other across the center of the molecule. **(c)** A schematic lays out the basic chemical makeup and bonding pattern of the molecule. **(d)** A detailed view of the base pairs, hydrogen bonds, and the antiparallel arrangement of the two helices. Note that in one strand, the deoxyribose-phosphate runs in the 5' to 3' direction and the other side is oriented from 3' to 5'.

9.1 MAKING CONNECTIONS

Deciphering the Structure of DNA

The search for the primary molecules of heredity was a serious focus throughout the first half of the twentieth century. At first, many biologists thought that protein was the genetic material. An important milestone occurred in 1944 when Oswald Avery, Colin MacLeod, and Maclyn McCarty purified DNA and demonstrated at last that it was indeed the blueprint for life. This was followed by an avalanche of research, which continues today.

"We Have Discovered the Secret of Life!"*

One area of extreme interest concerned the molecular structure of DNA. In 1951, American biologist James Watson and English physicist Francis Crick collaborated on solving the DNA puzzle. Although they did little of the original research, they were intrigued by several findings from other scientists. It had been determined by Erwin Chargaff that any model of DNA structure would have to contain deoxyribose, phosphate, purines, and pyrimidines arranged in a way that would provide variation and a simple way of copying itself. Watson and Crick spent long hours constructing models with cardboard cutouts and kept alert for any and every bit of information that might give them an edge.

Two English biophysicists, Maurice Wilkins and Rosalind Franklin, had been painstakingly collecting data on X-ray crystallographs of DNA for several years. With this technique, molecules of DNA bombarded by X rays

Dr. James Watson (left) and Dr. Francis Crick (right) stand next to their model that finally explained the structure of DNA in 1953.

produce a photographic image that can predict the three-dimensional structure of the molecule. After Dr. Wilkins allowed them to view their data, Watson and Crick noticed an unmistakable pattern: The molecule appeared to be a double helix. Gradually, the pieces of the puzzle fell into place, and a final model was assembled—a model that explained all of the qualities of DNA, including how it is copied. Although Watson and Crick were hailed for the clarity of their solution, it must be emphasized that their success was built on the considerable efforts of a number of English and American scientists. This historic discovery spawned ingenious research in all areas of molecular genetics that is still ongoing.

> **Quick Search**
> Find out more of the story at "The Secret of Life: Discovery of DNA Structure."

Since the discovery of the double helix in 1953, an extensive body of biochemical, microscopic, and crystallographic analysis has left little doubt that the model first proposed by Watson and Crick is correct. Scanning tunneling microscopes produce three-dimensional images of DNA that verify the helical shape and twists of DNA represented by models.

What particular requirements did Watson and Crick's model of DNA have to fit to be accurate? *Answer available at http://www. mhhe.com/talaro9*

*comment by Watson and Crick after publication of their monumental discovery.

complexity, DNA replication can be very rapid: This must be completed in a single generation time (around 20 minutes in *E. coli*).

The Significance of DNA Structure

The arrangement of nitrogen bases in DNA has two essential effects.

1. **Maintenance of the genetic message during reproduction.** The constancy of base-pairing guarantees that the correct order of the DNA bases will be retained during cell division. When the two strands are separated, each one provides a **template** (pattern or model) for the replication (exact copying) of a new molecule (figure 9.5). Because the sequence of one strand provides the correct pattern for its complementary strand, the codes can be duplicated with accuracy.
2. **Providing variety.** The order of bases along the length of the DNA strand provides information needed to produce RNA and protein molecules, which in turn are responsible for the phenotype of the cell. As we will see, changing the identity of the bases or their order in the DNA molecule can have a dramatic effect on the phenotype of the organism.

It is remarkable how such a seemingly simple set of codes can account for the extreme differences among forms as diverse as a virus, a bacterium, and a human. We know that the English language, based on 26 letters, can create an infinite variety of words, but how can an apparently complex genetic language such as DNA be based on just four nitrogen base "letters"? The answer lies in the fact that the four bases of DNA are arranged into much longer sequences. An average bacterial gene may contain 1,000 nucleotides: so while DNA is made up of fewer "letters," they are arranged into much longer "words." Mathematically speaking, 1,000 nucleotides can be arranged in $4^{1,000}$ different sequences, a number so large (1.5×10^{602}) that it provides nearly endless degrees of variation.

The Overall Replication Process

What features allow the DNA molecule to be exactly duplicated, and how is its integrity retained? DNA replication requires a careful orchestration of the actions of 30 different enzymes (partial list in **table 9.1**), which separate the strands of the existing DNA molecule, copy its template, and produce two complete daughter molecules.

TABLE 9.1	Some Enzymes Involved in DNA Replication and Their Functions
Enzyme	**Function**
Helicase	Unzipping the DNA helix
Primase	Synthesizing an RNA primer
DNA polymerase III	Adding bases to the new DNA chain; proofreading the chain for mistakes
DNA polymerase I	Removing RNA primers, replacing gaps between Okazaki fragments with correct nucleotides, repairing mismatched bases
Ligase	Final binding of nicks in DNA during synthesis and repair
Gyrase	Supercoiling

A simplified version of replication is shown in **figure 9.5** and includes the following:

1. uncoiling the parent DNA molecule, beginning at a predetermined point of origin;
2. unzipping the hydrogen bonds between the base pairs, thus separating the two strands and exposing the nucleotide sequence of each strand (which is normally buried in the center of the helix) to serve as templates; and
3. synthesizing two new strands by attachment of the correct **complementary** nucleotides to each single-stranded template.

A critical requirement of DNA replication is that each daughter molecule be identical to the parent in composition, but neither one is completely new; the strand that serves as a template is an original parental DNA strand. The preservation of the parent molecule in this way, termed **semiconservative replication,** helps explain the reliability and accuracy of replication.

Events in Replication

All chromosomes have a specific **origin of replication** site that serves as the place where replication will be initiated. It is recognized by a short sequence rich in adenine and thymine that, you will recall, are held together by only two hydrogen bonds rather than three. Because the origin of replication is AT-rich, less energy is required to separate the two strands than would be required if the origin were rich in guanine and cytosine.

The process of synthesizing a new daughter strand of DNA using the parental strand as a template is carried out by a giant enzyme complex that brings in the primary replication enzyme—**DNA polymerase III**—along with numerous accessory enzymes. The DNA polymerase III is responsible for deciphering and duplicating DNA codes, but it has some major conditions that will affect the overall process **(figure 9.6):**

- DNA polymerase cannot add nucleotides to a DNA template strand without a guide that can serve as the starting point for nucleotides to be bonded during synthesis.
- Before replication can begin, a piece of RNA called a primer is inserted at the origin of replication to provide the first nucleotide with a free 3′—OH group for binding.

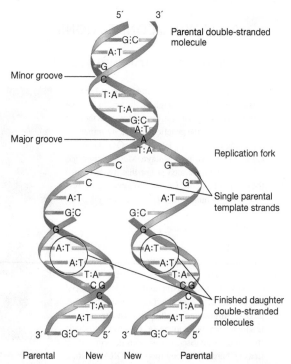

Figure 9.5 Simplified steps to show the semiconservative replication of DNA. The two strands of the parental double helix are unwound and separated. Each single strand will serve as a template (blue) to synthesize a new strand of DNA (red), starting at the replication fork. As synthesis proceeds, the correct nucleotides are added according to the pattern of the template. An A on the template will pair with a T on the new molecule, and a C will pair with a G. The finished daughter DNA molecules contain one strand of the newly synthesized DNA and the original template (parental) strand. This keeps the code intact because the same linear arrangement of the bases is maintained during this process. This process is covered in greater detail in figure 9.6.

- DNA polymerase can read only in the 3′ to 5′ direction on the template and can add nucleotides only in the 5′ to 3′ direction to the new strand. Because the two template strands are oriented in opposite directions, this will necessitate an alternative type of synthesis for the template strand that is oriented 5′ to 3′ (see lagging strand).

Prior to the start of replication, enzymes called **helicases** (unzipping enzymes) bind to the DNA at the origin. These enzymes untwist the helix and break the hydrogen bonds holding the two strands together, resulting in two separate strands, each of which will be used as a template for the synthesis of a new strand **(figure 9.6, step 1).**

Replication begins when RNA **primers** are synthesized by a primase at the origin of replication **(figure 9.6a).** DNA polymerase III will use this short strand of RNA as a starting point for adding nucleotides. In the circular DNA molecule of bacteria, there are two **replication forks,** each containing its own set of replication enzymes. Each fork requires two active DNA polymerases along with several other proteins and enzymes whose main functions are to stabilize the polymerase and provide a means of removing and replacing nucleotides. The enzyme complex encircles the DNA

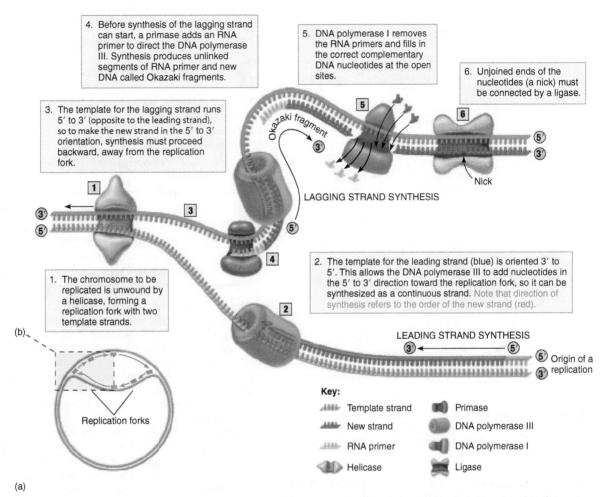

4. Before synthesis of the lagging strand can start, a primase adds an RNA primer to direct the DNA polymerase III. Synthesis produces unlinked segments of RNA primer and new DNA called Okazaki fragments.

5. DNA polymerase I removes the RNA primers and fills in the correct complementary DNA nucleotides at the open sites.

6. Unjoined ends of the nucleotides (a nick) must be connected by a ligase.

3. The template for the lagging strand runs 5′ to 3′ (opposite to the leading strand), so to make the new strand in the 5′ to 3′ orientation, synthesis must proceed backward, away from the replication fork.

Okazaki fragment

Nick

LAGGING STRAND SYNTHESIS

1. The chromosome to be replicated is unwound by a helicase, forming a replication fork with two template strands.

2. The template for the leading strand (blue) is oriented 3′ to 5′. This allows the DNA polymerase III to add nucleotides in the 5′ to 3′ direction toward the replication fork, so it can be synthesized as a continuous strand. Note that direction of synthesis refers to the order of the new strand (red).

(b)

Replication forks

LEADING STRAND SYNTHESIS

5′ Origin of a replication

Key:

Template strand	Primase
New strand	DNA polymerase III
RNA primer	DNA polymerase I
Helicase	Ligase

(a)

Process Figure 9.6 The assembly line of DNA replication in a circular bacterial chromosome. (a) A bacterial chromosome showing the overall pattern of replication. There are two replication forks where new DNA is being synthesized. (b) An enlarged view of the left replication fork to show the details of replication.

near the replication fork and synthesizes new DNA as guided by the parental strand. As synthesis proceeds, the forks are continually opened up to expose the template for replication.

Because DNA polymerase III can only synthesize new DNA in the 5′ to 3′ direction, just one strand, called the **leading strand,** can be synthesized continuously (**figure 9.6, step 2**). One enzyme does this by moving along the template strand in the 3′ to 5′ order toward the replication fork, adding nucleotides in the 5′ to 3′ order on the new strand.

The other template strand runs the opposite direction and cannot be used by the DNA polymerase to synthesize a continuous, unbroken strand of new DNA in the 5′ to 3′ order. This **lagging strand** will be synthesized in a series of shorter fragments that will later be connected into a continuous strand (**figure 9.6, steps 3** and **4**). It still requires primers, and each new fragment will require its own separate primer. The DNA polymerase adds nucleotides to the new strand in the 5′ to 3′ order, but it does this by going in a backward direction away from the fork. This manner of synthesis produces short fragments of DNA (100 to 1,000 bases long) called **Okazaki fragments** on the lagging strand. The lagging strand will be completed when

the enzyme, **DNA polymerase I,** removes the RNA primers from the Okazaki fragments, and fills in the missing segments with the correct complementary DNA nucleotides (**figure 9.6, step 5**). The replacement strand is not completely bonded to the finished part of the new strand, so an enzyme, **ligase,** makes these final phosphate-sugar connections (**figure 9.6, step 6**).

The addition of nucleotides proceeds at an astonishing pace, estimated in some bacteria to be 750 bases per second at each fork! As replication proceeds, one newly synthesized strand loops down (**figure 9.7a**). When the forks have gone full circle, a termination site shuts replication down. The two circular daughter molecules remain connected briefly but are nicked and separated by a helicase (**figure 9.7b**).

Like any language, DNA is occasionally "misspelled" when an incorrect base is added to the growing chain. Studies have shown that such mistakes are made once in approximately 10^8 to 10^9 bases,

Quick Search
Find out more by going to "DNA Interactive" and explore the process of replication—copying the code.

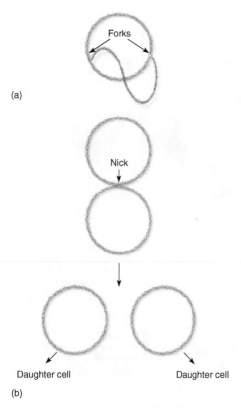

(a)

(b)

Figure 9.7 Completion of chromosome replication in bacteria.
(a) As replication proceeds, one strand loops down. (b) Final separation is achieved when an enzyme cuts and releases the two completed molecules. The daughter cells receive these during binary fission.

but most of these are corrected. If not corrected, they are referred to as mutations and can lead to serious cell dysfunction. Because continued cellular integrity is very dependent on accurate replication, cells have evolved their own proofreading function for DNA. DNA polymerase III, the enzyme that elongates the molecule, can also detect incorrect, unmatching bases; excise them; and replace them with the correct base. DNA polymerase I is involved in proofreading the molecule and repairing damaged DNA.

 Check Your Progress SECTION 9.1

1. Compare the genetic material of eukaryotes, bacteria, and viruses in terms of general structure, size, and mode of replication.
2. Characterize the organization of genetic material, going from the genome down to the gene.
3. Briefly describe how DNA is packaged to fit inside a cell.
4. What are the fundamental building blocks of DNA and how are they bonded together?
5. Describe what is meant by the antiparallel arrangement of DNA.
6. Explain the synthesis of the leading and lagging strands during DNA replication and identify the enzymes required for producing a finished product.
7. Name several characteristics of DNA structure that enable it to be replicated with such great accuracy generation after generation.

9.2 Applications of the DNA Code: Transcription and Translation

 Expected Learning Outcomes

7. Present an overview of the main aspects of the flow of genetic information in cells.
8. Explain the relationship between the structure of DNA and the structure of proteins.
9. Describe the different types of RNA and their basic functions in genetic expression.
10. Explain what happens during transcription.
11. Describe the genetic code, codons, and anticodons, and how they relate to one another.
12. Relate the participants and steps in translation (protein synthesis).
13. Distinguish major points of difference between prokaryotic and eukaryotic transcription and translation.

We have explored how the genetic language of the DNA molecule is conserved through replication. Next, we consider exactly how DNA is expressed. Given that the sequence of bases in DNA is a genetic code, just what is the nature of this code and how is it utilized? Although the genome is full of critical information, the DNA molecule itself cannot perform cell processes directly. Instead, its information is conveyed to RNA molecules, which carry out the instructions it contains. The concept that genetic information flows from DNA to RNA to protein has long been a central theme of molecular biology (**figure 9.8a**). It states that the master code of DNA is first used to synthesize RNA via a process called **transcription,** and the information contained in the RNA is then used to produce proteins in a process known as **translation.** The principal exceptions to this pattern are found in RNA viruses, which convert RNA to other RNA, and in retroviruses, which convert RNA to DNA.

We now know that these established concepts, though accurate, are still being scrutinized, and new discoveries are constantly adding to our understanding. In addition to the RNA used to produce proteins, a wide variety of specialized RNAs act by regulating gene function (**figure 9.8b**). We will introduce some of the expanded functions for RNA in 9.3 Making Connections, but we will start with its direct participation in protein synthesis.

The Gene-Protein Connection

The Triplet Code and the Relationship to Proteins

Several questions invariably arise concerning the relationship between genes and cell function. For instance, how does gene structure lead to the expression of traits in the individual, and what features of gene expression cause one organism to be so distinctly different from another? For answers, we must turn to the correlation between gene and protein structure. We know that each structural gene is an ordered sequence of nucleotides that codes for a protein. Because each protein is different, each gene must also differ somehow in its composition. In fact, the language of DNA exists in the order of groups of three consecutive bases, or **triplets,** on one DNA strand (**figure 9.9**). In short, one gene differs from another in the

Figure 9.8 Summary of the flow of genetic information in cells. DNA is the ultimate storehouse and distributor of genetic information. **(a)** DNA must be deciphered into a usable cell language. It does this by transcribing its code into RNA helper molecules that translate that code into protein. **(b)** Other sections of the DNA produce additional types of RNA molecules that regulate genes and their products.

order and number of its triplets. An equally important part of this concept is that each triplet represents a code for a particular amino acid. When the triplet code is transcribed and translated, it dictates the type and order of amino acids in a polypeptide (protein) chain.

To summarize the key points that connect DNA and protein function:

1. DNA is a blueprint that indicates which kinds of proteins to make and how to make them. This blueprint exists in the order of triplets along the DNA strands.
2. The order of triplets directs a protein's primary structure—the order and type of amino acids in the chain—which determines its characteristic shape and function.

Figure 9.9 Simplified view of the DNA-protein relationship. The DNA molecule is a continuous chain of base pairs, but the sequence must be interpreted in groups of three base pairs (a triplet). Each triplet as copied into mRNA codons will translate into one amino acid; consequently, the ratio of base pairs to amino acids is 3:1.

3. Proteins contribute significantly to the phenotype by functioning as enzymes and structural molecules.

The Major Participants in Transcription and Translation

Transcription, the formation of RNA using DNA as a template, and translation, the synthesis of proteins using RNA as a template, are highly complex. A number of components participate: most prominently, messenger RNA, transfer RNA, ribosomes, several types of enzymes, and a storehouse of raw materials. After first examining each of these components, we shall see how they come together in the assembly line of the cell.

RNAs: Tools in the Cell's Assembly Line

Ribonucleic acid (RNA) is an encoded molecule like DNA, but its general structure is different in several ways:

1. It is a single-stranded molecule that can assume secondary and tertiary levels of complexity due to bonds within the molecule, leading to specialized forms of RNA (mRNA, tRNA, and rRNA—**figure 9.10**).
2. RNA contains **uracil,** instead of thymine, as the complementary base-pairing mate for adenine. This does not change the inherent DNA code in any way because the uracil still follows the pairing rules.
3. Although RNA, like DNA, is structured with a backbone of alternating sugar and phosphate molecules, the sugar in RNA is **ribose** rather than deoxyribose (see figure 2.24).

The many functional types of RNA range from small regulatory pieces to large structural ones. All types of RNA are formed

(a) **Messenger RNA (mRNA)**
A short piece of messenger RNA (mRNA) illustrates the general structure of RNA: single strandedness, repeating phosphate-ribose sugar backbone attached to single nitrogen bases; use of uracil instead of thymine.

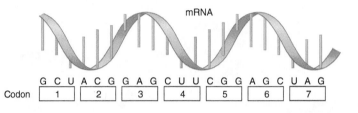

mRNA

G C U A C G G A G C U U C G G A G C U A G

Codon 1 2 3 4 5 6 7

(b) **Transfer RNA (tRNA)**
Left: The tRNA strand loops back on itself to form intrachain hydrogen bonds. The result is a cloverleaf structure, shown here in simplified form. At its bottom is an anticodon that specifies the attachment of a particular amino acid at the 3' end. Right: A three-dimensional view of tRNA structure.

Figure 9.10 Characteristics of messenger and transfer RNA.

through transcription of a DNA gene, but only mRNA is further translated into protein. See **table 9.2** for a comparison of major types of RNA and their functions. Other forms of RNA are introduced in section 9.3.

Messenger RNA: Carrying DNA's Message

Messenger RNA (mRNA) is a transcribed version of a structural gene or genes in DNA. It is synthesized by a process similar to synthesis of the leading strand during DNA replication, and the complementary base-pairing rules ensure that the code will be faithfully copied in the mRNA transcript. The message of this transcribed strand is later read as a series of triplets called **codons** (**figure 9.10a**), and the length of the mRNA molecule varies from about 100 nucleotides to several thousand. The details of transcription and the function of mRNA in translation are covered shortly.

Transfer RNA: The Key to Translation

Transfer RNAs (tRNA) are also complementary copies of specific regions of DNA; however, they differ from mRNA. Transfer RNAs typically range from 75 to 95 nucleotides in length, and they contain sequences of bases that form hydrogen bonds with complementary sections of the same tRNA strand. At these points, the molecule bends back upon itself into several *hairpin loops,* giving the molecule a secondary *cloverleaf* structure that folds even further into a complex, three-dimensional helix (**figure 9.10b**). This compact molecule acts as a translator that converts RNA language into protein language. The bottom loop of the cloverleaf exposes a triplet, the **anticodon,** that both designates the specificity of the tRNA and complements mRNA's codons. At the opposite end of the molecule is a binding site for the amino acid that is specific for that tRNA's anticodon. For each of the 20 amino acids, there is at least one

TABLE 9.2	**Major Types of Ribonucleic Acid Involved in Protein Synthesis**		
RNA Type	**Contains Codes For**	**Function in Cell**	**Translated**
Messenger (mRNA)	Sequence of amino acids in protein	Carries the DNA master code to the ribosome	Yes
Transfer (tRNA)	A cloverleaf tRNA to carry amino acids	Brings amino acids to ribosome during translation	No
Ribosomal (rRNA)	Several large structural rRNA molecules	Forms the major part of a ribosome and participates in protein synthesis	No
Primer	An RNA that can begin DNA replication	Primes DNA	No

specialized type of tRNA to carry it. Binding of an amino acid to its specific tRNA requires a specific enzyme that can correctly match each tRNA with its amino acid.

The Ribosome: A Mobile Molecular Factory for Translation

The prokaryotic (70S) ribosome is a particle composed of tightly packaged **ribosomal RNA (rRNA)** and protein. The rRNA component of the ribosome is also a long polynucleotide molecule. It forms complex three-dimensional figures that contribute to the structure and function of ribosomes. The interactions of proteins and rRNA create the two subunits of the ribosome that engage in final translation of the genetic code (see figure 9.12). A metabolically active bacterial cell can accommodate up to 20,000 of these minuscule factories—all actively engaged in reading the genetic program, taking in raw materials, and producing proteins at an impressive rate.

Transcription: The First Stage of Gene Expression

Like so many other genetic events, transcription is a marvel of efficiency. It is highly organized and guided by special codes on DNA itself. To describe it in more detail, we use the formation of mRNA in bacteria as a model. It is important to keep in mind that all types of RNA are synthesized by a similar process. The other RNAs have important functions; they just do not provide the code for the amino acids in a protein as mRNA does.

During transcription, an RNA molecule is synthesized using the codes on DNA as a guide or template. A large enzyme complex, **RNA polymerase,** is responsible for this process. This polymerase is more multipurpose than DNA polymerase, because the RNA enzyme works alone and does not require a helicase. It can bind to DNA and unwind it, as well as synthesize RNA (**figure 9.11**).

Transcription proceeds in three stages: *initiation, elongation,* and *termination.* Initiation requires the RNA polymerase to recognize a region on a gene called the **promoter region (figure 9.11, step 1).**

1. Each gene contains a specific promoter region and a leader sequence for guiding the beginning of transcription. Next is the region of the gene that codes for a polypeptide and ends with a series of terminal sequences that stop translation.

2. DNA is unwound at the promoter by RNA polymerase. Only one strand of DNA, called the template strand, supplies the codes to be transcribed by RNA polymerase. This strand runs in the 3′ to 5′ direction.

3. The RNA polymerase moves along the DNA strand, adding complementary nucleotides as dictated by the DNA template. The mRNA strand reads in the 5′ to 3′ direction.

4. The polymerase continues transcribing until it reaches a termination site, and the mRNA transcript is released to be translated. Note that the section of the transcribed DNA is rewound into its original configuration.

RNA polymerase binding site

Leader sequence | Initiation codon

Promoter region

Termination sequences

| T | A | C | G | A | C | T | G | A | T | G | C | G | A | C | T | G | A | T | G |
| A | T | G | C | T | G | A | C | T | A | C | G | C | T | G | A | C | T | A | C |

Intervening sequence of variable size

Termination sequence

RNA polymerase

Template strand

Sigma factor

Nontemplate strand

Unwinding of DNA

Direction of transcription

Nucleotide pool

Early mRNA transcript

Elongation

Late mRNA transcript

🌀 **Process Figure 9.11** The major events in transcription, using mRNA as a model.

This region consists of two sets of DNA sequences located just before the *initiation site*. The first sequence is about 35 nucleotides from the initiation site, and the second is about 10 nucleotides from it. The primary function of the promoter is to provide a position for initial binding of the RNA polymerase. A special protein molecule, the *sigma factor,* guides the RNA polymerase to the correct position on the promotor. These promoter sequences are not highly varied, and they tend to be rich in adenine and thymine base pairs, which have one less hydrogen bond than guanine-cytosine pairs, which facilitates the separation of the DNA strands.

Prior to the first synthesis step of transcription, the RNA polymerase begins to separate the two strands of the DNA helix and forms an open "bubble" for transcription **(figure 9.11, steps 2 and 3).** This bubble serves as the space where the bonds between the nucleotides of mRNA will actually be made. Only one strand of DNA—the **template strand**—is transcribed. This strand is the model used by the RNA polymerase to synthesize an mRNA molecule, similar to the process in DNA replication. The mRNA that is made by transcription of the template strand is a message for the correct sequence of amino acids to be combined during translation (protein synthesis). The other strand—the **nontemplate strand**—is sometimes called the sense, or coding, strand because its sequence is the same order as the mRNA (although it will have thymine instead of uracil). In some cases, this strand may serve a genetic function, but it is not transcribed. Which strand acts as the template varies from one gene to another. One important triplet appearing early in a DNA template is **TAC.** This will be transcribed into **AUG** on the mRNA, which we can see in figures 9.13 and 9.15 is the start codon, and it signals the location on the mRNA where translation starts. Note that the promotor sequences are not transcribed as part of the final mRNA molecule.

As elongation proceeds, the polymerase moves the transcription bubble forward, exposing subsequent sections of DNA. It simultaneously brings in nucleotides that are complementary to the DNA template and continues to assemble the mRNA strand. As with replication, this occurs in the 5′ to 3′ direction with regard to the growing mRNA. DNA that has already been transcribed rewinds back into its double helix structure **(figure 9.11, step 4).** The part of the mRNA strand that is already assembled remains attached to the enzyme complex but is kept out of the way of the processing machinery.

At termination, the polymerase recognizes a site on DNA near the end of the gene that signals the separation and release of the completed mRNA. It will go immediately to the translation phase on the ribosome. As we will see, this mRNA delivers its message in codons that are the master code for protein synthesis. The length of the final mRNA molecule depends upon the polypeptide that it encodes. The smallest one may consist of 100 nucleotides, an average one of 1,200 nucleotides, and the largest several thousand.

Translation: The Second Stage of Gene Expression

In translation, all of the elements needed to synthesize a protein, from the mRNA to the tRNAs with amino acids, are brought together on the ribosomes **(figure 9.12).** The process occurs in five

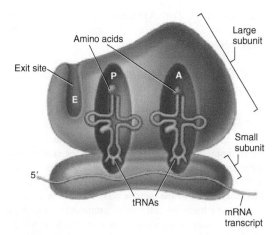

Figure 9.12 The "players" in translation. A ribosome serves as the stage for protein synthesis. Assembly of the small and large subunits results in specific sites for holding the mRNA and two tRNAs with their amino acids.

stages: initiation, elongation, termination, and protein folding and processing.

Initiation of Translation

In prokaryotic cells, the mRNA molecule leaves the DNA transcription site and is transported directly to ribosomes. Ribosomal subunits are specifically assembled in a way that forms sites to hold the mRNA and tRNAs. The ribosome thus recognizes these molecules and stabilizes reactions between them. The small subunit binds to the 5′ end of the mRNA and provides molecules to initiate translation. The large subunit holds the tRNAs and is actively involved in peptide bond formation by means of a specialized ribozyme, which is an RNA-based catalyst. The small subunit of the ribosome binds at a specific site on the mRNA and places the **start codon** AUG (rarely GUG) in correct alignment with the P site. This step provides the start signal for translation.

With the mRNA message in place on the assembled ribosome, the next step in translation involves entrance of tRNAs with their amino acids. The pool of cytoplasm around the region contains a complete array of tRNAs, previously charged by having the correct amino acid attached. The step in which the complementary tRNA meets with the mRNA code is guided by the two sites on the large subunit of the ribosome called the P site (left) and the A site (right).[1] Think of these sites as recessed spaces tucked within the two subunits of the ribosome, with each site accommodating a tRNA. The ribosome also has an exit or E site where used tRNAs are released.

The Master Genetic Code: The Message in Messenger RNA

By convention, the master genetic code is represented by the mRNA codons and the amino acids they specify **(figure 9.13).** Except in a very few cases (the genes of mitochondria and chloroplasts, for example), this code is universal, whether for prokaryotes, eukaryotes,

1. P stands for peptide site; A stands for aminoacyl (amino acid) site; E stands for exit site.

				Second Base Position					
		U		C		A		G	
U	UUU, UUC	Phenylalanine	UCU, UCC	Serine	UAU, UAC	Tyrosine	UGU, UGC	Cysteine	U, C
	UUA, UUG	Leucine	UCA, UCG		UAA, UAG	STOP**	UGA	STOP**	A
							UGG	Tryptophan	G
C	CUU, CUC	Leucine	CCU, CCC	Proline	CAU, CAC	Histidine	CGU, CGC	Arginine	U, C
	CUA, CUG		CCA, CCG		CAA, CAG	Glutamine	CGA, CGG		A, G
A	AUU, AUC	Isoleucine	ACU, ACC	Threonine	AAU, AAC	Asparagine	AGU, AGC	Serine	U, C
	AUA		ACA		AAA, AAG	Lysine	AGA, AGG	Arginine	A, G
	AUG*	START Methionine	ACG						
G	GUU, GUC	Valine	GCU, GCC	Alanine	GAU, GAC	Aspartic acid	GGU, GGC	Glycine	U, C
	GUA, GUG		GCA, GCG		GAA, GAG	Glutamic acid	GGA, GGG		A, G

* This codon initiates translation.
**For these codons, which give the orders to stop translation, there are no corresponding tRNAs with amino acids.

Figure 9.13 **The genetic code: Codons of mRNA that specify a given amino acid.** The master code for translation is provided by mRNA codons.

or viruses. It is worth noting that once the triplet code on mRNA is known, the original DNA sequence, the complementary tRNA code, and the types of amino acids in the protein are automatically known (**figure 9.14**). However, one cannot predict (backward) from protein structure what the exact mRNA codons are because of a factor called **redundancy** or **degeneracy,** meaning that a particular amino acid can be coded for by more than one codon.

In figure 9.13, the mRNA codons and their corresponding amino acid specificities are given. Because there are 64 different triplet codes[2] and only 20 different amino acids, it is expected that some amino acids are represented by several codons. For example, leucine and serine can each be represented by any of six different triplets, and only tryptophan and methionine are represented by a single codon. In such codons as leucine, only the first two nucleotides are required to encode the correct amino acid, and the third nucleotide does not change its sense. This property, called *wobble,* is thought to permit some variation or mutation without changing the message.

The Beginning of Protein Synthesis

With mRNA serving as the guide, the stage is finally set for actual protein assembly. The correct tRNA (labeled 1 on **figure 9.15**) enters the P site and binds to the **start codon (AUG)** presented by the mRNA. Rules of pairing dictate that the anticodon of this tRNA will complement the mRNA codon AUG; thus, the tRNA with

Figure 9.14 **Interpreting the DNA code.** If the DNA sequence is known, the mRNA codon can be surmised. If a codon is known, the anticodon and, finally, the amino acid sequence can be determined. The reverse is not possible (determining the exact codon or anticodon from amino acid sequence) due to the redundancy of the code.

2. $64 = 4^3$ (the 4 different nucleotides in all possible combinations of 3).

① Entrance of tRNAs 1 and 2

② Formation of peptide bond

③ Discharge of tRNA 1 at E site

④ First translocation; tRNA 2 shifts into P site; tRNA 3 enters ribosome at A

⑤ Formation of peptide bond

⑥ Discharge of tRNA 2; second translocation; tRNA 4 enters ribosome

⑦ Formation of peptide bond

⑧ Steps 3 to 5 are repeated until stop codon is reached and protein synthesis is terminated.

Process Figure 9.15 **The events in protein synthesis.**

anticodon UAC will first occupy site P. It happens that the amino acid carried by the initiator tRNA in bacteria is *formyl methionine* (fMet; see figure 9.13), though in many cases, it may not remain a permanent part of the finished protein.

Continuation and Completion of Protein Synthesis: Elongation and Termination

The mRNA formed during transcription provides a specific order of nucleotides (codons) called the *reading frame* that must be translated in that exact order. In general, the ribosome is mobile and moves along the mRNA from one codon to the next. This brings each succeeding codon into place on the ribosome and makes a space for the next tRNA to enter. The actual joining of the amino acids is carried out by a *ribozyme* (a catalytic RNA molecule) that is part of the large subunit of the ribosome. It forms a peptide bond between the amino acids on the adjacent tRNAs, and the polypeptide grows in length. The process is outlined here:

- Elongation begins with the filling of the A site by a second tRNA **(figure 9.15, step 1)**. The identity of this tRNA and its amino acid is dictated by the second mRNA codon.
- The entry of tRNA 2 into the A site brings the two adjacent tRNAs in favorable proximity for a peptide bond to form between the amino acids they carry. The fMet is transferred from the first tRNA to amino acid 2, resulting in two coupled amino acids called a dipeptide **(figure 9.15, step 2)**.
- For the next step to proceed, some room must be made on the ribosome, and the next codon in sequence must be brought into position for reading. This process is accomplished by *translocation,* the enzyme-directed shifting of the ribosome to the next position on the mRNA strand, which causes the blank tRNA (1) to be discharged from the ribosome **(figure 9.15, step 3)** at the E site.
- This shifts the tRNA holding the dipeptide into P position. Site A is temporarily left empty. The tRNA that has been released is now free to drift away and become recharged with an amino acid for later additions to this or another protein.
- The stage is now set for the insertion of tRNA 3 at site A as directed by the third mRNA codon **(figure 9.15, step 4)**. This insertion is followed once again by peptide bond formation between the dipeptide and amino acid 3 (making a tripeptide), splitting of the peptide from tRNA 2, and translocation **(figure 9.15, step 5)**.
- This releases tRNA 2, shifts mRNA to the next position, moves tRNA 3 to position P, and opens position A for tRNA 4 **(step 6)**. From this point on, peptide elongation proceeds repetitively by this same series of actions out to the end of the mRNA **(steps 7 and 8)**.

The termination of protein synthesis is not simply a matter of reaching the last codon on mRNA. It is brought about by the presence of at least one special codon occurring just after the codon for the last amino acid. Termination codons—UAA, UAG, and UGA—are codons for which there is no corresponding tRNA. Also termed **nonsense** or **stop codons,** they

Quick Search
Find out more by going to "VCAC: Molecular Processes: Translation the Movie" to see a video".

carry a necessary message: *Stop here.* When this codon is reached, a special enzyme breaks the bond between the final tRNA and the finished polypeptide chain, releasing it from the ribosome.

Before newly made proteins can carry out their structural or enzymatic roles, they often require finishing touches. Even before the peptide chain is released from the ribosome, it begins folding upon itself to achieve its biologically active tertiary conformation. Other alterations, called *posttranslational modifications,* may be necessary. Some proteins must have the starting amino acid (formyl methionine) clipped off; proteins destined to become complex enzymes have cofactors added; and some join with other completed proteins to form quaternary levels of structure.

The operation of transcription and translation is machinelike in its precision. Protein synthesis in bacteria is both efficient and rapid. At 37°C, 12 to 17 amino acids per second are added to a growing peptide chain. An average protein consisting of about 400 amino acids requires less than half a minute for complete synthesis. Further efficiency is gained when the translation of mRNA starts while transcription is still occurring **(figure 9.16)**. A single mRNA is long enough to be fed through more than one ribosome simultaneously. This permits the synthesis of hundreds of protein molecules from the same mRNA transcript arrayed along a chain of ribosomes. This **polyribosomal complex** is indeed an assembly line for mass production of proteins. Protein synthesis consumes an enormous amount of energy. Approximately 1,200 ATPs or ATP equivalents are consumed just for synthesis of an average-size protein.

Eukaryotic Transcription and Translation: Similar yet Different

Eukaryotes share many aspects of protein synthesis with prokaryotes. They show similarities in the operation of the ribosomes, the functions of start and stop codons, and the mass production of proteins by means of polyribosomes. But they do differ in significant ways. The start codon in eukaryotes is also AUG, but it codes for an alternate form of methionine. Another difference is that eukaryotic mRNAs code for just one protein, unlike bacterial mRNAs, which often contain information from several genes in series. Read **9.2 Making Connections** on page 273 to discover other exceptional aspects of eukaryotic genetics.

Prokaryotic and eukaryotic cells also vary in location and structure of genes. The presence of DNA in the nucleus of eukaryotic cells means that eukaryotic transcription and translation cannot be simultaneous as it is in prokaryotes. The mRNA transcript must pass through pores in the nuclear membrane and be carried to the ribosomes in the cytoplasm or on the endoplasmic reticulum for translation.

So far, we have introduced a simplified definition of a gene that fits well for most prokaryotes. The pattern of their genes is colinear, meaning that they consist of a series of triplets that encode proteins and do not require any processing.[3] Eukaryotic genes differ significantly in this characteristic because they are not colinear. Located along their genes are one to several intervening sequences of triplets, called **introns,** that do not code for protein.[4] Introns are

3. With colinearity, the triplet sequence can be read directly into a series of amino acids.

4. Introns are occasionally found in prokaryotes (cyanobacteria and archaea).

(a)

Start of translation

Growing polypeptides

1
2
3
4
5 6 7
Start

Polyribosomal complex

(b)

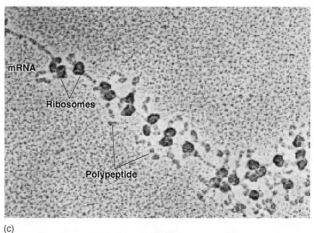

(c)

Figure 9.16 Speeding up the protein assembly line in bacteria. (a) The mRNA transcript encounters ribosomal parts immediately as it leaves the DNA. (b) The ribosomal factories assemble along the mRNA in a chain, each ribosome reading the message and translating it into protein. Many products will thus be well along the synthetic pathway before transcription has even terminated. (c) Photomicrograph of a polyribosomal complex in action. Note that the protein "tails" vary in length depending on the stage of translation (30,000×).

interspersed between coding regions, called **exons,** that will be translated into protein **(figure 9.17).** We can use words as examples. A short section of colinear prokaryotic gene might read TOM SAW OUR DOG DIG OUT; a eukaryotic gene that codes for the same portion would read TOM SAW XZKP FPL OUR DOG QZWVP DIG OUT. The recognizable words are the exons, and the non-sense letters represent the introns.

This unusual genetic architecture, also called a split gene, requires further processing before translation. Transcription of the entire gene with both exons and introns occurs first, producing a pre-mRNA. Next, an RNA-protein complex called a *spliceosome* recognizes the exon-intron junctions and enzymatically cuts through them in a process called RNA splicing. The action of this splicer enzyme loops the introns into lariat-shaped pieces,

Figure 9.17 The split gene of eukaryotes. Eukaryotic genes have an additional complicating factor in their translation. Their coding sequences, or exons (E), are interrupted at intervals by segments called introns (I) that are not part of that protein's code. Introns are transcribed but not translated, which necessitates their removal by RNA splicing enzymes before translation.

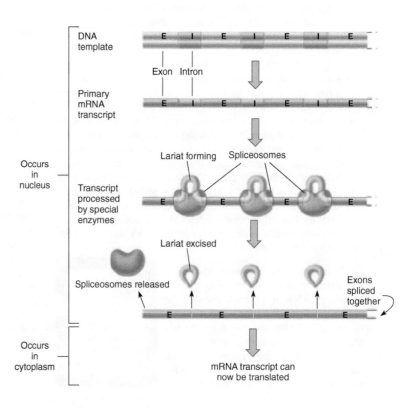

9.2 MAKING CONNECTIONS

Revising Some Rules of Genetics

What was true for E. coli *would be true for the elephant.*

 Jacques Monod, Nobel laureate and discover of the *lac* operon

Bacteria—with their small genomes and short generation times—have been ideal models for research into molecular genetics. From this research came elegant and universal rules governing the workings of DNA. This led to the "Central Dogma of Biology," which says that DNA is the repository of genetic information, RNA is a molecule that ferries information between DNA and the ribosome, and proteins produced from the RNA codes are responsible for carrying out the structural and metabolic needs of the cell. And all of this is still accurate.

 It is just that there is more to the story. Significant discoveries in eukaryotic organisms have revealed that certain aspects of their genetics have turned out to be somewhat more complex and varied. This does not change our introduction to microbial genetics for two reasons. First, the laws of genetics covered in this chapter do hold true for the vast majority of prokaryotic organisms. Second, this is an *introduction* to genetics and it is certainly fair to leave the exceptions, the unusual, and the overly complex for future courses. We would like to use this feature to introduce some of these revolutionary new findings.

The Genetic Code Is Universal with Some Exceptions

Based on early studies, it was assumed that the genetic code was the same in all cells and viruses, as no exceptions had ever been seen. Even more convincing, eukaryotic mRNAs were appropriately translated by bacterial cells, arguing for a single genetic dictionary. But later work with mitochondria isolated from yeast and humans found a slightly different code; for example, the stop codon UGA specifies the amino acid tryptophan in mitochondria. This discovery was followed by the detection of other exceptions to the genetic code in a few prokaryotic and eukaryotic organisms. This difference in the genetic code of mitochondria is one of the most compelling pieces of evidence supporting the endosymbiotic theory (see 5.1 Making Connections).

Genetic Expression Can Be Modified by Epigenetic Mechanisms

For years, geneticists have debated the effects of nature (genes) versus nurture (environment) on the development of organisms. Though both have profound influence, we now have greater understanding about the direct effects of nongenetic factors.

 The term *epigenetics* is used to designate factors that effect genetic expression other than the specific sequence of nucleotides in genes. One major epigenetic affect is in the manner that DNA coils around proteins during chromatin formation (see page 259). This layer of information is only now being fully appreciated and is still far from being completely understood. Epigenetic effects seem to work by increasing or decreasing the expression of certain genes by making them more or less accessible for transcription. For example, having methyl groups (—CH₃) attached to numerous cytosine nucleotides reduces the level of transcription of a section of DNA that is methylated (**figure *a***).

 To illustrate this effect, a study in mice determined that the mother's diet during gestation could greatly alter gene expression in her offspring. Genetically identical mothers (clones) were placed into two groups—one that was fed a diet high in the soy chemical genistein and the other a normal diet. The soy group had young mice with significant differences in color coat and weight. They were larger and yellower than the mice from the normal group. This was a permanent effect, because the soy group remained unchanged even when placed on a normal diet. The effect appears to be due to methylation of the embryonic genes by genistein during fetal development (**figure *b***).

90,000 Proteins . . . 21,000 Genes?

Humans have about 90,000 different proteins, and, going by our earlier understanding, we would have expected at least 90,000 different genes. Imagine the surprise most biologists felt when the Human Genome Project revealed that we have fewer than 21,000 protein-coding sequences, about 20,000 fewer than a simple corn plant.

 For some time, it has been known that eukaryotic genes consist of expressed sequences (exons) interspersed with intervening sequences (introns) and that the final mRNA need not contain every exon. Until our low gene count was revealed, however, no one realized how often a single gene could be used to make several different proteins. Utilizing *alternative splicing,* a cell can select which exons will be retained and spliced into a final mRNA. Like a Scrabble player deciding which lettered tiles to use to make a word, a cell can place any combination of the exons in a gene to produce many alternate mRNAs (and resulting proteins). It is currently estimated that three of every four human genes are edited in this way and that the prevalence of alternative splicing appears to increase with the complexity of an organism.

Suggest some reasons for having large parts of the genome silenced or unused. *Answer available at http://www.mhhe.com/talaro9*

(a) Section of gene with methylation that blocks its activation

Normal cytosine Methylated cytosine

(b) One example of epigenetic effects due to methylation of bases during early development

Mice from mothers fed a high-soy diet were larger and different-colored from mice whose mothers were fed a normal diet. All mice are genetically the same (clones).

excises them, and joins the exons end to end. By this means, a strand of mRNA with no intron material is produced. This completed mRNA strand can then proceed to the cytoplasm to be translated.

Several different types of introns have been discovered, some of which do code for cell substances. A great deal of non-protein-coding DNA is proving to be vital for cell function. In humans, this intron material represents 98% of the DNA found in chromosomes. Another surprising discovery is that some proteins have sections that are in reverse order from the DNA sequence that encoded them. Previously, it was considered a hard and fast rule that DNA sequence determined the mRNA and consequently amino acid sequence after the introns were removed. This new data revealed that cellular machinery can reverse the order of DNA transcription, essentially creating new proteins from the same gene. Many introns have been found to code for an enzyme called reverse transcriptase, which can convert RNA into DNA. Other introns are translated into endonucleases, enzymes that can snip DNA and allow insertions and deletions into the sequence.

Check Your Progress SECTION 9.2

8. How is the language of a gene expressed?
9. If a bacterial protein is 3,300 amino acids long, how many nucleotide pairs long is the gene sequence that codes for it?
10. Construct a table that compares the structure and functions of DNA and RNA.
11. Where does transcription begin?
12. What are the template and nontemplate strands of DNA?
13. Why is only one strand transcribed, and is the same strand of DNA always transcribed?
14. Distinguish between a codon and an anticodon.
15. Briefly describe the events in translation.
16. What are the functions of start and stop codons? Give examples.
17. Summarize how bacterial and eukaryotic cells differ in gene structure, transcription, and translation.
18. Discuss the roles of exons and introns.

9.3 Genetic Regulation of Protein Synthesis and Metabolism

 Expected Learning Outcomes

14. Explain the functions of operons in bacterial genetic control.
15. Describe the main features of the lactose operon and inducible operons.
16. Describe the main features of repressible operons.
17. Summarize some aspects of genetic control by RNA.

In chapter 8, we surveyed the metabolic reactions in cells and the enzymes involved in those reactions. At that time, we mentioned that some enzymes are regulated and that one form of regulation occurs at the genetic level. This control mechanism ensures that genes are active only when their products are required. In this way,

enzymes will be produced as they are needed and the waste of energy and materials in dead-end synthesis is prevented. A major form of gene regulation in prokaryotes is through systems called **operons.** An operon is a section of DNA that contains one or more structural genes along with a corresponding operator gene that controls transcription. Having this kind of setup will permit genes for a particular metabolic pathway to be induced or repressed in unison by the same regulatory element.

Operons are described as either inducible or repressible. The category of an operon is determined by how it is affected by the environment within the cell. Many catabolic operons are **inducible,** meaning that the operon is turned on (induced) by the substrate of the enzyme for which the structural genes code. In this way, the enzymes needed to metabolize a nutrient (lactose, for example) are only produced when that nutrient is present. **Repressible operons** often contain genes coding for anabolic enzymes, such as those used to synthesize amino acids. In the case of these operons, several genes in series are turned off (repressed) by the product synthesized by the enzyme.

The Lactose Operon: A Model for Inducible Gene Regulation in Bacteria

The best understood cell system for explaining control through genetic induction is the **lactose (*lac*) operon.** The system, first described in 1961 by François Jacob and Jacques Monod, accounts for the regulation of lactose metabolism in *Escherichia coli.* Many other operons with similar modes of action have since been identified, and together they furnish convincing evidence that a cell's metabolic actions can have great impact on gene expression.

The lactose operon has three important features (**figure 9.18**):

1. the **regulator,** composed of the gene that codes for a protein capable of repressing the operon (a **repressor**);
2. the *control locus,* composed of two areas, the promoter recognized by RNA polymerase (see figure 9.11) and the **operator,** a sequence that acts as an on/off switch for transcription; and
3. the *structural locus,* made up of three genes, each coding for a different enzyme needed to catabolize lactose. One of the enzymes, β-galactosidase, hydrolyzes the lactose into its monosaccharides; another, permease, brings lactose across the cell membrane.

The promoter, operator, and structural components lie adjacent to one another, but the regulator can be at a distant site.

In inducible systems such as the *lac* operon, the operon is normally in an *off mode* and does not initiate enzyme synthesis when the appropriate substrate is absent (**figure 9.18, step 1**). How is the operon maintained in this mode? The key is in the repressor protein that is encoded by the regulatory gene. This relatively large molecule is **allosteric,** meaning that its shape can change, depending on which active site and substrate are in play. A substrate binding to one active site can distort a different active site and prevent it from accepting its substrate (see figure 8.10b). In the absence of lactose, the repressor protein fits specifically into sites on the operator that cause it to form a temporary loop. This loop blocks access of the RNA polymerase to the DNA of the operator and prevents transcription. Think of the repressor as a lock on the operator, and if the

① Operon Off: No Lactose
In the absence of lactose, a repressor protein (the product of a regulatory gene located elsewhere) attaches to the operator of the operon. This effectively blocks transcription of structural genes downstream (to its right). Suppression of transcription (and translation) prevents the unnecessary synthesis of enzymes for processing lactose.

② Operon On: Lactose Present
Upon entering the cell, the substrate (lactose) becomes a genetic inducer by attaching to the repressor, which is rendered inactive and falls away. The operator is no longer closed off and its DNA becomes accessible to the RNA polymerase. The RNA polymerase transcribes the structural genes, and the mRNA is translated into enzymes that can act on the lactose substrate.

Process Figure 9.18 **The lactose operon in bacteria: How inducible genes are controlled by substrate.**

operator is locked, the structural genes cannot be transcribed. Importantly, the regulator gene is located in a separate site from the operator region and is not affected by this block on the operon.

If lactose is added to the cell's environment, it triggers several events that turn the operon *on.* First, the binding of lactose to the repressor protein causes a conformational change in the repressor that dislodges it from the operator segment **(figure 9.18, step 2).** This opens the operator up so that RNA polymerase can now bind to it and begin transcription. The structural genes are transcribed in a single unbroken transcript coding for all three enzymes. During translation, however, each protein is synthesized separately. Because lactose is ultimately responsible for stimulating the chain of events leading to protein synthesis, it is called an **inducer.**

As lactose is depleted, further enzyme synthesis is not necessary, so the order of events reverses. At this point, there is no longer sufficient lactose to inhibit the repressor; hence, the repressor

regains its shape for attachment to the operator. The operator is locked, and transcription of the structural genes and enzyme synthesis related to lactose both stop.

A fine but important point about the *lac* operon is that it functions only in the absence of glucose or if the cell's energy needs are not being met by the available glucose. Glucose is the preferred carbon source because it can be used immediately in growth and does not require induction of an operon. When glucose is present, a second regulatory system ensures that the *lac* operon is inactive, regardless of lactose levels in the environment.

A Repressible Operon

Bacterial systems for synthesis of amino acids, purines and pyrimidines, and other processes work on a principle that is the reverse of the *lac* operon—that of repression. Similar factors such as repressor

proteins, operators, and a series of structural genes are part of a repressible operon, but with some important differences. Unlike the *lac* operon, this operon is normally in the *on* mode and will be turned *off* only when the product of the pathway is no longer required. Excess product plays a role as a **corepressor** that slows the transcription of the operon.

A metabolically active cell that needs the amino acid arginine (arg) will serve to illustrate the operation of a repressible operon. Under these conditions, the *arg* operon is set to *on,* and arginine is being actively synthesized through the action of the operon's enzymatic products (**figure 9.19, step 1**). In such an active cell, the arginine will be used immediately, and the repressor will remain inactive (unable to bind the operator) because there is too little free arginine to activate it. As the cell's metabolism begins to slow down, however, the synthesized arginine is no longer used up and accumulates. The free arginine is then available to act as a corepressor by attaching to the repressor. This reaction changes the shape of the repressor, making it capable of binding

to the operator and stopping transcription. Arginine will cease to be synthesized until the cell once again requires it in metabolism (**figure 9.19, step 2/2**).

Non-Operon Control Mechanisms

Analogous gene control mechanisms in eukaryotic cells are not as well understood, but it is known that gene function can be altered by intrinsic regulatory segments similar to operons. Some molecules, called transcription factors, insert on the grooves of the DNA molecule and enhance transcription of specific genes. These transcription factors can regulate gene expression in response to environmental stimuli such as nutrients, toxin levels, or even temperature. Eukaryotic genes are also regulated during growth and development, leading to the hundreds of different tissue types found in higher multicellular organisms. Considerable interest has been generated in the functions of regulatory RNAs that exert control on several levels in both prokaryotic and eukaryotic cells (**9.3 Making Connections**).

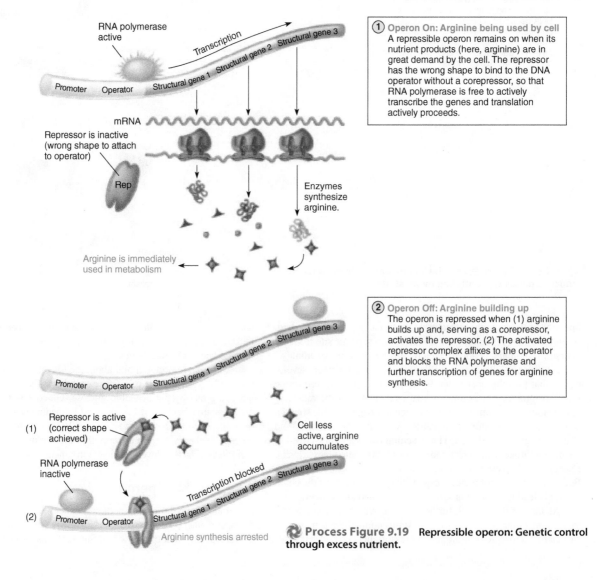

① **Operon On: Arginine being used by cell**
A repressible operon remains on when its nutrient products (here, arginine) are in great demand by the cell. The repressor has the wrong shape to bind to the DNA operator without a corepressor, so that RNA polymerase is free to actively transcribe the genes and translation actively proceeds.

② **Operon Off: Arginine building up**
The operon is repressed when (1) arginine builds up and, serving as a corepressor, activates the repressor. (2) The activated repressor complex affixes to the operator and blocks the RNA polymerase and further transcription of genes for arginine synthesis.

Process Figure 9.19 Repressible operon: Genetic control through excess nutrient.

9.3 MAKING CONNECTIONS

Is it Really an RNA World?

Evidence about the roles of RNAs in gene expression is accumulating rapidly. We have learned how the introns of eukaryotic mRNAs are removed by the catalytic RNA of the spliceosome complex, and the peptide bonds of proteins are catalyzed by ribosomal RNA. Based on our current understanding, it is clear that various forms of RNA dominate genetic control of transcription and translation. This type of RNA, called noncoding RNA (ncRNA) because it does not code for protein, regulates how the coded molecules are expressed.

Recently described ncRNAs in bacteria are **riboswitches**—short leader segments of mRNA that are transcribed but not expressed in a finished protein. Acting as a switch means that they can be turned on or off, depending on their folding pattern, which means they can both start or stop a step in gene expression. Some riboswitches work at the level of transcription and others alter translation, but the outcome of both is to affect protein synthesis. Riboswitches have a unique ability to sense and bind a specific molecule (ligand) such as an amino acid, vitamin, or cofactor, and this ligand changes their folding pattern. Certain riboswitches that terminate transcription are used by gram-positive bacteria to control synthesis of amino acids and some vitamins.

Riboswitches in gram-negative bacteria regulate translation at the ribosome. When the riboswitch is on, the leader sequence of mRNA forms a loop with itself that opens up the binding sequence and makes it available for the ribosome. The riboswitch can be turned off when a ligand binds to it and repositions the binding sequence. This makes the binding site inaccessible to the ribosome (**see figure**), thereby blocking translation. Like the *lac* operon, this mechanism will be reversed in the absence of the ligand, and translation can proceed. This riboswitch regulates synthesis of some vitamins.

Eukaryotes have their own versions of controls on transcription and translation. We are just beginning to understand the functions of small RNAs that contain around 20 to 25 nucleotides found in animal and plant cells. Small RNAs have been termed "gene silencers" because they shut down final products of gene expression. Examples are microRNAs and si (short interfering) RNAs, both of which control the fate of mRNA following transcription. Both types of small RNAs attach to mRNA and keep it from being translated. In some cases, they suppress mRNA functions, and in others, they actually bring in enzymes to destroy the mRNA. SiRNA is also known to signal the destruction of foreign RNA from viruses.

Another form of eukaryotic regulation acts at the level of the chromosomes, by means of reorganization and modification of the chromatin—a type of epigenetic effect. By fine-tuning the tightness and looseness of the chromatin structure, certain small RNAs can control which genes are accessible for function (see page 259). Other small RNAs are involved in methylation of DNA, which also modulates gene availability.

Knowledge of these novel types of RNA molecules has answered some questions that came out of genome sequencing studies. Most of the DNA in organisms was found *not* to code for functional proteins. This DNA was once considered "junk," but its percentage in humans was 85%! Obviously, in bacteria as well as in humans, it is far from junk. In fact, this DNA has been preserved in the same form for many millions of years of evolution, suggesting it has a very important function. We now know that much of it codes for these important RNA regulatory molecules.

In what ways could knowledge of these regulatory RNAs inspire new types of drug therapies? *Answer available at http://www.mhhe. com/talaro9*

Check Your Progress SECTION 9.3

19. What is an operon? Describe the functions of regulators, promoters, and operators.

20. Compare and contrast the *lac* operon and repressible operon systems.

21. For both figures 9.18 and 9.19, draw a simple stepwise diagram indicating the events that would reverse the operon's action.

22. At which levels of DNA regulation do small RNAs function?

9.4 Mutations: Changes in the Genetic Code

Expected Learning Outcomes

18. Define a mutation and explain how mutant forms are identified.

19. Explain the causes and types of mutations and their effects.

20. Describe some mutation repair mechanisms.

21. Compare beneficial and detrimental effects of mutations.

As precise and predictable as the rules of genetic expression seem, permanent changes do occur in the genetic code. Indeed, genetic change is the driving force of evolution by adding variation to populations of organisms. Changes may become evident in altered gene expression, such as in the appearance or disappearance of anatomical or physiological traits. For example, a pigmented bacterium can lose its ability to form pigment, or a strain of the malarial parasite can develop resistance to a drug. A phenotypic change that is due to an alteration in the genotype is called a **mutation.** On a strictly molecular level, a mutation is an alteration in the nitrogen base sequence of DNA. It can involve the loss of base pairs, the addition of base pairs, or a rearrangement in the order of base pairs. Do not confuse this with genetic recombination, in which microbes transfer whole segments of genetic information between themselves.

A microorganism that exhibits a natural, nonmutated characteristic is known as a **wild type,** or wild strain. If a microorganism bears a mutation, it is called a **mutant strain.** Mutant strains can show variance in morphology, nutritional characteristics, genetic control mechanisms, resistance to chemicals, temperature preference, and nearly any type of enzymatic function. Mutant strains are very useful for tracking genetic events, unraveling genetic organization, and pinpointing genetic markers.

The simplest way to detect mutant bacteria is to inoculate solid media containing differential or selective agents such as metabolic substrates or antibiotics. Growing a pure culture on a plate of media and observing the appearance of colonies can reveal strains of a species that express genetic variations. For instance, in cultures of wild-type *E. coli* grown on differential MacConkey agar, most of the isolated colonies will indicate a positive result for lactose fermentation, but invariably, there will be a small number of colonies that are negative and have lost the genes for using lactose. This colony can be readily pulled out for further study. Antibiotics are frequently added to media as selective agents for separating out strains of bacteria that are drug resistant. Figure 10.12 shows how this method works for detecting recombinant cells used in genetic engineering.

Another method for detecting and isolating mutant strains of microbes that grow in colonies is the *replica plating* technique **(figure 9.20).** This method is based on a variation between wild strains that can synthesize a nutrient, such as an amino acid, and mutant strains that cannot synthesize it. First a culture of test microbes is exposed to a chemical agent known to cause mutations and then plated on a complete medium that contains the particular nutrient. It is important for this to be done in a way that individual colonies are formed. Colony position on the plate is retained by pressing a pickup or replica carrier onto the colonies and then using the carrier to inoculate two plates in the same orientation. These two plates contain: (1) a complete medium containing the nutrient being tested for and (2) an incomplete medium that lacks it. Colonies that grow on the complete medium could be of either the wild or mutant type, but only the wild strains will grow on the incomplete medium. By comparing the two plates side by side, it is possible to locate the position of the colony on the complete medium that does not grow on the incomplete one. This mutant colony is now detectable and can be isolated.

Replica plating has been an effective technique to screen for phenotypic variants of bacteria and other microbes. It has the

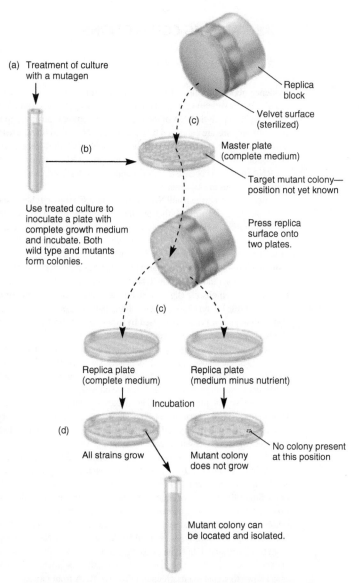

(a) Treatment of culture with a mutagen

(b)

(c)

Replica block

Velvet surface (sterilized)

Master plate (complete medium)

Target mutant colony—position not yet known

Use treated culture to inoculate a plate with complete growth medium and incubate. Both wild type and mutants form colonies.

Press replica surface onto two plates.

(c)

Replica plate (complete medium)

Replica plate (medium minus nutrient)

Incubation

(d)

All strains grow

Mutant colony does not grow

No colony present at this position

Mutant colony can be located and isolated.

Figure 9.20 The replica plating method for isolating mutant bacteria. This technique was developed by Joshua Lederberg. It is based on **(a)** exposing a culture to a mutagen, **(b)** plating the culture for isolated colonies on a master plate with complete nutrients, **(c)** pressing a sterile carrier onto the surface of the colonies to pick up a tiny clump of cells and pressing it again onto a plate of complete medium and then onto one of incomplete medium. **(d)** After growth, the two plates are compared. The colonies that occupy a specific position on the complete medium but are missing from that same position on the incomplete medium are mutant colonies that can be subcultured.

potential to provide information on a wide variety of metabolic characteristics. For example, it is used to detect mutants that vary in biochemical characteristics such as amino acid synthesis, substrate utilization, and sensitivity to antibiotics. Information on rates of mutation can also serve as the basis for carcinogen testing (see the Ames test, page 280).

Causes of Mutations

A mutation is described as spontaneous or induced, depending upon its origin. A **spontaneous mutation** is a random change in the DNA arising from errors in replication that occur without a known cause. The frequency of spontaneous mutations has been measured for a number of organisms. Mutation rates can vary considerably among organisms. Bacteria show rates ranging from 10^{-4} mutations per base per replication to 10^{-11} mutations per base per replication. The rapid rate of bacterial reproduction allows these mutations to be observed more readily in bacteria than in most eukaryotes.

Induced mutations result from exposure to known **mutagens,** which are primarily physical or chemical agents that damage DNA and interfere with its functioning **(table 9.3).** The carefully controlled use of mutagens has proved a useful way to induce mutant strains of microorganisms for study.

Chemical mutagenic agents act in a variety of ways to change the DNA. Agents such as acridine dyes insert completely across the DNA helices between adjacent bases. This results in distortion of the helix and can cause frameshift mutations. Analogs[5] of the nitrogen bases (5-bromodeoxyuridine and 2-aminopurine, for example) are chemical mimics of natural bases that are incorporated into DNA during replication. Addition of these abnormal bases leads to mistakes in base-pairing. Many chemical mutagens are also carcinogens, or cancer-causing agents (see the discussion of the Ames test on page 280).

Physical agents that alter DNA are primarily types of radiation. High-energy gamma rays and X rays introduce major physical changes into DNA, and it accumulates breaks that may not be repairable. Ultraviolet (UV) radiation induces abnormal bonds between adjacent pyrimidines so that normal replication of that region is blocked. Exposure to large doses of radiation can be fatal, which is why radiation is so effective in microbial control; it can also be carcinogenic in animals. The use of radiation to control microorganisms is described further in chapter 11.

5. An analog is a chemical structured very similarly to another chemical except for minor differences in functional groups.

TABLE 9.3	Selected Mutagenic Agents and Their Effects
Agent	**Effect**
Chemical	
Nitrous acid, bisulfite	Remove an amino group from some bases
Ethidium bromide	Inserts between the paired bases
Acridine dyes	Cause frameshifts due to insertion between base pairs
Nitrogen base analogs	Compete with natural bases for sites on replicating DNA
Radiation	
Ionizing (gamma rays, X rays)	Form free radicals that cause single or double breaks in DNA
Ultraviolet	Causes cross-links between adjacent pyrimidines

Categories of Mutations

Mutations range from large mutations, in which large genetic sequences are gained or lost, to small ones that affect only a single base on a gene. These latter mutations, which involve addition, deletion, or substitution of single bases, are called **point mutations.**

To understand how a change in DNA influences the cell, remember that the DNA code appears in a particular order of triplets (three bases) that is transcribed into mRNA codons, each of which specifies an amino acid. A permanent alteration in the DNA that is copied faithfully into mRNA and translated can change the structure of the protein. A change in a protein can likewise change the morphology and physiology of a cell. Most mutations have a harmful effect on the cell, leading to cell dysfunction or death; these are called lethal mutations. Neutral mutations produce neither adverse nor helpful changes. A small number of mutations are beneficial in that they provide the cell with a useful change in structure or physiology.

Any change in the code that leads to placement of a different amino acid is called a **missense mutation.** A missense mutation can do one of the following:

- create a faulty, nonfunctional (or less functional) protein,
- produce a protein that functions in a different manner, or
- cause no significant alteration in protein function.

A **nonsense mutation,** on the other hand, changes a normal codon into a stop codon that does not code for an amino acid and stops the production of the protein wherever it occurs. A nonsense mutation almost always results in a nonfunctional protein. A **silent mutation** alters a base but does not change the amino acid and thus has no effect. For example, because of the redundancy of the code, ACU, ACC, ACG, and ACA all code for threonine, so a mutation that changes only the last base will not alter the sense of the message in any way. A **back-mutation** occurs when a gene that has undergone mutation reverses (mutates back) to its original base composition.

Mutations also occur when one or more bases are inserted into or deleted from a newly synthesized DNA strand. This type of mutation, known as a **frameshift,** is so named because the reading frame of the mRNA has been changed. Frameshift mutations nearly always result in a nonfunctional protein because every amino acid after the mutation is different from what was coded for in the original DNA. Also note that insertion or deletion of bases in multiples of three (3, 6, 9, etc.) results in the addition or deletion of amino acids and does not disturb the reading frame. It can still disrupt the structure of the protein, depending on the change in the amino acid sequence. The effects of all of these types of mutations can be seen in **table 9.4.**

Repair of Mutations

Earlier, we indicated that DNA has a proofreading mechanism to repair mistakes in replication that might otherwise become permanent. Because mutations are potentially life-threatening, the cell has additional systems for finding and repairing DNA that has been damaged by various mutagenic agents and processes. Most ordinary DNA damage is resolved by enzymatic systems specialized for finding and fixing such defects.

DNA that has been damaged by ultraviolet radiation can be restored by photoactivation or light repair. This repair mechanism

TABLE 9.4	Classification of Major Types of Mutations
	Example

I. Wild-type (original, nonmutated) sequence THE BIG BAD DOG ATE THE FAT RED CAT

The wild-type sequence of a gene is the DNA sequence found in most organisms and is generally considered the "normal" sequence.

II. Categories of mutations based on type of DNA alteration

A. Substitution mutations

1. Missense THE BIG BAD DOG ATE THE FIT RED CAT

A missense mutation causes a different amino acid to be incorporated into a protein. Effects range from unnoticeable to severe, based on how different the two amino acids are.

2. Nonsense THE BIG BAD (stop)

A nonsense mutation converts a codon to a stop codon, resulting in premature termination of protein synthesis. Effects of this type of mutation are almost always severe.

B. Frameshift mutations

1. Insertion THE BIG BAB DDO GAT ETH EFA TRE DCA T

2. Deletion THE BIG BDD OGA TET HEF ATR EDC AT

Insertion and deletion mutations cause a change in the reading frame of the mRNA, resulting in a protein in which every amino acid after the mutation is affected. Because of this, frameshift mutations almost always result in a nonfunctional protein.

requires visible light and a light-sensitive enzyme, DNA photolyase, which can attach to sites of abnormal pyrimidine bonding and restore the original DNA structure. Ultraviolet repair mechanisms are successful only for a relatively small number of UV mutations. Mutations can be excised by a series of enzymes that remove the incorrect bases and add the correct ones. This process is known as *excision repair*. First, enzymes break the bonds between the bases and the sugar-phosphate strand at the site of the error. A different enzyme subsequently removes the defective bases one at a time, leaving a gap that will be filled in by DNA polymerase I and ligase. A repair system can also locate mismatched bases that were missed during proofreading: for example, C mistakenly paired with A, or G with T. The base must be replaced soon after the mismatch is made, or it will not be recognized by the repair enzymes.

Quick Search

See this process animated by going to the "DNA Nucleotide Excision Repair" video on YouTube.

The Ames Test

New agricultural, industrial, and medicinal chemicals are constantly being added to the environment, and exposure to them is widespread. The discovery that many such compounds are muta-

genic and that up to 83% of these mutagens are linked to cancer is significant. Although animal testing has been a standard method of detecting chemicals with carcinogenic potential, a more rapid screening system called the **Ames test**[6] is also commonly used. In this ingenious test, the experimental subjects are bacteria whose gene expression and mutation rate can be readily observed and monitored. The premise is that any chemical capable of mutating bacterial DNA can similarly mutate mammalian (and thus human) DNA and is therefore potentially hazardous. Many potential carcinogens (benzanthracene and aflatoxin, for example) are mutagenic agents only after being acted on by mammalian liver enzymes, so an extract of these enzymes is added to the test medium.

One indicator organism in the Ames test is a mutant strain of *Salmonella enterica*[7] that has lost the ability to synthesize the amino acid histidine, a defect highly susceptible to back-mutation because the strain also lacks DNA repair mechanisms. Mutations that cause reversion to the wild strain, which is capable of synthesizing histidine, occur spontaneously at a low rate. A test agent is considered a mutagen if it enhances the rate of back-mutation beyond levels that would occur spontaneously. **Figure 9.21** compares a standard version of the test with a multiwell method that streamlines result taking. The Ames test has proved invaluable for screening an assortment of environmental and dietary chemicals for mutagenicity and carcinogenicity without resorting to animal studies.

Positive and Negative Effects of Mutations

Many mutations are not repaired. How the cell copes with them depends on the nature of the mutation and the strategies available to that organism. Mutations are passed on to the offspring of organisms during reproduction and to new viruses during replication. They become a long-term part of the gene pool. Most mutations are harmful to organisms, but some can provide adaptive advantages.

If a mutation leading to a nonfunctional protein occurs in a gene for which there is only a single copy, as in haploid or simple organisms, the cell will probably die. This happens when certain mutant strains of *E. coli* acquire mutations in the genes needed to repair damage by UV radiation. Mutations of the human genome affecting the action of a single protein (mostly enzymes) are responsible for more than 3,500 diseases.

Although most spontaneous mutations are not beneficial, a small number contribute to the success of the individual and the population by creating variant strains with alternate ways of expressing a trait. Microbes are not "aware" of this advantage and do not direct these changes; they simply respond to the environment they encounter. In the long-range view, mutations and the variations they produce are the raw materials for change in the population and, thus, for evolution.

Mutations that create variants occur frequently enough that any population contains mutant strains for a number of characteristics, but as long as the environment is stable, these mutants will never comprise more than a tiny percentage of the population. When the environment changes, however, it can become hostile for the survival of certain individuals, and only those microbes

6. Named for its creator, Bruce Ames.

7. *S. enterica* inhabits the intestine of poultry and causes food poisoning in humans. It is used extensively in genetic studies of bacteria.

Culture of *Salmonella*
bacteria, histidine (–)

In the control setup, bacteria
are plated on a histidine-free
medium containing liver
enzymes but lacking the
test agent.

The experimental plate is
prepared the same way
except that it contains the test
agent.

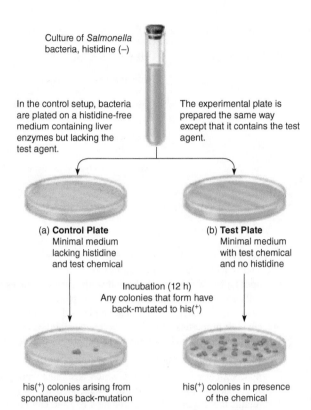

(a) **Control Plate**
Minimal medium
lacking histidine
and test chemical

(b) **Test Plate**
Minimal medium
with test chemical
and no histidine

Incubation (12 h)
Any colonies that form have
back-mutated to his(+)

his(+) colonies arising from
spontaneous back-mutation

his(+) colonies in presence
of the chemical

(c) The degree of mutagenicity of the chemical agent can be calculated by
comparing the number of colonies growing on the control plate with the
number on the test plate. Chemicals that induce an increased incidence
of back-mutation (right side) are considered carcinogens.

(d) Ames fluctuation tests using multiple wells; a blue well indicates no
back-mutation occurring; yellow indicates back-mutations.

Counting the number of (+) yellow wells provides the number of
back-mutations; the result on the right indicates a strong mutagen.

Figure 9.21 The Ames test. (a, b, c) In this traditional plate method,
a strain of *Salmonella enterica* that cannot synthesize histidine [his (–)] is the
test species. If the chemical causes an increase in mutation rate to histidine-
producing cells as compared to a control, the chemical is considered
mutagenic. **(d)** The newer well fluctuation test is based on the same basic
scheme, however, it has greater sensitivity and is easier to evaluate.

bearing protective mutations will be equipped to survive in the
new environment.

Such observations can be explained by the important biologi-
cal principles of natural selection and survival of the fittest. This
theory states that environmental pressure selects for organisms that
have greater adaptability due to beneficial mutations. They are
more likely to survive, reproduce, and pass the changed genes on
to succeeding generations. In time, these survivors become the
dominant members of the population as long as the mutation con-

tinues to favor their survival. One of the clearest models for natural
selection in action is acquired drug resistance in bacteria (dis-
cussed in chapter 12).

As we will see in section 9.5, bacteria have additional mecha-
nisms for changing their genetic makeup by sharing genes with
other bacteria through recombination.

Check your Progress SECTION 9.4

23. Explain what is meant by the terms mutation and mutant.
24. Describe the primary causes and types of mutations. Give an exam-
 ple of a mutation that is beneficial and one that is lethal or harmful.
25. Explain the purposes behind replica plating and the Ames test.

9.5 DNA Recombination Events

Expected Learning Outcomes

22. Explain recombination in bacteria and what it involves.
23. Describe the main features of conjugation and its outcomes.
24. Discuss what is required for bacterial transformation and its outcomes.
25. Identify the basic processes involved in transduction and the end results.
26. Discuss transposons and their importance to microorganisms.

Genetic recombination through sexual reproduction is an impor-
tant means of genetic variation in eukaryotes. Although bacteria
have no exact equivalent to sexual reproduction, they exhibit a
primitive means for sharing or recombining parts of their ge-
nomes. An event in which one bacterium donates DNA to another
bacterium is a type of genetic transfer termed **recombination,**
the end result of which is a new strain different from both the
donor and the original recipient strain. In general, any organism
that has acquired genes that originated in another organism is
called a **recombinant.**

Recombination in bacteria depends largely on their extreme ver-
satility in acquiring and expressing the genetic material of other bac-
teria and even other organisms. This capacity for genetic sharing has
tremendous effects on the diversity and evolution of bacteria. Unlike
spontaneous mutations, recombinations are generally beneficial.
They can provide additional genes for resistance to drugs and meta-
bolic poisons, new nutritional and metabolic schemes, increased vir-
ulence, and adaptations to changing environmental conditions.

Transmission of Genetic Material in Bacteria

DNA transfer between bacterial cells typically involves small
pieces of DNA in the form of **plasmids** or chromosomal fragments.
Plasmids are small, circular pieces of DNA that contain their own
origin of replication and therefore can replicate independently of
the bacterial chromosome. Plasmids are found in many bacteria (as
well as some fungi) and typically contain a few dozen genes. Al-
though plasmids are not necessary for bacterial survival, they often
carry adaptive genes, such as those for drug resistance.

TABLE 9.5	Types of Genetic Recombination in Bacteria		
Mode	**Factors Involved**	**Direct or Indirect***	**Examples of Genes Transferred**
Conjugation	Donor cell with pilus Fertility plasmid in donor Both donor and recipient alive Bridge forms between cells to transfer DNA.	Direct	Drug resistance; resistance to metals; toxin production; enzymes; adherence molecules; degradation of toxic substances; uptake of iron
Transformation	Free donor DNA (fragment or plasmid) Live, competent recipient cell, donor usually dead	Indirect	Polysaccharide capsule; unlimited with cloning techniques; metabolic enzymes
Transduction	Donor is lysed bacterial cell. Defective bacteriophage is carrier of donor DNA. Live recipient cell of same species as donor	Indirect	Exotoxins; enzymes for sugar fermentation; drug resistance

*Direct means the donor and recipient are in contact during exchange; indirect means they are not.

The Case Study on page 256 details a pathogen that has received dozens of resistance genes from other species. Chromosomal fragments that have escaped from a lysed bacterial cell are also commonly involved in the transfer of genetic information between cells. An important difference between plasmids and fragments is that, while a plasmid can be stably replicated and inherited, chromosomal fragments must integrate themselves into the bacterial chromosome in order to be replicated and eventually passed to progeny cells. The process of genetic recombination is relatively rare in nature, but its frequency can be increased in the laboratory, where the ability to transfer genes between organisms has become an important tool of research and technology.

Depending upon the mode of transmission, the means of genetic recombination in bacteria is called conjugation, transformation, or transduction. **Conjugation** requires the attachment of two cells and the formation of a bridge that can transport DNA. **Transformation** entails the transfer of naked DNA and requires no special vehicle. **Transduction** is DNA transfer mediated through the action of a bacterial virus (**table 9.5**).

Conjugation: Genetic Transmission Through Direct Contact

Conjugation is a mode of genetic recombination in which a plasmid or fragment of DNA is transferred from a donor cell to a recipient cell via a direct connection. Both gram-negative and gram-positive bacteria can conjugate, but only gram-negative cells operate with a specialized plasmid called a **fertility, or F factor.** This plasmid directs the synthesis of a unique **pilus,** also called a sex pilus,[8] that functions in most conjugation transfers. The recipient cell is usually a related bacterium with a recognition site on its surface for interacting with the pilus (**figure 9.22, step 1**).

A cell's role in conjugation is denoted by F^+ for the cell that has the F plasmid and by F^- for the cell that lacks it. Contact is made when a pilus grows out from the F^+ cell, attaches to the surface of the F^- cell, contracts, and draws the two cells together (figure 9.22, step 1). At the site where the pilus attaches the two cells, a mating or conjugative bridge is formed that serves as a

transfer system for the plasmid. The latest reliable information indicates that the pilus becomes part of a complex secretory system that opens a gateway between the cell walls and membranes of the two cells and serves as a passageway for the plasmid.

There are hundreds of conjugative plasmids with some variations in their properties. One of the best understood plasmids is the F factor in *E. coli*, which exhibits these patterns of transfer:

1. Because bacteria tend to conserve plasmids, the donor cell first makes a copy of the F factor, which is simultaneously transferred across the bridge (**figure 9.22, step 2**). This way, it retains the original plasmid, remains F^+, and can continue to conjugate with other bacteria. The F^- cell has been changed into an F^+ cell capable of producing a pilus and conjugating with other cells. No additional donor genes are transferred during this transfer.
2. In high-frequency recombination (Hfr) donors, the fertility factor has been integrated into the F^+ donor chromosome.

The term *high-frequency recombination* denotes that a cell with an integrated F factor transmits its chromosomal genes at a higher frequency than other cells. This is because the F factor can direct a more comprehensive transfer of part of the donor chromosome to a recipient cell. This transfer occurs through replication of the donor chromosome along with the F factor. One strand of DNA is retained by the donor, and the other strand is transported across to the recipient cell (**figure 9.22, step 3**). The F factor may not be transferred during this process. The transfer of an entire chromosome takes about 100 minutes, but the pilus bridge between cells is ordinarily broken before this time, and rarely is the entire genome of the donor cell transferred.

Conjugation has great biomedical importance. Special **resistance (R) plasmids,** or **factors,** that bear genes for resisting antibiotics and other drugs are commonly shared among bacteria through conjugation. Transfer of R factors can confer multiple resistance to antibiotics such as tetracycline, chloramphenicol, sulfonamides, and penicillin. This phenomenon is discussed further in chapter 12. Other types of R factors carry genetic codes for resistance to heavy metals (nickel and mercury) or for synthesizing virulence factors (toxins, enzymes, and adhesion molecules) that increase the pathogenicity of the bacterial strain. Conjugation studies have also provided a means to map the bacterial chromosome.

8. This term refers to its function in the mating of bacteria, but it has nothing to do with sexual reproduction, which is absent in bacteria.

Physical Conjugation

F factor Bacterial chromosome

F⁺

Sex pilus makes contact with F⁻ recipient cell.

F⁻

Sex pilus contracts, bringing cells together.

F⁺

F⁻

(1) The pilus of donor cell (top) attaches to receptor on recipient cell and retracts to draw the two cells together. This is the mechanism for gram-negative bacteria.

F Factor Transfer

Bridge made with pilus

Donor Recipient

F⁺ F⁻

F factor (plasmid)

Chromosome

F⁺ F⁻

F factor being copied

F⁺ F⁺

F factor

(2) Transfer of the F factor, or conjugative plasmid

Hfr Transfer

Pilus

Donor Recipient

Integrated F factor

Hfr cell

Chromosome

Partial copy of donor chromosome

Bridge broken Donated genes

(3) High-frequency (Hfr) transfer involves transmission of chromosomal genes from a donor cell to a recipient cell. The donor chromosome is duplicated and transmitted in part to a recipient cell, where it is integrated into the chromosome.

Process Figure 9.22 Conjugation: Genetic transmission through direct contact between two cells.

Gram-positive bacteria such as *Bacillus* and *Streptococcus* are known to recombine through conjugation. Because they lack pili, they must transport the plasmids via specialized proteins activated during adhesion of the two cells. The mechanisms involved are yet to be fully worked out.

Transformation: Capturing Free DNA from Solution

One of the cornerstone discoveries in microbial genetics was made in the late 1920s by the English biochemist Frederick Griffith working with *Streptococcus pneumoniae* and laboratory mice. The pneumococcus exists in two major strains based on the presence of the capsule, colonial morphology, and pathogenicity. Encapsulated strains bear a smooth (S) colonial appearance and are virulent; strains lacking a capsule have a rough (R) appearance and are non-

virulent. (Recall from chapter 4 that the capsule protects a bacterium from the phagocytic host defenses.) Griffith first showed that when mice were injected with a live, virulent (S) strain, they soon died **(figure 9.23a)**. Mice injected with a live, nonvirulent (R) strain remained alive and healthy **(figure 9.23b)**. Next he tried a variation on this theme. He heat-killed an S strain and injected it into mice, which remained healthy **(figure 9.23c)**. Then came the ultimate test: Griffith injected both dead S cells and live R cells into mice, with the result that the mice died from pneumococcal blood infection **(figure 9.23d)**. If killed bacterial cells do not come back to life and the nonvirulent live strain was harmless, why did the mice die? Although he did not know it at the time, Griffith had demonstrated that dead S cells, while passing through the body of the mouse, broke open and released some of their DNA (by chance, that part containing the genes for making a capsule). A few of the live R cells

subsequently picked up this loose DNA and were transformed by it into virulent, capsule-forming strains.

Later studies supported the concept that a chromosome released by a lysed cell breaks into fragments small enough to be accepted by a recipient cell and that DNA, even from a dead cell, retains its genetic code. This nonspecific acceptance by a bacterial cell of small fragments of soluble DNA from the surrounding environment is termed **transformation (figure 9.24).** Transformation is facilitated by special DNA-binding proteins on the cell wall that capture DNA from the surrounding medium. Cells that are capable of accepting genetic material through this means are termed **competent.** The new DNA is passed through a DNA uptake system in the cell wall and membrane. Within the cytoplasm, the donated strand is inserted into the chromosome of the recipient cell, now termed *transformed*. Natural transformation is found in several groups of gram-positive and gram-negative bacterial species. In addition to genes coding for the capsule, bacteria also exchange genes for antibiotic resistance and bacteriocin synthesis in this way.

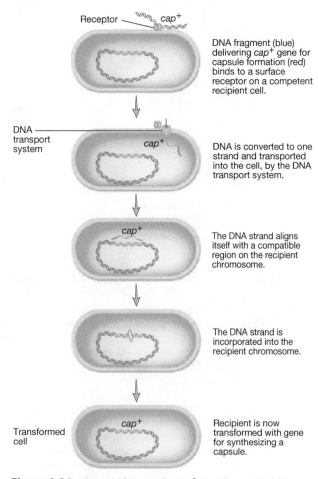

Figure 9.23 **Griffith's classic experiment in transformation.** In essence, this experiment proved that DNA released from a killed cell can be acquired by a live cell. The cell receiving this new DNA is genetically transformed—in this case, from a nonvirulent strain to a virulent one.

Figure 9.24 **Steps in bacterial transformation as seen in** *S. pneumoniae.* This shows how genes coding for capsule formation are brought into the cell and inserted into the chromosome. *Cap*⁺ indicates genes for forming a capsule.

Because transformation requires no special appendages, and the donor and recipient cells do not have to be in direct contact, the process is useful for certain types of recombinant DNA technology. With this technique, foreign genes from a completely unrelated organism are inserted into a plasmid, which is then introduced into a competent bacterial cell through transformation. These recombinations can be carried out in a test tube, and human genes can be experimented upon and even expressed outside the human body by placing them in a microbial cell. Transformation is often used in the production of genetically engineered organisms such as yeasts, plants, and mice and has been proposed as a future technique for curing genetic diseases in humans. These topics are covered in more detail in chapter 10.

Transduction: Viruses as Vectors

Bacteriophages (bacterial viruses) have been previously described as destructive bacterial parasites. Viruses can also serve as genetic vectors (an entity that can bring foreign DNA into a cell). The process by which a bacteriophage serves as the carrier of DNA from a donor cell to a recipient cell is **transduction.** Although it occurs naturally in a broad spectrum of bacteria, the participating bacteria in a single transduction event must be the same species because of the specificity of viruses for host cells.

There are two versions of transduction. In *generalized transduction* (**figure 9.25**), random fragments of disintegrating host DNA are taken up by the phage during assembly. Virtually any gene from the bacterium can be transmitted through this means. In *specialized transduction* (**figure 9.26**), a highly specific part of the host genome is regularly incorporated into the virus. This specificity is explained by the prior existence of a temperate prophage inserted in a fixed site on the bacterial chromosome. When activated, the prophage DNA separates from the bacterial chromosome, carrying a small segment of host genes with it. During a lytic cycle, these specific viral-host gene combinations are incorporated into the viral particles and carried to another bacterial cell. Instances of transduction include the transfer of drug resistance seen in *Staphylococcus* spp. and the transmission of gene regulators in gram-negative rods such as *Escherichia* and *Salmonella*.

Transposons: "The Case of the Jumping Genes" One type of genetic transferral of great interest involves transposable elements, or **transposons**. Transposons have the distinction of shifting from one part of the genome to another and so are termed "jumping genes." When the idea of their existence in corn plants was first postulated by the geneticist Barbara McClintock, it was greeted with wide skepticism, because it had long been believed that the location of a given gene was set and that genes did not or could not move around. Now it is evident that jumping genes are widespread among prokaryotic and eukaryotic cells and viruses. Results from analysis of human DNA indicates that they make up nearly 45% of the human genome.

All transposons share the general characteristic of traveling from one location to another on the genome—from one chromosomal site to another, from a chromosome to a plasmid, or from a plasmid to a chromosome (**figure 9.27**). Because transposons can occur in plasmids, they can also be transmitted from one cell to

Process Figure 9.25 Generalized transduction: Genetic transfer by means of a virus carrier. (1) A phage infects cell A (the donor cell) by normal means. **(2)** During replication and assembly, a phage particle incorporates a segment of bacterial DNA by mistake. **(3)** Cell A then lyses and releases the mature phages, including the genetically altered one. **(4)** The altered phage adsorbs to and penetrates another host cell (cell B), injecting the DNA from cell A rather than viral nucleic acid. **(5)** Cell B receives this donated DNA, which recombines with its own DNA. Because the virus is defective (biologically inactive as a virus), it is unable to complete a lytic cycle. The transduced cell survives and can use this new genetic material.

another in bacteria and a few eukaryotes. Some transposons replicate themselves before jumping to the next location, and others simply move without replicating first.

Transposons contain DNA that codes for the enzymes needed to remove and reintegrate the transposon at another site in the genome. Flanking the coding region of the DNA are sequences called

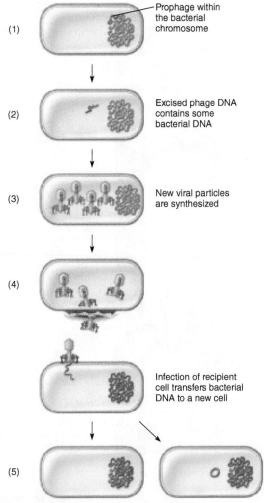

(1) Prophage within the bacterial chromosome

(2) Excised phage DNA contains some bacterial DNA

(3) New viral particles are synthesized

(4)

Infection of recipient cell transfers bacterial DNA to a new cell

(5)

Recombination results in two possible outcomes.

Process Figure 9.26 Specialized transduction: Transfer of specific genetic material by means of a virus carrier.
(1) Specialized transduction begins with a cell that contains a prophage (red). **(2)** When the virus enters a lytic cycle, it excises itself from its host cell, carrying along some host DNA. **(3)** Replication and assembly results in production of a chimeric virus containing viral and bacterial DNA. **(4)** Release of the recombinant virus and infection of a new host result in transfer of bacterial DNA between cells. **(5)** Recombination can occur between the new host chromosome and the virus DNA, resulting in either bacterial DNA or a combination of viral and bacterial DNA being incorporated into the bacterial chromosome.

inverted repeats, which mark the point at which the transposon is removed or reinserted into the genome. The smallest transposons consist of only these two genetic sequences and are often referred to as *insertion elements*. A type of transposon called *retrotransposon* can transcribe DNA into RNA and then back into DNA for insertion in a new location. Another example is the *integron*, which can carry large blocks of genetic material that are especially prominent in transmitting drug resistance.

(1)

(2) (3) (4)

Figure 9.27 Transposons: Shifting segments of the genome.
(1) A transposon exists as a small piece of DNA integrated into the host cell chromosome (red). **(2)** The transposon may excise itself and move from one location to another in the genome, maintaining itself as a single copy per cell. **(3)** It may also replicate prior to moving, leading to an increase in the copy number and a greater effect on the genome of the host. **(4)** Finally, the transposon may jump to a plasmid, which can then be transferred to another bacterial cell.

The overall effect of transposons—to scramble the genetic language—can be beneficial or adverse, depending upon such variables as where insertion occurs in a chromosome, what kinds of genes are relocated, and the type of cell involved. In bacteria, transposons are known to be involved in

- changes in traits such as colony morphology, pigmentation, and antigenic characteristics;
- replacement of damaged DNA; and
- the transfer of drug resistance in bacteria.

 Check Your Progress SECTION 9.5

26. Compare conjugation, transformation, and transduction on the basis of general method, donor, and recipient.
27. Explain the differences between general and specialized transduction, using drawings.
28. By means of a flowchart, show the possible jumps that a transposon can make. Show the involvement of viruses in its movement.

9.6 The Genetics of Animal Viruses

 Expected Learning Outcomes

27. Explain the major elements of viral genetics.
28. Compare aspects of the genetics of DNA and RNA viruses, using examples.

Viruses essentially consist of one or more pieces of DNA or RNA enclosed in a protective coating. They are genetic parasites that require access to their host cell's genetic and metabolic machinery to be replicated, transcribed, and translated, and they also have the potential for genetically changing the cells. Because they contain only those genes needed for the production of new viruses, the genomes of viruses tend to be very small and compact.

Viruses show significant variety in genetic patterns. In many viruses, the nucleic acid is linear in form; in others, it is circular. The genome of most viruses exists in a single molecule, though in a few, it is segmented into several smaller molecules. Most viruses contain normal double-stranded (ds) DNA or single-stranded (ss) RNA, but other patterns exist. There are ssDNA viruses, dsRNA viruses, and retroviruses, which work backward by making dsDNA from ssRNA. In some instances, viral genes overlap one another, and in a few DNA viruses, both strands contain a translatable message.

With few exceptions, replication of the DNA molecule of DNA animal viruses occurs in the nucleus, where the cell's DNA replication machinery lies, and the genome of RNA viruses is usually replicated in the cytoplasm. In all viruses, viral mRNA is translated into viral proteins on host cell ribosomes using host tRNA.

Replication Strategies in Animal Viruses

Replication, Transcription, and Translation of dsDNA Viruses

Replication of dsDNA viruses is divided into phases (**figure 9.28**). During the early phase, viral DNA enters the nucleus, where several genes are transcribed into a messenger RNA. Next, the mRNA transcript then moves into the cytoplasm to be translated into viral proteins (enzymes) needed to replicate the viral DNA. This replication usually occurs in the nucleus with the host cell's own DNA polymerase, though some viruses (herpes, for example) have their own. During the late phase, other viral genes are transcribed and translated into proteins required to form the capsid and other structures. The new viral genomes and capsids are assembled, and the mature viruses are released by budding or cell disintegration.

Double-stranded DNA viruses can interact directly with the DNA of their host cell. In some viruses, the viral DNA becomes silently *integrated* into the host's genome by insertion at a particular site on the host genome. Persistence of viral DNA may also lead to the transformation of the host cell into a cancer cell. Several DNA viruses, including hepatitis B (HBV), the herpesviruses, and papillomaviruses (warts), are known to be initiators of cancers and are thus termed **oncogenic.** The mechanisms of oncogenic **transformation** involve genes that can regulate cellular genomes and control the onset of cell division.

Replication, Transcription, and Translation of RNA Viruses

RNA viruses exhibit several differences from DNA viruses. Their genomes are smaller, they enter the host cell already in an RNA form, and the virus cycle occurs entirely in the cytoplasm for most viruses. RNA viruses can have one of the following genetic messages:

1. a positive-strand (+) genome that comes ready to be translated into proteins,

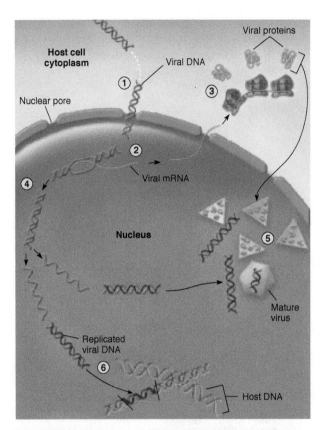

Figure 9.28 General stages in the multiplication of double-stranded DNA viruses. The virus penetrates the host cell and releases DNA, which, **(1)** enters the nucleus and **(2)** is transcribed by host cell enzymes into mRNA. **(3)** Viral mRNA leaves the nucleus and is translated into structural proteins; these proteins are transported into the nucleus. **(4)** Viral DNA is replicated repeatedly in the nucleus. **(5)** Viral DNA and proteins are assembled into a mature virus in the nucleus. **(6)** Because it is double-stranded, some viral DNA can insert itself into host DNA (latency). Some exceptions to this pattern occur in the poxviruses.

2. a negative-strand (−) genome that must be converted to a positive-strand before translation, and

3. a positive-strand (+) genome that can be converted to DNA or a dsRNA genome.

Positive-Strand Single-Stranded RNA Viruses (Figure 9.29)

The ssRNA of positive-strand viruses such as polio come ready to be translated, so it is immediately translated into a large protein and cleaved into individual functional units. One of these is an RNA polymerase that initiates the replication of the viral strand. Replication of a positive-message strand happens in two steps. First, a negative strand is synthesized using the positive strand as a template by the usual base-pairing mechanism. The resultant negative strand becomes a master template against which new positive daughter strands are made. Further translation of the viral genome

Figure 9.29 **Replication of positive-strand, single-stranded RNA viruses.** In general, these viruses do not enter the nucleus. **(1)** Penetration of viral RNA. **(2)** Because it is positive in message and single-stranded, the RNA can be directly translated on host cell ribosomes into various necessary viral proteins. **(3)** A negative genome is synthesized against the positive template to produce large numbers of positive genomes for final assembly. **(4)** The negative template is then used to synthesize a series of positive replicates. **(5)** RNA strands and proteins assemble into mature viruses.

produces large numbers of structural proteins for final assembly and maturation of the virus.

RNA Viruses with Reverse Transcriptase: Retroviruses

A most unusual class of viruses can reverse the order of the flow of genetic information. Thus far in our discussion, all genetic entities have shown the patterns DNA → DNA, DNA → RNA, or RNA → RNA. Retroviruses, including HIV, the cause of AIDS, and HTLV I, a cause of one type of human leukemia, synthesize DNA using their RNA genome as a template. They accomplish this by means of a **reverse transcriptase** that comes packaged with each virus particle. This enzyme synthesizes a single-stranded DNA against the viral RNA template and then directs the formation of a complementary strand of this ssDNA, resulting in a double strand of viral DNA. The dsDNA strand enters the nucleus, where it can be transcribed by the usual mechanisms into new viral ssRNA and used to assemble new viral particles.

When the DNA of some retroviruses becomes inserted into the host's DNA as a provirus, cells may be transformed and produce tumors. Insertion allows HIV to remain latent in an infected cell for several years (see figure 25.16).

✅ *Check Your Progress* SECTION 9.6

29. Explain why some viruses must enter the nucleus to replicate whereas others do not.
30. Explain the difference between positive-strand and negative-strand viral genomes.

CASE STUDY Part 2

The first cases of *A. baumannii* infections were reported in the 1970s. At that time, it was not considered a serious pathogen, and it was sensitive to most available drugs. How did it go from being an uncommon infectious agent to one that accounts for around 6% of nosocomial infections, and how did the number of MDR strains increase from 3% to 40%? It had not developed greater virulence.* It is actually relatively harmless for most healthy people with intact immune systems. It is an opportunist that attacks mainly immunocompromised patients with various underlying medical problems. This pathogen infects a variety of organs and systems, including respiratory, skin, urinary, and the bloodstream. Medical specialists suspect that its rapid evolution can be explained by the combination of four factors: the widespread distribution of the bacteria in the environment, the drug-rich environment of hospitals and clinics, the increase in severely compromised patients, and the pathogen's extreme genetic adaptability to challenges from new drugs.

For many years, the rise of "superbugs" has become a major concern of the medical community. The working definition of this term includes any bacterial species that have developed significant resistance to several drugs that would ordinarily have been given in therapy. Two of the *A. baumannii* strains described here are defined as multiple drug resistant (MDR), in that they resist a fairly broad range of drugs. One strain fits the category of extreme drug resistance (XDR), meaning that it is resistant to all possible drugs. Both versions of this pathogen have been added to the list of emerging diseases.

- What is meant by the term *opportunist*?
- Which genetic events have allowed *Acinetobacter* to become so resistant?

To conclude this Case Study, go to Perspectives on the Connect website.

These topics are discussed further in chapter 12.
To read more about the medical implications of this case, go to http://www.medscape.com/view article/575837.

──────

* *virulence* (veer′-yoo-lents) Ability of a microbe to invade and damage a host.

 Chapter Summary with Key Terms

9.1 Introduction to Genetics and Genes: Unlocking the Secrets of Heredity

A. **Genetics** is the study of **heredity** and can be studied at the level of the organism, **genome, chromosome, gene,** and **DNA.** Genes provide the information needed to construct **proteins,** which have structural or catalytic functions in the cell.

B. **DNA** is a long molecule in the form of a double helix. Each strand of the helix consists of a string of **nucleotides.**
1. A nucleotide consists of a **phosphate, deoxyribose sugar,** and **nitrogen base.** The bases form hydrogen bonds with their counterparts on the other strand.
2. **Adenine** base-pairs with **thymine** while **guanine** base-pairs with **cytosine.**
3. The order of the nucleotides specifies which amino acids will be used to construct proteins during the process of translation.

C. **Replication** of DNA–making copies of the genetic program.
1. Requires unwinding the double helix and exposing the nucleotides to serve as templates for synthesis of 2 identical molecules by **DNA polymerase.**
2. Is **semiconservative** and proceeds in the 5′ to 3′ direction of the newly synthesized DNA.

9.2 Applications of the DNA Code: Transcription and Translation

A. DNA is used to produce RNA (**transcription**) and RNA is then used to produce protein (**translation**).

B. RNA: Unlike DNA, RNA is single stranded, contains **uracil** instead of thymine and **ribose** instead of deoxyribose.
1. Major forms of RNA found in the cell include **mRNA, tRNA,** and **rRNA.**
2. The genetic information contained in DNA is copied to produce an RNA molecule. **Codons** in the mRNA pair with **anticodons** in the tRNA to specify what amino acids to assemble on the ribosome during translation.

C. *Transcription and Translation:*
1. Transcription occurs when **RNA polymerase** copies the template strand of a segment of DNA. RNA is always made in the 5′ to 3′ direction.
2. Translation occurs when the mRNA is used to direct the synthesis of proteins on the ribosome.
3. Codons in the mRNA pair with anticodons in the tRNA to assemble a string of amino acids. This occurs until a stop codon is reached.

D. *Eukaryotic Gene Expression:* Eukaryotic genes are composed of **exons** (expressed sequences) and **introns** (intervening sequences). The introns must be removed and the exons spliced together to create the final mRNA.

9.3 Genetic Regulation of Protein Synthesis and Metabolism

Protein synthesis is regulated through gene induction or repression, as controlled by an **operon.** Operons consist of several structural genes controlled by a common regulatory element.

A. **Inducible operons** such as the lactose operon are normally off but can be turned on by a lactose inducer.

B. **Repressible operons** are usually on but can be turned off when their end product is no longer needed.

C. Newly described types of RNA can serve in gene regulation.
1. Micro and small interfering RNAs can block the action of other RNAs and shut down gene expression in eukaryotes.
2. Riboswitches can also control RNA functions related to transcription and translation in bacteria.

9.4 Mutations: Changes in the Genetic Code

A. Changes in the genetic code occur primarily through mutation and recombination.

B. Inheritable changes in the genome of a microorganism are known as **mutations.** They usually entail an alteration in the nucleotide composition of the genetic material. Mutations may be **spontaneous** or **induced.**

C. Mutations are detected by the use of selective media and the replica plating technique.

D. **Point mutations** entail a change in one or a few bases and are categorized as **missense, nonsense, silent mutations,** and **back-mutations,** based on the effect of the change in nucleotide(s).

E. Many mutations, particularly those involving mismatched bases or damage from ultraviolet light, can be corrected using enzymes found in the cell.

F. The **Ames test** measures the mutagenicity of chemicals by their ability to induce mutations in bacteria.

9.5 DNA Recombination Events

A. Recombination involves the acquisition of new genetic material from an outside source.

B. Intermicrobial transfer and genetic recombination permit gene sharing between bacteria. Major types of recombination include **conjugation, transformation,** and **transduction.**

C. **Transposons** are DNA sequences that regularly move to different places within the genome of a cell, generating mutations and variations in chromosome structure.

9.6 The Genetics of Animal Viruses

A. Viruses contain various forms of DNA and RNA that are transcribed and translated by the genetic machinery of their host cells to form functioning viral particles.
1. Genomes of viruses are found in double-stranded (ds) DNA and single-stranded (ss) RNA forms. A few contain unusual ssDNA and dsRNA not found in cells.
2. DNA viruses tend to replicate in the nucleus while RNA viruses replicate in the cytoplasm. Retroviruses synthesize dsDNA using ssRNA as a template.

Level I. Knowledge and Comprehension

These questions require a working knowledge of the concepts in the chapter and the ability to recall and understand the information you have studied.

? Multiple-Choice Questions

Select the correct answer from the answers provided. For questions with blanks, choose the combination of answers that most accurately completes the statement.

1. What is the smallest unit of heredity (genotype)?
 a. chromosome c. codon
 b. gene d. nucleotide

2. A nucleotide contains which of the following?
 a. 5-carbon sugar d. b and c only
 b. nitrogen base e. all of these
 c. phosphate

3. The nitrogen bases in DNA are bonded to the
 a. phosphate c. ribose
 b. deoxyribose d. hydrogen

4. DNA replication is semiconservative because the _____ strand will become half of the _____ molecule.
 a. RNA, DNA c. sense, mRNA
 b. template, finished d. codon, anticodon

5. In DNA, adenine is the complementary base for _____, and cytosine is the complement for _____.
 a. guanine, thymine c. thymine, guanine
 b. uracil, guanine d. thymine, uracil

6. The base pairs are held together primarily by
 a. covalent bonds c. ionic bonds
 b. hydrogen bonds d. gyrases

7. Why must the lagging strand of DNA be replicated in short pieces?
 a. because of limited space
 b. otherwise, the helix will become distorted
 c. the DNA polymerase can synthesize in only one direction
 d. to make proofreading of code easier

8. Messenger RNA is formed by _____ of a gene on the DNA template strand.
 a. transcription c. translation
 b. replication d. transformation

9. Transfer RNA is the molecule that
 a. contributes to the structure of ribosomes
 b. adapts the genetic code to protein structure
 c. transfers the DNA code to mRNA
 d. provides the master code for amino acids

10. As a general rule, the first codon on a the DNA template strand that signals the start for a protein is
 a. TAC c. ATG
 b. AUG d. UAC

11. What components are involved in transcription?
 a. sigma factor d. only b and c
 b. RNA polymerase e. all of these
 c. promotor

12. The *lac* operon is usually in the _____ position and is activated by a/an _____ molecule.
 a. on, repressor c. on, inducer
 b. off, inducer d. off, repressor

13. For mutations to have an effect on populations of microbes, they must be
 a. inheritable d. a and b
 b. permanent e. all of these
 c. beneficial

14. Which of the following characteristics is *not* true of a plasmid?
 a. It is a circular piece of DNA.
 b. It is required for normal cell function.
 c. It is found in bacteria.
 d. It can be transferred from cell to cell.

15. Which genetic material could be transmitted naturally by all three methods of intermicrobial transfer?
 a. an *E. coli* chromosome d. a and c
 b. F factor e. all of these
 c. drug resistance genes

16. Which of these features is found in eukaryotes but not bacteria?
 a. polygene mRNAs c. stop codon
 b. introns d. AUG codon

17. Which of the following is present in prokaryotes but not eukaryotes?
 a. exons
 b. polyribosomes
 c. spliceosomes
 d. simultaneous transcription and translation

18. **Multiple Matching.** Fill in the blanks with all the letters of the words below that apply.
 _____ site of protein synthesis
 _____ carries the codon
 _____ carries the anticodon
 _____ a process synonymous with mRNA synthesis
 _____ bacteriophages participate in this transfer
 _____ duplication of the DNA molecule
 _____ process in which transcribed DNA code is deciphered into a polypeptide
 _____ involves plasmids

 a. replication f. mRNA
 b. tRNA g. transcription
 c. conjugation h. transformation
 d. ribosome i. translation
 e. transduction j. none of these

 Case Study Review

1. Which of the following is *not* a factor in the rise of drug-resistant *Acinetobacter baumannii*?
 a. It is very widespread in many habitats.
 b. It has acquired greater toxicity.
 c. It readily acquires genetic material from other species.
 d. The hospital environment brings together vulnerable patients and drugs.

2. Drug-resistance plasmids could be transferred in *A. baumannii* by which of the following mechanisms:
 a. conjugation pilus d. a and b
 b. bacteriophages e. a, b, and c
 c. capture by cell wall

3. Explain how it would be possible for *A. baumannii* to develop drug resistance to a drug in the body of a patient while he or she is receiving therapy.

 Writing Challenge

For each question, compose a one- or two-paragraph answer that includes the factual information needed to completely address the question. Check Your Progress questions can also be used for writing-challenge exercises.

1. Explain what is meant by the following diagram.

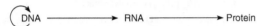

DNA ⟶ RNA ⟶ Protein

2. On paper, replicate the following segment of DNA:

 5′ A T C G G C T A C G T T C A C 3′
 3′ T A G C C G A T G C A A G T G 5′

 a. Show the direction of replication of the new strands and explain what causes lagging and leading strands to show different patterns of replication.
 b. Explain how this is semiconservative replication. Are the new strands identical to the original segment of DNA?

3. The following sequence represents triplets on DNA:

 TAC CAG ATA CAC TCC CCT GCG ACT

 a. Give the mRNA codons and tRNA anticodons that correspond with this sequence, and then give the sequence of amino acids in the polypeptide.
 b. Provide a different mRNA strand that can be used to synthesize this same protein.

4. Describe the actions of all of the enzymes involved in replication of a DNA molecule.

5. Compare and contrast the actions of DNA polymerase and RNA polymerase.

 Concept Mapping

An Introduction to Concept Mapping found at http://www.mhhe.com/talaro9 provides guidance for working with concept maps.

1. Supply your own linking words or phrases in this concept map, and provide the missing concepts in the empty boxes.

Level II. Application, Analysis, Evaluation, and Synthesis

These problems go beyond just restating facts and require higher levels of understanding and an ability to interpret, problem solve, transfer knowledge to new situations, create models, and predict outcomes.

Critical Thinking

Critical thinking is the ability to reason and solve problems using facts and concepts. These questions can be approached from a number of angles, and in most cases, they do not have a single correct answer.

1. Knowing that retroviruses operate on the principle of reversing the direction of transcription from RNA to DNA, propose a drug that might possibly interfere with their replication.

2. Using the piece of DNA in writing-challenge question 3, show a deletion, an insertion, a substitution, and nonsense mutations. Which ones are frameshift mutations? Are any of your mutations nonsense? Missense? (Use the universal code to determine this.)

3. Why will a mistake in the RNA code alone usually not result in a mutation?

4. The enzymes required to carry out transcription and translation are themselves produced through these same processes. Speculate which may have come first in evolution—proteins or nucleic acids—and explain your choice.

5. Why can one not reliably predict the sequence of nucleotides on mRNA or DNA by observing the amino acid sequence of proteins?

6. Activation, transcription, and translation of the *lac* operon will release which exact nutrients?

7. Explain the mechanisms by which RNA can control transcription, translation, and gene expression.

8. Explain how epigenetics is related to the expression:
phenotype = genotype + environment.

9. Use the concepts of chapters, letters, a library, words, and books to make an analogy that fits the levels of genetic structure and function.

Visual Challenge

1. From **figure 9.15, step 3.** Label each part of the illustration.

2. Examine figure 8.11, and explain which type of operon is functioning here. How would another operon differ from this?

CHAPTER **11**

Physical and Chemical Agents for Microbial Control

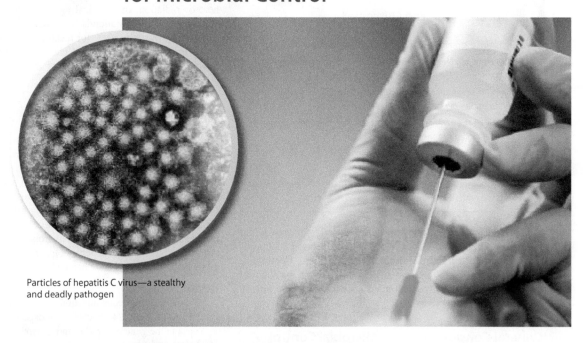

Particles of hepatitis C virus—a stealthy and deadly pathogen

 CASE STUDY Part 1 **The Billion Dollar Medical Error**

Late in 2007, a middle-aged man was hospitalized in Las Vegas with acute symptoms of **abdominal pain, nausea,** and **vomiting.** The attending physician also noticed that his eyes and skin were **jaundiced** (yellowed) and his urine was a dark color. Laboratory tests revealed an increased level of **liver enzymes** and **antibodies** to **hepatitis C virus** (HCV), and a **nucleic acid test** confirmed that **RNA** from HCV was present in his blood. Upon questioning, the patient denied having any of the **risk factors** for this infection such as **IV drug abuse** or **exposure to blood or blood products.** Further probing disclosed that he had recently undergone a dental procedure and had two **endoscopic examinations** of his gastrointestinal tract. This case was immediately reported to the Nevada Office of Epidemiology.

Within a month, two other cases of **acute** HCV infection were diagnosed. These patients also claimed to lack the risk factors that caused this infection and they, too, had recently had endoscope procedures performed at the same clinic as the first patient. The seriousness of these findings made it necessary to request assistance from the **Centers for Disease Control** and Prevention (CDC). The connection of the three patients to the same endoscopy center made this facility the prime focus of the investigation.

> "An RN-anesthetist was observed drawing a second dose of the drug from a large, multidose vial using the same syringe that had been used to take the first dose, although he did replace the needle."

The clinic had a large, thriving practice doing **colonoscopies** and other procedures on several thousand people each year. Because this raised the potential for other patients to have become infected with the virus, the CDC required that 63,000 persons who had a procedure in this clinic be immediately notified of their possible **exposure to the virus.**

It was essential to verify if the three patients were infected by the same **genetic strain** of HCV. When it turned out that the viruses were genetically identical, authorities were certain that the infections originated from the same **source.** Knowing that the three patients had never had any kind of contact, **epidemiologists** concluded that the clinic had to be the origin of the infection. This finding alone did not provide any clues as to what went wrong, but it had tremendous repercussions on the clinic, its patients, and the medical and insurance companies involved.

▶ *How are acute and chronic infections different, and why was it so important to differentiate them in this case?*

▶ *What sorts of procedures in a clinic might expose a person to bloodborne diseases?*

To continue the Case Study, go to page 348.

11.1 Controlling Microorganisms

 Expected Learning Outcomes

1. Summarize the major categories of microbial control and its purposes.

2. Evaluate the relative resistance of different groups of infectious agents.

3. Define and differentiate among the major terms for microbial control, citing examples of each.

4. Characterize the parameters of microbial death, and describe several factors that influence the rate of death.

5. Summarize what practices in microbial control influence the effectiveness of an antimicrobial agent.

6. Identify the targets of antimicrobial control agents, and explain what effects their modes of actions have.

Much of the time in our daily existence, we take for granted tap water that is drinkable, food that is not spoiled, shelves full of products to eradicate "germs," and drugs to treat infections. Controlling our degree of exposure to potentially harmful microbes is a monumental concern in our lives, and it has a long and eventful history (**11.1 Making Connections**).

General Considerations in Microbial Control

The methods of microbial control belong to the general category of *decontamination* procedures, in that they destroy or remove contaminants. In microbiology, contaminants are microbes present at a given place and time that are undesirable or unwanted. Most decontamination methods employ either physical agents, such as heat or radiation, or chemical agents, such as disinfectants and antiseptics. This separation is convenient, even though the categories overlap in some cases; for instance, radiation can cause damaging chemicals to form, and chemicals can generate heat. A flowchart (**figure 11.1**) summarizes the major applications and aims in microbial control.

Relative Resistance of Microbial Forms

The targets of microbial control processes are microorganisms capable of causing infection or spoilage that are constantly present in the external environment and on the human body. This targeted population is rarely simple or uniform; in fact, it often contains mixtures of microbes with extreme differences in resistance and harmfulness. Contaminants that can have far-reaching effects if not adequately controlled include bacterial vegetative cells and endospores, fungal hyphae and spores, yeasts, protozoan trophozoites and cysts, worms, viruses, and prions. This scheme compares the general resistance of these forms to physical and chemical methods of control:

Highest resistance

Prions: proteinaceous infectious particles (see the *Problem with Prions* on page 324); bacterial endospores, primarily from bacteria in the genera *Bacillus* and *Clostridium*.

Moderate resistance

Protozoan cysts; some fungal sexual spores (zygospores); some viruses. In general, naked viruses are more resistant than enveloped forms.

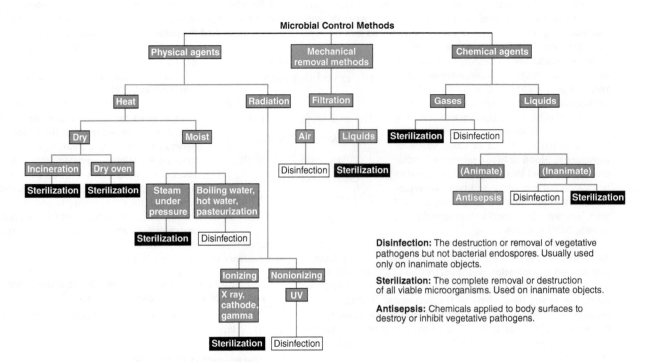

Figure 11.1 An overview of microbial control methods.

11.1 MAKING CONNECTIONS

Microbial Control Through the Ages

No one knows for sure when humans first applied methods that could control microorganisms, but perhaps the discovery and use of fire in prehistoric times were the starting points. We do know that records describing simple measures to control decay and disease appear from civilizations that existed several thousand years ago. We know, too, that these ancient people had no concept that germs caused disease, but they did have a mixture of beliefs; skills in observing natural phenomena; and, possibly, a bit of luck. This combination led them to carry out simple and sometimes rather hazardous measures that contributed to the control of microorganisms.

Salting, smoking, pickling, and drying foods, and exposing food, clothing, and bedding to sunlight were prevalent practices among early civilizations. The Egyptians showed surprising sophistication and understanding of decomposition by embalming the bodies of their dead with strong salts and pungent oils. They introduced filtration of wine and water as well. The Greeks and Romans burned clothing and corpses during epidemics, and they stored water in copper and silver containers. The armies of Alexander the Great reportedly boiled their drinking water and buried their wastes. Burning sulfur to fumigate houses and applying sulfur as a skin ointment also date approximately from this era.

During the great plague pandemic of the Middle Ages, it was commonplace to bury corpses in mass graves, burn the clothing of plague victims, and ignite aromatic woods in the houses of the sick in the belief that fumes would combat the disease. In a desperate search for some sort of protection, survivors wore peculiar garments and anointed their bodies with herbs, strong perfume, and vinegar. The children's rhyme "Ring-a-round a rosie" actually refers to many of the rituals related to the plague, such as filling the pockets of the victims with flowers ("pocket full of posies . . .") and burning the dead so as to reduce the

Illustration of protective clothing used by doctors in the 1700s to avoid exposure to plague victims. The beaklike portion of the hood contained volatile perfumes to protect against foul odors and possibly inhaling "bad air."

spread of the disease ("Ashes! Ashes! We all fall down"). These attempts may sound foolish and antiquated, but it now appears that they may have had some benefits. Burning wood releases formaldehyde, which could have acted as a disinfectant; herbs, perfume, and vinegar contain mild antimicrobial substances. Each of these early methods, although somewhat crude, laid the foundations for microbial control methods that are still in use today.

What are some modern techniques that are equivalent to these early techniques described here? *Answer available at http://www.mhhe. com/talaro9*

Several groups of bacteria lack endospores but have vegetative cells with increased resistance to microbial control agents. These include *Mycobacterium,* whose cell walls have thick, waxy layers that can block the entrance of many disinfectants. The cell walls of *Pseudomonas, Acinetobacter,* and other gram-negative pathogens have an outer membrane that also prevents penetration of some chemical agents. *Staphylococcus* species are among the most heat- and chemical-resistant of all bacteria due to their thick, protective peptidoglycan cell walls.

Least resistance

Most bacterial vegetative cells; fungal spores (other than zygospores) and hyphae; enveloped viruses; yeasts; and protozoan trophozoites

Actual comparative figures on the requirements for destroying various groups of microorganisms are shown in **table 11.1.** Bacterial endospores have traditionally been considered the most resistant microbial entities, being as much as 18 times harder to destroy than vegetative cells. Because of endospore resistance to microbial

TABLE 11.1	Relative Resistance of Bacterial Endospores and Vegetative Cells to Control Agents		
Method	**Endospores***	**Vegetative Forms***	**Relative Resistance****
Heat (moist)	120°C	80°C	1.5×
Radiation (X-ray) dosage	4,000 grays	1,000 grays	4×
Sterilizing gas (ethylene oxide)	1,200 mg/1	700 mg/1	1.7×
Sporicidal liquid (2% glutaraldehyde)	3 hours	10 min	18×

*Values are based on methods (concentration, exposure time, intensity) that are required to destroy the most resistant pathogens in each group.

**This number is a comparison of the conditions required to kill endospores versus vegetative cells and is an average of the most resistant pathogens in each group.

control and their widespread distribution, destroying them is the goal of sterilization (see definition in following section). Any process that kills endospores will invariably kill all less resistant microbial forms. Other methods of control (disinfection, antisepsis) target primarily microbes that are less hardy than endospores.

The Problem with Prions

The role of prions as infectious protein particles in certain progressive brain diseases (Creutzfeldt-Jakob disease) was first introduced in chapter 6. Not only are prions highly unusual in their actions, but they are also in a class of their own when it comes to "sterilization" procedures. This chapter defines *sterile* as the absence of all viable microbial life. But prions are not microbes, and most of the procedures described here are not sufficient to destroy them. Prions are extraordinarily resistant to heat, chemicals, and radiation. Instruments or other objects contaminated with these unique agents must be incinerated, at very high temperatures, or decontaminated with a combination of chemicals. The substances that have proved most effective are sodium hydroxide and hypochlorite (bleach) solutions that render them noninfectious after a significant period of exposure. When tissues, fluids, or instruments are suspected of containing prions, consultation with the CDC is recommended to ensure effective sterilization conditions.

In terms of routine sterilization procedures, this chapter considers bacterial endospores as the most resistant form of microbial life that will be targeted by antimicrobial agents. Prions are described in more detail in chapter 25.

Terminology and Methods of Microbial Control

Through the years, a growing terminology has emerged for describing and defining measures that control microbes. To complicate matters, the everyday use of some of these terms can at times be vague and inexact. For example, occasionally one may be directed to "sterilize" or "disinfect" a patient's skin, even though this usage does not fit the technical definition of either term. To lay the groundwork for the concepts in microbial control to follow, we present here a series of concepts, definitions, and usages in antimicrobial control.

Sterilization

Sterilization is a process that destroys or removes all viable microorganisms, including viruses. Any material that has been subjected to this process is said to be **sterile.** These terms should be used only in the strictest sense for methods that have been proved to sterilize. An object cannot be slightly sterile or almost sterile—it is either sterile or not sterile. Control methods that sterilize are generally reserved for inanimate objects, because sterilizing tissues within a living body would call for such harsh treatment that it would be highly dangerous and impractical. As we shall see in

Endospore of *Bacillus* sp

Quick Search
Find out more by searching for "What is Sterilization" on YouTube.

chapter 13, many parts of the body—the brain and other internal organs, for example—are naturally free of microbes.

Sterilized products—surgical instruments, syringes, and commercially packaged foods, just to name a few—are essential to human well-being. Although most sterilization is performed with a physical agent such as heat, a few chemicals called *sterilants* can be classified as sterilizing agents because of their ability to destroy spores.

At times, sterilization is neither practicable nor necessary, and only certain groups of microbes are of concern. Some antimicrobial agents eliminate only the susceptible vegetative states of microorganisms but do not destroy the more resistant endospore and cyst stages. Keep in mind that the destruction of spores is not always a necessity, because most of the infectious diseases of humans and animals are caused by non-spore-forming microbes.

Microbicidal Agents

The root *-cide,* meaning to kill, can be combined with other terms to define an antimicrobial agent aimed at destroying a certain group of microorganisms. For example, a **bactericide** is a chemical that destroys bacteria except for those in the endospore stage. It may or may not be effective on other microbial groups. A **fungicide** is a chemical that can kill fungal spores, hyphae, and yeasts. A **virucide** is any chemical known to inactivate viruses, especially on living tissue. A **sporicidal** agent can destroy bacterial endospores which makes it also a sterilizing agent.

Agents That Cause Microbistasis

The words *stasis* and *static* mean to stand still. They can be used in combination with various prefixes to denote a condition termed **microbistasis** in which microbes are temporarily prevented from multiplying but are not killed outright. Although killing or permanently inactivating microorganisms is the usual goal of microbial control, microbistasis can have meaningful applications. **Bacteriostatic** agents prevent the growth of bacteria on tissues or on objects in the environment, and *fungistatic* chemicals inhibit fungal growth. Materials used to control microorganisms in the body (antiseptics and drugs) usually have microbistatic effects because many microbicidal compounds can be highly toxic to human cells.

Germicides, Disinfection, Antisepsis

A **germicide,*** also called a *microbicide,* is any chemical agent that kills pathogenic microorganisms. A germicide can be used on inanimate (nonliving) materials or on living tissue, but it ordinarily cannot kill resistant microbial cells. Any physical or chemical agent that kills "germs" is said to have germicidal properties.

The related term **disinfection*** refers to the use of a physical process or a chemical agent—a **disinfectant**—to destroy vegetative pathogens but not bacterial endospores. It is important to note that disinfectants are normally used only on inanimate objects because, at the concentrations required to be effective, they can be toxic to living tissue. Disinfection processes can also remove the harmful products of microorganisms (toxins) from materials. Examples of

** germicide* (jer'-mih-syd) L. *germen,* germ, and *caedere,* to kill. Germ is a common term for a pathogenic microbe.
** disinfection* (dis"-in-fek'-shun) L. *dis,* apart, and *inficere,* to corrupt.

disinfection include applying a solution of 5% bleach to an examination table, exposing drinking water to UV radiation, and pasteurizing milk with heat.

In modern usage, **sepsis** is defined as the growth of microorganisms in the blood and other tissues. The term **asepsis*** refers to any practice that prevents the entry of infectious agents into sterile tissues and thus prevents infection. Aseptic techniques commonly practiced in health care range from sterile methods that exclude all microbes to **antisepsis.*** In antisepsis, chemical agents called **antiseptics** are applied directly to exposed body surfaces (skin and mucous membranes), wounds, and surgical incisions to destroy or inhibit vegetative pathogens. Examples of antisepsis include preparing the skin before surgical incisions with iodine compounds, swabbing a wound with hydrogen peroxide, and ordinary hand washing with a germicidal soap.

Methods That Reduce the Numbers of Microorganisms

While medical applications quite often require sterility, especially with regard to invasive instruments such as scalpels, clamps, dental hand tools, and the like, this high level of microbial control is often unwarranted and perhaps even unwanted. In many cases, it is more important to focus on reducing the size of a microbial population, or its *microbial load.* **Sanitization*** refers to any cleansing technique that removes debris, soil, microorganisms, and toxins, and in this way reduces the potential for infection and spoilage. Soaps and detergents are the most commonly employed sanitizers. From a practical standpoint, sanitization can have an advantage over sterilization. For example, in a restaurant you could be given a sterile fork with someone else's old food on it and a sterile glass with lipstick on the rim. Given that sanitization is in general far less expensive than sterilization, its cleansing effect has obvious advantages.

With living tissues the reduction in microbial load through mechanical means is referred to as **degermation.** This process usually involves scrubbing the skin or immersing it in chemicals, or both. Microorganisms are removed both mechanically and indirectly by emulsifying the oils that coat the skin and provide a habitat for their growth. Examples of degerming procedures include the surgical handscrub, the application of alcohol wipes, and the cleansing of a wound with germicidal soap and water. **Table 11.2** summarizes several of the important terms involved in microbial control.

What Is Microbial Death?

Death is a phenomenon that involves the permanent termination of an organism's vital processes. Signs of life in complex organisms such as animals are self-evident, and death is made clear by loss of nervous function, respiration, or heartbeat. In contrast, death in microscopic organisms that are composed of just one or a few cells is hard to detect, because they often reveal no conspicuous vital signs to begin with. Lethal agents (such as radiation and chemicals) do not necessarily alter the overt appearance of microbial cells. Even the loss of movement in a motile microbe cannot be used to indicate death. This fact has made it necessary to develop special qualifications that define and delineate microbial death.

The destructive effects of chemical or physical agents occur at the cellular and molecular level. As a cell is exposed to an agent such as intense heat or toxic chemicals, various cell structures break down, and the entire cell can sustain irreversible damage. At present, the most practical way to detect this damage is to determine if a microbial cell can still reproduce when exposed to a suitable environment. If the microbe has sustained metabolic or structural damage to such an extent that it can no longer reproduce, even in an ideal environment, then it is considered nonviable. **In most circumstances of testing, the permanent loss of reproductive capacity, even under optimal growth conditions, has become the working definition of microbial death.**[1]

* *asepsis* (ay-sep'-sis) Gr. *a,* no or none, and *sepsis,* decay.
* *antisepsis anti,* against.
* *sanitization* (san" ih-tih-zay'-shun) L. *sanitas,* health.

1. One drawback to using this definition of microbial death is that some microbes may have entered a viable but nonculturable state, making it difficult to know if the antimicrobial agent is microbicidal or microbistatic.

TABLE 11.2	**Microbial Control Terminology**	
Term	**Definition**	**Example**
Decontamination	The destruction, removal, or reduction in number of undesirable microbes	Asepsis, disinfection, sanitization, degermation
Sepsis	The growth of microorganisms in the tissues	Infected wounds, blood infection
Asepsis	Techniques that prevent the entry of microorganisms into sterile tissues	Cleansing the skin with iodine prior to surgery, using sterile needles
Antiseptic	Chemicals applied to body surfaces to destroy or inhibit vegetative pathogens	Iodophors, antibacterial soap, chlorhexidine
Disinfection	Destruction of vegetative pathogens on inanimate objects	5% bleach, boiling water
Sanitization	Cleansing technique that removes microorganisms and debris from inanimate surfaces	Dishwashing, laundering clothes
Degermation	Cleansing technique that removes microorganisms and debris from living tissue	Surgical handscrub, alcohol wipes
Sterilization	The removal or destruction of all viable microbes	Autoclaving, ionizing radiation (correctly applied)

Factors That Affect Death Rate

The ability to define microbial death has tremendous theoretical and practical importance. It allows medicine and industry to test the conditions required to destroy microorganisms, to pinpoint the ways that antimicrobial agents kill cells, and to establish standards of sterilization and disinfection in these fields. Hundreds of testing procedures have been developed for evaluating physical and chemical agents. Some of these can be found in **Appendix B.**

The cells of a culture show marked variation in susceptibility to a given microbicidal agent. Death of the whole population is not instantaneous but begins when a certain threshold of the microbicidal agent (some combination of time and concentration) is met. Death continues in a logarithmic manner as the time of exposure is increased (**figure 11.2**). Because many microbicidal agents target the cell's metabolic processes, active cells (younger, rapidly dividing) tend to die more quickly than those that are less metabolically active (older, dormant). Eventually, a point is reached at which survival of any cells is highly unlikely; this point is equivalent to sterilization.

The effectiveness of a particular agent is governed by several factors besides time. These additional factors influence the action of antimicrobial agents:

1. The number of microorganisms (**figure 11.2b**). A higher load of contaminants requires more time to destroy.

2. The nature of the microorganisms in the population (**figure 11.2c**). In most actual circumstances of disinfection and sterilization, the target population is not a single species of microbe but a mixture of bacteria, fungi, spores, and viruses, presenting a broad spectrum of microbial resistance.

3. The temperature and pH of the environment.

4. The concentration (dosage, intensity) of the agent. For example, UV radiation is most effective at 260 nm and most disinfectants are more active at higher concentrations.

5. The mode of action of the agent (**figure 11.2d**). How does it kill or inhibit microorganisms?

6. The presence of solvents, interfering organic matter, and inhibitors. Saliva, blood, and feces can inhibit the actions of disinfectants and even of heat.

Some Practical Concerns in Selecting Antimicrobial Agents

A remarkable variety of substances and objects require sterilization, disinfection, and other forms of decontamination. They range from durable materials made of glass and rubber to highly sensitive liquids such as blood plasma and even human tissues such as bone. Sometimes entire rooms with their contents and large pieces of equipment such as space vehicles and satellites may need to be sterilized. In accordance with an international agreement, all spacecraft

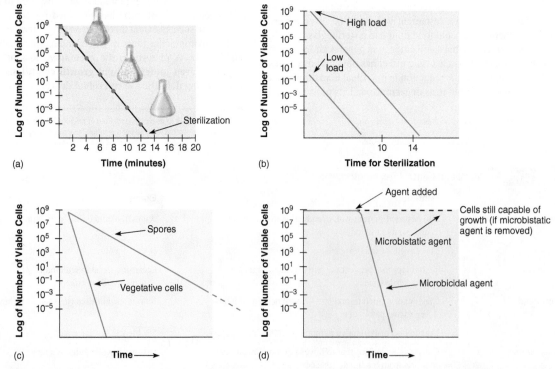

Figure 11.2 Factors that influence the rate at which microbes are killed by antimicrobial agents. **(a)** Length of exposure to the agent. During exposure to a chemical or physical agent, all cells of a microbial population, even a pure culture, do not die simultaneously. Over time, the number of viable organisms remaining in the population decreases logarithmically, giving a straight-line relationship on a graph. The point at which the number of survivors is infinitesimally small is considered sterilization. **(b)** Effect of the microbial load. **(c)** Relative resistance of spores versus vegetative forms. **(d)** Action of the agent, whether microbicidal or microbistatic.

landing on extraterrestrial bodies must have a highly reduced microbe load. This policy is to prevent the introduction of earth microbes that could potentially alter those environments or interfere with experiments being conducted by NASA. Parts of the probes are sterilized with heat, radiation, and certain chemicals (peroxide), and then maintained in very controlled clean rooms that require extreme precautions against contamination by workers. "Tour the JPL Clean Room" on Ustream **(figure 11.3).**

Literally hundreds of situations occur in the health care setting alone, where prevention of infection must be taken into consideration at all times. The CDC provides guidelines for recommended sterilization and disinfection procedures. The case study for this chapter provides a good example of some of the difficulties in ensuring that proper techniques are followed in every situation.

One of the first questions that arises when choosing a method is, What will render materials free of potential pathogens? For example, reusable dental instruments are highly contaminated with saliva, blood, and other fluids and tissues. These are all potential sources of infection, so it is critical that they be sterilized between patients with a method that will kill endospores.

The next concern is selecting the best method of sterilization. Because they are mostly made of metal, dental instruments can be sterilized with heat, although some forms of radiation and chemical treatments could also work. Clinics generally opt for a method such as steam sterilization that is simplest, fastest, and least expensive. This would not work on other types of delicate instruments such as endoscopes, which must be sterilized between patients using heat-free techniques.

On the other hand, certain single-use medical supplies such as plastic syringes and catheters used in hospitals and clinics come already sterilized and packaged at the factory. Because they are usually made of heat-sensitive plastics, this is done with penetrating radiation or chemicals. These items are not meant to be reused, but they still must be decontaminated before being discarded to prevent the transmission of disease. Disposal of such medical wastes is regulated by various governmental agencies.

Figure 11.3 NASA employees work in an ultraclean room at Jet Propulsion Lab (JPL) in Pasadena, California. Though not sterile, the levels of microbes in the air and on surfaces are kept to a minimum.

How Antimicrobial Agents Work: Their Modes of Action

An antimicrobial agent's adverse effect on cells is known as its **mode** (or **mechanism**) **of action.** Agents affect one or more cellular targets, inflicting damage progressively until the cell is no longer viable. Antimicrobials have a range of cellular targets, with the agents that are least selective in their targeting tending to be effective against the widest range of microbes (examples include heat and radiation). More selective agents (drugs, for example) tend to target only a single cellular component and are much more restricted as to the microbes they are effective against.

The cellular targets of physical and chemical agents fall into four general categories: (1) cell walls, (2) cell membranes, (3) protein and nucleic acid synthesis, and (4) protein structure and function.

The Effects of Agents on the Cell Wall

The cell wall maintains the structural integrity of bacterial and fungal cells. Several types of chemical agents damage the cell wall by blocking its synthesis, digesting it, or breaking down its surface. A cell deprived of a functioning cell wall becomes fragile and is lysed very easily. Examples of this mode of action include some antimicrobial drugs (penicillins) that interfere with the synthesis of the cell wall in bacteria (described in chapter 12). Detergents and alcohol can also disrupt cell walls, especially in gram-negative bacteria.

How Agents Affect the Cell Membrane

All microorganisms have a cell membrane composed of lipids and proteins, and even some viruses have an outer membranous envelope. As we learned in previous chapters, a cell's membrane provides a two-way system of transport. If this membrane is disrupted, a cell loses its selective permeability and can neither prevent the loss of vital molecules nor bar the entry of damaging chemicals. Loss of those functions usually leads to cell death. Chemicals called **surfactants*** work as microbicidal agents because they lower the surface tension of cell membranes. Surfactants are polar molecules such as detergents with hydrophilic and hydrophobic regions that can physically bind to the lipid layer and penetrate the internal hydrophobic regions of membranes. In effect, this process "opens up" the once tight interface, leaving leaky spots that allow harmful chemicals to seep into the cell and important ions to seep out **(figure 11.4).** Alcohols exert a related effect by dissolving membrane lipids and stripping membranes away from cells.

Agents That Affect Protein and Nucleic Acid Synthesis

Microbial life depends upon an orderly and continuous supply of proteins to function as enzymes and structural molecules. As we saw in chapter 9, these proteins are synthesized on the ribosomes during translation. Any chemical that blocks this process can affect function and survival. For example, certain drugs bind to the

* *surfactant* (sir-fak'-tunt) A word derived from **surf**ace-**act**ing age**nt.**

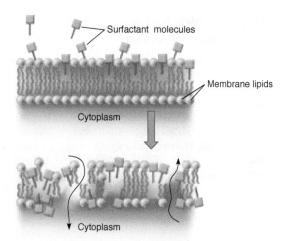

Figure 11.4 **Mode of action of surfactants on the cell membrane.** Surfactants inserting in the lipid bilayer disrupt it and create abnormal channels that alter permeability and cause leakage both into and out of the cell.

Figure 11.5 **Modes of action affecting protein function.** **(a)** The native (functional) state is maintained by bonds that create active sites to fit the substrate. Some agents denature the protein by breaking all or some secondary and tertiary bonds. Results are **(b)** complete unfolding or **(c)** random bonding and incorrect folding. **(d)** Some agents react with functional groups on the active site and interfere with bonding.

ribosomes of bacteria in a way that stops peptide bonds from forming. In its presence, many bacterial cells are inhibited from forming proteins required in growth and metabolism and are thus inhibited from multiplying. Many of the drugs used to treat infections are chemicals that block protein synthesis in microbes without adversely affecting human cells. This subject is discussed in greater detail in chapter 12.

The nucleic acids are likewise necessary for the continued functioning of microbes. DNA must be regularly replicated and transcribed in growing cells, and any agent that either impedes these processes or changes the genetic code is potentially antimicrobial. Some agents bind irreversibly to DNA, preventing both transcription and translation, whereas others are mutagenic agents. Gamma, ultraviolet, or X radiation causes mutations that result in permanent inactivation of DNA. Chemicals such as formaldehyde and ethylene oxide also interfere with DNA and RNA function.

Agents That Alter Protein Function

A microbial cell contains large quantities of proteins that function properly only if they remain in a normal three-dimensional configuration called the *native state*. The antimicrobial properties of some agents arise from their capacity to disrupt the structure of, or **denature,** proteins. In general, **denaturation** occurs when the bonds that maintain the secondary and tertiary structure of the protein are broken. Breaking these bonds will cause the protein to unfold or create random, irregular loops and coils (**figure 11.5**). One way that proteins can be denatured is through coagulation by moist heat (the same reaction seen in the irreversible solidification of the white of an egg when boiled). Chemicals such as strong organic solvents (alcohols, acids) also coagulate proteins. A few antimicrobial agents, such as metallic ions, attach to the active site of the protein and prevent it from interacting with its correct substrate. Regardless of the exact mechanism, such losses in normal

protein function can promptly arrest metabolism and exert broad effects on all types of microbes.

Check Your Progress SECTION 11.1

1. Explain the purposes of microbial control and differentiate between physical, mechanical, and chemical methods.
2. Compare sterilization with disinfection and sanitization. Describe the relationship of the concepts of sepsis, asepsis, and antisepsis.
3. Contrast various microbes and rate their variations in resistance to control agents.
4. Explain how the types and numbers of microorganisms can influence the effectiveness of control agents.
5. How is microbial death defined?
6. Why does a population of microbes not die instantaneously when exposed to an antimicrobial agent?
7. Distinguish between microbicidal and microbistatic effects on microbes, and tell why it is important to understand the difference.
8. Why are antimicrobial processes inhibited in the presence of extraneous organic matter?
9. Describe four modes of action of antimicrobial agents, and provide examples of how they work.

11.2 Physical Methods of Control: Heat

 Expected Learning Outcomes

7. List the major types of physical agents used in controlling microbes.

8. Describe the basic effects of temperature on microbes.

9. Define *moist* and *dry heat*, and explain their modes of action and relative effectiveness.

10. Differentiate between thermal death point and thermal death time, and provide examples of their uses.

11. Describe several moist heat methods and their chief applications for sterilization and disinfection.

12. Describe some methods using dry heat and its chief applications.

13. Explain how cold temperatures and desiccation are used in microbial control.

Microorganisms have adapted to a tremendous diversity of habitats on earth, some having severe conditions of temperature, moisture, pressure, and light. For microbes that normally withstand such extreme physical conditions, our usual attempts at control would probably have little effect. Fortunately for us, we are most interested in controlling microbes that flourish in the same environment in which humans live. The vast majority of these microbes are readily controlled by abrupt changes in their environment. Most prominent among antimicrobial physical agents is heat. Other less widely used agents include radiation and filtration. The following sections examine these and other methods, and explore their practical applications in medicine, commerce, and the home.

Effects of Temperature on Microbial Activities

A sudden departure from a microbe's temperature of adaptation is likely to have a detrimental effect on it. As a rule, temperatures that exceed the maximum growth temperature are microbicidal, whereas temperatures below the minimum growth temperature are microbistatic. This essentially means that, for most microbes, the effects of temperatures below minimum are reversible, whereas the effects of temperatures above maximum are not reversible, and most microbes will be destroyed by them.

The two physical states of heat used in microbial control are moist and dry. **Moist heat** occurs in the form of hot water, boiling water, or steam (vaporized water). In practice, the temperature of moist heat usually ranges from 60°C to 135°C. As we shall see, the temperature of steam can be regulated by adjusting its pressure in a closed container. The expression **dry heat** denotes air with a low moisture content that has been heated by a flame or electric heating coil. In practice, the temperature of dry heat ranges from 160°C to several thousand degrees Celsius.

Mode of Action and Relative Effectiveness of Heat

Moist heat and dry heat differ in their modes of action as well as in their efficiency. Moist heat operates at lower temperatures and shorter exposure times to achieve the same effectiveness as dry heat **(table 11.3).** Although many cellular structures are damaged by moist heat, its most microbicidal effects are the coagulation and denaturation of proteins, which quickly and permanently halt cellular metabolism.

Dry heat with a moderate temperature dehydrates the cell, removing the water necessary for metabolic reactions, and it alters protein structure. However, the lack of water actually increases the stability of some protein conformations, necessitating the use of higher temperatures when dry heat is employed as a method of microbial control. At very high temperatures, dry heat oxidizes cells, burning them to ashes. This method is the one used in the laboratory when a loop is flamed or in industry when medical waste is incinerated.

Heat Resistance and Thermal Death of Spores and Vegetative Cells

Bacterial endospores exhibit the greatest resistance, and vegetative states of bacteria and fungi are the least resistant to both moist and dry heat. Destruction of spores usually requires temperatures above boiling, although resistance varies widely. The following table compares some times and temperatures required to kill sporeformers using moist versus dry heat:

Moist Heat	Temp/Time	Dry Heat	Temp/Time
Bacillus subtilis	121°C/1 min	*Bacillus subtilis*	121°C/120 min
B. stearothermophilis	121°C/12 min	*B. stearothermophilis*	140°C/5 min
Clostridium botulinum	120°C/10 min	*Clostridium botulinum*	120°C/120 min
C. tetani	105°C/10 min	*C. tetani*	100°C/60 min

In general, reliable killing of the most heat-resistant species of sporeformers requires 121°C for 20 minutes in moist heat.

Vegetative cells also vary in their sensitivity to heat, though not to the same extent as spores. Among bacteria, the death conditions for moist heat range from 50°C for 3 minutes (*Neisseria gonorrhoeae*) to 60°C for 60 minutes (*Staphylococcus aureus*). It is worth noting that vegetative cells of sporeformers are just as susceptible as vegetative cells of non-sporeformers and that pathogens are neither more nor less susceptible than nonpathogens. Other microbes, including fungi, protozoa, and worms, are rather similar in their sensitivity to heat. Viruses can be surprisingly resistant to heat, with a tolerance range extending from 55°C for 2 to 5 minutes (adenoviruses) to 60°C for 600 minutes (hepatitis A virus). For practical purposes, all non-heat-resistant forms of bacteria, yeasts, molds, protozoa, worms, and viruses are destroyed by exposure to 80°C for 20 minutes.

TABLE 11.3	Comparison of Times and Temperatures to Achieve Sterilization with Moist and Dry Heat	
	Temperature	**Time to Sterilize**
Moist Heat	121°C	15 min
	125°C	10 min
	134°C	3 min
Dry Heat	121°C	600 min
	140°C	180 min
	160°C	120 min
	170°C	60 min

Practical Concerns in the Use of Heat: Thermal Death Measurements

Adequate sterilization requires that both temperature and length of exposure be considered. As a general rule, higher temperatures allow shorter exposure times, and lower temperatures require longer exposure times. A combination of these two variables constitutes the **thermal death time,** or **TDT,** defined as the shortest length of time required to kill all test microbes at a specified temperature. The TDT has been experimentally determined for the microbial species that are common or important contaminants in various heat-treated materials. Another way to compare the susceptibility of microbes to heat is the **thermal death point (TDP),** defined as the lowest temperature required to kill all microbes in a sample in 10 minutes.

Many perishable substances are processed with moist heat. Some of these products are intended to remain on the shelf at room temperature for several months or even years. The chosen heat treatment must render the product free of agents of spoilage or disease. At the same time, the quality of the product and the speed and cost of processing must be considered. For example, in the commercial preparation of canned green beans, one of the cannery's greatest concerns is to prevent growth of the agent of botulism. From several possible TDTs (that is, combinations of time and temperature) for *Clostridium botulinum* spores, the cannery must choose one that kills all spores but does not turn the beans to mush. These many considerations produce an optimal TDT for a given processing method. Commercial canneries heat low-acid foods at 121°C for 30 minutes, a treatment that sterilizes these foods. Because of such strict controls in canneries, cases of botulism from commercially canned foods are rare.

Common Methods of Moist Heat Control

The four ways that moist heat is employed to control microbes are

- steam under pressure,
- nonpressurized steam,
- boiling water, and
- pasteurization.

Sterilization with Steam Under Pressure At sea level, normal atmospheric pressure is 15 pounds per square inch (psi), or 1 atmosphere. At this pressure, water will boil (change from a liquid to a gas) at 100°C, and the resultant steam will remain at exactly that temperature, which is unfortunately too low to reliably kill all microbes. In order to raise the temperature of steam, it must be exposed to increased pressure. At higher pressures the temperature at which water boils and the temperature of steam both rise. For example, at a pressure of 20 psi (5 psi above normal), the temperature of steam is 109°C. As the temperature is increased to 10 psi above normal, the steam's temperature rises to 115°C, and at 15 psi above normal (a total of 2 atmospheres), it will be 121°C. It is not the pressure by itself that is killing microbes but the increased temperature it produces.

Such pressure-temperature combinations can be achieved only with a special device that can subject pure steam to pressures greater than 1 atmosphere. Health and commercial industries use an **autoclave** for this purpose, and a comparable home appliance is the pressure cooker. Autoclaves have a fundamentally similar plan: an enclosed metal chamber with an airtight door on one end and racks to hold materials **(figure 11.6).** Its construction includes a complex network of valves, pressure and temperature gauges, and ducts for regulating and measuring pressure and conducting the steam into the chamber.

(a)

(b)

Figure 11.6 Sterilization using steam under pressure. (a) An autoclave for sterilizing media and cultures. **(b)** Cutaway section, showing autoclave components and the flow of steam through the autoclave. From John J. Perkens, *Principles and Methods of Sterilization in Health Science,* 2nd ed., 1969. Courtesy of Charles C. Thomas, Publisher, Springfield, Illinois.

Sterilization is achieved when the steam condenses against the objects in the chamber and gradually raises their temperature.

Experience has shown that the most efficient pressure-temperature combination for achieving sterilization is 15 psi, which yields 121°C. It is possible to use higher pressure to reach higher temperatures (for instance, increasing the pressure to 30 psi raises the temperature to 132°C), but doing so will not significantly reduce the exposure time and can harm the items being sterilized.

The duration of the process is adjusted according to the bulkiness of the items in the load (thick bundles of material or large flasks of liquid) and how full the chamber is. The range of holding times varies from 10 minutes for light loads to 40 minutes for heavy or bulky ones; the average time is 20 minutes.

Nonpressurized Steam Selected substances that cannot withstand the high temperature of the autoclave can be subjected to *intermittent sterilization,* also called **tyndallization.**[2] This technique requires a chamber to hold the materials and a reservoir for boiling water. Items in the chamber are exposed to free-flowing steam for 30 to 60 minutes. This temperature is not sufficient to reliably kill spores, so a single exposure will not suffice. On the assumption that surviving spores will germinate into less resistant vegetative cells, the items are incubated at appropriate temperatures for 23 to 24 hours, and then again subjected to steam treatment. This cycle is repeated for 3 days in a row. Because the temperature never gets above 100°C, highly resistant spores that do not germinate could survive even after 3 days of this treatment.

Boiling Water: Disinfection A simple boiling water bath or chamber can quickly decontaminate items in the clinic and home. Because a single processing at 100°C will not kill all resistant cells, this method can be relied on only for disinfection and not for sterilization. Exposing materials to boiling water for 30 minutes will kill most non-spore-forming pathogens, including resistant species such as the tubercle bacillus and staphylococci. Probably the greatest disadvantage with this method is that the items can be easily recontaminated when removed from the water.

Pasteurization: Disinfection of Beverages Fresh beverages such as milk, fruit juices, beer, and wine are easily contaminated during collection and processing. Because microbes have the potential for spoiling these foods or causing illness, heat is frequently used to reduce the microbial load and destroy pathogens. **Pasteurization** is a technique in which heat is applied to liquids to kill potential agents of infection and spoilage, while at the same time retaining the liquid's flavor and food value.

A widely used pasteurization technique is the **flash method,** that exposes the liquid to heat exchangers at 71.6°C for 15 seconds. This first method is less likely to change flavor and nutrient content, and it is effective against certain resistant pathogens such as *Coxiella* and *Mycobacterium.* Although these treatments inactivate most viruses and destroy the vegetative stages of 97% to 99% of bacteria and fungi, they do not kill endospores or **thermoduric** microbes (mostly nonpathogenic lactobacilli, micrococci, and yeasts). Flash-pasteurized milk is not sterile after regular pasteurization. In fact, it

can contain 20,000 microbes per milliliter or more, which explains why even an unopened carton of milk will eventually spoil. The latest technologies can also produce *sterile milk* that has a longer storage life. This milk is processed with ultrahigh temperature (UHT)—134°C for 2 to 5 seconds.

One important aim in pasteurization is to prevent the transmission of milk-borne diseases from infected cows or milk handlers. The primary targets of pasteurization are non-spore-forming pathogens: *Salmonella* species (a common cause of food infection), *Campylobacter jejuni* (acute intestinal infection), *Listeria monocytogenes* (listeriosis), *Brucella* species (undulant fever), *Coxiella burnetii* (Q fever), *Mycobacterium bovis, M. tuberculosis,* and several enteric viruses.

Dry Heat: Hot Air and Incineration

Dry heat is not as versatile or as widely used as moist heat, but it has several important sterilization applications. The temperatures and times employed in dry heat vary according to the particular method, but in general, they are greater than with moist heat. **Incineration** in a flame or electric heating coil is perhaps the most rigorous of all heat treatments. The flame of a Bunsen burner reaches 1,870°C at its hottest point, and furnaces/incinerators operate at temperatures of 800°C to 6,500°C. Direct exposure to such intense heat ignites and reduces microbes and other substances to ashes and gas.

Incineration of microbial samples on inoculating loops and needles using a Bunsen burner is a very common practice in the microbiology laboratory. This method is fast and effective, but it is also limited to metals and heat-resistant glass materials. Tabletop infrared incinerators (see table 11.4), an alternative to Bunsen burners, are safer and prevent splatter of the inoculum.

The hot-air oven provides another means of dry-heat sterilization. The so-called *dry oven* is usually electric (occasionally gas) and has coils that radiate heat within an enclosed compartment. Heated, circulated air transfers its heat to the materials in the oven. Depending on the type of oven and the material being decontaminated, a cycle takes 12 minutes to 4 hours to complete and involves temperatures of 150°C to 180°C.

Table 11.4 presents an illustrated summary of the application of heat to control microbes.

The Effects of Cold and Desiccation

The principal benefit of cold treatment is to slow growth of cultures and microbes in food and other perishable materials during processing and storage. *It must be emphasized that cold merely retards the activities of most microbes.* Although it is true that some sensitive microbes are killed by cold temperatures, most are not adversely affected by gradual cooling, long-term refrigeration, or deep-freezing. In fact, freezing temperatures, ranging from −70°C to −135°C, provide an environment that can preserve cultures of bacteria, viruses, and fungi for long periods. Recall from chapter 7 that some psychrotrophs grow very slowly even at freezing temperatures and can continue to secrete toxic products. Pathogens able to survive several months in the refrigerator are *Staphylococcus aureus; Clostridium* species (sporeformers); *Listeria*; and several types of yeasts, molds, and viruses. Outbreaks of *Salmonella* food infection traced backed to refrigerated foods such as ice cream

2. Named for the British physicist John Tyndall, who did early experiments with sterilizing procedures.

TABLE 11.4	Applications Using Heat for Sterilization and Disinfection	
Form of Heat	Equipment Temperature/Time	Medical and Commercial Uses and Limitations
Moist heat: Employs steam or boiling water; mode of action coagulates proteins		
Steam under pressure	Autoclave, pressure cooker; 121°C, pressure of 15 psi for 10 to 40 minutes, depending on load size; kills endospores	Sterilization of heat-resistant materials made of glass, cloth, rubber, metal; media; a few plastics; canned food, spices Decontamination of cultures Not appropriate for moisture-repellent oil or powder
Unpressurized steam (Tyndallization)	Arnold's Sterilizer—100°C for 30 minutes on 3 days; items are incubated between treatments to allow endospores to germinate.	Limited uses in sterilizing some media and foods that cannot be autoclaved; can be used to disinfect but not sterilize some medical supplies
Pasteurization	Pasteurizer; flash method works at 71.6°C for 15 seconds; ultrahigh temperature (UHT) uses 134°C for a few seconds.	Disinfection of milk and dairy products to destroy milk-borne pathogens; UHT can sterilize for longer shelf life. Fruit juices, beer, and wine may be pasteurized to destroy contaminants and preserve the products.
Boiling water	Water bath or pan heated to 100°C; items may be placed in water for 30 minutes to kill vegetative pathogens.	Limited to disinfection and sanitization of heat-resistant household objects such as eating utensils, clothing, sick room supplies, baby supplies, bedding, and water in emergencies; problem with recontamination
Dry heat: Employs dried hot air, flame, or heat coil; works by dehydration or combustion		
Dry oven	Electric or gas chamber heated to 150°C to 180°C for 2 to 4 hours	Materials that can withstand hot temperatures and dehydration; glassware, metals, powders, oils Poor choice for liquids, rubber, plastics; time-consuming
Incineration	Bunsen burner flame up to 1,800°C; small infrared incinerators to 800°C Furnaces, incinerators up to 6,500°C	For sterilizing tips of inoculation instruments; limited to high-temperature metals Permanent disposal of waste material from laboratories; burning reduces bulky packages and garbage to ashes. For permanent disposal only

A small flash pasteurizer used by dairies for calves' milk.

Dry heat incineration. Infrared incinerator with shield to prevent spattering of microbial samples during flaming.

and eggs are testimony to the inability of cold temperatures to reliably kill pathogens.

Most vegetative cells directly exposed to normal room air gradually become dehydrated, or **desiccated.*** Delicate pathogens such as *Streptococcus pneumoniae,* the spirochete of syphilis, and

Neisseria gonorrhoeae can die after a few hours of air-drying, but many others are not killed and some are even preserved. Staphylococci and streptococci in dried secretions and the tubercle bacillus surrounded by sputum can remain viable in air and dust for lengthy periods. Many viruses (especially nonenveloped) and fungal spores can also withstand long periods of desiccation. Endospores of *Bacillus* and *Clostridium* are viable for millions of years under

* *desiccate* (des'-ih-kayt) To dry at normal environmental temperatures.

extremely arid conditions. Desiccation can be a valuable way to preserve foods because it greatly reduces the amount of water available to support microbial growth.

It is interesting to note that a combination of freezing and drying—**lyophilization***—is a common method of preserving microorganisms and other cells in a viable state for many years. Pure cultures are frozen instantaneously and exposed to a vacuum that rapidly removes the water. This method avoids the formation of ice crystals that would damage the cells. Although not all cells survive this process, enough of them do to permit future reconstitution of that culture.

As a general rule, chilling, freezing, and desiccation should not be construed as methods of disinfection or sterilization because their antimicrobial effects are erratic and uncertain, and one cannot be sure that pathogens subjected to them have been killed.

 Check Your Progress SECTION 11.2

10. What happens to microbes that encounter temperatures below their minimum and above their maximum growth temperatures?
11. Summarize the nature, mode of action, and effectiveness of moist and dry heat on spores and vegetative cells.
12. Explain the concepts of TDT and TDP, using examples.
13. What are the minimum TDTs for vegetative cells and endospores?
14. How can the temperature of steam be raised above 100°C? Which instrument is based on this technique and how is it used?
15. What are the primary purposes of pasteurization, and what is ultrapasteurization?
16. What are several microbial targets of pasteurization?
17. Explain why desiccation and cold are not reliable methods of disinfection but how they can still be effective in microbial control.

11.3 Physical Methods of Control: Radiation and Filtration

 Expected Learning Outcomes

14. Define *radiation* and assess the use of irradiation as a method of microbial control.
15. Differentiate between ionizing and nonionizing radiation in their modes of action.
16. Summarize the primary uses of ionizing and nonionizing radiation in sterilization and disinfection.
17. Describe the concept behind sterilization by filtration, including examples of applications.

Radiation as a Microbial Control Agent

Another way in which energy can serve as an antimicrobial agent is through the use of radiation. **Radiation** is defined as energy emitted from atomic activities and dispersed at high velocity through matter or space. It is characterized by a range of wavelengths known as the

* *lyophilization* (ly-off″-il-ih-za′-shun) Gr. *lyein,* to dissolve, and *philein,* to love.

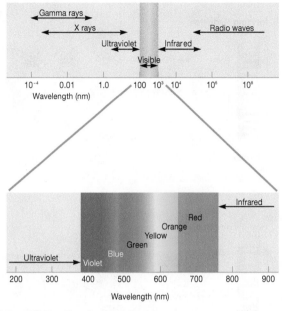

Figure 11.7 The electromagnetic spectrum. Waves range from the shortest gamma rays to the longest radio waves. Inset shows the spectrum of visible light between ultraviolet (UV) and infrared. Only ionizing radiation, UV, and infrared have applications in microbial control.

electromagnetic spectrum (**figure 11.7**). Although radiation exists in many energy states, we will consider only those types suitable for microbial control: gamma rays, X rays, and ultraviolet radiation.

Modes of Action of Ionizing Versus Nonionizing Radiation

The actual physical effects of radiation on microbes can be understood by visualizing the process of **irradiation,** or bombardment with radiation, at the cellular level (**figure 11.8**). When a cell is bombarded by certain waves or particles, its molecules absorb some of the available energy, leading to one of two consequences: (1) If the radiation ejects orbital electrons from an atom, it causes ions to form; this type of radiation is termed **ionizing radiation.** One of the most sensitive targets for ionizing radiation is DNA, which will undergo mutations on a broad scale. Secondary lethal effects appear to be chemical changes in organelles and the production of toxic substances. Gamma rays, X rays, and high-speed electrons are all ionizing in their effects. (2) **Nonionizing radiation,** best exemplified by UV, excites atoms by raising them to a higher energy state, but it does not ionize them. This atomic excitation, in turn, leads to the formation of abnormal bonds within molecules such as DNA and is thus a source of mutations (see figure 11.10).

Ionizing Radiation: Gamma Rays, X Rays, and Cathode Rays

Over the past several years, ionizing radiation has become safer and more economical to use, and its applications have expanded. It is a highly effective alternative for sterilizing materials that

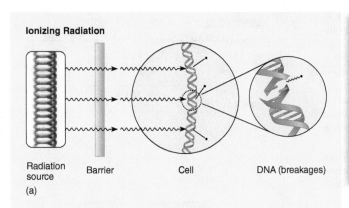

Ionizing Radiation

Radiation source | Barrier | Cell | DNA (breakages)
(a)

Nonionizing Radiation

(b)

DNA
(abnormal bonds)
See figure 11.10

UV does not penetrate
No effect on cell

Radiation source | Barrier
(c)

Figure 11.8 Cellular effects of irradiation. (a) Ionizing radiation can penetrate a solid barrier, bombard a cell, enter it, and dislodge electrons from molecules. Breakage of DNA creates massive mutations. **(b)** Nonionizing radiation enters a cell, strikes molecules, and excites them. The effect on DNA is mutation by formation of abnormal bonds. **(c)** A solid barrier cannot be penetrated by nonionizing radiation.

Irradiated raspberries left for 5 days at room temperature, still edible

Control, nonirradiated raspberries left for 5 days at room temperature, spoiled by mold

Figure 11.9 Sterilization with ionizing radiation. Many foods can be effectively sterilized by utilizing the penetrating power of ionizing radiation. The radura symbols applied to fresh foods signifies that the food has been irradiated and is required to be displayed on all food so treated.

sen dosage. The dosage of radiation is measured in grays (which has replaced the older term, *rads*). Depending on the application, exposure ranges from 5 to 50 kilograys (kGy; a kilogray is equal to 1,000 grays). Although all ionizing radiations can penetrate liquids and most solid materials, gamma rays are most penetrating, X rays are intermediate, and cathode rays least penetrating.

Irradiation as a Method of Microbial Control

Foods have been subject to irradiation in limited circumstances for more than 50 years. From flour to pork and ground beef, to fruits and vegetables, radiation is used to kill bacterial pathogens, insects, worms, and even to inhibit the sprouting of white potatoes. **Figure 11.9** demonstrates how irradiation of fruit can greatly reduce spoilage and improve shelf life.

As soon as radiation is involved, however, consumer concern arises that food may be made less nutritious, unpalatable, or even unsafe by subjecting it to ionizing radiation. But irradiated food has been extensively studied, and each of these concerns has been addressed.

Irradiation may lead to a small decrease in the amount of thiamine (vitamin B_1) in food, but this change is small enough to be inconsequential. The irradiation process does produce short-lived free radical oxidants, which disappear almost immediately (this same type of chemical intermediate is produced through cooking as well). Certain foods do not irradiate well and are not good candidates for this type of antimicrobial control. The white of eggs becomes milky and alfalfa seeds do not germinate properly. It should be emphasized that food is not made radioactive by the irradiation process, and many studies, in both animals and humans, have concluded that there are no ill effects from eating irradiated food. In fact, NASA relies on irradiated meat for its astronauts.

One of the potential benefits of irradiated foods has to do with infection control. It has been estimated that irradiation of 50% of the

Quick Search
Go online to view a video of "Food Irradiation."

are sensitive to heat or chemicals. Because it sterilizes in the absence of heat, irradiation is a type of **cold** (or low-temperature) **sterilization.**[3] Devices that emit ionizing rays include gamma-ray machines containing radioactive cobalt, X-ray machines similar to those used in medical diagnosis, and cathode-ray machines that operate like the vacuum tube in a television set. Items are placed in these machines and irradiated for a short time with a carefully cho-

3. To clarify the use of the word *cold*, in this context, it only means the absence of heat. Beer manufacturers have sometimes used this terminology as well. When they say that their product is "cold-filtered," they mean that it has been freed of contaminants via filtration, without heating.

meat and poultry in the United States would result in 900,000 fewer cases of infection, 8,500 fewer hospitalizations, and 350 fewer deaths each year. Radiation is currently approved in the United States for the reduction of bacterial pathogens such as *E. coli* and *Salmonella* in beef and chicken, reduction of *Trichinella* worms in pork, and the reduction of pathogens and pests on fruits and vegetables. An additional benefit of irradiation is that microbes responsible for food spoilage are killed along with pathogens, leading to an increased shelf life. In any event, no irradiated food can be sold to consumers without clear labeling that this method has been used (figure 11.9).

Sterilizing medical products with ionizing radiation is a rapidly expanding field. Drugs, vaccines, medical instruments (especially plastics), and other delicate materials can be irradiated without harming them. Its main advantages include speed, high penetrating power (it can sterilize materials through outer packages and wrappings), and the absence of heat. Its main disadvantages are potential dangers from factory exposure to radiation and possible damage to some materials. See table 11.5 for a summary of the applications of ionizing radiation.

Nonionizing Radiation: Ultraviolet Rays

Ultraviolet (UV) radiation ranges in wavelength from approximately 100 nm to 400 nm. It is most lethal from 240 nm to 280 nm (with a peak at 260 nm). In everyday practice, the source of UV radiation is the germicidal lamp, which generates radiation at 254 nm. Owing to its lower energy state, UV radiation is not as penetrating as ionizing radiation. Because UV radiation passes readily through air, slightly through liquids, and only poorly through solids, the object to be disinfected must be directly exposed to it for full effect.

As UV radiation passes through a cell, it is initially absorbed by DNA. Specific molecular damage occurs on the pyrimidine bases (thymine and cytosine), which form abnormal linkages with each other called **pyrimidine dimers (figure 11.10).** These bonds occur between adjacent bases on the same DNA strand and interfere with normal DNA replication and transcription. The results are inhibition of growth and cellular death. In addition to altering DNA directly, UV radiation also disrupts cells by generating toxic photochemical products called free radicals. These highly reactive molecules interfere with essential cell processes by binding to DNA, RNA, and proteins. Ultraviolet rays are a powerful tool for destroying fungal cells and spores, bacterial vegetative cells, protozoa, and viruses. Bacterial spores are about 10 times more resistant to radiation than are vegetative cells, but they can be killed by increasing the time of exposure.

Ultraviolet radiation is usually directed at disinfection rather than sterilization. Germicidal lamps can cut down on the concentration of airborne microbes by as much as 99%. Ultraviolet disinfection of air has proved effective in reducing postoperative infections, preventing the transmission of infections by respiratory droplets, and curtailing the growth of microbes in food-processing plants and slaughterhouses.

Ultraviolet irradiation of liquids requires special equipment to spread the liquid into a thin, flowing film that is exposed directly to a lamp. This method can be used to treat water (**figure 11.11**) and to purify other liquids (milk and fruit juices) as an alternative to heat. The surfaces of solid, nonporous materials such as walls and floors, as well as meat, nuts, tissues for grafting, and drugs, can be

Figure 11.10 **Formation of pyrimidine dimers by the action of ultraviolet (UV) radiation.** This shows what occurs when two adjacent thymine bases on one strand of DNA are induced by UV rays to bond laterally with each other. The result is a thymine dimer shown in greater detail. Dimers can also occur between adjacent cytosines and thymine and cytosine bases. If they are not repaired, dimers can prevent that segment of DNA from being correctly replicated or transcribed. High levels of dimerization are lethal to cells.

Figure 11.11 **An ultraviolet (UV) treatment system for disinfection of water.** Water is directed through channels at a water treatment plant, past racks of UV lamps (green glow). This system has a capacity of several million gallons per day and can be used as an alternative to chlorination. Home systems that fit under the sink are also available.

successfully disinfected with UV. Several types of small UV disinfection appliances have been marketed for personal items.

One major disadvantage of UV is its poor powers of penetration through solid materials such as glass, metal, cloth, plastic, and even paper. Another drawback to UV is the damaging effect of overexposure on human tissues, including sunburn, retinal damage, cancer, and skin wrinkling. These harmful results occur only if a person is directly exposed to the UV rays, but it necessitates placement of barriers to cut down on this possibility. **Table 11.5** summarizes UV applications.

Filtration—A Physical Removal Process

Filtration is an effective method to remove microbes from air and liquids. In practice, a fluid is strained through a filter with openings large enough for the fluid to pass through but too small for microorganisms to pass through (**figure 11.12a**).

TABLE 11.5	**Applications Using Radiation for Sterilization and Disinfection**	
Form of Radiation	**Equipment/Mode of Action**	**Medical and Commercial Uses and Limitations**
Ionizing radiation		
Sporicidal and penetrating	Cobalt radiation gives off gamma rays; others are X rays, cathode rays. Rays fragment DNA and create ionized bases; highly mutagenic.	Cold sterilization of packaged products such as medical supplies and instruments that cannot be heat sterilized Sterilization of foods, including fruits, lettuce and spinach, grains, spices, meats, and packaged meals Sterilization of drugs and vaccines Rapid and penetrating, prevents infection and spoilage
Nonionizing ultraviolet (UV) radiation		
Sporicidal and nonpenetrating	Germicidal lamps or generators set to deliver UV rays from 240 to 280 nm in wavelength; action creates abnormal bonds between adjacent thymines and cytosines and produces deletion mutations on DNA.	Mostly disinfection of air, some liquids, a few solids; reduces airborne pathogens in medical and dental offices, hospital rooms, and operating rooms Commercial use for clean rooms, food processing areas Works on liquids such as water, milk, drugs, vaccines if exposed to UV in thin layers Solid materials such as room surfaces, foods, tissue grafts, drugs, and instruments Lack of penetration through solids limits applications; direct exposure can be dangerous to eyes and skin.

Pallets of apples are being irradiated with a cobalt 60 machine that emits gamma rays.

Tabletop chamber generates ultraviolet rays to disinfect a toothbrush.

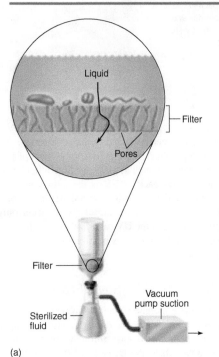

Liquid

Filter

Pores

Filter

Vacuum pump suction

Sterilized fluid

(a)

(b)

Figure 11.12 Membrane filtration. (a) Vacuum assembly for achieving filtration of liquids through suction. Inset shows filter as seen in cross section, with tiny passageways (pores) too small for the microbial cells to enter but large enough for liquid to pass through. **(b)** Scanning electron micrograph of *Enterococcus* trapped on the surface of a membrane filter (10,400×). Average cells measure about 0.5 μm to 1 μm in diameter, and average pore size is about 0.3 μm.

Most modern microbiological filters are thin membranes of cellulose acetate, polycarbonate, and a variety of plastic materials (Teflon, nylon) whose pore size can be carefully controlled and standardized. Ordinary substances such as charcoal, diatomaceous earth, or unglazed porcelain are also used in some applications. Viewed microscopically, most filters are perforated by very precise, uniform pores **(figure 11.12b).** The pore diameters vary from coarse (8 μm) to ultrafine (0.02 μm), permitting selection of the minimum particle size to be trapped. Those with even smaller pore diameters permit true sterilization by removing viruses, and some will even remove large proteins. A sterile liquid filtrate is typically produced by suctioning the liquid through a sterile filter into a presterilized container. These filters are also used to separate mixtures of microorganisms and to enumerate bacteria in water analysis.

Applications of Filtration Sterilization

Filtration sterilization is used to prepare liquids that cannot withstand heat, including serum and other blood products, vaccines, drugs, IV fluids, enzymes,

and media. Filtration has been employed as an alternative method for sterilizing milk and beer without altering their flavor. It is also an important step in water purification. Its use extends to filtering out particulate impurities (crystals, fibers) that can cause severe reactions in the body. It has the disadvantage of not removing soluble molecules (toxins) that can cause disease.

Filtration is also an efficient means of removing airborne contaminants that are a common source of infection and spoilage. High-efficiency particulate air (HEPA) filters are widely used to provide a flow of sterile air to hospital rooms and sterile rooms.

 Check Your Progress SECTION 11.3

18. Define radiation and irradiation.
19. Differentiate between the modes of action of ionizing radiation and ultraviolet radiation.
20. What are some advantages and disadvantages of ionizing radiation as a method of control?
21. Describe some applications of ionizing and ultraviolet radiation.
22. What are the advantages and disadvantages of using filtration as a method of control?

11.4 Chemical Agents in Microbial Control

 Expected Learning Outcomes

18. Define the terms that are used to describe different methods of chemical control of microbes.

19. Explain the desirable features of antimicrobial chemicals and what factors influence their effectiveness.

20. Describe the types of halogens, their modes of action, and their clinical and commercial applications.

21. Identify the characteristics of phenolic compounds and alcohols, explain how they act, and evaluate their primary uses.

22. Describe the characteristics of oxidizing agents and aldehydes, and summarize their main applications.

23. Differentiate among the sterilizing gases and aerosols, and describe how they are used.

24. Explain how detergents, soaps, and heavy metals can be employed in clinical, commercial, and household microbial control.

Chemical control of microbes probably emerged as a serious science in the early 1800s, when physicians used chloride of lime and iodine solutions to treat wounds and to wash their hands before surgery. At the present time, approximately 10,000 different antimicrobial chemical agents are manufactured; probably 1,000 of them are used routinely in the health care and home environments. A genuine need exists to avoid infection and spoilage, but the abundance of products available to "kill germs," "disinfect," "antisepticize," "clean and sanitize," "deodorize," "fight plaque," and "purify the air" indicates a preoccupation with eliminating microbes from the environment that, at times, seems excessive (**11.2 Making Connections**).

Antimicrobial chemicals occur in the liquid, gaseous, or even solid state. They serve as **disinfectants, antiseptics, sterilants** (chemicals that sterilize), degermers, or preservatives (chemicals that inhibit the deterioration of substances). In most cases, solid or gaseous antimicrobial chemicals are dissolved in water, alcohol, or a mixture of the two to produce a liquid solution. Solutions containing pure water as the solvent are termed **aqueous,** whereas those dissolved in pure alcohol or water-alcohol mixtures are termed **tinctures.**

Choosing a Microbicidal Chemical

The choice and appropriate use of antimicrobial chemical agents are of constant concern in medicine and dentistry. Although actual clinical practices of chemical decontamination vary widely, some desirable qualities in a germicide have been identified, including:

- rapid action in low concentrations,
- solubility in water or alcohol and long-term stability,
- broad-spectrum microbicidal action without being toxic to human and animal tissues,
- penetration of inanimate surfaces to sustain a cumulative or persistent action,
- resistance to becoming inactivated by organic matter,
- noncorrosive or nonstaining properties,
- sanitizing and deodorizing properties,
- affordability and ready availability, and
- nonoffensive odor.

As yet, no chemical can completely fulfill all of those requirements, but chlorhexidine and hydrogen peroxide approach this ideal. At the same time, we should question the rather overinflated claims made about certain commercial agents such as mouthwashes and disinfectant air sprays.

Germicides are evaluated in terms of their effectiveness in destroying microbes in medical and dental settings. The three levels of chemical decontamination procedures are *high, intermediate,* and *low* (**table 11.6**).

- High-level germicides kill endospores and, if properly used, are sterilants. Materials that necessitate high-level control are medical devices—for example, catheters, heart-lung equipment, and implants—that are not heat-sterilizable and are intended to enter body tissues during medical procedures.
- Intermediate-level germicides kill fungal (but not bacterial) spores, resistant pathogens such as the tubercle bacillus, and viruses. They are used to disinfect items (respiratory equipment, thermometers) that come into intimate contact with the mucous membranes but are noninvasive.
- Low levels of disinfection eliminate only vegetative bacteria, vegetative fungal cells, and some viruses. They are used to clean materials such as electrodes, straps, and furniture that touch the skin surfaces but not the mucous membranes.

Factors That Affect the Germicidal Activities of Chemical Agents

Several concepts of microbial control introduced in section 11.1 apply to germicides and other chemical agents. For instance, they target the same cellular structures and functions previously discussed: cell walls and membranes, proteins, and nucleic acids. The

TABLE 11.6	Qualities of Chemical Agents Used in Health Care			
Agent	Target Microbes	Level of Germicidal Activity	Toxicity	Comments
Chlorine	Sporicidal (slowly)	Intermediate	Gas is highly toxic; solution irritates skin	Inactivated by organics; unstable in sunlight
Iodine	Sporicidal (slowly)	Intermediate	Can irritate tissue; toxic if ingested	Iodophors* are milder forms
Phenolics	Some bacteria, viruses, fungi	Low to intermediate	Can be absorbed by skin; can cause CNS damage	Poor solubility; expensive
Chlorhexidine*	Most bacteria, some viruses, fungi	Low to intermediate	Low toxicity	Fast-acting, mild, has residual effects
Alcohols	Most bacteria, viruses, fungi	Intermediate	Toxic if ingested; a mild irritant; dries skin	Flammable, fast-acting
Hydrogen peroxide,* stabilized	Sporicidal	High (sterilant)	Toxic to eyes; toxic if ingested	Improved stability; works well in organic matter
Quaternary ammonium compounds	Some bactericidal, virucidal, fungicidal activity	Low	Irritating to mucous membranes; poisonous if taken internally	Weak solutions can support microbial growth; easily inactivated
Soaps	Certain very sensitive species	Very low	Nontoxic; few if any toxic effects	Used for removing soil, oils, debris
Mercurials	Weakly microbistatic	Low	Highly toxic if ingested, inhaled, absorbed	Easily inactivated
Silver nitrate	Bactericidal	Low	Toxic, irritating	Discolors skin
Glutaraldehyde*	Sporicidal	High (sterilant)	Can irritate skin; toxic if absorbed	Not inactivated by organic matter; unstable
Formaldehyde	Sporicidal	Intermediate to high	Very irritating; fumes damaging, carcinogenic	Slow rate of action; limited applications
Ethylene oxide gas*	Sporicidal	High (sterilant)	Very dangerous to eyes, lungs; carcinogenic	Explosive in pure state; good penetration; materials must be aerated
Dyes	Weakly bactericidal, fungicidal	Low	Low toxicity	Stains materials, skin

*These chemicals approach the ideal by having many of the following characteristics: broad spectrum, low toxicity, fast action, penetrating abilities, residual effects, stability, potency in organic matter, and solubility.

effectiveness of the agents depends on several factors. Among these are (1) the numbers and kinds of microbes that are present, (2) the kinds of materials that are being treated, (3) the time of exposure required, and (4) the strength and mode of action of the agent. Here, we focus on the latter two because of their importance to chemical agents.

Length of Exposure Most compounds require adequate contact time for the chemical to penetrate and to act on the microbes present. The composition of the material being treated can greatly affect this process. Smooth, solid objects are more rapidly disinfected than are those with pores or pockets that can trap soil. An item contaminated with common biological matter such as serum, blood, saliva, pus, fecal material, or urine presents an additional barrier to effective disinfection. Large amounts of this organic material can hinder penetration and, in some cases, can form bonds that reduce

a chemical's activity. Adequate cleaning of instruments and other reusable materials will ensure that the germicide or sterilant will better accomplish the job for which it was chosen.

Concentration of the Chemical Agent A chemical's strength or concentration is expressed in various ways, depending upon convention and the method of preparation. The content of many chemical agents can be formulated in more than one way. For dilutions, a small volume of the liquid chemical (solute) is diluted in a larger volume of solvent to achieve a certain ratio. For example, a common laboratory phenolic disinfectant such as Lysol is usually diluted 1:200; that is, one part of chemical (solute) has been added to 200 parts of water (solvent) by volume. Solutions such as chlorine that are effective in very diluted concentrations are expressed in parts per million (ppm). In percentage solutions, the solute is added to solvent by weight or volume to achieve a certain percentage in the solution.

11.2 MAKING CONNECTIONS

Pathogen Paranoia: "The Only Good Microbe Is a Dead Microbe"

The sensational publicity over influenza, MRSA skin infections, and noroviruses has had a dramatic impact on the public awareness of microorganisms. This glut of coverage has also had certain benefits, such as greater emphasis on hand washing, food handling, and personal hygiene. But sometimes a little knowledge can be dangerous. The trend also seems to have escalated into an obsessive fear of "germs" lurking around every corner and a fixation on eliminating microbes from the environment and the human body.

As might be expected, commercial industries have found a way to capitalize on those fears. Every year, a number of new products are released that incorporate antibacterial or germicidal "protection." A widespread array of cleansers and commonplace materials now contain antimicrobial chemicals. First, it was hand soaps and dishwashing detergents, and eventually, the list grew to include shampoos, laundry aids, hand lotions, foot pads for shoes, deodorants, sponges, kitty litter, acne medication, cutting boards, garbage bags, toys, toothpaste, and even building products.

One chemical agent routinely added to these products is a phenolic called *triclosan*. This substance is fairly mild and does indeed kill most pathogenic bacteria. However, it does not reliably destroy viruses or fungi and has been linked to cases of skin rashes due to hypersensitivity. Some published reports have also linked it to some forms of hormone and muscle disorders. Because concerns of its side effects have been raised, some hospitals have stopped using it, and the FDA is currently reviewing its safety.

Medical experts are concerned that the widespread overuse of these antibacterial chemicals could favor the survival and growth of resistant strains of bacteria. One study reported that pathogens such as *Mycobacterium tuberculosis* and *Clostridium* are naturally resistant to triclosan and that *E. coli* and *Staphylococcus aureus* have developed decreased sensitivity to it. One fear has been that overuse of this chemical could select for "super bugs" that can survive all attempts at disinfection.

Another outcome of overuse of environmental germicides is to reduce the natural contact with microbes that is required to maintain the normal microbial residents of the body and stimulate immunities. Con-

A three-dimensional model of triclosan, also known as Ultra-Fresh and Amicor, is a phenol-based chemical that destroys bacteria by disrupting cell walls and membranes.

stant use of these agents could shift the balance in the microbiota by killing off harmless or beneficial microbes.

An unfortunate side effect of negative views of microbes is how they foster the feeling that all microbes are harmful. We must not forget that most human beings manage to remain healthy despite the fact that they live in continual intimate contact with microorganisms. We really do not have to be preoccupied with microbes every minute or feel overly concerned that the things we touch, drink, or eat are sterile, as long as they are somewhat clean and free of pathogens. For most of us, resistance to infection is well maintained by our numerous host defenses.

Infectious disease specialists urge a happy medium approach. Instead of filling the home with questionable germicidal products, they encourage cleaning with traditional soaps and detergents, reserving more potent products to reduce the spread of infection in clinical settings.

Can you name other consequences of mass usage of antimicrobial chemicals in addition to those mentioned here? *Answer available at http://www.mhhe.com/talaro9*

Alcohol, for instance, is used in percentages ranging from 50% to 95%. In general, solutions of low dilution or high percentage have more of the active chemical (are more concentrated) and tend to be more germicidal, but expense and potential toxicity can necessitate using the minimum strength that is effective.

Standardized procedures for testing the effectiveness of germicides are summarized in **Appendix B.**

Categories of Chemical Agents

Several general groups of chemical compounds are widely used for antimicrobial purposes in medicine and commerce (table 11.6). Prominent agents include halogens, phenolic compounds, alcohols, oxidizers, aldehydes, gases, detergents, and heavy metals. These groups are surveyed in the following section from the standpoint of each agent's specific forms and modes of action. Applications and methods of delivery are described in tables.

The Halogen Antimicrobial Chemicals

The **halogens*** are fluorine, bromine, chlorine, and iodine, a group of nonmetallic elements with similar chemical properties. Although they can exist in either the ionic (halide) or nonionic state, most halogens exert their antimicrobial effect primarily in the nonionic state, not the halide state (chloride, iodide, for example). Because fluorine and bromine are difficult and dangerous to handle and no more effective than chlorine and iodine, only the latter two are used routinely in germicidal preparations. These elements are highly effective components of disinfectants and antiseptics because they are microbicidal and not just microbistatic, and they are sporicidal with longer exposure. For these reasons, halogens are the active ingredients in nearly one-third of all antimicrobial chemicals currently marketed.

* *halogens* (hay'-loh-jenz) Gr. *halos,* salt, and *gennan,* to produce.

Chlorine and Its Compounds Chlorine has been used for disinfection and antisepsis for approximately 200 years. The major forms used in microbial control are liquid and gaseous chlorine (Cl_2), hypochlorites (O^-Cl), and chloramines (NH_2Cl). In solution, these compounds combine with water and release hypochlorous acid (HOCl):

$$Cl_2 + H_2O \rightarrow HClO + HCl \text{ (hydrochloric acid)}$$
$$Ca(OCl)_2 + 2H_2O \rightarrow Ca(OH)_2 + 2HClO$$

Hypochlorous acid oxidizes the sulfhydryl (S—H) groups on the amino acid cysteine and breaks disulfide (S—S) bridges on numerous enzymes. The resulting denaturation of the enzymes is permanent and suspends metabolic reactions. It also damages the structure of DNA, RNA, and fatty acids.

Death of almost all microorganisms usually occurs within 30 minutes, although endospores may require several hours. Chlorine compounds are less effective and relatively unstable if exposed to light, alkaline pH, and excess organic matter.

Iodine and Its Compounds Iodine (I_2) is a pungent blue-black element that forms a brown-colored solution when dissolved in water. It rapidly penetrates the cells of microorganisms, where it disturbs a variety of metabolic functions by interfering with the disulfide bonds of proteins. This mode of action is similar to that seen in chlorine, although iodine is less susceptible to inactivation by organic material. All classes of microorganisms can be killed if proper exposure times and iodine concentrations are used.

See **table 11.7** for information on the main uses and forms of halogens.

TABLE 11.7	Applications of Halogen Compounds	
Form of Chlorine	**Primary Applications**	**How Delivered/Concerns**
Chlorine Gas (Cl_2)	Large-scale disinfection of drinking water, sewage, and wastewater	Chlorination to a concentration of 0.6 to 1.0 parts of chlorine per million parts of water destroys most vegetative pathogens.*
Hypochlorites (HClO) Bleach	Used extensively in sanitization and disinfection of food equipment, treatment of swimming pools, spas, drinking water, and fresh foods; for wound antisepsis and routine medical and household disinfection, deodorizing, and stain removal	Common household bleach is a 5% solution of sodium hypochlorite; dilutions of 1:10–1:1,000 are highly effective germicides.
Chloramines (Dichloramine, Halazone)	An alternative to pure chlorine in treating water supplies; also as sanitizers and disinfectants; for treating wounds and skin surfaces	Because standard gas chlorination of water is now believed to produce unsafe levels of trihalomethanes, some water districts are required to use chloramine treatment of water supplies.
Form of Iodine	**Primary Applications**	**How Delivered/Concerns**
Iodophors	Most common iodine for skin and mucous membranes; antiseptic prep for surgery and injections; for surgical handscrubs; to disinfect equipment and surfaces; possibly for burns; and may be an alternative preventive for eye infections in newborns	A complex of iodine and a neutral protein polymer provides slow release and reduced toxicity or irritation of tissues; less prone to staining. Common products are povidone-iodine (PVI; Betadine), which contain 2% to 10% of available iodine.
Aqueous or Tinctures	Topical antiseptic prior to surgery; sometimes for burned or injured skin	Weak solutions of 1% to 3% in water or in alcohol tinctures
	Medium-level disinfection for plastic instruments, thermometers; tablet form available for disinfection of contaminated water	Aqueous solutions or tinctures of 5% to 10%; somewhat limited by their toxicity and tendency to stain

Cantaloupes are disinfected with chlorine-treated water to kill *Salmonella* carried on their surfaces.

Patient has been treated with a povidone-iodine solution in preparation for surgery.

*Some cyst-forming protozoans such as *Giardia* and *Cryptosporidium* can survive this level of chlorination.

Phenol and Its Derivatives

Phenol (carbolic acid) is an acrid, poisonous compound derived from the distillation of coal tar. First adopted by Joseph Lister in 1867 as a surgical germicide, phenol was the major antimicrobial chemical until other phenolics with fewer toxic and irritating effects were developed. Solutions of phenol are now used only in certain limited cases, but it remains one standard against which other phe-nolic disinfectants are rated. The *phenol coefficient* quantitatively compares a chemical's antimicrobic properties to those of phenol. Substances chemically related to phenol are often referred to as phe-nolics. Hundreds of these chemicals are now available.

Phenolics consist of one or more aromatic carbon rings with added functional groups (**figure 11.13**). Among the most important are alkylated phenols (cresols), chlorinated phenols, and bisphenols. In high concentrations, they are cellular poisons, rapidly disrupting cell walls and membranes and precipitating proteins; in lower con-centrations, they inactivate certain critical enzyme systems. The phe-nolics are strongly microbicidal and will destroy vegetative bacteria (including the tuberculosis bacillus), fungi, and most viruses (not hepatitis B), but they are not reliably sporicidal. Their continued ac-tivity in the presence of organic matter and their detergent actions contribute to their usefulness. Unfortunately, the toxicity of many of the phenolics makes them too dangerous to use as antiseptics.

Figure 11.13 Examples of phenolic structures. All contain a basic aromatic ring, but they differ in the types of additional compounds such as Cl and CH₃.

Chlorhexidine

The compound chlorhexidine (Hibiclens, Hibitane) is a complex organic base containing chlorine and two phenolic rings. Its mode of action targets cell membranes by lowering surface tension and causing denaturation of proteins. At moderate to high concentra-tions, it is bactericidal for both gram-positive and gram-negative bacteria but inactive against spores. Its effects on viruses and fungi vary. It possesses distinct advantages over many other antiseptics because of its mildness, low toxicity, and rapid action, and it is not absorbed into deeper tissues to any extent. It is the antiseptic cleanser of choice to control *Staphylococcus* MRSA and *Acineto-bacter* outbreaks in hospitals.

Applications for phenolic compounds and chlorhexidine are given in **table 11.8.**

TABLE 11.8	Applications of Phenolics and Chlorhexidene	
Form of Phenolic	**Primary Applications**	**How Delivered/Concerns**
Lysol and Creolin	Common household versions of phenol; for low or intermediate levels of disinfection in the hospital	1% to 3% emulsions that are combined with soap; can be too toxic for antisepsis; tend to be absorbed by membranes into the blood
Bisphenols	Widely employed commercially, clinically, and in the home; Lysol spray often used in hospital and laboratory disinfection	Orthophenyl phenol is the major ingredient in disinfectant aerosol sprays. This same phenolic is also found in some compounds.
Hexachlorophene	Was once a widespread additive of cleansing soaps (pHisoHex) for hospital and home use; may be used to control outbreaks of skin infections	When hexachlorophene was found to be absorbed through the skin and a cause of neurological damage, it was no longer available without a prescription.
Triclosan (Dichlorophenoxyphenol)	Widely used antibacterial compound added to soaps, cosmetics, and many other household products	It acts as both disinfectant and antiseptic and is broad-spectrum in its effects.
Form of Chlorhexidine	**Primary Applications**	**How Delivered/Concerns**
Chlorhexidine (Hibiclens, Hibitane)	Alcoholic or aqueous solutions are now commonly used for hand scrubbing, preparing skin sites for surgical incisions and injections, and patient cleansing. Solutions also serve as an obstetric and neonatal wash, a wound degermer, a mucous membrane irrigant, and a preservative for eye solutions.	Complex base containing chlorine and two phenolic rings; mode of action targets cell membranes and protein structure. At moderate to high concentrations, destroys both gram-positive and gram-negative bacteria but not spores. It may be fungicidal and virucidal. It is milder and less toxic than phenolics and is not absorbed into the skin.

Alcohols as Antimicrobial Agents

Alcohols are colorless hydrocarbons with one or more —OH functional groups. Of several alcohols available, only ethyl and isopropyl are suitable for microbial control. Methyl alcohol is not particularly microbicidal, and more complex alcohols are either poorly soluble in water or too expensive for routine use. Alcohols are employed alone in aqueous solutions or as solvents for tinctures (with iodine, for example).

Alcohol's mechanism of action depends in part upon its concentration. Concentrations of 50% and higher dissolve membrane lipids, disrupt cell surface tension, and compromise membrane integrity. Alcohol that has entered the protoplasm denatures proteins through coagulation but only in alcohol-water solutions of 50% to 95%. Alcohol is the exception to the rule that higher concentrations of an antimicrobial chemical have greater microbicidal activity. Because water is needed for proteins to coagulate, alcohol shows a greater microbicidal activity at 70% concentration (that is, 30% water) than at 100% (0% water). Absolute alcohol (100%) dehydrates cells and inhibits their growth but is generally not a protein coagulant.

Although useful in intermediate- to low-level germicidal applications, alcohol does not destroy bacterial spores at room temperature. Alcohol can, however, destroy resistant vegetative forms, including tuberculosis bacteria and fungal spores, provided the time of exposure is adequate. Alcohol tends to inactivate enveloped viruses more readily than nonenveloped viruses such as poliovirus and hepatitis A virus.

Hydrogen Peroxide and Related Germicides

Hydrogen peroxide (H_2O_2) is a colorless, caustic liquid that decomposes in the presence of light, metals, or catalase into water and oxygen gas. Early formulations were unstable and inhibited by organic matter, but manufacturing methods now permit synthesis of H_2O_2 so stable that even dilute solutions retain activity through several months of storage.

The germicidal effects of hydrogen peroxide are due to the direct and indirect actions of oxygen. Oxygen forms hydroxyl free radicals (—OH), which, like the superoxide radical (see chapter 7), are highly toxic and reactive to cells. Although most microbial cells produce catalase to inactivate the metabolic hydrogen peroxide, it cannot neutralize the amount of hydrogen peroxide entering the cell during disinfection and antisepsis. Hydrogen peroxide is bactericidal, virucidal, fungicidal, and, in higher concentrations, sporicidal.

A number of clinical procedures involve delicate reusable instruments such as endoscopes and dental handpieces. Because these devices can become heavily contaminated by tissues and fluids, they need to undergo sterilization, not just disinfection, between patients to prevent transmission of infections such as hepatitis, tuberculosis, and HIV. These expensive diagnostic tools (a colonoscope may cost $5,000 to $10,000) have created another dilemma. They may trap infectious agents where they cannot be easily removed; and they are delicate, complex, and difficult to clean. Traditional methods are either too damaging to the instruments (heat) or too slow to sterilize them in a timely fashion between patients (ethylene oxide gas). The need for effective rapid sterilization has led to the development of sterilizing cabinets that contain liquid sterilants such as hydrogen peroxide or peracetic acid **(figure 11.14).** A vaporized form of hydrogen peroxide is

Figure 11.14 Automated processor using peracetic acid to chemically sterilize reusable, immersible, heat-sensitive, critical and semi-critical devices. The cleaned medical device, such as an endoscope, is placed in the chamber and treated for about 23 minutes.

effective as an environmental sterilant used in decontaminating large spaces and objects (see figure 11.3).

Coverage on the applications of alcohols and peroxides is provided in **table 11.9.**

Aldehyde Sterilants and Disinfectants

Organic substances bearing a —CHO functional group (a strong reducing group) on the terminal carbon are called aldehydes. The two aldehydes used most often in microbial control are *glutaraldehyde* and *formaldehyde.*

Glutaraldehyde is a yellow liquid with a mild odor. The molecule's two aldehyde groups favor the formation of polymers. The mechanism of activity involves cross-linking protein molecules on the cell surface. In this process, amino acids are alkylated, meaning that a hydrogen atom on an amino acid is replaced by the glutaraldehyde molecule itself. This irreversibly disrupts the activity of enzymes and other proteins within cells. Glutaraldehyde is rapid and broad-spectrum, and is one of the few chemicals officially accepted as a sterilant and high-level disinfectant. It kills spores in 3 hours and fungi and vegetative bacteria (even *Mycobacterium* and *Pseudomonas*) in a few minutes. Viruses, including the most resistant forms, appear to be inactivated after relatively short exposure times. A special device known as a chemiclave (similar to an autoclave) vaporizes the solution under pressure to sterilize delicate instruments without heat. Glutaraldehyde retains its potency even in the presence of organic matter, is noncorrosive, does not damage plastics, and is less toxic or irritating than formaldehyde. Its principal disadvantage is that it is somewhat unstable, especially with increased pH and temperature.

Formaldehyde is a sharp, irritating gas that readily dissolves in water to form an aqueous solution called **formalin.** Pure formalin is a 37% solution of formaldehyde gas dissolved in water. The chemical is microbicidal through its attachment to nucleic acids and functional groups of amino acids. Formalin is an intermediate- to high-level disinfectant, but its extreme toxicity (it is classified as a carcinogen) and irritating effects on the skin and mucous membranes greatly limit its clinical usefulness.

Another aldehyde, ortho-phthalaldehyde (OPA), has been approved by the EPA as a high-level disinfectant. OPA is a pale blue liquid with a barely detectable odor. It has a mechanism of action similar to glutaraldehyde, is stable and nonirritating, and, for most uses, is much faster acting than glutaraldehyde. It is effective against

TABLE 11.9	Applications of Alcohols and Peroxides (and Other Oxidizing Agents)	
Form of Alcohol*	**Primary Applications**	**How Delivered/Concerns**
Ethyl Alcohol (Ethanol, Grain Alcohol)	Skin degerming agent and antiseptic; surfactant action removes skin oil, soil, and some microbes sheltered in deeper skin layers; occasionally used to disinfect electrodes and face masks	Solutions of 70% to 95% are germicidal, inexpensive, nonirritating; limited by its rate of evaporation. Items need to be first cleaned and then soaked in alcohol for 15 to 20 minutes.
Isopropyl Alcohol (Rubbing Alcohol)	Some disinfection of objects, surfaces; limited skin cleansing	More microbicidal and less expensive than ethanol, but these benefits must be weighed against its toxicity; inhaling its vapors can adversely affect the nervous system.
Form of Oxidizing Agent	**Primary Applications**	**How Delivered/Concerns**
Hydrogen Peroxide (H_2O_2)	Versatile uses as an antiseptic, including skin and wound cleansing, bedsore care, and mouthwashing; disinfectant for soft contact lenses, surgical implants, plastics, bedding, and room interiors	3% hydrogen peroxide—most common form—is useful in treating infections by anaerobic bacteria because of the lethal effects of the oxygen released.
Sterilizing H_2O_2	Vaporized H_2O_2 is a major type of sterilant; hydrogen peroxide plasma sterilizers used for industrial parts or medical items; for isolators, clean rooms, and space vehicles	Hydrogen peroxide (35%) penetrates into delicate medical instruments, kills the most resistant microbes, and does not corrode small parts; vapors are sporicidal.
Peracetic Acid	Used to sterilize rooms, space shuttle; a chemical sterilant for medical devices	Oxidizing agent—similar actions to hydrogen peroxide
Ozone (O_3)	A gas used to disinfect air, water, industrial air conditioners, and cooling towers	Difficult to handle in gaseous form

A nurse takes advantage of an alcohol gel hand cleansing station. These are very common in hospitals and clinics to encourage hand antisepsis.

Disinfection of contact lenses with peroxide-based cleaner. Note the bubbles produced, indicating the release of oxygen gas.

*Both forms of alcohol are in alcohol gels used for universal precautions and hand degerming in hospitals.

vegetative bacteria, including *Mycobacterium* and *Pseudomonas*, fungi, and viruses. Chief among its disadvantages are an inability to reliably destroy spores and a tendency to stain proteins, including those in human skin.

Gaseous Sterilants and Disinfectants

Processing inanimate substances with chemical vapors, gases, and aerosols provides a versatile alternative to heat or liquid chemicals. Currently, those vapors and aerosols having the broadest applications are ethylene oxide (ETO), propylene oxide, and chlorine dioxide.

Ethylene oxide and its relative propylene oxide (PO) are colorless gases at room temperature. The structure of ETO is shown below:

$$CH_2 - CH_2$$
$$\diagdown \, O \diagup$$

It is very explosive in air, a feature that can be eliminated by combining it with a high percentage of carbon dioxide or fluorocarbon. Like the aldehydes, ETO is a very strong alkylating agent, and it reacts vigorously with functional groups of DNA and proteins. Through these actions, it blocks both DNA replication and enzymatic actions. Ethylene oxide is one of a very few gases generally accepted for chemical sterilization because, when employed according to strict procedures, it is a sporicide. A specially designed ETO sterilizer is equipped with a chamber, gas ports, and temperature, pressure, and humidity controls (**figure 11.15**). Ethylene oxide is rather penetrating but relatively slow-acting, requiring from 90 minutes to 3 hours. Some items absorb ETO residues and must be aerated with sterile air for several hours after exposure to remove as much residual gas as possible. For all of its effectiveness, ETO has some unfortunate features. Its explosiveness makes it dangerous to handle; it can damage the lungs, eyes, and mucous membranes

Figure 11.15 Sterilization using an ethylene oxide sterilizer. The machine is equipped with gas canisters containing ethylene oxide (ETO) and carbon dioxide, a chamber to hold items, and mechanisms that evacuate gas and introduce air.

if contacted directly; and it is rated as a carcinogen by the government. Both ETO and propylene oxide are used mainly as disinfectant-sterilants for some foods and plastic items.

Chlorine dioxide is another gas used for sterilization. Despite the name, chlorine dioxide works in a completely different way from the chlorine compounds discussed earlier in the chapter. It is a strong alkylating agent, which disrupts proteins and is effective against vegetative bacteria, fungi, viruses, and endospores. Although chlorine dioxide is used for the treatment of drinking water, wastewater, food-processing equipment, and medical waste, its best known use was in the decontamination of several government offices after the anthrax attack of 2001.

Betapropiolactone (BPL) is a substance somewhat similar to ETO in applications. It is rapidly microbicidal when used as an aerosol or liquid to disinfect whole rooms and instruments, sterilize bone and arterial grafts, and inactivate viruses in vaccines.

A summary of applications for aldehydes and sterilizing gases is presented in **table 11.10.**

TABLE 11.10	Applications of Aldehydes and Sterilant Gases	
Form of Aldehyde	**Primary Applications**	**How Delivered/Concerns**
Glutaraldehyde	A sterilant for materials usually damaged by heat. Examples include respiratory therapy equipment, hemostats, fiberoptic endoscopes, kidney dialysis equipment, and dental instruments; an alternate vaccine preservative, and sanitizer for poultry carcasses.	Solutions diluted to 2% are relatively mild but require 2 to 4 hours soaking. Usual commercial products are Cidex, Sporocidin. Instrument sterilization involves precleaning along with autoclaving to inactivate hepatitis B and other blood-borne viruses.
Formalin	Limited uses as a disinfectant for surgical instruments; used in aquaculture to kill fish parasites and control growth of algae and fungi; it is one active ingredient in embalming fluid (with an alcohol and a phenolic).	May be used as 8% tincture; objects intended for contact with the body must be thoroughly rinsed to remove the formalin residue, which is toxic and carcinogenic.
Ortho-phthalaldehyde (OPA)	High-level disinfectant similar in uses and effects to glutaraldehyde	Faster acting and more stable than glutaraldehyde but less sporicidal
Form of Gas	**Primary Applications**	**How Delivered/Concerns**
Ethylene Oxide (ETO)	An official sterilant for heat-sensitive plastics and delicate instruments in hospitals and industries— prepackaged medical supplies and disposable Petri dishes; used extensively to disinfect foods, spices, dried fruits, and drugs	Carboxide and cryoxide are commercial products; gas is explosive and must be used with a stabilizer; ETO is rather toxic to humans; penetrating but slow, requiring 1 to 3 hours of exposure inside a special chamber.
Propylene Oxide	Sterilization of foods such as nuts, powders, starches, and spices	Similar physical properties and mode of action to ETO but safer because it breaks down into a relatively harmless substance.
Chlorine Dioxide	Air and surface sterilant; for treatment of water, food-processing equipment, and medical waste; the decontamination of whole rooms and space probes	Similar in action to ETO but does not require a chamber; thus, effective for large spaces or objects.

Technician treats surgical instruments with glutaraldehyde prior to heat sterilization.

Examples of prepackaged medical supplies sterilized in an ethylene oxide sterilizer

CLINICAL CONNECTIONS

The Quest for Sterile Skin

About 130 years ago, before sterile gloves were a routine part of medical procedures, the hands remained bare during surgery. Even then, medical practitioners understood the risk for infections and attempted to "steril-ize" the hands of surgeons and their assistants. Several stringent (and probably very painful) techniques involving strong chemical germicides and vigorous scrubbing were practiced. Here are a few examples.

In Schatz's method, the hands and forearms were first cleansed by brisk scrubbing with liquid soap for 3 to 5 minutes, then soaked in a saturated solution of permanganate at a temperature of 110°F until they turned a deep mahogany brown. Next, the limbs were immersed in satu-rated oxalic acid until the skin became decolorized. Then, as if this were not enough, the hands and arms were rinsed with sterile limewater and washed in warm bichloride of mercury for 1 minute.

Or, there was Park's method (more like torture). First, the surfaces of the hands and arms were rubbed completely with a mixture of cornmeal and green soap to remove loose dirt and superficial skin. Next, a paste of water and mustard flour was applied to the skin until it began to sting. This potion was rinsed off in sterile water, and the hands and arms were then soaked in hot bichloride of mercury for a few minutes, during which the solution was rubbed into the skin.

Another method once earnestly suggested for getting rid of micro-organisms was to expose the hands to a hot-air cabinet to "sweat the germs" out of skin glands. Pasteur himself advocated a quick flaming of the hands to maintain asepsis.

The old dream of sterilizing the skin was finally reduced to some basic realities: The microbes entrenched in the epidermis and skin glands cannot be completely eradicated even with the most intense ef-forts, and the skin cannot be sterilized without also seriously damaging it. Because this is true for both medical personnel and their patients, the chance always exists that infectious agents can be introduced during

Heavy growth of microbial colonies on a plate of blood agar prepared by having a classroom of 30 students touch its surface. The result was a mixed population of bacteria and fungi, many of which could be pathogens (clear zones of hemolysis).

invasive medical procedures. Safe surgery had to wait until 1890, when rubber gloves were first made available for placing a sterile barrier around the hands. Of course, this did not mean that skin cleansing and antiseptic procedures were abandoned or downplayed. A thorough scrubbing of the skin with antiseptic soap is still needed to remove the most dangerous source of infections—the superficial contaminants constantly picked up from whatever we touch.

What would be some of the more serious problems associated with sterilizing or trying to sterilize the skin? *Answer available at http://www.mhhe.com/talaro9*

Chemicals with Surface Action: Detergents and Soaps

Detergents are polar molecules that act as surfactants. Most anionic detergents have limited microbicidal power. This includes most soaps. Much more effective are positively charged (cationic) deter-gents, particularly the **quaternary ammonium compounds** (usu-ally shortened to *quats*). The activity of cationic detergents arises from the attachment of four organic radicals (the origin of the term quaternary) to a central, positively charged nitrogen atom. At least one of these radicals is a long-chain hydrocarbon surfactant that disrupts the cell membranes of sensitive microbes (see table 11.11). After a few minutes of contact, the cells burst and die.

The effects of detergents are varied. When used at high enough concentrations, quaternary ammonium compounds are effective against some gram-positive bacteria, viruses, fungi, and algae. In low concentrations, they exhibit only microbistatic effects. Draw-backs to the quats include their ineffectiveness against the tubercu-losis bacterium, hepatitis virus, *Pseudomonas,* and spores at any

concentration. Furthermore, their activity is greatly reduced in the presence of organic matter, and they require alkaline conditions to function. As a result of these limitations, quats are rated only for low-level disinfection in the clinical setting.

Soaps are alkaline compounds made by combining the fatty acids in oils with sodium or potassium salts. In usual practice, soaps are weak microbicides, and they destroy only highly sensitive forms such as the agents of gonorrhea, meningitis, and syphilis. The com-mon hospital pathogen *Pseudomonas* is so resistant to soap that various species grow abundantly in soap dishes.

Soaps function primarily as cleansing agents and sanitizers in industry, the home, and the medical setting. Vigorously brush-ing the hands with germicidal soap over a 15-second period is an effective way to remove dirt, oil, and surface contaminants as well as some resident microbes, but it is unable to remove the skin microbiota (**Clinical Connections** and **figure 11.16**).

See **table 11.11** for coverage on the main uses of detergents and soaps.

346 **Chapter 11** Physical and Chemical Agents for Microbial Control

Figure 11.16 Graph showing some effects of hand scrubbing. Comparison of scrubbing over several days with a nongermicidal soap versus a germicidal soap. Germicidal soap has persistent effects on skin over time, reducing and keeping the microbial count low. Soap alone does not cause a sustained reduction in the microbial count, it even raises it. This effect is presumably due to the exposure of skin layers with higher levels of normal residents.

Heavy Metal Compounds

Various forms of the metallic elements mercury, silver, gold, copper, arsenic, and zinc have been applied in microbial control over several centuries. These are often referred to as heavy metals because of their relatively high atomic weight. However, from this list, only preparations containing mercury and silver still have any significance as germicides. Although some metals (zinc, iron) are actually needed in small concentrations as cofactors on enzymes, the higher molecular weight metals (mercury, silver, gold) can be very toxic, even in minute quantities (parts per million). This property of having antimicrobial effects in exceedingly small amounts is called an **oligodynamic* action (figure 11.17).** Heavy metal germicides contain either an inorganic or an organic metallic salt, and they come in the form of aqueous solutions, tinctures, ointments, or soaps.

Mercury, silver, and most other metals exert microbicidal effects by binding onto functional groups of proteins and inactivating them, rapidly bringing metabolism to a standstill (see figure 11.5c). This mode of action can destroy many types of microbes, including vegetative bacteria, fungal cells and spores, algae, protozoa, and viruses (but not endospores). A newer use of metals is their incorporation into medical supplies and hospital facilities. Silver is now added to catheters, IV lines, and prostheses to prevent

* *oligodynamic* (ol″-ih-goh-dy-nam′-ik) Gr. *oligos,* little, and *dynamis,* power.

TABLE 11.11	Applications of Detergents and Soaps	
Form of Detergents or Soaps	**Primary Applications**	**How Delivered/Concerns**
Quaternary Ammonium Compounds (Quats)	Mixed with cleaning agents to disinfect and sanitize floors, equipment surfaces, and restrooms; for sanitizing restaurant utensils, food-processing equipment, and clothing; common preservatives in ophthalmic solutions and cosmetics	Names include benzalkonium chloride (Zephiran) and cetylpyridinium chloride (Ceepryn); in dilutions ranging from 1:100 to 1:1,000; the level of disinfection is too low for disinfecting medical instruments.
Soaps	Cleansing agents and sanitizers in industry and the home; preparing instruments for heat sterilization; degerming patients' skin, routine hand washing by medical and dental personnel, surgical and preoperative hand scrubbing	Alkaline salts of fatty acids; weak germicides with superior sudsing and wetting properties; can remove large amounts of surface soil, grease, and other debris; antimicrobial chemicals added to make germicidal soaps with greater disinfection power

Proper hand washing with soap is one of the most important control methods for health care and personal hygiene.

Quick Search
Go to CDC TV and watch the "Put Your Hands Together" video about the importance of hand washing.

Silver amalgam Gold foil

Figure 11.17 Demonstration of the oligodynamic action of heavy metals. A pour plate inoculated with saliva has small fragments of heavy metals pressed lightly into it. During incubation, clear zones indicating growth inhibition developed around both fragments. The slightly larger zone surrounding the amalgam (used in tooth fillings) probably reflects the synergistic effect of the silver and mercury it contains.

biofilm formations and infections. Studies have demonstrated that copper has superior killing powers over chrome and aluminum when added to metal parts of lavatory fixtures, doors, and doorknobs. It destroys the most problematic drug-resistant pathogens such as MRSA, as well as *Clostridium difficile* vegetative cells, influenza virus, and gram-negative opportunists.

The main drawbacks to heavy metals are (1) metals are very toxic to humans if ingested, inhaled, or absorbed through the skin, even in small quantities, for the same reasons that they are toxic to microbial cells; (2) they commonly cause allergic reactions; (3) large quantities of biological fluids and wastes neutralize their actions; and (4) microbes can develop resistance to metals.

Table 11.12 provides an overview of applications for heavy metals.

Dyes as Antimicrobial Agents

Dyes are important in staining techniques and as selective and differential agents in media; they are also a primary source of certain drugs used in chemotherapy. Their antimicrobial effects are apparently due to the way they insert into nucleic acids and cause mutations. There is also some evidence they can interfere with cell wall synthesis. Because aniline dyes such as crystal violet and malachite green are most active against gram-positive species of bacteria and some fungi, they are incorporated into solutions and ointments to treat skin infections (ringworm, for example). The yellow acridine dyes, acriflavine and proflavine, are sometimes utilized for antisepsis and wound treatment in medical and veterinary clinics. For the most part, dyes will continue to have limited applications because they stain and have a narrow spectrum of activity.

Acids and Alkalis

Conditions of very low or high pH can destroy or inhibit microbial cells, but they are limited in applications due to their corrosive, caustic, and hazardous nature. Alkaline solutions are good for cleaning and some types of disinfection because they inactivate proteins. Ammonium hydroxide is a major component of detergents and cleansers, and a strong sodium hydroxide solution is one of the few substances that reliably destroys prions. Organic acids are widely used in food preservation because they prevent spore germination and bacterial and fungal growth and because they are generally regarded as safe to eat. Acetic acid (in the form of vinegar) is a pickling agent that inhibits bacterial growth; propionic acid is commonly incorporated into breads and cakes to retard molds; lactic acid is added to sauerkraut and olives to prevent growth of anaerobic bacteria (especially the clostridia); and benzoic and sorbic acids are added to beverages, syrups, and margarine to inhibit yeasts.

For a look at the antimicrobial chemicals found in some common household products, see **table 11.13.**

TABLE 11.12	Applications of Heavy Metals	
Form of Metal	**Primary Applications**	**How Delivered/Concerns**
Organic Mercury	Thimerosal (Merthiolate) and nitromersol (Metaphen) are weak antiseptics and infection preventives; may be preservatives in cosmetics and ophthalmic solutions	Tinctures (0.001% to 0.2%) are fairly effective but a poor choice for broken skin because they are toxic and can delay healing. Mercurochrome is now considered among the poorest of antiseptics.
Silver Sulfadiazine Ointment	Added to dressings, it effectively prevents infection in second- and third-degree burn patients.	A yellow ointment containing silver salts and a sulfa drug
Silver Nitrate (AgNO₃)	Primarily as a topical germicide for mouth ulcers and occasionally root canals	1% to 2% solutions have been used as antiseptics, but they discolor skin and other tissues.
Metallic Silver	Incorporated into catheters to prevent urinary tract infections in the hospital; added to paint, plastics, and steel as a way to control microbial survival on items such as toilet seats, stethoscopes, and even walls and floors in homes	
Colloidal Silver	Mild germicidal ointments or rinses for the mouth, nose, eyes, and vagina	

TABLE 11.13	Active Ingredients of Various Commercial Antimicrobial Products	
Product	**Specific Chemical Agent**	**Antimicrobial Category**
Lysol and Clorox Sanitizing Wipes	Dimethyl benzyl ammonium chloride	Detergent (quat)
Tilex and Lysol Mildew Remover	Sodium hypochlorites	Halogen
Ajax and Dial Antibacterial Hand Soap	Triclosan	Phenolic
Lysol Disinfecting Spray	Alkyl dimethyl benzyl ammonium/ethanol	Detergent (quat)/alcohol
ReNu Contact Lens Solution	Polyaminopropyl biguanide	Chlorhexidine
Wet Ones Antibacterial Moist Towelettes	Benzethonium chloride	Detergent (quat)
Noxzema Triple Clean	Triclosan	Phenolic
Scope Mouthwash	Ethanol	Alcohol
Purell Instant Hand Sanitizer	Ethanol	Alcohol
Pine-Sol	Pine oil and surfactant	Aldehydes, alcohols
Allergan Eye Drops	Sodium chlorite	Halogen

 Check Your Progress SECTION 11.4

23. Describe situations that require high-level disinfection and those for which medium- or low-level disinfection is adequate.

24. What is the difference between a tincture and an aqueous solution?

25. Name one chemical for which the general rule that a higher concentration is more effective is *not* true.

26. Define *sterilant*, and name the principal sporicidal chemical agents.

27. Summarize the chief forms and uses of chlorine compounds.

28. What are the superior characteristics of iodophors over free iodine solutions?

29. What are the modes of action of alcohols and phenolics?

30. Why is hydrogen peroxide solution so effective against anaerobes?

31. Give the uses and disadvantages of the heavy metal chemical agents, glutaraldehyde, and the sterilizing gases.

32. What does it mean to say that a chemical has an oligodynamic action, and which compounds have this effect?

 CASE STUDY **Part 2**

The preliminary investigations linked nine cases and 106 possible cases to the facility. It was the largest outbreak of health care-associated hepatitis ever reported. Not only were 63,000 clinic patients tested for HCV, all of them were directed to have additional tests for hepatitis B virus (HBV) and human immunodeficiency virus (HIV).

In the meantime, the big question was: What went wrong at the endoscopy center? Teams of epidemiologists reviewed the records on the days the patients had procedures. Essentially, their investigation identified four potential problem areas and possible modes of transmission: staff to patient, contaminated equipment, IV technique, and method of preparing syringes for sedation drugs.

First, they tested all of the health care workers at the clinic for HCV. Endoscopes are frequently suspected in outbreaks because they have to be reused and disinfected between patients. They found that the endoscopes were scrubbed with an enzymatic cleaner, soaked in glutaraldehyde for 30 minutes, and flushed with alcohol. Other equipment was either new and sterile or disinfected in the clinic. The IV lines were inserted in a standard fashion with sterile needles and syringes. Protocols for preparing drugs for sedation were not standardized and varied among the RN-anesthetists who did the procedures.

A report was made about an RN-anesthetist who was observed taking out a second dose of the drug from a large, multidose vial using the same syringe that had been used to take the first dose, although he did replace the needle. Often, these partly used vials were stored and reused on other patients.

In 2010, a judge awarded the claimants in a lawsuit the huge sum of $500 million to be paid by the drug manufacturer and distributor for negligence in packaging of the drug. Several patients were awarded an additional $500 million in a civil lawsuit against the health maintenance organization that hired the endoscopy clinic. In 2013, the owner and the anesthetist were tried and convicted on a number of criminal charges. The owner was found guilty of second-degree murder because one of the patients died from the effects of his HCV infection. Both men will probably spend the rest of their lives in jail.

- Why was it necessary to also test the patients for HBV and HIV?

- Why is it a mistake to use the same syringe, even with a new, sterile needle?

To conclude this Case Study, go to Perspectives on the Connect website.

Additional coverage of these topics can be found in chapters 13 and 25.

A summary of this case can be found at http://www.cdc.gov/mmwr/preview/mmwrhtml/mm5719a2.htm.

 Chapter Summary with Key Terms

11.1 Controlling Microorganisms

A. **Decontamination** procedures involve the destruction or removal of contaminants. Contaminants are defined as microbes present at a given place and time that are undesirable or unwanted.

B. **Sterilization** is a process that destroys or removes all microbes, including viruses.
 1. A **bactericide** is a chemical that destroys bacteria.
 2. **Bacteriostatic** agents inhibit or prevent the growth of bacteria on tissues or on other objects in the environment.
 3. A **germicide** or **microbicide** is a chemical that will kill any pathogenic microorganisms.

C. **Disinfection** refers to a physical or chemical process that destroys vegetative pathogens but not bacterial endospores on objects. An **antiseptic** is a chemical applied to living tissues to render them free of pathogens.

D. **Sanitization** is forceful cleaning that removes contaminants and makes objects hygienic and safe to use. **Degermation** is the same process applied to the body to remove potential pathogens.

E. Several factors influence the rate at which antimicrobial agents work. These factors are:
 1. Exposure time to the agent
 2. Numbers of microbes present
 3. Relative resistance of microbes (for example, endospores versus vegetative forms)
 4. Activity of the agent (microbicidal versus microbistatic)

F. How antimicrobial agents work: their **modes of action.** Agents affect cell wall synthesis, membrane permeability, and protein and nucleic acid synthesis and function.

11.2 Physical Methods of Control: Heat

A. Moist heat denatures proteins and DNA while destroying membranes.
 1. *Sterilization:* **Autoclaves** utilize steam under pressure (121°C) to sterilize heat-resistant materials, whereas intermittent sterilization uses steam at 100°C to sterilize more delicate items.
 2. *Disinfection:* **Pasteurization** subjects liquids to temperatures below 100°C and is used to lower the microbial load in liquids. Boiling water can be used to destroy vegetative pathogens in the home.

B. Dry heat, using higher temperatures than moist heat, can also be used to sterilize.
 1. **Incineration** can be carried out using a Bunsen burner or incinerator. Temperatures range between 800°C and 6,500°C.
 2. *Dry ovens* operate at temperatures of 150°C to 180°C.

C. Cold temperatures (refrigeration and freezing) are microbistatic and are commonly used to preserve food, media, and cultures.

D. Drying and **desiccation** lead to (often temporary) metabolic inhibition by reducing water in the cell.

11.3 Physical Methods of Control: Radiation and Filtration

A. *Radiation:* Energy in the form of **radiation** can be used for **cold sterilization,** which works by killing microbes without heat.
 1. **Ionizing radiation,** such as gamma rays and X rays, has deep penetrating power and works by causing breaks in the DNA of target organisms.

 2. **Nonionizing radiation** uses **ultraviolet** waves with very little penetrating power and works by creating dimers between adjacent pyrimidines, which interferes with replication.

B. *Using Filtration to Remove Microbes:* Filtration involves the physical removal of microbes by passing a gas or liquid through a fine filter, and can be used to sterilize air as well as heat-sensitive liquids.

11.4 Chemical Agents in Microbial Control

A. Chemicals are divided into disinfectants, **antiseptics,** sterilants, **sanitizers,** and **degermers** based on their level of effectiveness and the surfaces to which they are applied.

B. Antimicrobial chemicals are found as solids, gases, and liquids. Liquids can be either **aqueous** (water based) or **tinctures** (alcohol based).

C. **Halogens** are chemicals based on elements from group VII of the periodic table.
 1. Chlorine gas, hypochlorites, and chloramines all work by disrupting disulfide bonds and, given adequate time, are sporicidal.
 2. Iodine compounds include free iodine (I_2) and **iodophors.** Iodine has a mode of action similar to chlorine and can also be sporicidal.

D. **Phenolics** work by disrupting cell membranes and precipitating proteins. They are bactericidal, fungicidal, and virucidal but not sporicidal. Bisphenols are mild forms for disinfection and antisepsis.

E. **Chlorhexidine** (Hibiclens, Hibitane) is a surfactant and protein denaturant with broad microbicidal properties, although it is not sporicidal. Solutions of chlorhexidine are used as skin degerming agents for preoperative scrubs, skin cleaning, and burns.

F. Ethyl and isopropyl **alcohol,** in concentrations of 50% to 90%, are useful for microbial control. Alcohols act as **surfactants,** dissolving membrane lipids and coagulating proteins of vegetative bacterial cells and fungi. They are not sporicidal.

G. **Hydrogen peroxide** produces highly reactive hydroxyl free radicals that damage protein and DNA while also decomposing to O_2 gas, which is toxic to anaerobes. Strong solutions of H_2O_2 are sporicidal.

H. Aldehydes such as **glutaraldehyde** and formaldehyde kill microbes by alkylating protein and DNA molecules.

I. Gases and aerosols such as **ethylene oxide (ETO),** propylene oxide, and chlorine dioxide are strong alkylating agents, all of which are sporicidal.

J. **Detergents** and **soaps**
 1. Cationic detergents known as **quaternary ammonium compounds (quats)** act as surfactants that alter the membrane permeability of some bacteria and fungi. They are not sporicidal.
 2. Soaps function by removing grease and soil that contain microbes.

K. **Heavy metals:** Solutions of silver and mercury kill vegetative cells (but not spores) despite being highly diluted (**oligodynamic action**) by inactivating proteins.

L. **Dyes, acids,** and **alkalis** can also inhibit or destroy microbes.

350 **Chapter 11** Physical and Chemical Agents for Microbial Control

Level I. Knowledge and Comprehension

These questions require a working knowledge of the concepts in the chapter
and the ability to recall and understand the information you have studied.

? Multiple-Choice Questions

Select the correct answer from the answers provided. For questions with blanks, choose the combination of answers that most accurately completes the statement.

1. A microbicidal agent has what effect?
 a. sterilizes
 b. inhibits microorganisms
 c. is toxic to human cells
 d. destroys microorganisms

2. Microbial control methods that kill _____ are able to sterilize.
 a. viruses
 b. the tubercle bacillus
 c. endospores
 d. cysts

3. Any process that destroys the non-spore-forming contaminants on inanimate objects is
 a. antisepsis
 b. disinfection
 c. sterilization
 d. degermation

4. Sanitization is a process by which
 a. the microbial load on objects is reduced
 b. objects are made sterile with chemicals
 c. utensils are scrubbed
 d. skin is debrided

5. An example of an agent that lowers the surface tension of cells is
 a. phenol
 b. chlorine
 c. alcohol
 d. formalin

6. High temperatures _____ and low temperatures _____.
 a. sterilize, disinfect
 b. kill cells, inhibit cell growth
 c. denature proteins, burst cells
 d. speed up metabolism, slow down metabolism

7. The primary action of _____ heat is to _____.
 a. dry, destroy cell walls
 b. moist, kill vegetative cells
 c. dry, dissolve lipids
 d. moist, denature proteins

8. The temperature-pressure combination for an autoclave is
 a. 100°C and 4 psi
 b. 121°C and 15 psi
 c. 131°C and 9 psi
 d. 115°C and 3 psi

9. Microbe(s) that is/are the target(s) of pasteurization include(s)
 a. *Clostridium botulinum*
 b. *Mycobacterium* species
 c. *Salmonella* species
 d. both b and c

10. Ionizing radiation removes _____ from atoms.
 a. protons
 b. waves
 c. electrons
 d. ions

11. The primary mode of action of nonionizing radiation is to
 a. produce superoxide ions
 b. make pyrimidine dimers
 c. denature proteins
 d. break disulfide bonds

12. The most versatile method of sterilizing heat-sensitive liquids is
 a. UV radiation
 b. exposure to ozone
 c. beta propiolactone
 d. filtration

13. _____ is the iodine antiseptic of choice for wound treatment.
 a. Eight percent tincture
 b. Five percent aqueous
 c. Iodophor
 d. Potassium iodide solution

14. A chemical with sporicidal properties is
 a. phenol
 b. alcohol
 c. quaternary ammonium compound
 d. glutaraldehyde

15. Silver sulfadiazine is used
 a. in antisepsis of burns
 b. as a mouthwash
 c. to treat genital gonorrhea
 d. to disinfect water

16. Detergents are
 a. high-level germicides
 b. low-level germicides
 c. excellent antiseptics
 d. used in disinfecting surgical instruments

17. Which of the following is an approved sterilant?
 a. chlorhexidine
 b. betadyne
 c. ethylene oxide
 d. ethyl alcohol

📁 Case Study Review

1. How would one best describe the state of being a *carrier* of HCV?
 a. It is on the skin and transmitted through direct contact.
 b. The person shows symptoms and is jaundiced.
 c. The person has a chronic infection of the liver and harbors the virus.
 d. The person has had contact with blood in a medical setting.

2. The main issue in the case of clinic-acquired HCV infections was:
 a. use of unclean equipment
 b. a high number of carriers
 c. contamination of drugs
 d. health workers who were IV drug abusers

3. Outline the chain of events involved in the transmission of HCV from an infected patient to several other patients through the actions of a medical worker.

 Writing Challenge

For each question, compose a one- or two-paragraph answer that includes the factual information needed to completely address the question. Check Your Progress questions can also be used for writing-challenge exercises.

1. What is wrong with this statement: "Prior to vaccination, the patient's skin was sterilized with alcohol"? What would be the more correct wording?

2. Would it be proper to say that a patient has been disinfected? Why or why not?

3. Think of three situations in which the same microbe would be considered a serious contaminant in one case and completely harmless in another.

4. Explain what features of endospores make them so resistant to microbial control, and how sterilizing techniques work to destroy them.

5. Explain some of the problems involved in sterilizing delicate and heat-sensitive instruments such as endoscopes, syringes, needles, catheters, and other instruments.

6. The shelf life and keeping qualities of fruit and other perishable foods are greatly enhanced through irradiation, saving industry and consumers billions of dollars. How would you personally feel about eating irradiated fruit? How about spices that had been sterilized with ETO?

 Concept Mapping

An Introduction to Concept Mapping found at http://www.mhhe.com/talaro9 provides guidance for working with concept maps.

1. Construct your own concept map using the following words as the *concepts*. Supply the linking words between each pair of concepts.

halogens	sporicidal
oligodynamic	chemical
surfactants	physical
alcohol	silver
phenolics	

 Level II. Application, Analysis, Evaluation, and Synthesis

These problems go beyond just restating facts and require higher levels of understanding and an ability to interpret, problem solve, transfer knowledge to new situations, create models, and predict outcomes.

 Critical Thinking

Critical thinking is the ability to reason and solve problems using facts and concepts. These questions can be approached from a number of angles, and in most cases, they do not have a single correct answer.

1. For each item on the following list, give a reasonable method of sterilization. You cannot use the same method more than three times for the whole list. The method must sterilize, not just disinfect; and the method must not destroy the item or render it useless unless there is no other choice. After considering a workable method, think of a method that would not work. Note: Where an object containing something is given, you must sterilize everything (for example, both the jar and the petroleum jelly [Vaseline] in it). Some examples of methods are autoclave, ethylene oxide gas, dry oven, and ionizing radiation.

room air	a pot of soil
serum	plastic Petri dishes

heat-sensitive drugs	inside of a refrigerator
cloth dressings	wine
leather shoes from a thrift shop	a jar of Vaseline
a cheese sandwich	fruit in plastic bags
a flask of nutrient agar	milk
an entire room (walls, floor, etc.)	orchid seeds
rubber gloves	metal instruments
disposable syringes	mail contaminated with
carcasses of cows with	anthrax spores
"mad cow" disease	

352 **Chapter 11** Physical and Chemical Agents for Microbial Control

2. Using pasteurization techniques as a model, compare the TDTs and explain the relationships between temperature and length of exposure.

3. It may seem contradictory that lyophilization can be used to preserve foods yet also be used to keep cultures of microbes viable. Explain how these applications can be reconciled.

4. A supermarket/drugstore assignment: Look at the labels of 10 different products used to control microbes, and make a list of their active ingredients, their suggested uses, and information on toxicity and precautions.

5. Devise an experiment that will differentiate between bactericidal and bacteriostatic effects.

6. There is quite a bit of concern that chlorine used as a water purification chemical presents serious dangers. What alternative methods covered by this chapter could be used to purify water supplies and keep them safe from contamination?

7. Was the source patient in the case study most likely acutely or chronically infected? Explain.

8. Research this Case Study: In 2012, a company in New England that manufactured injectable steroids supplied thousands of contaminated vials to hospitals and clinics. Over 700 patients developed serious brain or systemic fungal infections and 40 died. Discuss what went so terribly wrong at the pharmacy.

Visual Challenge

1. From **chapter 2, figure 2.20.** Study this illustration of a cell membrane. In what ways could alcohol (Hint: a solvent) damage this membrane? How would that harm the cell?

2. Explain this graph that charts the reactions of a mesophilic bacterium to temperature. Blue shows the survival curve and brown the growth curve.

CHAPTER **12** Drugs, Microbes, Host—The Elements of Chemotherapy

HIV (green spheres) budding off the surface of an infected white blood cell

Microscopic view reveals colorful crystals of the anti-HIV drug Retrovir (also known as azidothymidine)

 CASE STUDY Part 1 **An Ounce of Prevention and a Pound of Cure**

Joan Mitchell, a 48-year-old registered nurse, had safely removed needles from intravenous **catheters** hundreds of times, yet all of those years of care and experience seemed to evaporate in an instant. The needle accidently jabbed with some force into her arm. She immediately reported it and began the **standard precautions** for a **needle stick.** She washed the site of the laceration with water and **betadyne,** as indicated by hospital protocol.

Needle sticks are a regular occurrence in hospitals and clinics, and usually the greatest concern is the possibility of **infectious agents** being carried by the offending needle. Unfortunately for the nurse, the patient had been suffering from **acquired immune deficiency syndrome** (AIDS) caused by **human immunodeficiency virus** (HIV). Within 2 hours, it was necessary for her to begin a regimen of **anti-HIV drugs** that are routinely given for **postexposure prophylaxis.** The drug chosen was a combination of lamivudine and zidovudine (Combivir), a pill containing two different **reverse transcriptase inhibitors.** She was tested right away for HIV to establish a baseline for the possibility of a prior infection, and it came back negative.

Despite treatment, the AIDS patient died unexpectedly of respiratory failure due to *Pneumocystis* pneumonia. Unfortunately, his

> "The needle accidently jabbed with some force into her arm."

medical history did not indicate other infections he may have had, and this lack of information turned the next several weeks into a nightmare for the nurse. She was supposed to take the Combivir for 6 weeks, but it caused **severe side effects,** including nausea, headache, muscle pain, weakness, abdominal pain, and rash. She discontinued taking it after 2 weeks with the hope that it had succeeded in preventing HIV infection.

During the next month, the site of nurse Mitchell's injury became **abscessed** and painful, and she suffered from a **fever** up to 102°F. Since the wound was obviously infected, her doctor **biopsied** it and had routine **bacterial** and **fungal cultures** made, but they came back negative. The course of **dicloxacillin** did not seem to be working. Signs that the infection was spreading came in the form of an **enlarged lymph node** in her armpit.

▶ What is meant by prophylactic drug treatment, and what are its purposes?

▶ Why is it necessary for two drugs to be given in the Combivir treatment?

To continue the Case Study, go to page 383.

12.1 Principles of Antimicrobial Therapy

Expected Learning Outcomes

1. State the goals of antimicrobial therapy.
2. Discuss the origins of antimicrobial drugs.
3. Differentiate between antibiotics, synthetic drugs, and semisynthetic drugs.
4. Describe some of the special strategies of antimicrobial therapy.
5. Explain what is meant by a drug's spectrum and how narrow- and broad-spectrum drugs differ.
6. Summarize the five modes of action of antimicrobial drugs, with specific examples of their effects.

TABLE 12.1	Characteristics of the Ideal Antimicrobial Drug

- Selectively toxic to the microbe but nontoxic to host cells
- Microbicidal rather than microbistatic
- Remains potent long enough to act and is not broken down or excreted prematurely
- Is not subject to the development of antimicrobial resistance
- Complements or assists the activities of the host's defenses
- Remains active even when diluted in body fluids and tissues
- Readily delivered to the site of infection
- Reasonably priced
- Does not disrupt the host's health by causing allergies or predisposing the host to other infections

Over a century ago in the United States, one out of three children was expected to die of an infectious disease before the age of 5. Early death or severe lifelong debilitation from scarlet fever, diphtheria, tuberculosis, meningitis, and many other bacterial diseases was a fearsome yet undeniable fact of life to most of the world's population.

The introduction of modern drugs to control infections in the 1930s was a medical revolution that has added significantly to the life span and health of humans. It is no wonder that for many years, antibiotics in particular were regarded as miracle drugs. In later discussions, we evaluate this misconception in light of the shortcomings of drug therapy. Although antimicrobial drugs have greatly reduced the incidence of certain infections, they have definitely not eradicated infectious disease and probably never will. In fact, in some parts of the world, mortality rates from infectious diseases are as high as before the arrival of antimicrobial drugs. Nevertheless, humans have been taking medicines to try to control diseases for thousands of years (**12.1 Making Connections**).

Quick Search

Look for "Antibiotics, Seven Wonders of the Microbe World" on the internet.

The goal of **antimicrobial chemotherapy**[1] is deceptively simple: administer a drug to an infected person that destroys the infective agent without harming the host's cells. In actuality, this goal is rather difficult to achieve, because many often contradictory factors must be taken into account. The ideal drug should be easily administered and able to reach the infectious agent anywhere in the body. It should be able to kill the infectious agent rather than merely inhibit its growth and remain active in the body as long as needed, yet be safely and easily broken down and excreted. In short, the perfect drug does not exist, but by balancing drug characteristics against one another, a satisfactory compromise can be achieved (**table 12.1**).

The Origins of Antimicrobial Drugs

The origin of modern antimicrobial drugs is varied. Some, called **antibiotics,** are substances produced by the natural metabolic processes of some microorganisms that can inhibit or destroy other microorganisms. Nature is a prolific producer of antimicrobial drugs. Antibiotics come primarily from aerobic spore-forming bacteria and fungi. By inhibiting the growth of other microorganisms in the same habitat (antagonism), antibiotic producers presumably enjoy less competition for nutrients and space. The greatest numbers of antibiotics are derived from bacteria in the genera *Streptomyces* and *Bacillus* and molds in the genera *Penicillium* and *Cephalosporium* (**figure 12.1** and **table 12.2**). Species of *Streptomyces* are the most prolific producers of all. They are the source of two-thirds of antibiotics; about 9,000 different bioactive compounds have been isolated from them.

Antimicrobial drugs are described with regard to their origin, range of effectiveness, and whether they are naturally produced or

Figure 12.1 **Colonies of two prolific producers of antibiotics.** The tendency of these microbes to secrete the antibiotic onto their surfaces is an important factor in isolation and production of the drugs. Left: The mold *Penicillium notatum* with yellowish droplets containing penicillin. Right: The bacterium *Streptomyces coelicolor* with dark blue droplets containing actinorhodin, an experimental antibiotic.

1. The word *chemotherapy,* meaning the use of chemicals in therapy, is often associated with the treatment of cancer, but its official meaning also includes antimicrobial treatment.

12.1 MAKING CONNECTIONS

From Witchcraft to Wonder Drugs

Early human cultures relied on various types of primitive medications concocted from plant, animal, and mineral products that had been found, usually through trial and error or accident, to have some curative effect upon ailments. In one ancient Chinese folk remedy, a fermented soybean curd was applied to skin infections. The Greeks used wine and plant resins (myrrh and frankincense), rotting wood, and various mineral salts to treat diseases. Some folk medicines were effective, but others either had no effect or were even harmful. It is interesting that the Greek word *pharmakeutikos* originally meant the practice of witchcraft. These ancient remedies were handed down from generation to generation, but it was not until the Middle Ages that a specific disease was first treated with a specific chemical. Dosing syphilitic patients with inorganic arsenic and mercury compounds may have proved the ancient axiom: *Graviora quaedum sunt remedia periculus* ("Some remedies are worse than the disease").

Paul Ehrlich was the first scientist to formulate basic theoretical concepts in chemotherapy in the late 1800s. Ehrlich had observed that certain dyes affixed themselves to specific microorganisms and not to animal tissues. This observation led to the profound idea that if a drug was properly selective in its actions, it would zero in on and destroy a microbial target and leave human cells unaffected. His first discovery was an arsenic-based drug that was very toxic to the spirochete of syphilis but, unfortunately, to humans as well. After 606 attempts he arrived at a compound he called *salvarsan*. This drug had some therapeutic merit and was used for a few years, but it eventually had to be discontinued because it was still not selective enough in its toxicity. Ehrlich's work had laid important foundations for many of the developments to come.

Another pathfinder in early drug research was Gerhard Domagk, whose discoveries in the 1930s launched a breakthrough in therapy that marked the true beginning of broad-scale usage of antimicrobial drugs. Domagk showed that the red dye prontosil was chemically changed by the body into a compound with specific activity against bacteria. This substance was sulfonamide—the first *sulfa* drug. Once the structure of this drug was determined, it became possible to synthesize it on a wide scale and to develop scores of other sulfonamide drugs. Although these drugs had immediate applications in therapy (and still do), still another fortunate discovery ushered in the "age of antibiotics."

A pioneer in the discovery of antibiotics. A Scottish physician, Sir Alexander Fleming, accidently discovered penicillin in a culture plate contaminated with mold. From this mold he extracted the antibiotic, setting the scene for the development of the drug 10 years later.

The discovery of antibiotics dramatically demonstrates how developments in science and medicine often occur through a combination of accident, persistence, collaboration, and vision. In 1928 in the London laboratory of Sir Alexander Fleming, a plate of *Staphylococcus aureus* became contaminated with the mold *Penicillium notatum*. Observing these plates, Fleming noted that the colonies of *Staphylococcus* were evidently being destroyed by some activity of the nearby mold colonies. Struck by this curious phenomenon, he extracted from the fungus a compound he called penicillin and showed that it was responsible for the inhibitory effects.

A decade after his discovery, English chemists Howard Florey and Ernst Chain worked out methods for industrial production of penicillin to help in the war effort. Clinical trials conducted in 1941 ultimately proved penicillin's effectiveness, and by 1945 the drug had been used to save hundreds of thousands of lives. This event paved the way for an era of drug research and development that soon made penicillin only one of a large assortment of antimicrobial drugs. But in time, because of extreme overuse and misunderstanding of its capabilities, penicillin also became the model for one of the most serious drug problems—namely, drug resistance.

Name some potential "therapies" you could employ to prevent and treat infections if you were cast away on a deserted island. *Answer available at http://www.mhhe.com/talaro9*

chemically synthesized. A few of the more important terms you will encounter are found in **table 12.3.**

In this chapter, we describe different types of antibiotic drugs, their mechanism of action, and the types of microbes on which they are effective.

Common Drug Strategies

You will encounter the terms **prophylaxis, combined therapy,** and drug **synergy** in several areas of the chapter. Each idea has its own special niche in drug therapy. With prophylaxis, drugs are administered to *prevent* an infection from happening. This is brought into play in cases of known or possible exposure. For example, certain dental

patients are often pretreated with antibiotics prior to instrument procedures that could leak saliva into the bloodstream.

Combined therapy, also known as combination therapy, is a protocol for taking more than two drugs at a time to treat an infection. This is the usual method of treatment for tuberculosis, HIV/AIDS, and gonorrhea. Its main rationale is to prevent the survival of drug-resistant microbes, but it is also used for treating mixed infections by microbes that differ in the correct drug of choice.

Another advantage comes from the synergistic effect that two drugs working together can often provide. Synergy can produce an improved result over either drug used alone, and this enhanced effectiveness means that smaller quantities of the drugs can be used. Figure 12.18*b* shows a test result for this effect.

TABLE 12.2	**Selected Microbial Sources of Antibiotics**	
Producer Genus	**Type of Microbe**	**Drugs Formed**
Penicillium	Mold	Penicillins Griseofulvin
Cephalosporium	Mold	Cephalosporins
Micromonospora	Bacteria	Gentamicin
Bacillus	Bacteria	Bacitracin Polymyxin B
Chromobacterium	Bacteria	Aztreonam
Streptomyces	Filamentous bacteria	Streptomycin Erythromycin Tetracycline Vancomycin Chloramphenicol Amphotericin B

TABLE 12.3	**Terminology of Chemotherapy**
Chemotherapeutic drug	Any chemical used in the treatment, relief, or prophylaxis of a disease
Prophylaxis*	Use of a drug to prevent potential for infection of a person at risk
Antimicrobial chemotherapy*	The use of chemotherapeutic drugs to control infection
Antimicrobials	All-inclusive term for any antimicrobial drug, regardless of its origin
Antibiotics*	Substances produced by the natural metabolic processes of some microorganisms that can inhibit or destroy other microorganisms
Semisynthetic drugs	Drugs that are chemically modified in the laboratory after being isolated from natural sources
Synthetic drugs	Antimicrobial compounds synthesized in the laboratory through chemical reactions
Narrow spectrum (limited spectrum)	Antimicrobials effective against a limited array of microbial types; for example, a drug effective mainly on gram-positive bacteria
Broad spectrum (extended spectrum)	Antimicrobials effective against a wide variety of microbial types; for example, a drug effective against both gram-positive and gram-negative bacteria

* *prophylaxis* (proh″-fih-lak′-sis) Gr. *prophylassein,* to keep guard before. A process that prevents infection or disease in a person at risk.
* *chemotherapy* (kee″-moh-ther′-uh-pee) Gr. *chemieia,* chemistry, and *therapeia,* service to the sick. Use of drugs to treat disease.
* *antibiotic* (an-tee′-by-aw″-tik) Gr. *anti,* against, and *bios,* life.

Interactions Between Drugs and Microbes

The goal of antimicrobial drugs is either to disrupt the cell processes or structures of bacteria, fungi, and protozoa or to inhibit the virus multiplication cycle. Most of the drugs used in chemotherapy interfere with the function of enzymes required to synthesize or assemble macromolecules, but a few destroy structures already formed in the cell. Above all, drugs should be **selectively toxic,** which means they can kill or inhibit the growth of microbes without simultaneously damaging host tissues. This concept of selective toxicity is central to chemotherapy. The best drugs are those that act specifically on microbial structures or functions not found in vertebrate cells. Examples of drugs with excellent selective toxicity are those that block the synthesis of the cell wall in bacteria (penicillins). They have low toxicity and few direct effects on human cells because human cells lack a cell wall and are thus unaffected by this action of the antibiotic. Among the most toxic to human cells are drugs that act upon a structure common to both the infective agent and the host cell, such as the cell membrane (for example, amphotericin B used to treat fungal infections). As the characteristics of the infectious agent become more similar to those of the host cell, selective toxicity becomes more difficult to achieve and undesirable side effects are more likely to occur. We examine the subject of toxicity in section 12.5.

Mechanisms of Drug Action

The primary basis of chemotherapy is to target an infectious agent with a chemical that irreversibly damages or inhibits it. This knowledge guides drug development as well. Most classes of antimicrobic drugs are active against some unique feature of microbial structure or metabolism. Observe **table 12.4** and take note of the diversity of cell types and possible effects of drug action. Overall, there are five major components that are useful drug targets in an actively dividing cell. These are the cell wall and membrane, the

genetic material, protein synthesis, and metabolic pathways. We cover the effects of drugs on these cell components based on this outline and **figure 12.2:**

1. inhibition of cell wall synthesis,
2. breakdown of the cell membrane structure or function,
3. interference with functions of DNA and RNA,
4. inhibition of protein synthesis, and
5. blockage of key metabolic pathways.

These targets are not completely discrete, and some have overlapping effects. For example, if DNA transcription is inhibited, protein synthesis will be as well. Viruses are a special case and have very specialized targets for drugs (see table 12.6).

The Spectrum of an Antimicrobial Drug One result of drugs acting upon a particular microbial structure or function is that each drug has a particular range of activity. This has been termed the drug's *spectrum.* Traditionally, **narrow-spectrum** drugs are effective on a small range of cell types. This is usually because they target a specific component that is found only in certain bacteria. For instance, bacitracin blocks the elongation of the peptidoglycan in gram-positive bacteria but has no effect on gram-negative bacteria because of the outer membrane on their

TABLE 12.4	General Actions of Drugs on Microbial Groups					
Microbe Type	Drug Groups/ Examples	Effects of Drugs	Microbe Type	Drug Groups/ Examples	Effects of Drugs	
Bacteria	Penicillins	Cell wall damage and lysis	Fungi	Amphotericin B	Loss of membrane permeability	
	Cephalosporins	Cell wall damage and lysis		Azoles	Loss of membrane permeability	
	Bacitracin	Cell wall damage and lysis		Flucytosine	Inhibits DNA and RNA synthesis	
	Aminoglycosides	Inhibit ribosomal protein synthesis	Protozoa	Quinines	Buildup of toxic wastes in the parasite's cells	
	Macrolides					
	Erythromycin	Inhibits ribosomal protein synthesis		Metronidazole	Buildup of toxic free radicals	
	Vancomycin	Cell wall damage and lysis	Helminths	Bendazoles	Inhibit glucose metabolism	
	Tetracyclines	Inhibit protein synthesis on ribosomes		Diethylcarbamide	Kills larval forms	
	Chloramphenicol	Inhibits protein synthesis on ribosomes		Piperazine	Paralyzes muscular system	
				Niclosamide	Loosens worm hold	
	Fluoroquinolones	Block replication of DNA		Ivermectin	Inhibits neuromuscular system	
	Rifampin	Stops mRNA synthesis	Viruses	Oseltamivir	Prevents viral budding	
	Sulfa drugs	Inhibit folic acid metabolism		Cyclovirs	Stop viral replication	
	Trimethoprim	Inhibits folic acid metabolism		Azidothymidine	Blocks DNA formation from RNA	

cell wall that serves as a barrier to the drug. Polymyxin breaks down the outer membrane on gram-negative cells but does not target gram-positive ones.

Drugs that are effective against a wider range of microbes are termed medium or broad spectrum, depending on the particular drug. For example, the **medium-spectrum** drug ampicillin is effective on both gram-positive and gram-negative bacteria, but not all types. **Broad-spectrum** drugs such as tetracycline have the greatest range of activity. They work on most gram-negative and gram-positive bacteria, rickettsias, mycoplasmas, and spirochetes. The broad-spectrum drugs usually exert their effects on common cell components such as ribosomes, which are found in all cells and mitochondria. Consult **Table 12.5** to see an array of antibacterial drugs and their spectra.

TABLE 12.5	Spectrum of Activity for Antibacterial Drugs					
Spectrum of Action	Gram-Positive Bacteria	Gram-Negative Bacteria	Rickettsias	Chlamydias	Mycoplasmas	Examples of Drugs with This Spectrum
Broad	+	+	+	+	+	Tetracyclines Quinolones Chloramphenicol Doripenem
Intermediate	+	+	−	V*	V*	Ampicillin Cephalexin (Keflex) Sulfa/trimethoprim Macrolides (erythromycin)
Narrow Group 1	+	−	−	−	−	Penicillin G, V Vancomycin Bacitracin Rifampin Isoniazid (for TB)
Narrow Group 2	−	+	−	−	−	Polymyxin Streptomycin Cefaclor Aztreonam

*Some drugs in the list are effective on these microbes.

Figure 12.2 Major targets of drugs acting on bacterial cells. Each mode of action correlates with the numbered section where it is discussed in the text.

1. Antimicrobial Drugs That Affect the Bacterial Cell Wall The cell walls of most bacteria contain a rigid girdle of peptidoglycan, which protects the cell against rupture from hypotonic environments. Active cells must constantly synthesize new peptidoglycan and transport it to its proper place in the cell envelope. Drugs such as penicillins and cephalosporins react with one or more of the enzymes required to complete this process, causing the cell to develop weak points at growth sites and to become osmotically fragile **(figure 12.3)**. Antibiotics that produce this effect are considered bactericidal, because the weakened cell is subject to lysis. It is essential to note that most of these antibiotics are active only in young, growing cells, because old, inactive, or dormant cells do not synthesize peptidoglycan. (One exception is a new class of antibiotics termed "-penems.")

Penicillins and cephalosporins bind and block peptidases that cross-link the glycan molecules, thereby interrupting the completion of the cell wall **(figure 12.3b).** Penicillins that do not penetrate the outer membrane are less effective against gram-negative bacteria. Broad-spectrum penicillins (carbenicillin) and cephalosporins (ceftriaxone) can pass into the cell walls of gram-negative species. Cycloserine inhibits the formation of the basic peptidoglycan subunits, and vancomycin hinders the elongation of the peptidoglycan.

2. Antimicrobial Drugs That Disrupt Cell Membrane Function
A cell with a damaged membrane invariably dies from disruption in metabolism or lysis. It does not even have to be actively dividing to be destroyed. The antibiotic classes that damage cell membranes usually have specificity for particular microbial groups, based on differences in the types of lipids in their cell membranes.

Polymyxins interact with membrane phospholipids and cause leakage of proteins and nitrogen bases, particularly in gram-negative bacteria **(figure 12.4)**. The polyene antifungal antibiotics (amphotericin B and nystatin) form complexes with the sterols on fungal membranes, which causes abnormal openings and seepage of small ions. Unfortunately, this selectivity is not exact, and the similarities in membranes of microbial and animal cells means that most of these antibiotics can be quite toxic to humans cells.

3. Antimicrobial Drugs That Affect Nucleic Acid Synthesis
As you learned in chapter 9, the metabolic pathway that generates DNA and RNA is a long, enzyme-catalyzed series of reactions. Like any complicated process, it is subject to breakdown at many different points along the way, and inhibition at any point in the sequence can block subsequent events. Antimicrobial drugs interfere with nucleic acid synthesis by blocking synthesis of nucleotides, inhibiting replication, or stopping transcription. Because functioning DNA and RNA are required for proper translation as well, the effects on protein metabolism can be far-reaching.

Several antimicrobials inhibit DNA synthesis. The broad-spectrum quinolones inhibit DNA unwinding enzymes or helicases, thereby stopping DNA replication and repair. Certain antiviral drugs are **analogs*** of purines and pyrimidines which will insert in the viral nucleic acid like a normal base. When synthesis can no

* *analog* (an'-uh-log) A compound whose configuration closely resembles another compound required for cellular reactions.

Peptidoglycan
(cell wall)

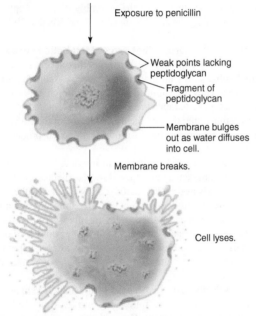

(a) Normal untreated cells. Left and center views
are *Staphylococcus* cells; right view is the molecular
structure of peptidoglycan, with chains of NAM
(*N* muramic acid) and NAG (*N* glucosamine)
linked together by cross bridges (green).

Exposure to penicillin

Weak points lacking
peptidoglycan

Fragment of
peptidoglycan

Membrane bulges
out as water diffuses
into cell.

Membrane breaks.

Cell lyses.

(b) Effects of treatment with penicillin. Left side shows the
breakdown of a *Staphylococcus* cell exposed to penicillin.
Center view shows actual cells undergoing lysis and cell death.
Right indicates how penicillin blocks the formation of the cross
bridges and dismantles the framework that holds the cell wall
together.

10,000X

10,000X

Figure 12.3 **Effects of penicillin on bacterial cell walls.**

Polymyxin B

Cell
membrane

longer continue, viral replication is blocked (see table 12.6). The
antifungal drug flucytosine is an analog of uracil that creates dys-
functional RNA. By inhibiting an enzyme that acts in purine syn-
thesis, it also stops DNA replication. This double assault shuts
down metabolism and causes cell death.

4. Antimicrobial Drugs That Block Protein Synthesis Most
drugs that inhibit protein synthesis react with the ribosome-mRNA
complex. Although human cells also have ribosomes, the ribosomes
of eukaryotes are different in size and structure from those of pro-
karyotes, so these antimicrobials usually have a selective action
against bacteria. One potential therapeutic consequence of drugs

Figure 12.4 **Effects of drugs on membranes.** The detergent
action of polymyxin. Polymyxin binds to the outer and cell membranes
and forms abnormal openings that cause them to leak their contents
and lyse.

that bind to the prokaryotic ribosome is the damage they can do to eukaryotic mitochondria, which contain a prokaryotic type of ribosome.

Two possible targets of ribosomal inhibition are the 30S subunit and the 50S subunit (**figure 12.5**). Aminoglycosides (streptomycin, gentamicin, for example) insert on sites on the 30S subunit

and cause the misreading of the mRNA, leading to abnormal proteins. Tetracyclines block the attachment of tRNA on the A acceptor site and effectively stop further synthesis of that protein. Other antibiotics attach to sites on the 50S subunit in a way that prevents the formation of peptide bonds (chloramphenicol) or inhibits translocation of the subunit during translation (erythromycin). The oxazolidinones are a newer drug class that affect the assembly of the completed ribosome by blocking the attachment site for the 50S and 30S subunits.

> **Quick Search**
> Find "Antibiotic and Protein Interactions" that animates the effects of antibiotics on ribosomes.

5. Antimicrobial Drugs That Affect Metabolic Pathways Sulfonamides and trimethoprim are drugs that act by mimicking the normal substrate of an enzyme in a process called **competitive inhibition.** They are supplied to the cell in high concentrations to ensure that a needed enzyme is constantly occupied by the **metabolic analog** rather than by the true substrate of the enzyme. As the enzyme is no longer able to produce a needed product, cellular metabolism slows or stops.

Sulfonamides and trimethoprim interfere with folate metabolism by blocking enzymes required for the synthesis of tetrahydrofolate, which is needed by bacterial cells for the synthesis of folic acid and the eventual production of DNA and RNA and amino acids. Trimethoprim and sulfonamides are often given simultaneously to achieve a synergistic effect so that a lower dosage of each drug can be used. **Figure 12.6** illustrates sulfonamides' competition with PABA for the active site of the enzyme that synthesizes the folic acid precursor.

The selective toxicity of these compounds is explained by the fact that mammals derive folic acid from their diet and so do not possess this enzyme system. This makes it possible to inhibit bacterial and protozoan parasites, which must synthesize folic acid, while leaving the human host unaffected.

Figure 12.5 Sites of inhibition on the prokaryotic ribosome and major antibiotics that act on these sites. All have the general effect of blocking protein synthesis. Blockage actions are indicated by ×.

✅ *Check Your Progress* SECTION 12.1

1. Differentiate between antibiotics and synthetic drugs.
2. Differentiate between narrow-spectrum and broad-spectrum antibiotics.
3. Can you determine why some drugs have narrower spectra than others? (Hint: Look at their mode of action.)
4. What kind of tests would determine whether a particular antimicrobial is broad or narrow spectrum?
5. What is the major source of antibiotics and what appears to be the natural function of antibiotics in microbes that produce them?
6. What drug characteristics are most important to consider in therapy?
7. Why is it better for a drug to be microbicidal than microbistatic?
8. Explain the major modes of action of antimicrobial drugs, and give an example of each.
9. Explain the concept of competitive inhibition, and describe how a metabolic analog molecule inhibits metabolism.
10. What are the end effects of drugs that block transcription?

(a) The metabolic pathway needed to synthesize tetrahydrofolic acid (THFA) contains two enzymes that are chemotherapeutic targets. Under normal circumstances, PABA acts as a substrate for the enzyme pteridine synthetase, the product of which is needed for the eventual production of folic acid.

Structural differences

Sulfanilamide PABA

(b) Left: Formula of a sulfanilamide molecule compared alongside one of PABA. Note that, despite a similarity in overall shape, sulfa drugs cannot be used to make folic acid. Right: The sulfa drug molecules can insert into the active site in the enzyme that would ordinarily fit the PABA. This will work only when the sulfa molecules are more prevalent and can outcompete with the PABA and keep the enzyme sites filled. Since little or no PABA can bind, the synthesis of folic acid will be inhibited.

Figure 12.6 Competitive inhibition as a mode of action. This example shows how sulfa drugs block a metabolic pathway bacteria use to synthesize folic acid.

12.2 Survey of Major Antimicrobial Drug Groups

 Expected Learning Outcomes

7. Describe the classes of antibacterial drugs that act on the cell wall and membrane, and list some of their applications.

8. Describe the classes of antibacterial drugs that act on DNA or RNA, and characterize their uses.

9. Indicate which types of antibacterial drugs block protein synthesis, and explain how they are used.

10. Describe some new classes of antibacterial drugs and their applications.

Scores of antimicrobial drugs are marketed in the United States. Although the medical and pharmaceutical literature contains a wide array of names for antimicrobials, most of them are variants of a small number of drug families. About 280 different antimicrobial drugs are currently classified in around 22 drug families. Drug reference books may give the impression that there are 10 times that many because various drug companies assign different trade names

to the very same generic drug. Ampicillin, for instance, is available under 50 different names. Most antibiotics are useful in controlling bacterial infections, although we shall also consider a number of antifungal, antiviral, and antiprotozoan drugs. Summaries of drug choices are located in later chapters on infectious agents.

Antibacterial Drugs That Act on the Cell Wall

The **beta-lactam*** group of antibiotics all contain a 3-carbon, 1-nitrogen ring that is highly reactive. Its primary mode of action is to interfere with proteins involved in synthesis of the cell wall, leading to lysis and cell death. More than half of all antimicrobic drugs are beta-lactams, with the penicillins and cephalosporins being the most prominent representatives.

Beta-lactam ring

Structure of penicillin G

* *beta-lactam* (bey'-tuh-lak'-tam) The chemical name of a molecular group found in a number of drug families.

362 **Chapter 12** Drugs, Microbes, Host—The Elements of Chemotherapy

Penicillin and Its Relatives

The **penicillin** group of antibiotics, named for the parent compound, is a large, diverse group of compounds, most of which end in the suffix *-cillin*. Although penicillins could be completely synthesized in the laboratory from simple raw materials, it is more practical and economical to obtain natural penicillin through microbial fermentation. The natural product can then be used either in unmodified form or to make semisynthetic derivatives. *Penicillium chrysogenum* is the major source of the drug. All penicillins consist of three parts: a beta-lactam ring, a thiazolidine ring, and a variable side chain that dictates its microbicidal activity (**figure 12.7** and **12.2 Making Connections**).

Subgroups and Uses of Penicillins The characteristics of selected penicillin drugs are shown in figure 12.7. Penicillin G was the first antibiotic and is the parent compound for all "-cillin" drugs. It is narrow spectrum and considered the drug of choice for infections by sensitive gram-positive bacteria (streptococci) and some gram-negative bacteria (meningococci). A close relative, penicillin V, has similar uses but has been modified to be stable in the stomach acid and so can be taken orally. Other narrow-spectrum penicillins include dicloxacillin, methicillin, and nafcillin.

Semisynthetic penicillins such as ampicillin and amoxicillin have been chemically altered with side chains that help them move across the outer membrane of gram-negative cell walls. This increases their spectrum and makes them useful in treating many types of gram-negative infections. Ticarcillin and piperacillin have such an extended spectrum that they can be substituted for combinations of antibiotics.

Many bacteria produce enzymes that are capable of destroying the beta-lactam ring of penicillin. The enzymes are referred to as **penicillinases** or **beta-lactamases,** and they make the bacteria that possess them resistant to many penicillins. Penicillinase-resistant penicillins such as methicillin, nafcillin, and cloxacillin are useful in treating infections caused by some penicillinase-producing bacteria.

All of the "-cillin" drugs are relatively mild and well tolerated because of their specific mode of action on cell walls (which humans lack). The primary problems in therapy include allergy (which is altogether different from toxicity) and resistant strains of pathogens. Clavulanic acid is a chemical that inhibits beta-lactamase enzymes, thereby increasing the longevity of beta-lactam antibiotics in the presence of penicillinase-producing bacteria. For this reason, clavulanic acid is often added to semisynthetic penicillins to augment their effectiveness. For example, *Clavamox* is a combination of amoxicillin and clavulanate marketed under the trade name Augmentin. *Zosyn,* a similar combination of the beta-lactamase inhibitor tazobactam and piperacillin, is used for a wide variety of systemic infections. These combined medications show an extended spectrum because of the synergy of the two drugs working together.

The Cephalosporin Group of Drugs

The **cephalosporin** antibiotics currently account for one-third of all antibiotics administered. Cephalosporins are similar to penicillins; they have a beta-lactam structure that can be synthetically altered (**figure 12.8**) and have a similar mode of action. The generic names of these compounds are often recognized by the presence of the root *cef, ceph,* or *kef* in their names.

Subgroups and Uses of Cephalosporins The cephalosporins are versatile. They are relatively broad spectrum, resistant to most penicillinases, and cause fewer allergic reactions than penicillins. Although some cephalosporins are given orally, many are poorly absorbed from the intestine and must be administered **parenterally,*** by injection into a muscle or a vein.

Four generations of cephalosporins exist, with each group being more effective against gram-negative organisms than the generation before it. In addition, succeeding generations typically have improved dosing schedules and fewer side effects. First-generation cephalosporins (cephalothin and cefazolin) are most effective against gram-positive cocci and a few gram-negative bacteria. Second-generation forms (cefaclor and cefonicid) are more effective than the first-generation forms in treating infections by gram-negative bacteria such as *Enterobacter, Proteus,* and *Haemophilus.* Third-generation cephalosporins, such as *cephalexin* (Keflex) and *ceftriaxone* (Rocephin), are broad spectrum with especially well-developed activity against enteric bacteria that produce beta-lactamases. Fourth-generation drugs, such as cefepime, have the widest range of antimicrobial properties. They are effective with both gram-negative and gram-positive bacterial infections and are rapidly microbicidal.

Carbapenems and Monobactams Other beta-lactam drugs are the carbapenems or "penems" and aztreonam. *Imipenem* and *ertapenem* are broad-spectrum antibiotics with a mode of action

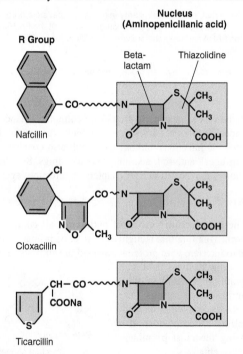

Nucleus
(Aminopenicillanic acid)

R Group

Nafcillin

Cloxacillin

Ticarcillin

Figure 12.7 Chemical structure of penicillins. The basic nucleus of penicillin drugs (blue box) consists of a thiazolidine ring (green) and a beta-lactam ring (red), but specific types differ in the nature of the side chain (R group), which is also responsible for differences in each compound's activity against gram-negative cells.

* *parenterally* (par-ehn′-tur-ah-lee) Gr. *para,* beyond, and *enteron,* intestine. A route of drug administration other than the gastrointestinal tract.

R Group 1	Basic Nucleus	R Group 2
	S or O	Cephalothin (first generation*)
	2nd	Cefotiam (second generation)
	3rd	Moxalactam (third generation)
	4th	Cefepime (fourth generation)

*New improved versions of drugs are referred to as new "generations."

Figure 12.8 The structure of cephalosporins. Like penicillin, their main nucleus consists of a beta-lactam ring (red) and a second ring (yellow). However, unlike penicillins, they have two sites for placement of R groups (at positions 3 and 7). This makes possible several generations of molecules with greater versatility in function and complexity in structure.

similar to penicillin but with greater resistance to beta-lactamases. They are active in very low concentrations and can be taken by mouth with few side effects except for allergies. Starting in 2001, some carbapenem-resistant strains of gram-negative enteric bacteria began to emerge in hospital outbreaks. These pathogens, termed CRE, have continued to increase in numbers and are currently a serious concern (see 12.4 Making Connections).

Aztreonam, a monobactam, is a narrow-spectrum antibiotic for treating pneumonia, septicemia, and urinary tract infections by gram-negative aerobic bacilli. Aztreonam is especially useful when treating persons who are allergic to penicillin, because it is chemically different and does not cross-react with antibodies made to penicillin.

Miscellaneous Non-Beta-Lactam Cell Wall Inhibitors *Vancomycin* is a narrow-spectrum antibiotic most effective in treating staphylococcal infections in cases of penicillin and methicillin resistance or in patients with an allergy to penicillins. It has also been chosen to treat *Clostridium* infections in children and endocarditis (infection of the lining of the heart) caused by *Enterococcus faecalis.* Because it is very toxic and hard to administer, vancomycin is usually restricted to the most serious, life-threatening conditions.

Bacitracin is a narrow-spectrum peptide antibiotic produced by a strain of *Bacillus subtilis.* Its primary effect is to block the elongation of

the peptidoglycan in gram-positive bacteria. Since it was first isolated, its greatest claim to fame has been as a major ingredient in a common drugstore antibiotic ointment (Neosporin) for combating superficial skin infections by streptococci and staphylococci. For this purpose, it is usually combined with neomycin (an aminoglycoside) and polymyxin.

Isoniazid (INH) works by interfering with the synthesis of mycolic acid, a necessary component of the cell wall of acid-fast organisms. It is used to treat infections with *Mycobacterium tuberculosis* but is effective only against growing cells. It is often prescribed with rifampin (see section on drugs that act on RNA) and other drugs to treat tuberculosis. Oral doses are indicated for both active tuberculosis and prophylaxis in cases of a positive TB test. Ethambutol, a closely related compound, is another antituberculosis drug added to treatment regimens.

Another essential tuberculosis drug is *rifampin.* The primary action of this drug is in blocking the action of RNA polymerase, thereby preventing transcription. It is somewhat limited in spectrum because the molecule cannot pass through the cell envelope of many gram-negative bacilli. It is mainly used to treat infections by selected gram-positive rods and cocci and a few gram-negative bacteria. Rifampin figures most prominently in treating mycobacterial infections, especially tuberculosis and leprosy, but it is usually given in combination with other drugs to prevent development of resistance. Rifampin is also recommended for prophylaxis in *Neisseria meningitidis* carriers and their contacts, and it is occasionally used to treat *Legionella, Brucella,* and *Staphylococcus* infections.

Antibiotics That Damage Bacterial Cell Membranes

Bacillus polymyxa is the source of the **polymyxins,** narrow-spectrum peptide antibiotics with a unique fatty acid component that contributes to their detergent activity (see figure 12.4). Only two polymyxins—B and E (also known as colistin)—have any routine applications, and even these are limited by their toxicity to the kidney. Either drug can be indicated to treat drug-resistant infections caused by gram-negative rods such as *Pseudomonas aeruginosa* and *Acinetobacter baumannii.* It is also one of the topical agents in ointments to prevent skin infections, such as Neosporin.

Drugs That Act on DNA or RNA

Much excitement was generated by a class of synthetic drugs chemically related to quinine called **fluoroquinolones.** These drugs work by binding to DNA gyrase and a related enzyme, topoisomerase

12.2 MAKING CONNECTIONS

A Modern Quest for Designer Drugs

Once the first significant antibiotic was developed, the world immediately witnessed a scientific scramble to find more. This search was advanced on several fronts. Hundreds of investigators began the laborious task of screening samples from soil, dust, muddy lake sediments, rivers, estuaries, oceans, plant surfaces, compost heaps, sewage, skin, and even the hair and skin of animals for antibiotic-producing bacteria and fungi. This intense effort has paid off over the past 50 years, because more than 10,000 antibiotics have been discovered (although surprisingly, only a relatively small number have actually been used clinically). Finding a new antimicrobial substance is only a first step. The complete pathway of drug development from discovery to therapy takes between 12 and 24 years and costs several billion dollars.

Antibiotics are products of fermentation pathways in many microorganisms. Among the greatest producers of antibiotics are the fungi, members of the soil-dwelling bacterial genera *Streptomyces* and the spore-forming bacteria. The role of antibiotics in the lives of these microbes must be important because the genes for antibiotic production are preserved in evolution. Some experts theorize that antibiotic-releasing microorganisms can inhibit or destroy nearby competitors or predators; others propose that antibiotics play a part in spore formation. Whatever benefit the microbes derive, these compounds have been extremely profitable for humans. Every year, the pharmaceutical industry farms vast quantities of microorganisms and harvests their products to treat diseases caused by other microorganisms. Researchers have facilitated the work of nature by selecting mutant species that yield more abundant or useful products, by varying the growth medium, or by altering the procedures for large-scale industrial production.

Another approach in the drug quest is to chemically manipulate molecules by adding or removing functional groups. Drugs produced in this way are designed to have advantages over related drugs. Using this **semisynthetic** method, a natural product of the microorganism is joined with various preselected functional groups. The antibiotic is reduced to its basic molecular framework (called the nucleus), and to this nucleus specially selected side chains (R groups) are added.

A case in point is the metamorphosis of the semisynthetic penicillins. The nucleus is an inactive penicillin derivative called aminopenicillanic acid, which has a special bonding site for addition of R groups. A particular carboxylic acid (R group) added to this nucleus can "fine-tune" the penicillin, giving it special characteristics. For instance, some R groups will make the product resistant to penicillinase (methicillin), some confer a broader activity spectrum (ampicillin), and others make the product acid resistant (penicillin V). Cephalosporins and tetracyclines also exist in several semisynthetic versions. The potential for using bioengineering techniques to design drugs seems almost limitless, and, indeed, several drugs have already been produced by manipulating the genes of antibiotic producers.

Explain why development of effective drugs takes so many years.
Answer available at http://www.mhhe.com/talaro9

A plate with several discrete colonies of soil bacteria was sprayed with a culture of *Escherichia coli* and incubated. Zones of inhibition (clear areas with no growth) surrounding several colonies indicate colonies that produce antibiotics.

R Groups

(a) Aminopenicillanic acid

(b) Methicillin

(c) Ampicillin

(d) Penicillin V

IV—both of which are essential for replication of the bacterial DNA. While DNA gyrase tends to be the primary target in gram-negative organisms, topoisomerase is targeted in gram-positive cells. It is not known how these drugs target different enzymes in different cell types, but this mode of action ensures that fluoroquinolones provide broad-spectrum effectiveness. In addition to being broad spectrum and highly potent, the drugs are readily absorbed from the intestine.

The principal quinolones, *norfloxacin* and *ciprofloxacin* (Cipro) have been successful in therapy for urinary tract infections, sexually transmitted diseases, gastrointestinal infections, osteomyelitis, respiratory infections, and soft tissue infections. Newer drugs in this category are sparfloxacin and levofloxacin. These agents are especially recommended for pneumonia, bronchitis, and sinusitis. Now that concerns have arisen regarding the overuse of quinolone drugs, the CDC is recommending careful monitoring of their use to prevent the emergence of ciprofloxacin-resistant bacteria (see 12.4 Making Connections). Side effects that can limit the use of quinolones include seizures and other brain disturbances.

Drugs That Interfere with Protein Synthesis
The Aminoglycoside Drugs

Antibiotics composed of one or more amino sugars and an aminocyclitol (6-carbon) ring are referred to as **aminoglycosides (figure 12.9).** These complex compounds are exclusively the products of various species of soil **actinomycetes** in the genera *Streptomyces* and *Micromonospora*.

Subgroups and Uses of Aminoglycosides The aminoglycosides have a relatively broad antimicrobial spectrum because they inhibit protein synthesis by binding to one of the ribosomal subunits. They are especially useful in treating infections caused by aerobic gram-negative rods and certain gram-positive bacteria. *Streptomycin* is among the oldest of the drugs but has gradually been replaced by

newer forms with less mammalian toxicity. It is still the antibiotic of choice for treating bubonic plague and tularemia, and is considered an effective antituberculosis agent. *Gentamicin* is less toxic and is widely administered for infections caused by gram-negative rods (*Escherichia, Pseudomonas, Salmonella,* and *Shigella*). Two relatively new aminoglycosides, tobramycin and amikacin, are also used for gram-negative infections, with tobramycin especially useful for treating *Pseudomonas* infections in cystic fibrosis patients.

Tetracycline Antibiotics

The first antibiotic in this class was aureomycin. It was used to synthesize terramycin, tetracycline, and several semisynthetic derivatives, commonly known as the **tetracyclines (figure 12.10a).** Their action of binding to ribosomes and blocking protein synthesis accounts for the broad-spectrum effects in the group.

Subgroups and Uses of Tetracyclines The scope of microorganisms inhibited by tetracyclines is very broad. It includes gram-positive and gram-negative rods and cocci, aerobic and anaerobic bacteria, mycoplasmas, rickettsias, and spirochetes. Tetracycline compounds such as *doxycycline* and *minocycline* are administered orally to

(a) Tetracyclines

(b) Chloramphenicol

(c) Erythromycin

Figure 12.10 Structures of three antibiotics that act on prokaryotic ribosomes. (a) Tetracyclines. These are named for their regular group of four rings. The several types vary in structure and activity by substitution at the four R groups. **(b)** Chloramphenicol. **(c)** Erythromycin, an example of a macrolide drug. Its central feature is a large lactone ring to which two hexose sugars are attached.

Figure 12.9 The structure of an aminoglycoside: Streptomycin. Colored portions of the molecule are found in all numbers of this drug class.

366 **Chapter 12** Drugs, Microbes, Host—The Elements of Chemotherapy

treat several sexually transmitted diseases, Rocky Mountain spotted fever, Lyme disease, typhus, *Mycoplasma* pneumonia, cholera, leptospirosis, acne, and even some protozoan infections. A newer derivative of minocycline—*tigecycline* was developed to treat serious hospital skin and soft tissue infections in cases of drug resistance (*Acinetobacter* and MRSA). Although generic tetracycline is low in cost and easy to administer, its use can be limited by its side effects. In addition to gastrointestinal disruption due to changes in the normal flora and staining of the teeth, ingestion during pregnancy can interfere with fetal bone development (see table 12.9).

Chloramphenicol

Chloramphenicol is a potent broad-spectrum antibiotic with a unique nitrobenzene structure (**figure 12.10*b***). Its primary effect on cells is to block peptide bond formation and protein synthesis. It is one type of antibiotic that is no longer derived from the natural source but is entirely synthesized through chemical processes. Although this drug is as broad spectrum as the tetracyclines, it is so toxic to human cells that its uses are restricted. A small number of people undergoing long-term therapy with this drug incur irreversible damage to the bone marrow that usually results in a fatal form of aplastic anemia.[2] Its administration is now limited to typhoid fever, brain abscesses, and rickettsial and chlamydial infections for which an alternative therapy is not available. Chloramphenicol should never be given in large doses repeatedly over a long time period, and the patient's blood must be monitored during therapy.

Macrolides and Related Antibiotics

Erythromycin is a representative of antibiotics termed macrolides.[3] Its structure consists of a large lactone ring with sugars attached (**figure 12.10*c***). This drug has a moderate spectrum and fairly low toxicity. Its mode of action is to block protein synthesis by attaching to the 50S subunit of the ribosome. It is administered orally for *Mycoplasma* pneumonia, legionellosis, *Chlamydia* infections, pertussis, and diphtheria, and as a prophylactic drug prior to intestinal surgery. It also offers a useful substitute for dealing with penicillin-resistant streptococci and gonococci and for treating syphilis and acne. Newer semisynthetic macrolides include *clarithromycin* and *azithromycin* (Zithromax). Both drugs are useful for middle ear, respiratory, and skin infections and have been approved for *Mycobacterium* (MAC) infections in AIDS patients. Clarithromycin has additional applications in controlling infections and gastric ulcers caused by *Helicobacter pylori*. Azithromycin is one of the most-prescribed antibiotics in the world. It is used in respiratory, gastrointestinal, and sexually transmitted infections. One serious side effect is heart arrhythmias, which limits its use in sensitive people.

Clindamycin is a broad-spectrum antibiotic derived from lincomycin. The tendency of clindamycin to cause adverse reactions in the gastrointestinal tract limits its applications to (1) serious infections in the large intestine and abdomen due to anaerobic bacteria (*Bacteroides* and *Clostridium*), (2) infections with penicillin-resistant staphylococci, and (3) acne medications applied to the skin.

Drugs That Block Metabolic Pathways

Several of the drugs that interfere with metabolism are synthetic. These antimicrobials as a group do not originate from bacterial or fungal fermentations. Some were synthesized from aniline dyes, and others were originally isolated from plants. Although they have been largely replaced by antibiotics, a few of them remain essential to chemotherapy.

The most important drugs in this class are the **sulfonamides,** or **sulfa drugs.** Their name is derived from sulfanilamide, an early form of the drug (**figure 12.11**). These drugs function as metabolic analogs to block the synthesis of folic acid by bacteria (see figure 12.6). Dozens of these drugs have been developed, most of them narrow spectrum. Because of its solubility, sulfisoxazole is an effective choice for treating shigellosis, urinary tract infections, and certain protozoan infections. Silver sulfadiazine ointment and solution are prescribed for treatment of burns and eye infections. Another drug, *trimethoprim,* inhibits a second enzymatic step in the synthesis of folic acid. Because of this, trimethoprim is often given in combination with sulfamethoxazole to take advantage of the synergistic effect of the two drugs (Septra, Bactrim). This combination is one of the primary treatments for *Pneumocystis jiroveci* pneumonia (PCP) in AIDS patients, urinary tract infections, and otitis media.

Sulfones are compounds chemically related to the sulfonamides but lacking their broad-spectrum effects. They still remain important as key drugs in treating Hansen's disease (leprosy). The most active form is dapsone, usually given in combination with rifampin and clofazimine (an antibacterial dye) over long periods.

Newly Developed Classes of Antibiotics

Although most new antibiotics are formulated from the drug classes that already exist, a few classes of drugs with novel actions against bacteria have been added to drug regimens.

Fosfomycin trimethamine is a phosphoric acid agent effective as alternate treatment for urinary tract infections caused by enteric bacteria. It works by inhibiting an enzyme necessary for cell wall synthesis.

Figure 12.11 The structures of some sulfonamides. Boxed side chains attach at the —ONH group of the nucleus. **(a)** Sulfacetamide, **(b)** sulfadiazine, and **(c)** sulfisoxazole.

2. A failure of the blood-producing tissue that results in very low levels of blood cells.

3. Macrolide antibiotics get their name from the type of chemical ring structure (macrolide ring) they all possess.

Synercid is an antibiotic from the streptogramin group of drugs that contains two active chemicals (quinupristin and dalfopristin) that together exert a synergistic action on certain bacteria. It has bactericidal effects against *Staphylococcus* and *Enterococcus* species that cause endocarditis and surgical infections, and against resistant strains of *Streptococcus*. It is one of the main choices when other drugs are ineffective due to resistance. Synercid works by binding to sites on the 50S ribosome, inhibiting peptide transfer and elongation.

Daptomycin (Cubicin) is a lipopeptide directed mainly against gram-positive bacteria, acting to disrupt multiple aspects of membrane function. Many experts are urging physicians to use these medications only when no other drugs are available to slow the development of drug resistance.

Another new class of drugs, the ketolides, is similar to macrolides like erythromycin but has a different ring structure. The main representative, *telithromycin* (Ketek), is used for respiratory tract infections caused by macrolide-resistant bacteria.

The *oxazolidinone* class of drugs operates using a unique mechanism, namely to inhibit the *initiation* of protein synthesis. It does this by interfering with the interaction between the mRNA and the two ribosomal subunits necessary for the initiation of translation. The sole drug in this class, linezolid (sold under the trade name Zyvox), has been used to treat infections caused by two of the most difficult clinical pathogens, methicillin-resistant *Staphylococcus aureus* (MRSA) and vancomycin-resistant *Enterococcus* (VRE). Because this drug is synthetic and not found in nature, it is hoped that drug resistance will be slow to develop.

Drugmakers have developed a new antituberculosis drug for the first time in 40 years. Called bedaquiline (Sirturo), this drug will be restricted to use only for multidrug-resistant and extremely drug-resistant TB cases that are currently on the rise.

 Check Your Progress SECTION 12.2

11. Construct a chart that summarizes the modes of action and applications of the major groups of antibacterial drugs (antibiotics and synthetics).

12. Why do the penicillin and cephalosporin groups of drugs have milder toxicity than other antibiotics? What are their primary side effects?

12.3 Drugs to Treat Fungal, Parasitic, and Viral Infections

 Expected Learning Outcomes

11. Categorize antimicrobial drugs that are effective against fungi, and describe how they are used.

12. Discuss the categories of drugs used to treat parasite infections, and describe their applications.

13. Discuss some of the difficulties in giving antiviral drug treatments.

14. Identify several categories of antiviral drugs, and explain how they are used.

Antifungal Drugs

Because the cells of fungi are eukaryotic, they present special problems in chemotherapy. For one, the great majority of chemotherapeutic drugs are designed to act on bacteria and are generally ineffective in combating fungal infections. For another, the similarities between fungal and human cells often mean that drugs toxic to fungal cells are also capable of harming human tissues. A few agents with special antifungal properties have been developed for treating systemic and superficial fungal infections. Five main drug groups currently in use are the macrolide polyene antibiotics, griseofulvin, synthetic azoles, flucytosine, and echinocandins **(figure 12.12)**. See table 22.4 for a complete outline of antifungal drugs.

Polyenes bind to fungal membranes and cause loss of selective permeability. They are specific for fungal membranes because fungal membranes contain a particular sterol component called ergosterol, while human membranes do not. The toxicity of polyenes is not completely selective, however, because mammalian cell membranes contain compounds similar to ergosterol that bind polyenes to a small extent.

Macrolide polyenes, represented by *amphotericin B* (Fungizone) (named for its acidic and basic—amphoteric—properties) and nystatin (for New York State, where it was discovered), have a structure that mimics the lipids in some cell membranes. Amphotericin B is by far the most versatile and effective of all antifungals. Not only does it work on most fungal infections, including skin and mucous membrane lesions caused by *Candida albicans,* but it is one of the few drugs that can be injected to treat systemic fungal infections such as histoplasmosis and cryptococcus meningitis. A significant drawback to the widespread use of amphotericin centers on its serious side effects, which can include fatigue and irregular heartbeat.

(a)

(b) (c)

Figure 12.12 Some antifungal drug structures. (a) Polyenes. The example shown is amphotericin B, a complex steroidal antibiotic that inserts into fungal cell membranes. **(b)** Ketoconazole, an azole that inhibits synthesis of ergosterol, a component of the fungal cell membrane. **(c)** Flucytosine, a structural analog of cytosine that inhibits DNA and protein synthesis.

Nystatin (Mycostatin) is used only topically or orally to treat candidiasis of the skin and mucous membranes, but it is not useful for subcutaneous or systemic fungal infections or for ringworm.

Griseofulvin is an antifungal product especially active in certain dermatophyte infections such as athlete's foot. The drug is deposited in the epidermis, nails, and hair, where it inhibits fungal growth. Because complete eradication requires several months and griseofulvin is relatively nephrotoxic, this therapy is given only for the most stubborn cases. A newer drug for treatment of ringworm and athlete's foot, terbinifine (Lamisil), is an inhibitor of ergosterol synthesis that is readily deposited in skin and nails. Unfortunately, it must also be taken for an extended period and has a number of side effects, including hepatotoxicity.

The **azoles** are broad-spectrum antifungal agents with a complex ringed structure that also inhibit ergosterol and cell membrane synthesis. They have fewer adverse side effects when compared with other antifungal drugs. The most effective drugs are ketoconazole (Nizoral), fluconazole (Diflucan), clotrimazole (Gyne-Lotrimin), miconazole (Monistat), voriconazole (VFEND), and itraconazole (Sporanox). Ketoconazole is used orally and topically for cutaneous mycoses, vaginal and oral candidiasis, and some systemic and invasive mycoses. Fluconazole can be used in selected patients for AIDS-related mycoses such as aspergillosis and cryptococcus meningitis. Clotrimazole and miconazole are used mainly as topical ointments for infections in the skin, mouth, and vagina. Itraconazole is generally used orally for fungal infections of the nails and systemic candidiasis. Because voriconazole crosses the blood-brain barrier, it is the treatment of choice for fungal meningitis.

Flucytosine is an analog of the nucleotide cytosine that has antifungal properties. It is rapidly absorbed after oral therapy, and it is readily dissolved in the blood and cerebrospinal fluid. Alone, it can be used to treat certain cutaneous mycoses. Many fungi are resistant to flucytosine, so it is usually combined with amphotericin B to effectively treat systemic mycoses.

After many years of testing, a new antifungal drug category has been introduced. *Echinocandins,* such as caspofungin, damage the cell walls of several types of fungi, thereby making them sensitive to lysis. A significant advantage of this mode of action is that it cannot target human cells.

Antiparasitic Chemotherapy

The enormous diversity among protozoan and helminth parasites and their corresponding therapies reaches far beyond the scope of this textbook; however, a few of the more common drugs are surveyed here and described again for particular diseases in chapter 23. Presently, a small number of approved and experimental drugs are used to treat malaria, leishmaniasis, trypanosomiasis, amebic dysentery, and helminth infections, but the need for new and better drugs has spurred considerable research in this area.

Antimalarial Drugs: Quinine and Its Relatives

Quinine, a toxic chemical extracted from the bark of the cinchona tree, was the principal treatment for malaria for hundreds of years, but it has largely been replaced by the synthesized quinolines, mainly *chloroquine* and *primaquine,* which have less toxicity to humans. Because of the several species of *Plasmodium* (the ma-

laria parasite) and many stages in its life cycle, no single drug is universally effective for every species and stage, and each drug is restricted in application. For instance, primaquine eliminates the liver phase of infection, and chloroquine suppresses acute attacks associated with infection of red blood cells. It is also given as a prophylactic treatment in endemic regions. Chloroquine is usually taken in combination with another drug to reduce the chances of parasite resistance.

Structure of quinine

Mefloquine is a semisynthetic analog of quinine used to treat infections caused by chloroquine-resistant strains of *Plasmodium,* an increasing problem in Southeast Asia. The latest drug approved for treating uncomplicated malaria is a combination of artimisinin and lumefantrine called *Coartem.* It was designed to prevent drug resistance and has become the drug of choice in many parts of the world.

Chemotherapy for Other Protozoan Infections

A widely used amoebicide, metronidazole (Flagyl), is effective in treating mild and severe intestinal infections and hepatic disease caused by *Entamoeba histolytica.* It appears to inactivate essential metabolic enzymes of the pathogens. Given orally, it also has applications for infections by *Giardia lamblia* and *Trichomonas vaginalis.* Other drugs with antiprotozoan activities are quinacrine (a quinine-based drug), sulfonamides, and tetracyclines.

Antihelminthic Drug Therapy

Treating helminthic infections has been one of the most challenging of all chemotherapeutic tasks. Flukes, tapeworms, and roundworms are much larger parasites than other microorganisms and, being animals, have greater similarities to human physiology. Also, the usual strategy of using drugs to block their reproduction is usually not successful in eradicating the adult worms. The most effective drugs immobilize, disintegrate, or inhibit the metabolism of all stages of the life cycle.

Mebendazole and *thiabendazole* are broad-spectrum antiparasitic drugs used to treat several types of roundworm infections. These drugs work locally in the intestine to inhibit the function of the microtubules of worms, eggs, and larvae, which interferes with their glucose utilization and disables them. The compounds *pyrantel* and *piperazine* paralyze the muscles of intestinal roundworms. Niclosamide destroys the scolex and the adjoining proglottids of tapeworms, thereby loosening the worm's holdfast. In these forms of therapy, the worms are unable to maintain their grip on the intestinal wall and are expelled along with the feces by the normal peristaltic action of the bowel. A drawback to the use of the drug is the severe abdominal cramps that often accompany treatment. Two newer antihelminthic drugs are *praziquantel,* a treatment for various tapeworm and fluke infections, and *ivermectin,* a veterinary drug now used for strongyloidiasis and oncocercosis in humans.

Antiviral Chemotherapeutic Agents

The chemotherapeutic treatment of viral infections presents unique problems. Throughout our discussion of infections caused by bacteria, fungi, protozoa, and helminths, we've emphasized differences in structure and metabolism that guide drug choice. With viruses, we are dealing with an infectious agent that relies upon the host cell for the vast majority of its metabolic functions. Disrupting viral function may require that we disrupt the metabolism of the host cell to a much greater extent than is desirable. Put another way, selective toxicity with regard to viral infection can be difficult to achieve because a single metabolic system is responsible for the well-being of both virus and host. A few viral diseases such as measles, mumps, and hepatitis are routinely prevented by effective vaccinations. Unfortunately, vaccines are unavailable for many serious viral diseases, creating a real need for antiviral medications.

Over the past few years, several antiviral drugs have been developed that target specific points in the infectious cycle of viruses. But due to marked differences among the viruses, antiviral compounds tend to be limited in their spectrum.

Most antiviral drugs are designed to block a step in completion of the virus cycle. Major modes of action include

1. barring penetration of the virus into the host cell;
2. blocking replication, transcription, and/or translation of viral genetic material; and
3. preventing the normal maturation of viral particles.

Although antiviral drugs protect uninfected cells by keeping viruses from being synthesized and released, most are unable to eliminate extracellular viruses or those in a latent state. A summary covering the actions of several antiviral drugs appears in **table 12.6**.

Drugs for Treating Influenza

Zanamivir (*Relenza*) and oseltamivir (*Tamiflu*) are broader-spectrum antiinfluenza medications that block neuraminidase actions in both influenza A and influenza B viruses. Without the functions of neuraminidase, the virus cannot be budded off and released from the host cell, so cells cannot produce active viruses. Both types of drugs may be used prophylactically and must be given early in an infection to be most effective (table 12.6; go to http://www.pharmasquare.org/flash/Tamiflu.html animation).

Amantadine and its relative, rimantadine, have been essentially discontinued as flu treatments because the current viral strains have developed almost complete resistance to them. They function by blocking envelope receptors that are essential for the uncoating and release of RNA from the influenza A virus.

Antiherpes Drugs

Many antiviral agents mimic the structure of nucleotides (i.e., act as *analogs*) and compete for sites on replicating DNA. Once one of these nucleotide analogs is incorporated into the growing chain of DNA, replication of that strand stops, interrupting the viral life cycle. **Acyclovir** (Zovirax) and the related compounds *valacyclovir* (Valtrex), *famciclovir* (Famvir), and *penciclovir* (Denavir) all work in this manner and (with small exceptions from drug to drug) can be used either orally or topically to treat common herpesvirus infections such as oral and genital herpes, chickenpox, and shingles. A related drug, *ganciclovir* (Cytovene) is used parenterally to treat cytomegalovirus infection in patients with compromised immune systems.

An interesting aspect of some of these antiviral agents (specifically valacyclovir and famciclovir) is that they are activated by an enzyme encoded by the virus itself, making the drug active only in virally infected cells. The enzyme thymidine kinase is used by the virus to process nucleosides before incorporating them into viral RNA or DNA. When the inactive drug enters a virally infected cell, the virus's own thymidine kinase converts it to a working antiviral agent. In cells without viruses, the drug is never activated and normal DNA replication is allowed to continue.

Drugs for Treating HIV Infection and AIDS

The global epidemic of HIV disease has been a powerful stimulus for drug discovery. Most of the newer drugs being introduced are designed for HIV and AIDS. There is now a considerable array of drugs and drug combinations to manage HIV, which can make treatment very complicated. All of the drugs target a specific part of the multiplication cycle of HIV (table 12.6). There are currently drugs that can inhibit or block every strategic step in the virus cycle. One of the most important targets is the **reverse transcriptase (RT)** enzyme that HIV brings into the host cell. Recall from chapter 9 that HIV is a retrovirus with an RNA genome. Upon entering a host, the RNA is used as a template by reverse transcriptase to produce a DNA copy of this RNA. This activity offers two types of targets for anti-HIV drugs. The first involves *nucleoside reverse transcriptase analogs* (NRTIs) that directly stop DNA synthesis, and the second comes from *nonnucleoside reverse transcriptase inhibitors* (NNRTIs) that interfere with the function of the reverse transcriptase enzyme itself.

Zidovudine was the first NRTI and the first drug developed to treat HIV and AIDS. It is an analog of thymine that becomes incorporated into the DNA strand of HIV but terminates synthesis because it does not offer the correct binding sites.

NNRTIs accomplish a similar goal in preventing reverse transcription of the HIV RNA, but they bind to the enzyme itself and prevent its reactive site from synthesizing DNA. They are usually given together or in combination with NRTIs.

Another enzyme essential to the virus's release is HIV protease, which is involved in cutting the proteins that are an essential part of the virus structure (capsids, enzymes). The class of drugs called *protease inhibitors* has the effect of blocking this enzyme and causing the assembly of faulty viruses that are not infective.

Newer classes of anti-HIV drugs are two that block entry or fusion of the virus at the beginning of its invasion and one that prevents viral integration into the host genome. The drug *maraviroc* keeps HIV out of cells by preventing the viruses from adhering to host cells, and without this step, they cannot invade. Enfuvirtide (*Fuzeon*) prevents infection when it stops the envelope of the virus from fusing with the host cell after it has attached.

Another important enzyme targeted for HIV therapy is *HIV integrase*. This enzyme is essential for the final step in HIV DNA processing. Integrase inhibitors prevent this viral DNA from being incorporated or integrated into a host cell's chromosome. Because this step must occur for full viral function, the cycle is terminated by this action.

TABLE 12.6 Actions of Selected Antiviral Drugs*

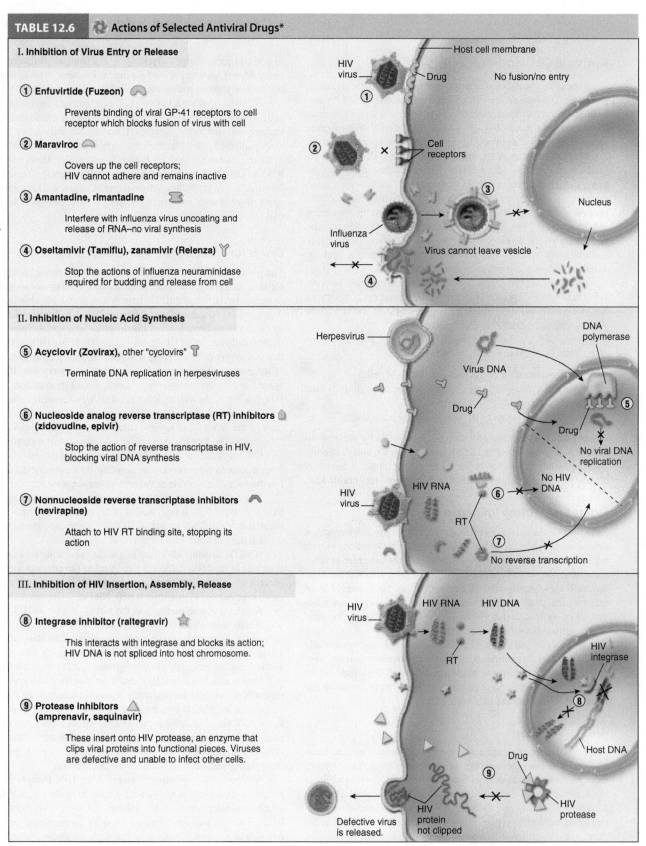

I. Inhibition of Virus Entry or Release

① **Enfuvirtide (Fuzeon)**

Prevents binding of viral GP-41 receptors to cell receptor which blocks fusion of virus with cell

② **Maraviroc**

Covers up the cell receptors; HIV cannot adhere and remains inactive

③ **Amantadine, rimantadine**

Interfere with influenza virus uncoating and release of RNA–no viral synthesis

④ **Oseltamivir (Tamiflu), zanamivir (Relenza)**

Stop the actions of influenza neuraminidase required for budding and release from cell

II. Inhibition of Nucleic Acid Synthesis

⑤ **Acyclovir (Zovirax), other "cyclovirs"**

Terminate DNA replication in herpesviruses

⑥ **Nucleoside analog reverse transcriptase (RT) inhibitors (zidovudine, epivir)**

Stop the action of reverse transcriptase in HIV, blocking viral DNA synthesis

⑦ **Nonnucleoside reverse transcriptase inhibitors (nevirapine)**

Attach to HIV RT binding site, stopping its action

III. Inhibition of HIV Insertion, Assembly, Release

⑧ **Integrase inhibitor (raltegravir)**

This interacts with integrase and blocks its action; HIV DNA is not spliced into host chromosome.

⑨ **Protease inhibitors (amprenavir, saquinavir)**

These insert onto HIV protease, an enzyme that clips viral proteins into functional pieces. Viruses are defective and unable to infect other cells.

Labels within figure:
- Host cell membrane
- HIV virus
- Drug
- No fusion/no entry
- Cell receptors
- Nucleus
- Influenza virus
- Virus cannot leave vesicle
- Herpesvirus
- DNA polymerase
- Virus DNA
- Drug
- No viral DNA replication
- No HIV DNA
- HIV RNA
- HIV virus
- RT
- No reverse transcription
- HIV virus
- HIV RNA
- HIV DNA
- HIV integrase
- Host DNA
- Drug
- HIV protease
- Defective virus is released.
- HIV protein not clipped

*Details of viral cycles are omitted for ease in observing drug effects.

TABLE 12.7	Overview of Anti-HIV Drugs, Effects, and Examples	
Category of Anti-HIV Drug	**Effects of Drug on Virus**	**Examples of Drugs**
Nucleoside reverse transcriptase inhibitors (NRTIs)	Chemical analogs are inserted into the HIV DNA and terminate its synthesis; this is a type of competitive inhibition.	Retrovir (azidothymidine [AZT], zidovudine), lamivudine (Epivir), abacavir, didanosine, stavudine, tenofovir, emtricitabine (Emtriva)
Nonnucleoside reverse transcriptase inhibitors (NNRTIs)	Drugs interact with reverse transcriptase and block its active site; this is a type of noncompetitive inhibition.	Nevirapine, efavirenz, delavirdine, rilpivirine
Protease Inhibitors	HIV protease that completes viral assembly is blocked, leading to incomplete and dysfunctional viruses.	Amprenavir, atazanavir, darunavir, indinavir, saquinavir
Entry or Fusion Blockers	Maraviroc covers an entry receptor on the human cell (CCR5) and keeps the virus from binding; enfuvirtide (Fuzeon) stops the viral envelope from fusing with the cell membrane.	Maraviroc, enfuvirtide
Integrase Inhibitors	Drugs interact with HIV integrase, which is required for the viral DNA to be inserted (integrated) into the human chromosome; this stops the action of the viral DNA.	Raltegravir, elvitegravir

The strategy for HIV and AIDS treatment currently involves some form of combined therapy or HAART (highly active antiretroviral therapy) that reduces the development of drug resistance. Combinations are available with two, three, or four drugs together in one pill. Most have at least one NRTI and one NNRTI, and some have protease inhibitors and an integrase inhibitor. They are used to treat ongoing HIV infection and AIDS, and for pre- and postexposure prophylaxis. **Table 12.7** summarizes HIV drug types, their modes of action, and examples.

Interferons A sensible alternative to artificial antiviral drugs has been a human-based substance, **interferon (IFN).** Interferon is a glycoprotein produced primarily by fibroblasts and leukocytes in response to various immune stimuli. It has numerous biological activities, including antiviral and anticancer properties. Studies have shown that it is a versatile part of animal host defenses, having a major role in natural immunities. Its mechanism is discussed in chapter 14.

The first investigations of interferon's antiviral activity were limited by the extremely minute quantities that could be extracted from human blood. Several types of interferon (Betaseron, Roferon) are currently produced by the recombinant DNA technology techniques outlined in chapter 10. Extensive clinical trials have tested interferon's effectiveness in viral infections and cancer. Some of the known therapeutic benefits of interferon include

1. reducing the time of healing and some of the complications in certain infections (mainly of herpesviruses);
2. preventing or reducing some symptoms of cold and papillomaviruses (warts);
3. slowing the progress of certain cancers, including bone cancer and cervical cancer, and certain leukemias and lymphomas; and
4. treating a rare cancer called hairy-cell leukemia, hepatitis C (a viral liver infection), genital warts, and Kaposi's sarcoma in AIDS patients.

Medical science is giving close scrutiny to alternate methods of preventing or treating infections beyond the usual antibiotics and synthesized drugs (**12.3 Making Connections**).

 Check Your Progress SECTION 12.3

13. Construct a chart to outline the applications of major groups of antifungal drugs, antiparasitic drugs, and antiviral drugs.
14. Explain why there are fewer antifungal, antiparasitic, and antiviral drugs than antibacterial drugs.
15. What is the strategy behind taking several different types of drugs to treat HIV?
16. Summarize the origins and biological actions of interferon-based drugs.

12.4 Interactions Between Microbes and Drugs: The Acquisition of Drug Resistance

 Expected Learning Outcomes

15. Describe the development of drug resistance, and explain how it is acquired.
16. Explain the major mechanisms by which microbes become resistant to drugs.
17. Discuss some of the ways for reducing levels of drug resistance.
18. Discuss how drug resistance spreads through a population of microbes and the long-term effects of this.

One unfortunate outcome of the use of antimicrobials is the development of microbial **drug resistance,** an adaptive response in which microorganisms begin to tolerate an amount of drug that would

12.3 MAKING CONNECTIONS

Alternative Antimicrobial Therapies

"The enemy of my enemy is my friend."

This old saying might well describe a novel way to kill bacteria using viruses. This technique, called phage therapy, was first attempted over a hundred years ago after the discovery of bacteriophages. The concept behind it is rather simple: When you expose bacterial cells to their specific viruses, the viruses will invade and destroy them. If you apply the viruses in large quantity to treat a human or animal infection, they could lyse the bacteria and cure the infection. Phage therapy went out of favor for many years except in Russia, but it is currently making a comeback worldwide. An important push for renewed interest is the search for solutions to the high levels of drug resistance among bacteria. Bacteria do not become resistant to viruses. Other significant advantages are that viruses are very narrow spectrum—they can target just one species of bacteria—and they would not be toxic to humans as are many drugs.

For now, phage therapy is restricted in the United States to removing contaminants from meats, reducing the incidence of *Salmonella* and *Escherichia coli* in young farm animals, treating skin infections, and sanitizing food. In some clinics, it is in experimental trials for treatment of skin ulcers, wounds, and urinary tract infections. It will require extensive testing before it becomes a first-line therapy.

Other novel approaches to controlling infections include the use of **probiotics*** and **prebiotics.** Probiotics are preparations of live microorganisms that are fed to animals and humans to modify the resident intestinal bacteria. These microorganisms can replace microbes lost during antimicrobial therapy or simply augment the normal microbiota that is already there. Culture-enriched dairy products are the latest commercial source of probiotics. Several new types of yogurt now claim specific health benefits from eating high numbers of special strains of bacteria. According to some published research findings, the ingestion of *Bifidobacterium lactis regularis* can help to maintain regular bowel function, and *Lactobacillus casei immunitas* may

boost the immune function of the gut. Purposely eating such high numbers of bacterial cells—estimated at from 1 billion to 10 billion per serving—is quite a departure from the usual view of microbes as disease agents. Bon appetit!

A probiotic approach is frequently used in female patients with recurring urinary tract infections. There is evidence that vaginal inserts or perineal swabs of *Lactobacillus* can restore a healthy acidic environment to the region and displace disease-causing microorganisms. Probiotics also seem to inhibit the development of food allergies.

Prebiotics are nutrients that encourage the growth of beneficial microbes in the intestine. For instance, fruit sugars such as fructans are thought to encourage the growth of *Bifidobacterium* in the large intestine and to discourage the growth of potential pathogens. Clearly, the use of these agents is a different type of antimicrobial strategy than we are used to, but it may have its place in a future in which traditional antibiotics are more problematic.

New attention is being paid to the curative properties of honey. Several studies have found that it appears to limit infection but even more, it can speed the healing of wounds and burns through its beneficial effects on the immune system. When applied to wounds, honey helps remove wound debris and promotes the growth of new tissue. A type of wound dressing marketed as Medihoney (antimicrobial active Manuka honey) has been approved by the FDA. Other home remedies that show pharmacologic potential are pomegranate, cranberry, and grape juices and bitter orange leaves.

Describe several benefits of using nondrug regimens and foods to treat or prevent infections. *Answer available at http://www.mhhe.com/talaro9*

* *probiotic* (proh′-by-ah-tik′) Gr. *pro*, for, and *bios*, life.

ordinarily be inhibitory. The development of mechanisms for resisting antimicrobial drugs is a result of the genetic versatility and adaptability of microbial populations. The property of drug resistance can be intrinsic as well as acquired. Intrinsic drug resistance can best be exemplified by the fact that bacteria must, of course, be resistant to any antibiotic that they produce. This type of resistance is limited, however, to a small group of organisms and is generally not a problem with regard to antimicrobial chemotherapy. Of much greater importance is the acquisition of resistance to a drug by a microbe that was previously sensitive to the drug. In our context, the term *drug resistance* will refer to this last type of acquired resistance.

How Does Drug Resistance Develop?

Contrary to popular belief, antibiotic resistance is not a recent phenomenon. Resistance to penicillin developed in some bacteria as early as 1940, 3 years before the drug was even approved for public use. The scope of the problem became apparent in the 1980s and

1990s when scientists and physicians observed treatment failures on a large scale.

Microbes become newly resistant to a drug after one of the following events occurs: (1) spontaneous mutations in critical chromosomal genes, or (2) acquisition of entire new genes or sets of genes via transfer from another species. Chromosomal drug resistance usually results from spontaneous random mutations in bacterial populations. The chance that such a mutation will be advantageous is minimal, and the chance that it will confer resistance to a specific drug is lower still. Nevertheless, given the huge numbers of microorganisms in any population and the constant rate of mutation, such mutations do occur. The end result varies from slight changes in microbial sensitivity, which can be overcome by larger doses of the drug, to complete loss of sensitivity.

Resistance through intermicrobial transfer originates from chromosomal genes and plasmids called **resistance (R) factors** being transferred through the processes we considered in chapter 9: conjugation, transformation, or transduction **(figure 12.13).** Studies

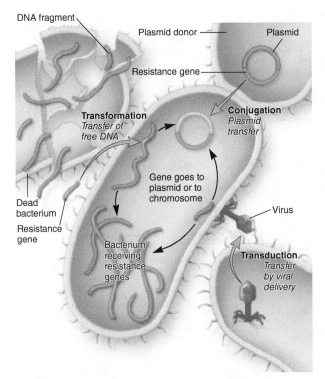

Figure 12.13 **Transfer of drug resistance.** Bacteria transmit R factors, often containing numerous genes for drug resistance by means of conjugation, transduction, and transformation. The widespread occurrence of such exchanges accounts for the rapid spread of drug resistance.

have shown that plasmids encoded with drug resistance are naturally present in microorganisms before they have been exposed to the drug. Such traits are "lying in wait" for an opportunity to be expressed and to confer adaptability on the species. Many bacteria also maintain transposable drug-resistance sequences (transposons) that are duplicated and inserted from one plasmid to another or from a plasmid to the chromosome. Chromosomal genes and plasmids containing codes for drug resistance are faithfully replicated and inherited by all subsequent progeny. This sharing of resistance genes accounts for the rapid proliferation of drug-resistant species. A growing body of evidence points to the ease and frequency of gene transfers in biofilms between totally unrelated bacteria living in the body's microbiota and the environment.

Specific Mechanisms of Drug Resistance

Inside a bacterial cell, the net effect of these genetic transfers is one of the following, which actually causes the bacterium to be resistant (note that the numbers that follow correspond to the numbers seen in **figure 12.14**):

> **Quick Search**
> Explore this topic by going to "Animation of Antibiotic Resistance" on YouTube.

1. Inducement of alternate enzymes can inactivate the drug (only occurs when new genes are acquired).
2. Permeability or uptake of drug into bacterium is decreased or eliminated.

CLINICAL CONNECTIONS

Biofilms and Drug Resistance

In chapters 4 and 7, we described the development of microbial biofilms in various habitats. Recall that in these complex communities, certain "pioneer" microbes anchor themselves to a substrate by secreting a sticky matrix. This initial colonization stimulates a network of other microbes to migrate into the film.

It is estimated that around 60% of infections involve biofilms containing single or multiple species of microbes. Often the infections occur on natural tissues—for example, bacterial infections of the heart valves, middle ear, and teeth. The increased use of indwelling medical devices has created yet another habitat in which biofilms may become tenaciously attached. Catheters, artificial valves, and prosthetic devices can harbor persistent biofilm colonizations that are very difficult to treat and remove.

Microbes in infectious biofilms may be hundreds of times more drug resistant than the same free, unattached microbes. For one thing, microbes are protected by the impenetrable nature of the extracellular matrix—drugs may be blocked from entry. We also know that microbes communicate and regulate resistance mechanisms such as drug pumps, and the contact within the biofilm facilitates the transfer of drug-resistant plasmids and genes. Numerous studies have discovered the presence of persisters—microbes that remain embedded in the infection long after the drug has been discontinued, only to erupt at a later time in a new infection. These factors alone or in combination allow the persistence of the biofilm and a long-term source of infection for the patient.

With knowledge of biofilms, drug companies are researching newer drug strategies that can prevent or disrupt their formation. One concept already in use is to incorporate antimicrobic chemicals into implants, catheters, and other metal or plastic devices to inhibit microbial growth.

Would broad-spectrum or narrow-spectrum drugs be more effective in treating infections involving biofilms? Explain your reasoning. *Answer available at http://www.mhhe.com/talaro9*

3. The microbe engages special drug transport pumps that remove the drug.
4. Binding sites for drug are decreased in number or affinity (can occur via mutation or acquisition of new genes).
5. An affected metabolic pathway is shut down or an alternate pathway is used (occurs due to mutation of original enzyme[s]).

Some bacteria can become resistant indirectly by lapsing into dormancy or, in the case of penicillin, by converting to a cell-wall-deficient form (L form) that penicillin cannot affect. A number of infections, including endocarditis, urinary infections, otitis media, osteomyelitis, and pneumonias are more resistant to drugs because they develop as biofilms (see **Clinical Connections** above).

Drug Inactivation Mechanisms

Microbes inactivate drugs by producing enzymes that permanently alter drug structure. One example, bacterial exoenzymes called *beta-lactamases*, hydrolyze the beta-lactam ring structure of some penicillins and cephalosporins, rendering the drugs inactive. Two

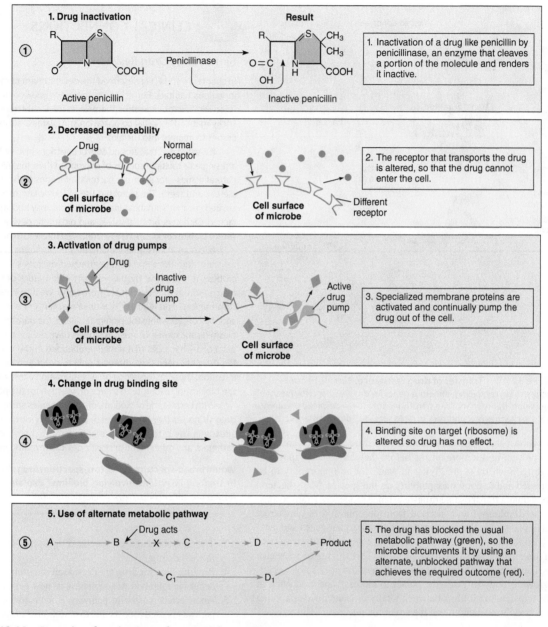

Figure 12.14 Examples of mechanisms of acquired drug resistance.

beta-lactamases—penicillinase and cephalosporinase—disrupt the structure of certain penicillin or cephalosporin molecules so their activity is lost (**figure 12.14, part 1**). So many strains of *Staphylococcus aureus* produce penicillinase that regular penicillin is rarely a possible therapeutic choice. Now that some strains of *Neisseria gonorrhoeae*, called PPNG,[4] have also acquired penicillinase, alternative drugs are required to treat gonorrhea. A large number of other gram-negative species are inherently resistant to some of the penicillins and cephalosporins because of naturally occurring beta-lactamases.

Decreased Drug Permeability or Increased Drug Elimination

The resistance of some bacteria can be due to a mechanism that prevents the drug from entering the cell and acting on its target. For example, the outer membrane of the cell wall of certain gram-negative bacteria is a natural blockade for some of the penicillin drugs. Resistance to the tetracyclines can arise from plasmid-encoded proteins that pump the drug out of the cell. Aminoglycoside resistance is known to develop through changes in drug permeability caused by point mutations in proteins of the transport system or outer membrane (**figure 12.14, parts 2 and 3**).

4. Penicillinase-producing *Neisseria gonorrhoeae*.

Many bacteria possess multidrug-resistant (MDR) pumps that actively transport drugs and other chemicals out of cells. These pumps are proteins encoded by plasmids or chromosomes. They are stationed in the cell membrane and expel molecules by a proton-motive force similar to ATP synthesis (figure 12.14, part 3). They confer drug resistance on many gram-positive pathogens (*Staphylococcus, Streptococcus*) and gram-negative pathogens (*Pseudomonas, E. coli*). Because they lack selectivity, one type of pump can expel a broad array of antimicrobial drugs, detergents, and other toxic substances.

Change of Drug Receptors

Because most drugs act on a specific target such as protein, RNA, DNA, or membrane structure, microbes can circumvent drugs by altering the nature of this target. Bacteria can become resistant to aminoglycosides when point mutations in ribosomal proteins arise (**figure 12.14, part 4**). Erythromycin and clindamycin resistance is associated with an alteration on the 50S ribosomal binding site. Penicillin resistance in *Streptococcus pneumoniae* and methicillin resistance in *Staphylococcus aureus* are related to an alteration in the binding proteins in the cell wall. Several species of enterococci have acquired resistance to vancomycin through a similar alteration of cell wall proteins. Fungi can become resistant by decreasing their synthesis of ergosterol, the principal receptor for certain antifungal drugs.

Changes in Metabolic Patterns

The action of antimetabolites can be circumvented if a microbe develops an alternative metabolic pathway or enzyme (**figure 12.14, part 5**). Sulfonamide and trimethoprim resistance develops when microbes deviate from the usual patterns of folic acid synthesis. Fungi can acquire resistance to flucytosine by completely shutting off certain metabolic activities.

Natural Selection and Drug Resistance

So far, we have been considering drug resistance at the cellular and molecular levels, but its full impact is felt only if this resistance oc-

curs throughout the cell population. Let us examine how this might happen and its long-term therapeutic consequences.

Any large population of microbes is likely to contain a few individual cells that are already drug resistant because of prior mutations or transfer of plasmids (**figure 12.15a**). As long as the drug is not present in the habitat, the numbers of these resistant forms will remain low because they have no particular growth advantage. But if the population is subsequently exposed to this drug (**figure 12.15b**), sensitive individuals are inhibited or destroyed, and resistant forms survive and proliferate. As the population continues to grow, offspring of these resistant microbes will inherit this drug resistance. In time, the replacement population will have more of the drug-resistant forms and can eventually become completely resistant (**figure 12.15c**). In ecological and evolutionary terms, the environmental factor (in this case, the drug) has put selection pressure on the population, allowing the more "fit" microbe (the drug-resistant one) to survive and grow. The end result is a population that has evolved to a condition of drug resistance.

Natural selection for drug-resistant forms is apparently a common phenomenon. It takes place most frequently in various natural habitats, medical environments, and it also can occur within the bodies of humans and animals during drug therapy. See **12.4 Making Connections** to find out some of the current implications of drug resistance. **Table 12.8** summarizes a number of actions that are being considered to slow its development.

 Check Your Progress SECTION 12.4

17. Explain the phenomenon of drug resistance from the standpoint of microbial genetics (include a description of R factors).
18. Describe the five basic mechanisms of drug resistance.
19. Explain why biofilm infections are often resistant to drugs.
20. Name several ways that drug resistance can be prevented by medical personnel and patients (see table 12.8).

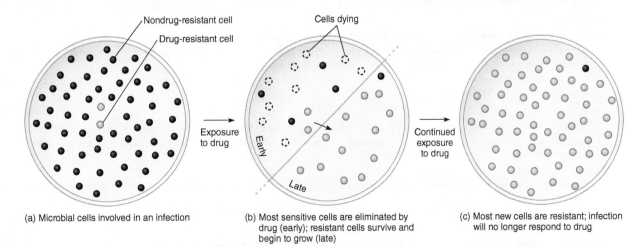

(a) Microbial cells involved in an infection

(b) Most sensitive cells are eliminated by drug (early); resistant cells survive and begin to grow (late)

(c) Most new cells are resistant; infection will no longer respond to drug

Figure 12.15 A model of natural selection for drug resistance. (a) Generally, any population of microbes will harbor a few cells carrying a prior mutation that confers drug resistance. **(b)** Environmental pressure (here, exposure to the drug) selects for survival of these cells. **(c)** In time, the resistant cells become the dominant cells.

12.4 MAKING CONNECTIONS

The Rise of Drug Resistance

"The steady rise of resistance in the last five years represents a ticking time bomb that ranks alongside terrorism as a threat to the nation."
Sally Davies, Chief Medical Officer, UK

It is a fact of nature that if a large number of microbes are exposed to a variety of drugs, there will always be some genetically favored strains or types that survive in the presence of those drugs. One could even say that microbes are merely practicing their livelihoods—to adapt and survive. Our very use of drugs is indeed a catalyst that speeds their evolution into drug resistance.

Approximately 2 million hospital-acquired infections causing 90,000 fatalities occur every year. About 70% of these infections are caused by bacteria resistant to at least one drug. For many years, concerned observers reported the gradual development of drug resistance in a number of pathogens, but during the past decade, the scope of the problem has escalated. It is now a common event to discover microbes that have become resistant to relatively new drugs in a very short time.

The clinical setting is a prolific source of drug-resistant strains of bacteria. This environment continually exposes large numbers of pathogens to a wide variety of drugs. The hospital also maintains patients with weakened defenses, making them highly susceptible to infections. A classic example occurred with *Staphylococcus aureus* and penicillin. In the 1950s, hospital strains began to show resistance to this drug, and because of indiscriminate use, these strains became nearly 100% resistant to penicillin within 30 years. This was followed by the appearance of MRSA (methicillin-resistant *S. aureus*) strains, which can tolerate nearly all antibiotics. To complicate this problem, strains of MRSA found their way from the clinic into the community. Up until recently, MRSA has been sensitive to the drug vancomycin. Then, in 2002, the first cases of complete resistance to this drug were reported (VRSA).

In 2012, a new health care crisis arose over carbapenem-resistant Enterobacteriaceae (CRE). This description refers to resistance among members of this family of gram-negative rods to the carbapenem drugs (imipenem, ertapenem), which had traditionally been used in cases of drug resistance to other beta-lactam drugs. Many new resistant strains of *Klebsiella pneumoniae, Enterobacter cloacae,* and *Escherichia coli* have emerged as significant hospital-acquired pathogens (see figures). In this setting, enteric bacteria cause infections of the bloodstream and urinary tract. The fatality rate for some patients is 40%. Similar to *Acinetobacter,* which was featured in the Case Study on page 256, the genes for carbapenem resistance are readily and rapidly transmitted by means of several mechanisms. Since 2001, the number of cases has risen by three to five times.

Drugs in Animal Feeds

Another practice that has contributed significantly to growing drug resistance is the addition of antimicrobials to livestock feed, with the idea of decreasing infections and thereby improving animal health and size. Enteric bacteria such as *Salmonella, E. coli,* and enterococci that live as normal intestinal residents of these animals readily share resistance plasmids and are constantly selected and amplified by exposure to drugs. These pathogens subsequently "jump" to humans and cause drug-resistant infections, oftentimes at epidemic proportions. In a deadly outbreak of *Salmonella* infection in Denmark, the pathogen was found to be resistant to seven different antimicrobials. The opportunistic pathogen called VRE (vancomycin-resistant enterococcus) has been traced to the use of a vancomycin-like drug in cattle feed. It is now one of the most tenacious of hospital-acquired infections for which there are few drug choices.

Worldwide Drug Resistance

The drug dilemma has become a widespread problem, affecting all countries and socioeconomic groups. In general, the majority of infectious diseases, whether bacterial, fungal, protozoan, or viral, are showing

TABLE 12.8 Strategies to Limit Drug Resistance of Microorganisms

Drug Usage

- Physicians have the responsibility for making an accurate diagnosis and prescribing the correct drug therapy.
- Compliance with physicians' guidelines: The patient should take the correct dosage, by the best route, for the appropriate period. This diminishes the selection for mutants that can resist low drug levels and ensures elimination of the pathogen.
- Combined therapy with two or more drugs together increases the chances that at least one of the drugs will be effective and that a strain resistant to either drug will not be able to persist.

Drug Research

- Research focuses on developing shorter-term, higher-dose antimicrobials that are more effective, less expensive, and have fewer side effects.
- Pharmaceutical companies continue to seek new antimicrobial drugs with structures that are not readily inactivated by microbial enzymes or drugs with modes of action that are not readily circumvented.

Long-Term Strategies

- Proposals to reduce the abuse of antibiotics range from educational programs for medical workers to requiring justification for prescribing certain types of antibiotics.
- Especially valuable antimicrobials may be restricted in their use to only one or two types of infections.
- The addition of antimicrobials to animal feeds must be curtailed worldwide.
- Government programs that make effective therapy available to low-income populations should be increased.
- Vaccines should be used whenever possible to provide alternative protection.

increases in drug resistance. In parts of India, the main drugs used to treat cholera (furazolidone, ampicillin) have gone from being highly effective to essentially useless in 10 years. In Southeast Asia, 98% of gonococcus infections are multidrug resistant. Many strains of the malaria parasite have become resistant to the mainstay drug chloroquine, which means that it must be combined with an alternate drug or not given at all. The influenza drugs amantadine and rimantadine had to be discontinued because the virus had become almost completely resistant to these medications. In some parts of Africa, the TB bacillus has such extreme resistance that there are no effective treatments available. To add to the problem, global travel and globalization of food products mean that drug resistance can be spread around the world in a short time.

In the United States alone, the extra cost for treating drug-resistant infections is around $10 billion per year. In many developing countries, drugs are mishandled by overuse and underuse, either of which can contribute to drug resistance. Many countries that do not regulate the sale of prescription drugs make them readily available to purchase over the counter. For example, the antituberculosis drug INH (isoniazid) is sometimes used as a "lung vitamin" to improve health, and antibiotics are often taken in the wrong dose for undiagnosed conditions. These countries serve as breeding grounds for drug resistance that can eventually be carried to other countries.

"Bad Bugs–No Drugs"

The development of new antimicrobial drugs is considered the only viable way to gain some advantage in this situation, often referred to as the "bad bugs–no drugs" problem. A case in point is the alarming trend of pathogens known collectively as ESKAPE. This acronym comes from the first letters of their generic names, but it also tells us that these six pathogens are very successful at escaping the effects of drugs and are getting better at it all the time. The microbes—*Enterococcus*, *Staphylococcus aureus*, *Klebsiella*, *Acinetobacter*, *Pseudomonas*, and *Enterobacter*—make up the majority of hospital-acquired infections and are also the most drug-resistant bacteria in the hospital environment. It is not unusual to find extremely drug-resistant strains or "superbugs" for which there are only two, one, and sometimes no drugs available. Even more problematic is that right now, there are no new drugs that could control these pathogens making their way through the pipeline of development. To avert a public health crisis, a number of governments are actively working with pharmaceutical companies on drug discovery and development, sometimes called the "new bugs–new drugs" approach. It may be our only hope.

What are some of the reasons that microbes develop drug resistance so rapidly? *Answer available at http://www.mhhe.com/talaro9*

Examples of CRE (carbapenem-resistant Enterobacteriaceae) pathogens

Colonies of Klebsiella pneumoniae *Colonies of Escherichia coli* *Colonies of Enterobacter cloacae*

12.5 Interactions Between Drugs and Hosts

Expected Learning Outcomes

19. Summarize the adverse effects of drugs on the human body.

20. Describe some of the toxic effects of drugs on organs and tissues.

21. Discuss how drugs can cause damaging immune responses.

22. Explain the ways that drugs alter the normal microbiota and the results.

Until now, this chapter has focused on the interactions between antimicrobials and the microorganisms they target. During an infection, the microbe is living in or on a host; therefore, the drug is administered to the host though its target is the microbe. Because of this, the effect of the drug on the host must always be considered.

Although selective antimicrobial toxicity is the ideal constantly being sought, chemotherapy by its very nature involves contact with foreign chemicals that can harm human tissues. In fact, estimates indicate that at least 5% of all persons taking an antimicro-

bial drug experience some type of serious adverse reaction to it. The major **side effects** of drugs fall into one of three categories: direct damage to tissues through toxicity, allergic reactions, and disruption in the balance of normal microbial flora. The damage incurred by antimicrobial drugs can be short term and reversible or permanent, and it ranges in severity from cosmetic to lethal.

Toxicity to Organs

Drugs can adversely affect the following organs: the liver (hepatotoxic), kidneys (nephrotoxic), gastrointestinal tract, cardiovascular system and blood-forming tissue (hemotoxic), nervous system (neurotoxic), respiratory tract, skin, bones, and teeth.

Because the liver is responsible for metabolizing and detoxifying foreign chemicals in the blood, it can be damaged by a drug or its metabolic products. Injury to liver cells can result in enzymatic abnormalities, fatty liver deposits, hepatitis, and liver failure. The kidney is involved in excreting drugs and their metabolites. Some drugs irritate the nephron tubules, creating changes that interfere with their

filtration abilities. Drugs such as sulfonamides can crystallize in the kidney and form stones that obstruct the flow of urine.

The most common complaint associated with oral antimicrobial therapy is diarrhea, which can progress to severe intestinal irritation or colitis. Although some drugs directly irritate the intestinal lining, the usual gastrointestinal complaints are caused by disruption of the intestinal microflora (discussed in a subsequent section).

Many drugs given for parasitic infections are toxic to the heart, causing irregular heartbeats and even cardiac arrest in extreme cases. Chloramphenicol can severely depress blood-forming cells in the bone marrow, resulting in either a reversible or a permanent (fatal) anemia. Some drugs hemolyze the red blood cells, others reduce white blood cell counts, and still others damage platelets or interfere with their formation, thereby inhibiting blood clotting.

Quick Search
Find the video "Important Side Effects and Toxicities" on YouTube.

Certain antimicrobials act directly on the brain and cause seizures. Others, such as aminoglycosides, damage nerves (very commonly, the eighth cranial nerve), leading to dizziness, deafness, or motor and sensory disturbances. When drugs block the transmission of impulses to the diaphragm, respiratory failure can result.

The skin is a frequent target of drug-induced side effects. The skin response can be a symptom of drug allergy or a direct toxic effect. Some drugs interact with sunlight to cause photodermatitis, a skin inflammation. Tetracyclines are contraindicated (not advisable) for children from birth to 8 years of age because they bind to the enamel of the teeth, creating a permanent gray to brown discoloration (**figure 12.16**). Pregnant women should avoid tetracyclines because they cross the placenta and can be deposited in the developing fetal bones and teeth.

Allergic Responses to Drugs

One of the most frequent drug reactions is heightened sensitivity, or **allergy.** This reaction occurs because the drug acts as an antigen (a foreign material capable of stimulating the immune system) and stimulates an allergic response. This response can be provoked by the intact drug molecule or by substances that develop from the body's metabolic alteration of the drug. In the case of penicillin, for instance, it is not the penicillin molecule itself that causes the allergic response but a product, *benzylpenicilloyl.* Allergic reactions have been reported for every major type of antimicrobial drug, but the penicillins account for the greatest number of antimicrobial allergies, followed by the sulfonamides.

People who are allergic to a drug become sensitized to it during the first contact, usually without symptoms. Once the immune system is sensitized, a second exposure to the drug can lead to a reaction such as a skin rash (hives); respiratory inflammation; and, rarely, anaphylaxis, an acute, overwhelming allergic response that develops rapidly and can be fatal. This topic is discussed in greater detail in chapter 16.

Suppression and Alteration of the Microbiota by Antimicrobials

Most normal, healthy body surfaces, such as the skin, large intestine, outer openings of the urogenital tract, and oral cavity, provide numerous habitats for a virtual "garden" of microorganisms. These normal colonists or residents, called the microbiota, consist mostly of harmless or beneficial bacteria, but a small number can potentially be pathogens. Although we defer a more detailed discussion of this topic to chapter 13 and later chapters, here we focus on the general effects of drugs on this population.

If a broad-spectrum antimicrobial is administered to treat infection, it will destroy microbes regardless of their roles in maintaining a balance, affecting not only the targeted infectious agent but also many others in sites far removed from the original infection (**figure 12.17**).

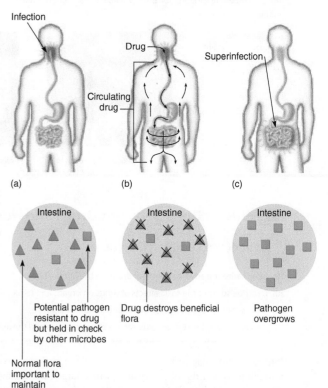

Figure 12.17 **The role of antimicrobials in disrupting microbiota and causing superinfections. (a)** A primary infection in the throat is treated with an oral antibiotic. **(b)** The drug is carried to the intestine and is absorbed into the circulation. **(c)** The primary infection is cured, but drug-resistant pathogens have survived and create an intestinal superinfection.

Figure 12.16 Drug-induced side effect. An adverse effect of tetracycline given to young children is the permanent brownish discoloration of tooth enamel continuing into adulthood.

TABLE 12.9	Major Adverse Toxic Reactions to Common Drug Groups
Antimicrobial Drug	**Primary Damage or Abnormality Produced**
Antibacterials	
Penicillin G	Skin allergy
Ampicillin	Diarrhea and enterocolitis
Cephalosporins	Inhibition of prothrombin synthesis
	Decreased circulation
	Nephritis
Tetracyclines	Diarrhea and enterocolitis
	Discoloration of tooth enamel
	Reactions to sunlight (photosensitization)
Chloramphenicol	Injury to red and white blood cell precursors
Aminoglycosides (streptomycin, gentamicin)	Diarrhea and enterocolitis; loss of hearing, dizziness, kidney damage
Azithromycin	Heart arrhythmias
Isoniazid	Hepatitis
	Seizures
	Dermatitis
Sulfonamides	Formation of kidney crystals; blockage of urine flow
	Hemolysis
	Reduction in number of platelets
Polymyxin	Damage to membranes of kidney tubules
	Weakened muscular responses
Quinolones (floxacins)	Headache, dizziness, GI distress, tendonitis
Rifampin	Damage to hepatic cells
	Dermatitis
Antifungals	
Amphotericin B	Disruption of kidney filtration
Flucytosine	Decreased number of white blood cells
Antiprotozoan Drugs	
Metronidazole	Nausea, vomiting
Chloroquine	Vomiting
	Headache
	Itching
Antihelminthics	
Niclosamide	Nausea, abdominal pain
Pyrantel	Irritation
	Headache, dizziness
Antivirals	
Acyclovir	Seizures, confusion
	Skin rash
Amantadine	Nervousness, light-headedness
	Nausea
AZT	Immunosuppression, anemia
Protease inhibitors	Hepatic damage
	Abnormal deposition of fats
	Diabetes

When this therapy destroys beneficial resident species, resistant microbes that were once in small numbers begin to overgrow and cause disease. This complication is called a **superinfection.**

Some common examples demonstrate how a disturbance in microbial flora leads to replacement flora and superinfection. A broad-spectrum cephalosporin used to treat a urinary tract infection by *E. coli* will cure the infection, but it will also destroy the lactobacilli in the vagina that normally maintain a protective acidic environment there. The drug has no effect, however, on *Candida albicans,* a yeast that also resides in normal vaginas. Released from the inhibitory environment provided by lactobacilli, the yeasts proliferate and cause symptoms. *Candida* can cause similar superinfections of the oropharynx (thrush) and the large intestine.

Oral therapy with tetracyclines, clindamycin, and broad-spectrum penicillins and cephalosporins is associated with a serious and potentially fatal condition known as *antibiotic-associated colitis* (pseudomembranous colitis). This condition is due to the overgrowth in the bowel of *Clostridium difficile,* an endospore-forming bacterium that is resistant to the antibiotic. It invades the intestinal lining and releases toxins that induce diarrhea, fever, and abdominal pain.

Refer to **table 12.9** for a general summary of major drug groups and their side effects.

 Check Your Progress SECTION 12.5

21. Why do drugs that act on bacterial and fungal membranes generally have high toxicity?
22. Describe the series of events that gives rise to a superinfection, using an example.
23. What characteristic of antibiotics and other drugs causes hypersensitivity and allergic reactions?
24. Explain why it is better to use a narrow-spectrum drug instead of a broad-spectrum one, if possible.

12.6 Considerations in Selecting an Antimicrobial Drug

 Expected Learning Outcomes

23. Outline some important factors to consider in drug therapy.
24. Describe the principles behind sensitivity testing for infectious agents.
25. Explain the uses of the minimum inhibitory concentration and the therapeutic index in drug selection.
26. Discuss medical considerations in final drug selection.
27. Summarize the problems in managing antimicrobial drugs.

Before actual antimicrobial therapy can begin, consideration must be given to at least three factors:

1. the nature of the microorganism causing the infection,
2. the degree of the microorganism's susceptibility (also called sensitivity) to various drugs, and
3. the overall medical condition of the patient.

Identifying the Agent

Identification of infectious agents from body specimens should be attempted as soon as possible. It is especially important that such specimens be taken before any antimicrobial drug is given, to prevent loss of the infectious agent. Direct examination of body fluids, sputum, or stool can provide a rapid detection method for bacteria or fungi. A doctor often begins the therapy on the basis of such immediate findings. The choice of drug will be based on experience with drugs that are known to be effective against the microbe. For instance, if a sore throat appears to be caused by *Streptococcus pyogenes,* the physician may prescribe penicillin, because this species seems to be almost universally sensitive to it so far. If the infectious agent is not or cannot be isolated, epidemiological statistics may be required to predict the most likely agent in a given infection. For example, *Streptococcus pneumoniae* accounts for the majority of cases of meningitis in children, followed by *Neisseria meningitidis* and *Haemophilus influenzae.*

Testing for the Drug Susceptibility of Microorganisms

Testing is essential in those groups of bacteria commonly showing resistance, primarily *Staphylococcus* species, *Neisseria gonorrhoeae, Streptococcus pneumoniae, Enterococcus faecalis,* and the aerobic gram-negative enteric bacilli. However, not all infectious agents require antimicrobial sensitivity testing. When certain groups, such as group A streptococci and most anaerobic bacteria are known to be uniformly susceptible to penicillin G, testing may not be necessary unless the patient is allergic to penicillin. Testing methods are available for fungi (see figure 12.21), protozoa, and viruses, although testing may not be done as often for these groups.

Selection of a proper antimicrobial agent begins by demonstrating the in vitro activity of several drugs against the infectious agent by means of standardized methods. In general, these tests involve exposing a pure culture of the bacterium to several different drugs and observing the effects of the drugs on growth.

The *Kirby-Bauer* technique is an agar diffusion test that provides useful data on antimicrobial susceptibility. In this test, the surface of a plate of special medium is spread with the test bacterium, and small discs containing a premeasured amount of antimicrobial are dispensed onto the bacterial lawn. After incubation, the zone of inhibition surrounding the discs is measured and compared with a standard for each drug **(figure 12.18).** The profile of antimicrobial sensitivity, or *antibiogram,* provides data for drug selection. The Kirby-Bauer procedure is less effective

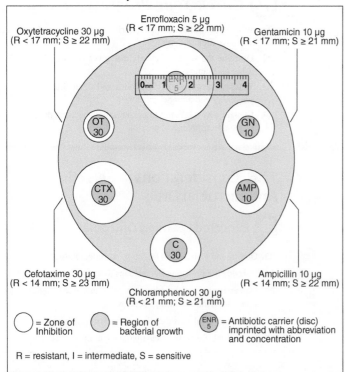

Kirby-Bauer Disc Diffusion Test

Enrofloxacin 5 µg
(R < 17 mm; S ≥ 22 mm)

Oxytetracycline 30 µg
(R < 17 mm; S ≥ 22 mm)

Gentamicin 10 µg
(R < 17 mm; S ≥ 21 mm)

OT 30

GN 10

CTX 30

AMP 10

C 30

Cefotaxime 30 µg
(R < 14 mm; S ≥ 23 mm)

Ampicillin 10 µg
(R < 14 mm; S ≥ 22 mm)

Chloramphenicol 30 µg
(R < 21 mm; S ≥ 21 mm)

○ = Zone of Inhibition

○ = Region of bacterial growth

(ENR 5) = Antibiotic carrier (disc) imprinted with abbreviation and concentration

R = resistant, I = intermediate, S = sensitive

(a) Example and evaluation of an agar diffusion sensitivity test. If the test bacterium is sensitive to a drug, a zone of inhibition develops around its disc. The larger the size of this zone, the greater is the bacterium's sensitivity to the drug. The diameter of each zone is measured in millimeters and evaluated for susceptibility or resistance by means of a comparative standard (R, I, or S).

(b) Result for gram-negative *Klebsiella pneumoniae*, with zones of inhibition indicating sensitivity to cefotaxime (CTX) and ampicillin and clavulanic acid (AMC). Observe the expanded zone between these two drugs that indicates their enhanced action, or synergy, when combined.

(c) Result for gram-positive *Staphylococcus aureus* using gentamicin (GM, left) and aztreonam (ATM, right). Although the bacteria are sensitive to both drugs, the GM has a few colonies growing in the zone of inhibition, indicating some cells that have developed resistance to that concentration of the drug.

Figure 12.18 Techniques for preparation and interpretation of disc diffusion tests.

Figure 12.19 Etest®: A quantitative method for determining sensitivity. This test uses a plastic strip that contains a premeasured gradient of a drug and is labeled with a scale that indicates increasing concentrations of the drug in μg. When the strips are placed on a plate swabbed with the test microbe and incubated, an oval area called the ellipse of inhibition develops adjacent to the strip. The lowest point on the scale (lowest concentrations are toward the middle of the plate) where the ellipse begins to form corresponds with the MIC. (IP = imipenem and TZ = ceftazidime). Etest® and the Etest gradient strip are registered trademarks of AB BIODISK.

for bacteria that are anaerobic, highly fastidious, or slow-growing (*Mycobacterium*).

An alternative quantitative system that provides a quantitative rating of drug effectiveness is the *Etest®* (**figure 12.19**). In addition to providing a precise numerical rating (the MIC), this method allows testing for a wide variety of drugs and microbial types, including anaerobes, mycobacteria, and fungi.

More sensitive and quantitative results can also be obtained with tube dilution tests. First the antimicrobial is diluted serially in tubes of broth, and then each tube is inoculated with a small uniform sample of pure culture, incubated, and examined for growth (turbidity). The smallest concentration of drug in the series that visibly inhibits growth is called the **minimum inhibitory concentration,** or

MIC. The MIC is useful in determining the smallest effective dosage of a drug and in providing a comparative index against other antimicrobials (**figures 12.20** and **12.21**, and **table 12.10**). In many

Figure 12.20 Tube dilution test for determining the minimum inhibitory concentration (MIC). The antibiotic is diluted through tubes of liquid nutrient so that the concentration in successive tubes ranges from 6.4 μg/ml to 0.1 μg/ml. All tubes are inoculated with an identical amount of a test bacterium and then incubated. The first tube on the left is a control that lacks the drug and shows cloudiness indicative of normal growth. Reading from left to right, the MIC is the dilution of the first tube in the series that has no growth (is not cloudy).

Figure 12.21 Microbroth dilution in a multiwell plate adapted for a pathogenic yeast. Drugs being tested are amphotericin B (AmB), flucytosine (5FC), fluconazole (Fluc), azole drugs (itraconazole [itra], ketoconazole [Keto], Voriconazole [vori], and caspofungin (caspo). Pink indicates growth and blue, no growth. Reading across numbers 2–12 are increasing concentrations of the drugs in μg/ml. Row 1 has no drug. The first dilution with no growth is crossed out, indicating the MIC for that drug. Results are given in the box on the left.

TABLE 12.10	Comparative MICs (μg/ml) for Common Drugs and Pathogens				
Bacterium	**Penicillin G**	**Ampicillin**	**Sulfamethoxazole**	**Tetracycline**	**Cefaclor**
Staphylococcus aureus	4.0	0.05	3.0	0.3	4.0
Enterococcus faecalis	3.6	1.6	100.0	0.3	60.0
Neisseria gonorrhoeae	0.5	0.5	5.0	0.8	2.0
Escherichia coli	100.0	12.0	3.0	1–4.0	3.0
Pseudomonas aeruginosa	>500.0	>200.0	>100.0	>100.0	4.0
Salmonella species	12.0	6.0	10.0	1.0	0.8
Clostridium perfringens	0.16	NA	NA	3.0	12.0

NA = not available

clinical laboratories, these antimicrobial testing procedures are performed in automated machines that can test dozens of drugs and microbes simultaneously.

The MIC and the Therapeutic Index

The results of antimicrobial sensitivity tests guide the physician's choice of a suitable drug. If therapy has already commenced, it is imperative to determine if the tests bear out the use of that particular drug. Once therapy has begun, it is important to observe the patient's clinical response, because the in vitro activity of the drug is not always correlated with its in vivo effect. When antimicrobial treatment fails, the failure is due to

1. the inability of the drug to diffuse into that body compartment (the brain, joints, skin);
2. a few resistant cells in the culture that did not appear in the sensitivity test; or
3. an infection caused by more than one pathogen (mixed), some of which are resistant to the drug.

If therapy does fail, a different drug, combined therapy, or a different method of administration must be considered.

Many factors influence the choice of an antimicrobial drug besides microbial sensitivity to it. The nature and spectrum of the drug, its potential adverse effects, and the condition of the patient can be critically important. When several antimicrobial drugs are available for treating an infection, final drug selection advances to a new series of considerations. In general, it is better to choose the narrowest-spectrum drug of those that are effective if the causative agent is known. This decreases the potential for superinfections and other adverse reactions.

Because drug toxicity is of concern, it is best to choose the drug with high selective toxicity for the infectious agent and low human toxicity. The **therapeutic index (TI)** is defined as the ratio of the dose of the drug that is toxic to humans as compared to its minimum effective (therapeutic) dose. The closer these two figures are (the smaller the ratio), the greater is the potential for toxic drug reactions. For example, a drug that has a therapeutic index of

$$\frac{10\,\mu g/ml : \text{toxic dose}}{9\,\mu g/ml\,(\text{MIC})} \quad \boxed{\text{TI} = 1.1}$$

is a riskier choice than one with a therapeutic index of

$$\frac{10\,\mu g/ml}{1\,\mu g/ml} \quad \boxed{\text{TI} = 10}$$

Drug companies recommend dosages that will inhibit the microbes but not adversely affect patient cells. When a series of drugs being considered for therapy have similar MICs, the drug with the highest therapeutic index usually has the widest margin of safety.

Patient Factors in Choosing an Antimicrobial Drug

The physician must also take a careful history of the patient to discover any preexisting medical conditions that will influence the activity of the drug or the response of the patient. A history of

CLINICAL CONNECTIONS

An Antimicrobial Drug Dilemma

We began this chapter with a view of the exciting strides made in antimicrobial therapy, but we must be realistic about its downside. There is now a worldwide problem in the management of antimicrobial drugs, which rank second only to nervous system drugs in overall usage. The remarkable progress in treating many infectious diseases has spawned a view of antimicrobials as a "cure-all" for infections as diverse as the common cold and acne. And, although it is true that nothing is as dramatic as curing an infectious disease with the correct antimicrobial drug, in many instances, drugs have no effect and can even be harmful. The depth of this problem can perhaps be appreciated better with a few facts:

1. Roughly 200 million prescriptions for antimicrobials are written in the United States every year. One study found that 75% of antimicrobial prescriptions are for pharyngeal, sinus, lung, and upper respiratory infections. A fairly high percentage of these are viral in origin, and antibacterial drugs will have little or no effect.
2. Drugs are often prescribed without benefit of culture or susceptibility testing, even when such testing is clearly warranted.
3. Therapy is often applied in a "shotgun" approach for minor infections, which involves administering a broad-spectrum drug that destroys our protective resident microbes instead of a more specific narrow-spectrum one. This practice can lead to superinfections and other adverse reactions.
4. More expensive newer drugs are chosen when a less costly older one would be just as effective.
5. Tons of excess antimicrobial drugs produced in this country are exported to other countries, where controls are not as strict. Nearly 200 different antibiotics are sold over the counter in Latin American and Asian countries. Self-medication without understanding the correct medical indication is largely ineffectual, and unhealthy, but, worse yet, it is partly responsible for emergence of drug-resistant bacteria that subsequently cause epidemics.

The medical community recognizes the motivation for immediate therapy to protect a sick patient and for defensive medicine to provide the very best care possible. But in the final analysis, every allied health professional should be critically aware not only of the admirable and utilitarian nature of antimicrobials but also of their limitations.

What efforts can people make in their everyday lives to help to solve these problems? *Answer available at http://www.mhhe.com/talaro9*

allergy to a certain class of drugs should preclude the administration of that drug and any drugs related to it. Underlying liver or kidney disease will ordinarily necessitate the modification of drug therapy, because these organs play such an important part in metabolizing or excreting the drug. Infants, the elderly, and pregnant women require special precautions. For example, age can diminish gastrointestinal absorption and organ function, and most antimicrobial drugs cross the placenta and could affect fetal development.

The intake of other drugs must be carefully scrutinized, because incompatibilities can result in increased toxicity or failure of

one or more of the drugs. For example, the combination of aminoglycosides and cephalosporins increases nephrotoxic effects; antacids reduce the absorption of isoniazid; and the interaction of tetracycline or rifampin with oral contraceptives can abolish the contraceptive's effect. Some drugs (penicillin with certain aminoglycosides, or amphotericin B with flucytosine) act synergistically, so that reduced doses of each can be used.

Other concerns in choosing drugs include any genetic or metabolic abnormalities in the patient, the site of infection, the route of administration, and the cost of the drug.

Even when all the information is in, the final choice of a drug is not always straightforward. Consider the case of an elderly alcoholic patient with pneumonia caused by *Klebsiella* and complicated by diminished liver and kidney function. All drugs must be given parenterally because of prior damage to the gastrointestinal lining and poor absorption. Drug tests show that the infectious agent is sensitive to fourth-generation cephalosporins, gentamicin, imipenem, and ticarcillin. The patient's history shows previous allergy to the penicillins, so these would be ruled out. Cephalosporins are associated with serious bleeding in elderly patients, so this may not be a good choice. Aminoglycosides such as gentamicin are nephrotoxic and poorly cleared by damaged kidneys. Imipenem is probably the best choice because of its broad spectrum and low toxicity.

 Check Your Progress SECTION 12.6

25. How are dilution susceptibility tests and disc diffusion tests used to determine microbial drug sensitivity?
26. Briefly describe the Kirby-Bauer test and its purpose.
27. What would you surmise if you examined a Kirby-Bauer assay and found individual colonies of the plated microbe growing within the zone of inhibition?
28. Explain the relationship between the minimum inhibitory concentration and the therapeutic index and what is optimum for each.
29. Discuss the general factors to consider in selecting an appropriate antimicrobial drug.

 Chapter Summary with Key Terms

12.1 Principles of Antimicrobial Therapy

A. **Chemotherapeutic drugs** are used to control microorganisms in the body. Depending on their source, these drugs are described as **antibiotics,** either **semisynthetic** or synthetic.

B. Based on their mode and spectrum of action, they are described as **broad spectrum** or **narrow spectrum** and microbistatic or microbicidal.

C. Strategic approaches to the use of chemotherapeutics include
 1. **Prophylaxis,** where drugs are administered to *prevent* infection in susceptible people.
 2. **Combined therapy,** where two or more drugs are given simultaneously, either to prevent the emergence of resistant species or achieve **synergism.**

 CASE STUDY Part 2

Eventually, nurse Mitchell had a routine skin test for tuberculosis, and rather surprisingly, developed a raised red patch that indicated TB positive. A new specimen taken from the wound verified *Mycobacterium tuberculosis.* Unknown to the medical staff was the fact that the AIDS patient had been suffering from both *Pneumocystis* **and** tuberculosis lung infections. This now explained his sudden death, because tuberculosis is a deadly risk factor for AIDS patients, and he had not received any therapy for TB. The blood in the needle must have contained a high level of tubercle bacilli that were inoculated into the nurse's arm when it penetrated the skin.

Diagnosis of the tuberculosis skin infection called for an entirely different drug regimen. The dicloxacillin given early on was ineffective because this relative of penicillin does not have a mode of action that works on *M. tuberculosis.* Major problems with drug treatment for tuberculosis are (1) the pathogen can already have or can develop drug resistance, and (2) it takes longer than most pathogenic bacteria to be eliminated.

This means that it was necessary to test for drug sensitivity, to choose drugs that would prevent resistance from happening, and to administer the drugs for several months. When tests indicated that the culture was sensitive to isoniazid, rifampin, and pyrazinamide, the nurse was started on this three-drug combined pill for 2 months, followed by 4 additional months on isoniazid and rifampin alone. By the end of this treatment, the infection was cured, and she was relieved of her worst fears when a final HIV test came out negative.

- Suggest some reasons that the cause of nurse Mitchell's infection was not immediately evident.
- What are the purposes of doing drug sensitivity tests for TB?

To conclude this Case Study, go to Perspectives on the Connect website.

For more information on infections from needle sticks, go to http://emedicine.medscape.com/article/784812-overview. For additional coverage of tuberculosis, go to chapter 19; for HIV and AIDS, go to chapter 25.

D. *Interactions between Drugs and Microbes*
 1. The ideal antimicrobial is **selectively toxic,** highly potent, stable, and soluble in the body's tissues and fluids.
 2. It does not disrupt the immune system or microflora of the host and is exempt from drug resistance.

12.2 Survey of Major Antimicrobial Drug Groups

A. *Drugs That Act on the Cell Envelope*
 1. **Penicillins** are beta-lactam-based drugs originally isolated from the mold *Penicillium chrysogenum.* The natural form is penicillin G, although various semisynthetic forms, such as ampicillin and methicillin, vary in their spectrum and applications.
 a. Penicillin is bactericidal, blocking completion of the cell wall, which causes eventual rupture of the cell.

384 **Chapter 12** Drugs, Microbes, Host—The Elements of Chemotherapy

b. Major problems encountered in penicillin therapy include allergic reactions and bacterial resistance to the drug through **beta-lactamase.**

2. **Cephalosporins** include both natural and semisynthetic drugs initially isolated from the mold *Cephalosporium.* Cephalosporins inhibit peptidoglycan synthesis (like penicillin) but have a much broader spectrum.

3. Bacitracin and **polymyxin** are narrow-spectrum antibiotics.
 a. Bacitracin prevents cell wall synthesis in gram-positive organisms and is used in antibacterial skin ointments.
 b. Polymyxin interferes with the cell membrane. It is added to skin ointments and can be used to treat *Pseudomonas* infections.

4. Vancomycin interferes with the early stages of cell wall synthesis and is used for life-threatening, methicillin-resistant staphylococcal infection.

5. Isoniazid (INH) blocks the synthesis of cell wall components in *Mycobacteria.* It is used in the treatment of tuberculosis.

B. *Drugs That Affect Nucleic Acid Synthesis*

1. Fluoroquinolones (ciprofloxacin) represent a new class of broad-spectrum synthetic drugs that have proven useful in a variety of infections.

2. Rifampin interferes with RNA polymerase (thereby affecting transcription) and is primarily used for tuberculosis and leprosy infections.

C. *Drugs That Inhibit Protein Synthesis*

1. **Aminoglycosides** include several narrow-spectrum drugs isolated from unique bacteria found in the genera *Streptomyces.* Examples include streptomycin, gentamicin, tobramycin, and amikacin.

2. **Tetracyclines** and chloramphenicol are very broad-spectrum drugs isolated from *Streptomyces.* Both interfere with translation but their use is limited by adverse effects.

3. Erythromycin and clindamycin both affect protein synthesis. Erythromycin is a broad-spectrum alternative for use with penicillin-resistant bacteria, while clindamycin is used primarily for intestinal infection by anaerobes.

D. *Antimetabolite Drugs*

1. **Sulfonamides** are synthetic drugs that act as **metabolic analogs, competitively inhibiting** enzymes needed for nucleic acid synthesis.

2. Trimethoprim is often used in combination with sulfa drugs.

3. Dapsone is a narrow-spectrum drug used (often in combination with rifampin) to treat leprosy.

E. *Newly Developed Antibiotics* are useful when bacteria have developed resistance to more traditional drugs.

1. Fosfomycin inhibits cell wall synthesis and is effective against gram-negative organisms.

2. Synercid inhibits translation and is most effective against gram-positive cocci.

3. Ketek is a new ketolide antibiotic with broad-spectrum effects.

4. Oxazolidinones are another new class of synthetic drug that work by inhibiting the start of protein synthesis. They are useful for treatment of staphylococci that are resistant to other drugs (MRSA and VRE).

12.3 Drugs to Treat Fungal, Parasitic, and Viral Infections

A. *Antifungal Drugs*

1. Amphotericin B and nystatin disrupt fungal membranes by detergent action.

2. **Azoles** are synthetic drugs that interfere with membrane synthesis. They include ketoconazole, fluconazole, and miconazole.

3. Flucytosine inhibits DNA synthesis. Due to fungal resistance, flucytosine must usually be used in conjunction with amphotericin.

B. *Drugs for Protozoan Infections*

1. Quinine or the related compounds chloraquine, primaquine, or mefloquine are used to treat infections by the malarial parasite *Plasmodium.*

2. Other antiprotozoan drugs include metronidazole, suramin, melarsopral, and nitrifurimox.

C. *Drugs for Helminth Infections* include mebendazole, thiabendazole, praziquantel, pyrantel, piperizine, and niclosamide.

D. *Drugs for Viral Infections* inhibit viral penetration, multiplication, or assembly. Because viral and host metabolism are so closely related, toxicity is a potential adverse reaction.

1. **Acyclovir,** valacyclovir, famciclovir, and ribavirin act as nucleoside analogs, inhibiting viral DNA replication, especially in herpesviruses.

2. Tamiflu acts to stop uncoating of the influenza A virus.

3. Two varieties of reverse transcriptase inhibitors, protease inhibitors, integrase inhibitors, and entry/fusion inhibitors are the main categories of anti-HIV drugs, usually given in combinations of two or three.

4. Interferon is a naturally occurring protein with both antiviral and anticancer properties.

12.4 Interactions Between Microbes and Drugs: The Acquisition of Drug Resistance

A. Microbes can lose their sensitivity to a drug through the acquisition of **resistance (R) factors.** Drug resistance takes the form of drug inactivation, decreased permeability to drug or increased elimination of drug from the cell, change in drug receptors, or change of metabolic patterns.

B. New approaches to antimicrobial therapy include the use of **probiotics** and **prebiotics.**

12.5 Interactions between Drugs and Hosts

Side effects of chemotherapy include organ toxicity, allergic responses, and alteration of microflora.

12.6 Considerations in Selecting an Antimicrobial Drug

A. Rapid identification of the infectious agent is important.

B. The pathogenic microbe should be tested for its susceptibility to different antimicrobial agents. This involves using standardized methods such as the *Kirby-Bauer* and **minimum inhibitory concentration (MIC)** techniques. The **therapeutic index** factors in the toxicity of a drug as compared with its MIC so as to guide proper drug selection.

C. Medical conditions of the patient such as age, allergy, disease, and pregnancy are also important guides.

D. The inappropriate use of drugs on a worldwide basis has led to numerous medical and economic problems.

Level I. Knowledge and Comprehension

These questions require a working knowledge of the concepts in the chapter and the ability to recall and understand the information you have studied.

? Multiple-Choice Questions

Select the correct answer from the answers provided. For questions with blanks, choose the combination of answers that most accurately completes the statement.

1. A compound synthesized by bacteria or fungi that destroys or inhibits the growth of other microbes is a/an
 a. synthetic drug
 b. antibiotic
 c. antimicrobial drug
 d. competitive inhibitor

2. Which statement is *not* an aim in the use of drugs in antimicrobial chemotherapy? The drug should
 a. have selective toxicity
 b. be active even in high dilutions
 c. be broken down and excreted rapidly
 d. be microbicidal

3. Microbial resistance to drugs is acquired through
 a. conjugation
 b. transformation
 c. transduction
 d. all of these

4. R factors are _____ that contain a code for _____.
 a. genes, replication
 b. plasmids, drug resistance
 c. transposons, interferon
 d. plasmids, conjugation

5. When a patient's immune system becomes reactive to a drug, this is an example of
 a. superinfection
 b. drug resistance
 c. allergy
 d. toxicity

6. An antibiotic that disrupts the normal flora can cause
 a. the teeth to turn brown
 b. aplastic anemia
 c. a superinfection
 d. hepatotoxicity

7. Most antihelminthic drugs function by
 a. weakening the worms so they can be flushed out by the intestine
 b. inhibiting worm metabolism
 c. blocking the absorption of nutrients
 d. inhibiting egg production
 e. all of these

8. Select a drug or drugs that can prevent a viral nucleic acid from being replicated.
 a. azidothymidine
 b. acyclovir
 c. amantadine
 d. both a and b

9. Which of the following effects do antiviral drugs *not* have?
 a. killing extracellular viruses
 b. stopping virus synthesis
 c. inhibiting virus maturation
 d. blocking virus receptors

10. Which of the following modes of action would be most selectively toxic?
 a. interrupting ribosomal function
 b. dissolving the cell membrane
 c. preventing cell wall synthesis
 d. inhibiting DNA replication

11. The MIC is the _____ of a drug that is required to inhibit growth of a microbe.
 a. largest concentration
 b. standard dose
 c. smallest concentration
 d. lowest dilution

12. An antimicrobial drug with a _____ therapeutic index is a better choice than one with a _____ therapeutic index.
 a. low, high
 b. high, low

13. **Matching.** Select the mode of action for each drug in the left column; all but one choice is used.

 _____ sulfonamides
 _____ zidovudine
 _____ penicillin
 _____ tetracycline
 _____ erythromycin
 _____ quinolone
 _____ amantadine
 _____ polymyxin

 a. reverse transcriptase inhibitor
 b. blocks the attachment of tRNA on the ribosome
 c. interferes with uncoating of the viral envelope
 d. interferes with synthesis of folic acid
 e. breaks down cell membrane integrity
 f. prevents the ribosome from translocating
 g. blocks synthesis of peptidoglycan
 h. inhibits DNA gyrase

Case Study Review

1. What was the purpose of giving postexposure prophylaxis to the nurse?
 a. to treat AIDS
 b. to prevent pneumocystis pneumonia
 c. to prevent HIV replication in cells
 d. to stimulate an immune response

2. What is a probable reason that tuberculosis therapy must continue for several months?
 a. to prevent drug resistance
 b. to keep the infection from spreading
 c. the TB bacillus grows very slowly
 d. the drugs are slow acting

3. Summarize the major problems with drug therapy as demonstrated in this case.

 Writing Challenge

For each question, compose a one- or two-paragraph answer that includes the factual information needed to completely address the question. Check Your Progress questions can also be used for writing-challenge exercises.

1. Using the diagram as a guide, briefly explain how the three factors in drug therapy interact.

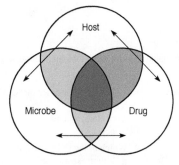

2. Observe table 12.4 with regard to type of microbe and structures or functions that are affected by drugs. Write a short paragraph that explains the different ways in which drugs can affect microbes and how this affects selectivity of drugs and their spectrum.

3. Drugs are often given to surgical patients, to dental patients with heart disease, or to healthy family members exposed to contagious infections.
 a. What word would you use to describe this use of drugs?
 b. What is the purpose of this form of treatment?
 c. Explain some potential undesired effects of this form of therapy.
 d. Define probiotics and give some ways they are used.

4. Write an essay covering some of the main concerns in antimicrobial drug therapy, including resistance, allergies, superinfections, and other adverse effects.

5. a. Explain the basis for combined therapy.
 b. Give reasons why it could be helpful to use combined therapy in treating HIV infection.

6. Explain the whys and hows of creating a semisynthetic antibiotic.

7. Summarize the primary reasons that we find ourselves in a "drug dilemma" with regard to antimicrobial drugs.

 Concept Mapping

An Introduction to Concept Mapping found at http://www.mhhe.com/talaro9 provides guidance for working with concept maps.

1. Supply your own linking lines and phrases in this concept map.

> Penicillin

> Amphotericin B Metronidazole Sulfamethoxazole–trimethoprim

> Protozoa Fungi Bacteria

2. Use 6 to 10 bolded words of your choice from the Chapter Summary to create a concept map. Finish it by providing linking words.

 Level II. Application, Analysis, Evaluation, and Synthesis

These problems go beyond just restating facts and require higher levels of understanding and an ability to interpret, problem solve, transfer knowledge to new situations, create models, and predict outcomes.

 Critical Thinking

Critical thinking is the ability to reason and solve problems using facts and concepts. These questions can be approached from a number of angles, and in most cases, they do not have a single correct answer.

1. Occasionally, one will hear the expression that a microbe has become "immune" to a drug.
 a. What is a better way to explain what is happening?
 b. Explain a simple test one could do to determine if drug resistance was developing in a culture.

2. a. Your pregnant neighbor has been prescribed a daily dose of oral tetracycline for acne. Do you think this therapy is advisable for her? Why or why not?

 b. A woman has been prescribed a broad-spectrum oral cephalosporin for a strep throat. What are some possible consequences in addition to cure of the infected throat?

 c. A man has a severe case of sinusitis that is negative for bacterial pathogens. A physician prescribes an oral antibacterial drug for treatment. What is right or wrong with this therapy?

3. You have been directed to take a sample from a growth-free portion of the zone of inhibition in the Kirby-Bauer test and inoculate it onto a plate of nonselective medium.
 a. What does it mean if growth occurs on the new plate?
 b. What if there is no growth?

4. From the results shown in figure 12.21, determine which drugs could be used to treat the yeast infection. Taking into account their adverse side effects, which drug would probably be the best choice?

5. Explain why drugs that interfere with the prokaryotic ribosome can have harmful side effects on a human patient.

6. In cases in which it is not possible to culture or drug test an infectious agent (such as middle ear infection), how would the appropriate drug be chosen?

7. Reviewing drug characteristics, choose an antimicrobial for each of the following situations (explain your choice):
 a. for an adult patient suffering from *Mycoplasma* pneumonia
 b. for a child with bacterial meningitis (drug must enter into cerebrospinal fluid)
 c. for a patient who has chlamydiosis and an allergy to azithromycin
 d. for treating a child with Rocky Mountain spotted fever
 e. for PPNG drug-resistant gonorrhea

8. a. Using table 12.10 as a reference, find and explain the differences between the results for *Staphylococcus* and *Pseudomonas*. Are any of these drugs broad spectrum?
 b. Explain the difference in the MIC of *E. coli* for penicillin versus ampicillin.
 c. Refer to figure 12.18*a*, take measurements, and interpret the results.

Visual Challenge

For the following figures a–e, research the chapter and book to find an appropriate drug to treat an infection with the microbe shown, and explain what its effects on the microbe will be.

Envelope Capsid DNA core

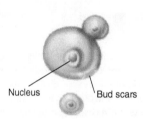

Nucleus Bud scars

(a) Figure 18.1 (b) Figure 6.8*b* (c) Figure 5.15*c*

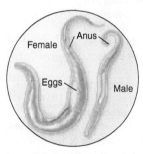

Female Anus

Eggs Male

(d) Figure 5.26*c* (e) Figure 5.28

CHAPTER **13** Microbe-Human Interactions
Infection, Disease, and Epidemiology

Salmonella sp.

Culture of *Salmonella* on XLD agar

Left: *Salmonella enterica* bacilli adhering to host cells with their flagella (pink strands); right: bacilli being engulfed by host cell membrane

 CASE STUDY Part 1 A Recipe for *Salmonella* Surprise

Starting in September 2008, reports of ***Salmonella enterica* infections** began to trickle into the **CDC's Reportable and Notifiable Diseases** division, increasing steadily to a peak in late December, and tapering back to a small number in April 2009. The final tally was 714 **cases** reported from 46 states. The victims ranged in age from 2 months to 98 years, and nine people died. What was responsible for this wave of **gastrointestinal disease?** The first suspicions would fall on the usual suspects—contaminated beef, eggs, or chicken—but by January, it was clear that all cases originated from an unsuspected **vehicle:** peanut butter products.

Infected people interviewed about their food history all told a similar story. About 12 to 48 hours after ingesting peanut butter or snacks, they developed **acute symptoms** of **enteritis,** including nausea and vomiting, followed by severe abdominal cramping and diarrhea. At least half had a **fever** of 103°F or higher. Over 100 patients had to be hospitalized and some were gravely ill. The deaths occurred primarily in the elderly and young children.

Salmonella enterica, **serotype Typhimurium** was isolated from all of the stool samples tested. In addition, laboratories in several states isolated this serotype from unopened containers of peanut butter. A serotype is an isolate with a small variation in the molecules **(antigens)** that stimulate an immune reaction, and it is one way to categorize the strains within a species. There are over 2,300 different serotypes in this species, Typhimurium being a major one. This

> "A worker in the plant reported that cockroaches falling into the dry roasted peanuts was a constant problem and rat droppings were often seen in the processing area."

serotype has additional genetic subtypes that can narrow down the origin of the **pathogen** even more.

Epidemiologists from the CDC, Food and Drug Administration (FDA), and local public health agencies teamed up to identify the origin of the **outbreak.** Some of the questions they asked were: What was the specific subtype of *Salmonella* Typhimurium, and was there a **common source** for all cases? What was the pathogen's **reservoir** and how did it get into the peanut products?

The specific subtype was analyzed by **PulseNet,** a network that uses genetic finger-printing to determine if isolated cultures from different sources are an exact match. It uses these data to track the **incidence** of new cases of **foodborne** infections and is an early warning system to indicate if new cases correspond to a **sporadic** or **epidemic** pattern. Tests determined that all of the peanut butter–associated cases in the reports originated from a single brand of peanut butter or paste sold by Peanut Corp. of America. This finding resulted in one of the largest food-related recalls on record, with over 1,000 different products containing some form of peanuts being removed from stores.

▶ *What term refers to the 12 to 48 hours between eating and symptoms?*

▶ *How would one distinguish if the outbreak were sporadic or epidemic?*

To continue the Case Study, go to page 421.

13.1 We Are Not Alone

 Expected Learning Outcomes

1. Describe some of the major interactions between humans and the microbes that share our habitats.
2. Identify and define the terms associated with infectious diseases.
3. Discuss the characteristics of the normal microbiota and the types of functions they serve.
4. Briefly relate the sources and conditions that influence the development of microbiota in the major body systems.
5. Identify which bodily sites remain free of living organisms, and explain why this is necessary.
6. Explain the germ-free condition and how it is important to microbiologists.

The human body exists in a state of dynamic equilibrium with microorganisms. The healthy individual is able to maintain a balanced coexistence with them. But on occasion, the balance is disrupted, allowing microorganisms to cause an infection or disease. In this chapter, we explore each component of the human-microbe relationship, beginning with the nature and function of normal microbial residents, moving to the stages of infection and disease, and closing with a study of epidemiology and the patterns of disease in populations. These topics will set the scene for chapters 14 and 15, which deal with host defenses, and for later chapters, which examine the agents of infectious disease.

Many of the interactions between the human body and microorganisms involve the development of biofilms (see 4.1 Making Connections). These associations result from the binding of microbial cells to our cells and often to those of other microorganisms in various ways. As we discuss topics in this chapter, keep in mind that colonization of the body involves a constant "give and take" between us and them. The most significant of these interactions can be summarized as follows:

- Microbes provide a protective and stabilization effect on body surfaces by establishing themselves as normal residents.
- Microbes are involved in maturation of host defenses and development of the immune system.
- Microbes can invade and grow in sterile tissues where they cause disease by damaging tissues and organs.

Contact, Colonization, Infection, Disease

In chapter 7, we first considered several of the basic interrelationships between humans and microorganisms. Most of the microbial inhabitants benefit from the nutrients and protective habitat the body provides. Our microbial partnerships run the gamut from mutualism to commensalism to parasitism and can have beneficial, neutral, or harmful effects.

Microbes that engage in mutual or commensal associations with humans belong to the **normal resident microbiota.** Other terms in common use are **indigenous* microflora,** normal flora,

* *indigenous* (in-dih′-juh-nus) Belonging or native to.

and commensals. Even though these resident microbes have colonized the body, they remain in the outer surfaces without penetrating into sterile tissues or fluids. When a microbe has penetrated the host defenses, invaded sterile tissues, and multiplied, the result is an **infection,** and the microbe is considered an infectious agent or **pathogen.** If the infection causes damage or disruption to tissues and organs, it is now considered an **infectious disease.** Note that a disease is defined as any deviation from health. There are hundreds of different diseases caused by such factors as infections, diet, genetics, and aging. In this chapter, however, we discuss only diseases arising from the disruption of a tissue or organ caused by microbes or their products.

Figure 13.1 provides a diagrammatic view of the potential phases in infection and disease. Because of numerous factors relating to host resistance and degree of pathogenicity, not all contacts lead to infection and not all infections lead to disease. In fact, contact without infection and infection without disease are the rule.

Before we consider further details of infection and disease, let us examine what happens when microbes colonize the body, thereby establishing a long-term, usually beneficial, relationship.

Resident Microbiota: The Human as a Habitat

The human body offers a seemingly endless variety of microenvironments and niches, with wide variations in temperature, pH, nutrients, moisture, and oxygen tension from one area to another. With such a wide range of habitats, it should not be surprising that the body supports an abundance of microbes. In fact, it is so favorable that our bodies hold 10 times more microbes than our own cells. The importance of this relationship has recently become the focus of a comprehensive initiative (**13.1 Secret World of Microbes**).

As shown in **table 13.1,** most areas of the body in contact with the outside environment harbor resident microorganisms. Mucosal surfaces provide a particularly attractive surface for attachment. Most other body sites, including internal organs, tissue, and the fluids they contain, are generally microbe-free (**table 13.2**). In fact, the presence of microbes in these areas is usually indicative of infection.

The vast majority of microbes that come in contact with the body are removed or destroyed by the host's defenses long before they are able to colonize a particular area. Those organisms that occupy the body for only short periods are known as **transients.** The remaining microbes that do become established more permanently are considered **residents.** One of their most important adaptations is to avoid the attention of the body's defenses. The resident organisms have coevolved along with their human hosts toward a complex relationship in which the effects of normal microflora are generally not harmful to the host, and vice versa.

Although generally stable, the microbiota fluctuate with general health, age, variations in diet, hygiene, hormones, and drug therapy. In many cases, the microbiota actually benefit the human host by preventing the overgrowth of harmful microorganisms. A

Quick Search
Seek out "The Human Microbiome and What We Do to It" on YouTube.

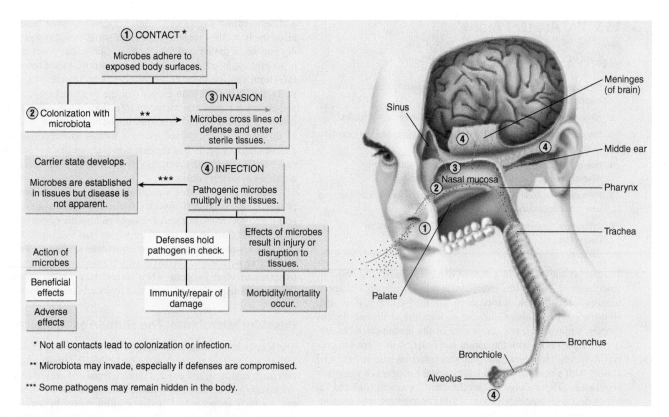

Figure 13.1 **Associations between microbes and humans.** Effects of contact with microbes can progress in a variety of directions, ranging from no effect to colonization, and from infection to disease and immunity. The example shown here follows the possible events in the case of contact with a pathogen such as *Streptococcus pneumoniae* (the pneumococcus). This bacterium can be harbored harmlessly in the upper respiratory tract, but it may also invade and infect the ear, cranium, and respiratory tract.

TABLE 13.1	Sites That Harbor Normal Resident Microbes

- Skin and its contiguous mucous membranes
- Upper respiratory tract (oral cavity, pharynx, nasal mucosa)
- Gastrointestinal tract (mouth, colon, rectum, anus)
- Outer opening of urethra
- External genitalia
- Vagina
- External ear and canal
- External eye (lids, lash follicles)

TABLE 13.2	Sterile (Microbe-Free) Anatomical Sites and Fluids

All Internal Tissues and Organs

Heart and circulatory system	Bones
Liver	Ovaries/testes
Kidneys and bladder	Glands (pancreas, salivary)
Lungs	Sinuses
Brain and spinal cord	Middle and inner ear
Muscles	Internal eye

Fluids Within an Organ or Tissue

Blood
Urine in kidneys, ureters, bladder
Cerebrospinal fluid
Saliva prior to entering the oral cavity
Semen prior to entering the urethra
Amniotic fluid surrounding the embryo and fetus

common example is the fermentation of glycogen by lactobacilli, which keep the pH in the vagina acidic enough to prevent the overgrowth of the yeast *Candida albicans* and other pathogens. A second example is seen in the large intestine, where a protein produced by *Escherichia coli* can prevent the growth of pathogenic bacteria such as *Salmonella* and *Shigella.*

The generally antagonistic effect "good" microbes have against intruder microorganisms is called **microbial antagonism.** Microbiota that exist in an established biofilm are unlikely to be displaced by incoming microbes. This antagonistic protection may simply be

a result of a limited number of attachment sites in the host site, all of which are stably occupied by normal flora. Antagonism may also result from the chemical or physiological environment created by the resident microbiota, which is hostile to other microbes.

In experiments performed with mice, scientists discovered that a species of the intestinal bacterium *Bacteroides* controlled the host's production of a defense compound that suppressed other microbes in the area. This is an extreme case of microbial antagonism, but the general phenomenon is of great importance to human health.

Generally, the normal residents will have beneficial or benign effects only if the host is in good health, with a fully functioning immune system, and if the microbiota remain in their natural microhabitat within the body. Hosts with compromised immune systems could very easily be infected by these residents (see table 13.4). We see this outcome when AIDS patients contract pneumonia by *Streptococcus pneumoniae* bacteria, often carried as normal residents in the nasopharynx. Other microbiota-associated infections can occur when residents are introduced to a site that was previously sterile, as when *E. coli* from the large intestine gets into the bladder, resulting in a urinary tract infection.

Initial Colonization of the Newborn

The uterus and its contents are normally sterile during embryonic and fetal development and remain essentially germ-free until just before birth. The event that first exposes the infant to microbes is the breaking of the fetal membranes, at which time microbes from the mother's vagina can enter the womb. Comprehensive exposure occurs during the birth process itself, when the baby unavoidably comes into intimate contact with the birth canal (**figure 13.2**). Within 8 to 12 hours after delivery, the newborn typically has been colonized by bacteria such as streptococci, staphylococci, and lactobacilli, acquired primarily from its mother. The skin, gastrointestinal tract, and portions of the respiratory and genitourinary tracts all continue to be colonized as contact continues with family members, health care personnel, the environment, and food.

The nature of the microbiota initially colonizing the large intestine depends upon whether the baby is bottle- or breast-fed. Bottle-fed infants (receiving milk or a milk-based formula) tend to acquire a mixed population of coliforms, lactobacilli, enteric streptococci, and staphylococci. In contrast, the intestinal residents of breast-fed infants consists primarily of *Bifidobacterium* species whose growth is favored by a growth factor from mother's milk. This bacterium metabolizes sugars into acids that protect the infant from infection by certain intestinal pathogens.

Milestones that contribute to further development of the microbiota are eruption of teeth, weaning, and introduction of the first solid food. Although exposure to microbes is unavoidable and even necessary for the maturation of the infant's microbial residents, contact with pathogens is dangerous. The neonate does not yet have the full protection they provide and, owing to its immature immune defenses, is extremely susceptible to infection.

Indigenous Microbiota of Specific Regions

Although we tend to speak of the microbiota as a single unit, it is a complex mixture of thousands of species, differing somewhat in quality and quantity from one individual to another. Studies have shown that most people harbor certain specially adapted bacteria,

Figure 13.2 The origins of microbiota in newborns. A newborn presents a rich and varied collection of habitats. Exposure to the environment through the birthing process, parents, health care workers, and visitors leads to colonization of the newborn by numerous microbes.

fungi, and protozoa and, occasionally, viruses and arthropods. **Table 13.3** provides an overview of the primary locations and types of normal residents.

Viruses as Normal Microbiota

The role of viruses as normal residents is complicated by their usual reputation as infectious agents. In addition, they are harbored inside cells, which makes them very different from most resident microbes. But we now know that they can be harmless and even beneficial inhabitants of the body. Discoveries from the human genome sequencing project have shown that about 8% to 10% of the genetic material consists of endogenous retroviruses (ERVs). It has been postulated that these ERVs started out as ancient infections, but through coevolution, the virus established a mutualistic existence with the human genetic material. In time, the viruses may have become an important factor in development and gene expression of their hosts.

Colonizers of the Human Skin

The skin is the largest and most accessible of all organs. Its major layers are the epidermis, an outer layer of dead cells continually being sloughed off and replaced, and the dermis, which lies atop the

13.1 Secret World of Microbes
The Human Microbiome—A Superorganism

Microbiologists have recognized for many years that the microbes residing on the human body exert profound effects on health and disease. This is to be expected, because they outnumber our cells by 10 times and occupy about 2% to 5% of our body's mass. Knowledge of this intimate coexistence inspired the concept of a superorganism—the merger of humans and their microbiota into a single, functioning, interactive unit that shares nutrients, metabolism, genetic information, and stays in constant communication. Up until recently, we have had an incomplete understanding of the scientific details of our interactions with them and many of their functions. A complete picture has been hampered by having to rely on knowledge of cultured microbes, and many species that cannot be cultured have not been explored to any extent.

This all began to change when the National Institutes of Health launched a massive program to study the superorganism from a different perspective. The project, called the **Human Microbiome Project (HMP),** uses advanced technology in metagenomics to analyze the genomes of as many of the microbial residents as possible. Researchers took samples from 300 healthy volunteers, primarily from such locations as the oral cavity, skin, nose, digestive tract, and vagina. By extracting and sequencing the DNA, it was possible to identify a number of microbes that we already knew were part of the microbiota and to tabulate many others that were entirely new and unknown. After 5 years of analysis, the researchers estimated that the human body is home to at least 10,000 different species of microbes. Even more astonishing was the isolation of 8 million distinct microbial genes, which is 360 times more than our own genome holds. This means that, genetically, we are more microbe than we are human! The collective total of genetic material from all microbiota has been termed the human **microbiome.**

Preliminary results of the study released in 2012 provide some interesting insights. Representatives of all microbial groups were isolated, including bacteria (the largest group), archaea (the smallest group), fungi, protozoa, and viruses. Most of the microbes have a mutualistic relationship and do not cause disease, although a few pathogens, such as *Staphylococcus aureus* and *Helicobacter pylori,* were among the isolates. Although many bacteria were common to all volunteers, the precise content of microbiota is apparently unique to each individual, one that begins developing at birth and varies with age and sex. Because of these studies, we now know that many unculturable bacteria will not grow on artificial media because they have lost genes required for certain metabolic processes that are now derived from their hosts.

Approximately 500 species of bacteria and yeasts were associated with the skin, with notable differences depending on the location sampled. For example, the skin of the hands and body creases had much greater microbial diversity than areas such as the ear and navel. Most bacterial isolates are members of four phyla: Actinobacteria, Firmicutes, Proteobacteria, and Bacteroidetes (discussed in chapter 4). See the accompanying figure for the sites sampled and the proportion of bacterial groups found in each site.

The intestinal microbiota is the largest and most varied, containing 500 to 1,000 different species of bacteria, fungi, archaea, and protozoa. The dominant phyla in this habitat are the Firmicutes and Bacteroidetes. Most of them occupy the colon, where they influence a number of physiological activities. The most common member is a species of *Bacteroides* that helps digest complex carbohydrates and contributes to the development of the protective mucous layer. There is evidence that these bacteria also signal intestinal cells to regulate development of the intestine in newborns. Other types of bacteria apparently communicate with cells of the immune system and assist in its development.

The HMP has reemphasized the idea that a balanced microbiota is protective, and that a disturbed microbiota increases the susceptibility to a number of diseases. A well-established example can be seen with the colitis caused by *Clostridium difficile* that arises when the normal intestinal residents have been eliminated by antibiotic therapy. Several studies are investigating the impact of an altered microbiota on other intestinal diseases such as irritable bowel syndrome, Crohn's disease, and colorectal cancer. Some findings indicate that composition of the microbiome can influence fat cell metabolism and can be a factor in obesity in certain individuals. There are also new data to show that the skin microbiota in diseases such as psoriasis, eczema, and acne differs significantly from that found in normal subjects. As hundreds of researchers continue to unravel the secrets of the microbiome, they are already on a quest for new strategies and therapies that may prevent these diseases and many others linked to our fellow passengers.

What effects on the development of our microbiome might be expected from excessive cleanliness in our habits and habitats? *Answer available at http://mhhe.com/talaro9*

subcutaneous layer of tissue **(figure 13.3a).** Depending on its location, skin also contains hair follicles and several types of glands; and the outermost surface is covered with a protective, waxy cuticle that can help microbes adhere. The normal microbiota reside only in or on the dead cell layers, and except for in follicles and glands, it does not extend into the dermis or subcutaneous levels. The nature of the population varies according to site. Oily, moist skin supports a more prolific flora than dry skin. Humidity, occupational exposure, and clothing also influence its character. Transition zones where the skin joins with the mucous membranes of the nose, mouth, and external genitalia harbor a particularly rich set of microbial colonists.

Ordinarily, there are two cutaneous populations. The **transients** cling to the skin surface but do not ordinarily grow there. They are acquired by routine contact and vary markedly from person to person and over time. The transients include any microbe a person has picked up, often species that do not ordinarily live on the body, and are greatly influenced by the hygiene of the individual.

The resident populations live and multiply in deeper layers of the epidermis and in glands and follicles **(figure 13.3b).** The composition of the resident microbiota is more stable, predictable, and less influenced by hygiene than are the transients. The

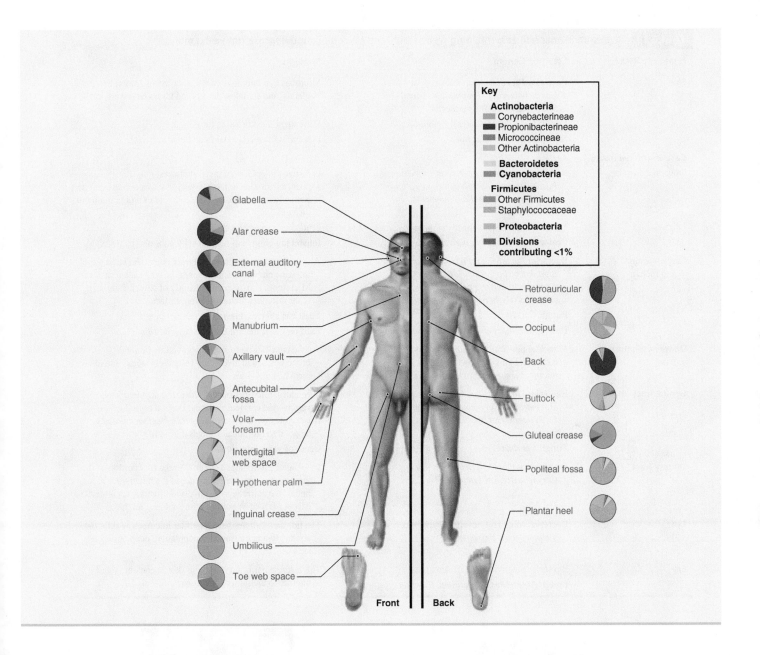

normal skin residents consist primarily of bacteria (notably *Staphylococcus, Corynebacterium,* and *Propionibacterium*) and yeasts. Moist skin folds, especially between the toes, tend to harbor fungi, whereas lipophilic mycobacteria and staphylococci are prominent in sebaceous[1] secretions of the axilla, external genitalia, and external ear canal. One species, *Mycobacterium smegmatis,* lives in the waxy secretion, or *smegma,* on the external genitalia of men and women.

Microbial Residents of the Gastrointestinal Tract

The gastrointestinal (GI) tract receives, moves, digests, and absorbs food and removes waste. It encompasses the oral cavity, esophagus, stomach, small intestine, large intestine, rectum, and anus. Stating that the GI tract harbors residents may seem to contradict our earlier statement that internal organs are generally sterile, but it is not an exception to the rule. How can this be true? In reality, the GI tract is a long, hollow tube (with numerous pockets and curves), bounded by the mucous membranes of the oral cavity on one

1. From *sebum,* a lipid material secreted by glands in the hair follicles.

TABLE 13.3	Life on Humans: Sites Containing Well-Established Microbiota and Representative Examples	
Anatomic Sites	**Common Genera**	**Remarks**
Skin	**Bacteria:** *Pseudomonas, Micrococcus, Corynebacterium, Propionibacterium, Staphylococcus, Streptococcus*	Microbes live only in upper dead layers of epidermis, glands, and follicles; dermis and layers below are sterile.
	Fungi: *Candida, Malassezia, Rhodotorula*	Dependent on skin lipids for growth
	Arthropods: *Demodex* mite	Present in sebaceous glands and hair follicles
Gastrointestinal Tract		
Oral cavity	**Bacteria:** *Streptococcus, Neisseria, Veillonella, Fusobacterium, Lactobacillus, Bacteroides, Actinomyces, Eikenella, Treponema, Haemophilus*	Colonize the epidermal layer of cheeks, gingiva, pharynx; surface of teeth; found in saliva in huge numbers Some members involved in dental caries and periodontal diseases
	Fungi: *Candida* spp.	*C. albicans* can cause thrush
	Protozoa: *Entamoeba gingivalis*	Inhabit the gingiva of persons with poor oral hygiene
Large intestine and rectum	**Bacteria:** *Bacteroides, Fusobacterium, Bifidobacterium, Clostridium,* fecal streptococci and staphylococci, *Lactobacillus,* coliforms (*Escherichia, Enterobacter*), *Proteus* spp.	Areas of lower gastrointestinal tract other than large intestine and rectum have sparse or nonexistent residents. Microbiota consist predominantly of strict anaerobes; other microbes are aerotolerant or facultative.
	Fungi: *Candida*	Yeast can survive this habitat, but not molds.
	Protozoa: *Entamoeba coli, Trichomonas hominis*	Feed on waste materials in the large intestine
Upper Respiratory Tract	Microbial population exists in the nasal passages, throat, and pharynx; owing to proximity, microbes are similar to those of oral cavity.	Trachea may harbor a sparse population; bronchi, bronchioles, and alveoli are essentially sterile due to local host defenses.
Genital Tract	**Bacteria:** *Lactobacillus, Streptococcus,* diphtheroids (*Corynebacterium* and relatives) *Escherichia, Gardnerella*	In females, microbes occupy the external genitalia and vaginal and cervical surfaces; internal reproductive structures normally remain sterile. Vaginal colonists respond to hormonal changes during life.
	Fungi: *Candida*	Cause of yeast infections
Urinary Tract	**Bacteria:** *Staphylococcus, Streptococcus, Corynebacterium, Lactobacillus*	In females, microbiota exist only in the first portion of the urethral mucosa; the remainder of the tract is sterile. In males, the entire reproductive and urinary tract is sterile except for a short portion of the anterior urethra.
Eye	**Bacteria:** coagulase-negative Staphylococci, *Streptococcus, Neisseria*	The lids and follicles harbor similar microbes as skin; the conjunctiva has a transient population; deep tissues are sterile.
Ear	**Bacteria:** Staphylococci, diphtheroids	The external ear is similar to the skin in content; areas internal to the tympanum are generally sterile.
	Fungi: *Aspergillus, Penicillium, Candida,* yeasts	

(b)

Figure 13.3 The landscape of the skin. (a) The epidermis, along with associated glands and follicles (colored), provides rich and diverse habitats. Noncolored regions (dermis and subcutaneous layers) are free of microbes. **(b)** A highly magnified view (7,500×) of skin layers reveals rod- and coccus-shaped bacteria adhering to skin cells (blue).

extreme and those of the anus on the other. Because the innermost surface of this tube is exposed to the environment, it is topographically outside the body, so to speak.

The shifting conditions of pH and oxygen tension and differences in the microscopic anatomy of the GI tract are reflected by the variations in or distribution of the microbiota (**figure 13.4**). Some microbes remain attached to the mucous epithelium or its associated structures, and others dwell in the **lumen.*** Although the abundance of nutrients invites microbial growth, the only areas that harbor appreciable permanent microbes are the oral cavity, large intestine, and rectum. The esophagus contains an extremely light load of flora, primarily bacteria swallowed with saliva. The stomach acid inhibits most microbes, although small numbers of lactobacilli and *Helicobacter* can become established there. The small intestine has a sparse population of lactobacilli and streptococci except for its terminal segment, which has flora more similar to the adjacent large intestine.

Microbiota of the Mouth

The oral cavity has unique residents that are among the most diverse and abundant of the body. Microhabitats, including the cheek epithelium, gingiva, tongue, floor of the mouth, and tooth enamel, provide numerous adaptive niches. By one estimate, there are more than 600 species residing there. The most common residents are aerobic *Streptococcus* species—*S. sanguis, S. salivarius, S. mitis*—that colonize the smooth superficial epithelial surfaces. Two species, *S. mutans* and *S. sanguis,* make a major contribution to dental caries by forming sticky dextran slime layers in the presence of simple sugars. The adherence of dextrans to the tooth surface establishes the basis for a biofilm that attracts other bacteria.

Eruption of the teeth establishes an anaerobic habitat in the gingival crevice that favors the colonization by anaerobic bacteria that can be involved in dental caries and periodontal[2] infections. The instant that saliva is secreted from ducts into the oral cavity, it becomes laden with resident and transient flora. Saliva normally has a high bacterial count (up to 5×10^9 cells per milliliter), a fact that tends to make mouthwashes rather ineffective and a human bite quite dangerous.

Microbiota of the Large Intestine

Microbes inhabiting the intestinal tract have complex and profound interactions with the host. The large intestine (cecum and colon) and the rectum harbor a huge population of microbes ($10^8 - 10^{11}$ per gram of feces). So abundant and prolific are these microbes that they constitute 30% or more of the fecal volume. Even an individual on a long-term fast passes feces consisting primarily of bacteria.

The appendix has been considered an organ without much use, but recent research is verifying its importance in replenishment of the normal microbiota (**Clinical Connections**). The state of the intestinal environment favors strictly anaerobic bacteria

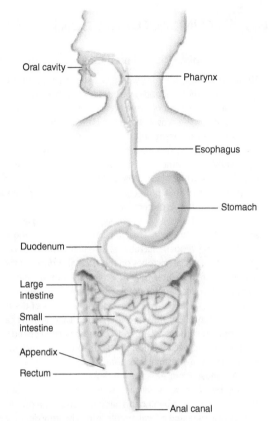

Oral cavity

Pharynx

Esophagus

Stomach

Duodenum

Large intestine

Small intestine

Appendix

Rectum

Anal canal

Figure 13.4 Distribution of microbes in the GI tract. Areas of the gastrointestinal tract that shelter major communities of resident microbes are highlighted in color. Noncolored areas do not harbor residents in significant numbers.

(*Bacteroides, Bifidobacterium, Fusobacterium,* and *Clostridium*). **Coliforms*** such as *E. coli, Enterobacter,* and *Citrobacter* are present in smaller numbers. Many species ferment waste materials in the feces, generating vitamins (B$_{12}$, K, pyridoxine, riboflavin, and thiamine) and acids (acetic, butyric, and propionic) of potential value to the host. Occasionally significant are bacterial digestive enzymes that convert disaccharides to monosaccharides or promote steroid metabolism.

Intestinal bacteria contribute to intestinal odor by producing **skatole,*** amines, and gases (CO_2, H_2, CH_4, and H_2S). Intestinal gas is known in polite circles as *flatus,* and the expulsion of it as *flatulence.* Some of the gas arises through the action of bacteria on dietary carbohydrate residues from vegetables such as cabbage, corn, and beans. The bacteria produce an average of 8.5 liters of gas daily, but only a small amount is ejected in flatus. Combustible gases occasionally form an explosive mixture in the presence of oxygen that has reportedly ignited during intestinal surgery and ruptured the colon!

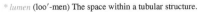

* *lumen* (loo'-men) The space within a tubular structure.
2. Situated or occurring around the tooth.

* *coliform* (koh'-lih-form) L. *colum,* a sieve. Gram-negative, facultatively anaerobic, and lactose-fermenting microbes.
* *skatole* (skat'-ohl) Gr. *skatos,* dung. One chemical that gives feces their characteristic stench.

CLINICAL CONNECTIONS

The Appendix: A Safe Haven for Microbiota?

The appendix, a 4-inch-long wormlike pouch that sprouts from the junction between the small and large intestine, has been written off for years as a lingering remnant of tissue without any real functions. Evidence offered for its uselessness is that it can be removed without real medical consequences. In recent times, the medical establishment has been reconsidering the accuracy of this claim. For one thing, immunologists have known for some time that the appendix contains a significant population of white blood cells, and they consider it a modest form of lymphatic organ that protects the intestines from pathogens in the same way that tonsils protect the respiratory tract.

Studies at Duke University have produced strong evidence that the appendix has an additional role to play—that of harboring and supporting the normal resident microbiota. Researchers uncovered an extensive biofilm of beneficial microbes on the internal surfaces of the organ that periodically reinoculates the large intestine and maintains the correct composition necessary for normal colon function. This way, the colon's own biofilms could be rapidly replaced after a case of diarrhea or other intestinal disruption. These experts reason that humans can still function normally without an appendix because we don't need it as much in light of our improved medical care and sanitation, which greatly reduce the incidence of intestinal infections.

An unusual but effective therapy for a serious form of diarrhea caused by *Clostridium difficile* involves the transplantation of fecal microbiota. The idea behind this has been around for hundreds of years, but it involves taking a fecal sample from a healthy donor and implanting it directly into the infected colon near the appendix during a colonoscopy procedure. This technique is often more successful than taking antibiotics alone for this disease. It likely restores the normal microbial residents of the colon and the appendix, which inhibits the growth of the pathogen.

What could be some unintended but harmful consequences of implanting one person's intestinal microbiota into another person's colon? *Answer available at http://www.mhhe.com/talaro9*

Late in childhood, some people lose the ability to secrete the enzyme lactase. When they ingest milk or other lactose-containing dairy products, lactose is acted upon instead by intestinal bacteria, and severe intestinal distress can result. The recommended treatment for this deficiency is avoiding these foods or eating various lactose-free substitutes.

Inhabitants of the Respiratory Tract

The first microorganisms to colonize the upper respiratory tract (nasal passages and pharynx) are predominantly oral streptococci. *Staphylococcus aureus* preferentially resides in the nasal entrance, nasal vestibule, and anterior nasopharynx, and *Neisseria* species take up residence in the mucous membranes of the nasopharynx behind the soft palate **(figure 13.5).** Lower still are

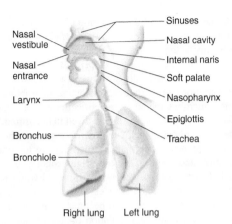

Figure 13.5 Colonized regions of the respiratory tract. The moist mucous blanket of the nasopharynx has well-entrenched resident microbes (indicated by color). Some colonization occurs in the upper trachea, but lower regions of bronchi, bronchioles, and lungs lack resident microbes.

assorted streptococci and species of *Haemophilus* that colonize the tonsils and lower pharynx. Conditions lower in the respiratory tree (bronchi and lungs) are unfavorable habitats for permanent residents.

Microbiota of the Genitourinary Tract

The regions of the genitourinary tract that harbor microflora are the vagina and outer opening of the urethra in females and the anterior urethra in males **(figure 13.6).** The internal reproductive organs are kept sterile through physical barriers such as the cervical plug and other host defenses. The kidney, ureter, bladder, and upper urethra are presumably kept sterile by urine flow and regular bladder emptying. The shortness of the urethra in women (about 3.5 cm long), frequently leads to urinary tract infections. The principal residents of the urethra are nonhemolytic streptococci, staphylococci, corynebacteria, and occasionally, coliforms.

The vagina presents a notable example of how changes in physiology can greatly influence the composition of the normal microbiota. An important factor influencing these changes in women is the hormone estrogen. Estrogen normally stimulates the vaginal mucosa to secrete glycogen, which certain bacteria (primarily *Lactobacillus* species) ferment, thus lowering the pH to about 4.5. Before puberty, a girl produces little estrogen and little glycogen and has a vaginal pH of about 7. These conditions favor the establishment of diphtheroids,[3] staphylococci, streptococci, and some coliforms. As hormone levels rise at puberty, the vagina begins to deposit glycogen, and the microbiota shift to the acid-producing lactobacilli. It is thought that the acidic pH of the vagina during this time prevents the establishment and invasion of microbes with potential to harm a developing fetus. The estrogen-glycogen effect continues, with minor disruption,

3. Any nonpathogenic species of *Corynebacterium*.

Uterine tube

Ovary

Uterus

Rectum

Urinary bladder

Vagina

Urethra

Anus

External reproductive organs

(a)

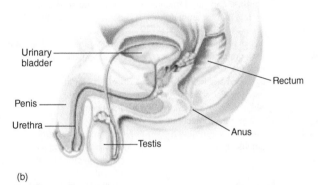

Urinary bladder

Rectum

Penis

Urethra

Anus

Testis

(b)

Figure 13.6 **Microbiota of the reproductive tract. (a)** Female and **(b)** male genitourinary residents (location indicated by color).

throughout the childbearing years until menopause, when the microbiota return to a mixed population similar to that of prepuberty. These transitions are not abrupt but occur over several months to years.

Maintenance of the Normal Microbiota

There is no question that the normal residents are essential to the health of humans and other animals. When living in balance with their host, the flora create an environment that may prevent infections and can enhance certain host defenses. In general, the microbes replace themselves naturally on a regular basis to maintain the types and numbers in their zones. However, because the exact content of the microbiota is not fixed, a number of changes can disrupt this balance. Use of broad-spectrum antibiotics, changes in diet, and underlying disease all have the potential of altering the makeup of the microbiota and tilting toward disease. A growing trend in therapy is the use of live cultures of known microbes in the form of **probiotics** (discussed in chapter 12). This essentially involves introducing pure cultures of known microbes into the body through ingestion or inoculation. The microbes chosen for this process are known to be beneficial and are considered nonpathogenic.

For a look into laboratory studies that address the effects of microbiota, see **13.1 Making Connections.**

 Check Your Progress SECTION 13.1

1. Describe the significant relationships that humans have with microbes.
2. Explain what is meant by the terms microbiota and microbiome and summarize their importance to humans.
3. Differentiate between contamination, colonization, infection, and disease, and explain some possible outcomes in each.
4. How are infectious diseases different from other diseases?
5. Outline the general body areas that are sterile and those regions that harbor normal resident microbiota.
6. Differentiate between transient and resident microbes.
7. Explain the factors that cause variations in the microbiota of the newborn intestine and the vaginal tract.

13.2 Major Factors in the Development of an Infection

Expected Learning Outcomes

7. Review the main stages in the development of an infection.
8. Distinguish between different states of pathogenicity and differentiate it from virulence.
9. Differentiate among the different portals of entry, and give examples of pathogens that invade by these means.
10. Explain what is meant by the infectious dose, using examples.
11. Describe the process of adhesion and various mechanisms by which microbes use it to gain entry.
12. Identify and discuss invasive factors and virulence factors.
13. Compare and contrast the major characteristics of exotoxins and endotoxins.

In this section, we trace the course of an infection, a sequence of events that is summarized in **figure 13.7.** Pathogens are parasitic microbes whose relationship with a host results in infection and disease. The type and severity of infection depend on both the pathogenicity of the organism and the condition of the host. Pathogenicity, you will recall, is a broad concept that describes an organism's potential to cause infection or disease and is used to divide pathogenic microbes into one of two general groups. **True pathogens** (primary pathogens) are capable of causing disease in healthy persons with normal immune defenses. They are generally associated with a specific, recognizable disease, which may vary in severity from mild (colds) to severe (malaria) to fatal (rabies). Examples of true pathogens include the influenza virus, plague bacillus, and meningococcus.

Opportunistic pathogens cause disease when the host's defenses are compromised[4] or when they become established in a part of the body that is not natural to them. Opportunists are not considered pathogenic to a normal healthy person and, unlike primary pathogens, do not generally possess well-developed virulence properties. Examples of opportunistic pathogens include *Pseudomonas* species and *Candida albicans*. Factors that greatly

4. People with weakened immunity are often termed *immunocompromised.*

13.1 MAKING CONNECTIONS

A Germ-Free Existence

For years, questions lingered about how essential the microbiota are to normal life and what functions they might serve. The need for animal models to further investigate these questions led eventually to development of laboratory strains of *germ-free,* or **axenic***, mammals and birds. After the young mammals are taken from the mother aseptically by cesarean section, they are immediately transferred to a sterile isolator or incubator. The newborns must be fed by hand through gloved ports in the isolator until they can eat on their own, and all materials entering their chamber must be sterile. Rats, mice, rabbits, guinea pigs, monkeys, and dogs are some of the mammals raised in the germ-free state.

Experiments with germ-free animals are of two basic varieties: (1) general studies on how the lack of normal microbial residents influences the nutrition, metabolism, and anatomy of the animal; and (2) **gnotobiotic*** studies, in which the germ-free subject is inoculated either with a single type of microbe to determine its individual effect or with several known microbes to determine interrelationships. Results are validated by comparing the germ-free group with a conventional, normal control group. **Table 13.A** summarizes some major conclusions arising from studies with germ-free animals.

A dramatic characteristic of germ-free animals is that they live longer and have fewer diseases than normal controls, as long as they remain in a sterile environment. From this standpoint, it is clear that the microbiota are not needed for survival and may even be the source of infectious agents. At the same time, it is also clear that axenic life is highly impractical.

Additional studies have revealed that microbiota contribute significantly to the development of the immune system. When germ-free animals are placed in contact with normal control animals, they gradually develop resident microbes similar to that of the controls. However, germ-free subjects are less tolerant of microorganisms and can die from infections by relatively harmless species. This susceptibility is due to the immature character of the immune system of germ-free animals. These animals have a reduced number of certain types of white blood cells and slower antibody response.

* axenic (aye-zeen′-ik) Gr. *a,* not and *xeno,* strange or foreign
* gnotobiotic (noh″-toh-by-aw′-tik) Gr. *gnotos,* known and *biosis,* life

Sterile enclosure for rearing and handling germ-free animals

TABLE 13.A	Effects of the Germ-Free State
Germ-Free Animals Display	**Significance**
Enlargement of the cecum; other degenerative diseases of the intestinal tract of rats, rabbits, chickens	Microbes are needed for normal intestinal development.
Vitamin deficiency in rats	Microbes are a significant nutritional source of vitamins.
Underdevelopment of immune system in most animals	Microbes are needed to stimulate development of certain host defenses.
Absence of dental caries and periodontal disease in dogs, rats, hamsters	Microbes are essential in caries formation and gum disease.
Heightened sensitivity to enteric pathogens (*Shigella, Salmonella, Vibrio cholerae*) and to fungal infections	Normal bacterial residents are antagonistic against pathogens.
Lessened susceptibility to amebic dysentery	Normal resident microbes facilitate the completion of the life cycle of the amoeba in the gut.
Less body fat	Normal microbiota help to break down indigestible carbohydrates and increase fat storage in the body.

One puzzling observation revolved around the fact that germ-free mice had as much as 42% less body fat than their normal counterparts. Later experiments revealed that indigenous bacteria acted to increase the body fat of mice in two ways. First, certain bacteria in the gut helped to digest complex carbohydrates, making extra calories available to the mice. Second, these same bacteria secreted a substance that, by acting on mouse hormones, caused the animal to store more fat than it otherwise would.

Gnotobiotic experiments have clarified the dynamics of several infectious diseases. For years, the precise involvement of microbes in dental caries had been ambiguous. Studies with germ-free rats, hamsters, and beagles confirmed that caries development is influenced by heredity, a diet high in sugars, and poor oral hygiene. Even when all these predisposing factors are present, however, germ-free animals still remain free of caries unless they have been inoculated with specific bacteria.

Why is a cesarean section necessary for developing axenic mammals?
Answer available at http://www.mhhe.com/talaro9

predispose a person to infections, both primary and opportunistic, are shown in **table 13.4.**

The relative severity of the disease caused by a particular microorganism depends on the **virulence*** of the microbe. Although

the terms *pathogenicity* and *virulence* are often used interchangeably, virulence is the accurate term for describing the degree of pathogenicity. The virulence of a microbe is determined by its ability to establish itself in the host and cause damage. There is much involved in both of these steps. To establish themselves in a host, microbes must enter the host, attach firmly to host tissues, and

* virulence (veer-yoo-lents) L. *virulentia,* virus, poison.

Figure 13.7 **A flow diagram that relates the events in entry, establishment, and exit of infectious agents.**

TABLE 13.4	Factors That Weaken Host Defenses and Increase Susceptibility to Infection*

- Old age and extreme youth (infancy, prematurity)
- Genetic defects in immunity and acquired defects in immunity
- Surgery and organ transplants
- Organic disease: cancer, liver malfunction, diabetes
- Chemotherapy/immunosuppressive drugs
- Physical and mental stress
- Other infections

*These conditions compromise defense barriers or immune responses.

survive the host defenses. To cause damage, microbes invade tissues, produce toxins, or induce a host response that is actually injurious to the host. Any characteristic or structure of the microbe that contributes to the infection or disease state is called a **virulence factor.** Virulence can be due to a single factor or to multiple factors. In some microbes, the causes of virulence are clearly established, but in others, they are not. In the following section, we examine the effects of virulence factors and their roles in the progress of an infection.

As with many concepts, the idea of a pathogen being true or opportunistic is a convenience to simplify discussion. In reality, pathogenicity actually extends along a range from low to high. To recognize this, the CDC has adopted a system of biosafety categories for pathogens based on their degree of pathogenicity and the relative danger in handling them. This system assigns microbes to one of four levels or classes. Microbes not known to cause disease in humans are assigned to class 1, and highly contagious viruses that pose an extreme risk to humans are classified as class 4. Microbes of intermediate virulence are assigned to class 2 or 3. Details of this system are presented in more detail in **table B-1 of the Appendix.**

Becoming Established: Phase One—Portals of Entry

To initiate an infection, a microbe enters the tissues of the body by a characteristic route, the **portal of entry (figure 13.8),** usually a cutaneous or membranous boundary. The source of the infectious agent can be **exogenous,** originating from a source outside the

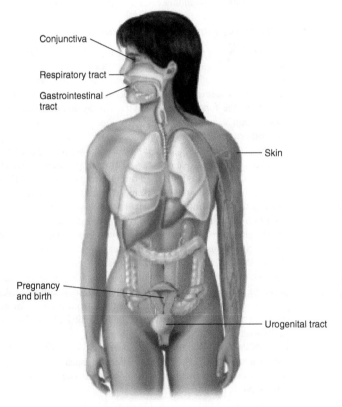

Figure 13.8 **Portals of entry.** Infectious microbes enter the body through characteristic routes. Most microbes have adapted to a specific portal.

body such as the environment or another person or animal, or **endogenous,** already existing on or in the body from microbiota or a latent infection.

For the most part, the portals of entry are the same anatomical regions that also support resident microbes: the skin, gastrointestinal tract, respiratory tract, and urogenital tract. The majority of pathogens have adapted to a specific portal of entry, one that provides a habitat for further growth and spread. This adaptation can be so restrictive that if certain pathogens enter the "wrong" portal, they will not be infectious. For instance, inoculation of the nasal

mucosa with the influenza virus invariably gives rise to the flu, but if this virus contacts only the skin, no infection will result. Likewise, contact with athlete's foot fungi in small cracks in the toe webs can induce an infection, but inhaling the fungus spores will not infect a healthy individual.

Occasionally, an infective agent can enter by more than one portal. For instance, *Mycobacterium tuberculosis* enters through both the respiratory and gastrointestinal tracts, and pathogens in the genera *Streptococcus* and *Staphylococcus* have adapted to invasion through several portals of entry such as the skin, urogenital tract, and respiratory tract. Understand that the same pathogen entering different portals of entry will likely lead to different infections or diseases. Infection of a skin follicle by *Staphylococcus aureus* will produce an abscess, but its invasion of the respiratory tract causes a serious form of pneumonia.

Infectious Agents That Enter the Skin

The skin is a very common portal of entry. The actual sites of entry are usually nicks, abrasions, and punctures (many of which are tiny and inapparent) rather than smooth, unbroken skin. *Staphylococcus aureus* (the cause of boils), *Streptococcus pyogenes* (an agent of impetigo), the fungal dermatophytes, and agents of gangrene and tetanus gain access through damaged skin. The cold sore virus (herpes simplex) enters through the mucous membranes near the lips.

Some infectious agents create their own passageways into the skin using digestive enzymes. For example, certain helminth worms burrow through the skin directly to gain access to the tissues. Other infectious agents enter through bites. The bites of insects, ticks, and other animals offer an avenue to a variety of viruses, rickettsias, and protozoa. An artificial means for breaching the skin barrier is contaminated hypodermic needles by intravenous drug abusers. Users who inject drugs are predisposed to a disturbing list of well-known diseases: hepatitis, HIV/AIDS, tetanus, tuberculosis, osteomyelitis, and malaria. A resurgence of some of these infections is directly traceable to drug use. Contaminated needles often contain bacteria from the skin or environment that induce heart disease (endocarditis), lung abscesses, and chronic infections at the injection site.

Although the conjunctiva, the outer protective covering of the eye, is a relatively good barrier to infection, bacteria such as *Chlamydia trachomatis* (trachoma), and *Neisseria gonorrhoeae* readily attach to this membrane.

The Gastrointestinal Tract as Portal

The gastrointestinal tract is the portal of entry for pathogens contained in food, drink, and other ingested substances. They are adapted to survive digestive enzymes and abrupt pH changes. Most enteric pathogens possess specialized mechanisms for entering and localizing in the mucosa of the small or large intestine. The best-known enteric agents of disease are gram-negative rods in the genera *Salmonella, Shigella, Vibrio,* and certain strains of *Escherichia coli.* Viruses that enter through the gut are poliovirus, hepatitis A virus, echovirus, and rotavirus. Important enteric protozoans are *Entamoeba histolytica* (amebiasis) and *Giardia lamblia* (giardiasis). Although the anus is not a typical portal of entry, it becomes one in people who practice anal sex.

The Respiratory Portal of Entry

The oral and nasal cavities are also the gateways to the respiratory tract, the portal of entry for the greatest number of pathogens. Because there is a continuous mucous membrane surface covering the upper respiratory tract, the sinuses, and the auditory tubes, microbes are often transferred from one site to another. The extent to which an agent is carried into the respiratory tree is based primarily on its size. In general, small cells and particles are inhaled more deeply than larger ones.

Infectious agents with this portal of entry include the bacteria of streptococcal sore throat, meningitis, diphtheria, and whooping cough and the viruses of influenza, measles, mumps, rubella, chickenpox, and the common cold. Pathogens that are inhaled into the lower regions of the respiratory tract (bronchioles and lungs) can cause pneumonia, an inflammatory condition of the lung. Bacteria (*Streptococcus pneumoniae, Klebsiella, Mycoplasma*) and fungi (*Cryptococcus* and *Pneumocystis*) are a few of the agents involved in pneumonias. Other agents causing unique recognizable lung diseases are *Mycobacterium tuberculosis* and fungal pathogens such as *Histoplasma.*

Urogenital Portals of Entry

The urogenital tract is the portal of entry for pathogens that are contracted by sexual means (intercourse or intimate direct contact). In the past, a judgmental attitude toward women and a somewhat Victorian attitude toward sex led to these diseases being referred to as venereal, from Venus, the Latin name of the goddess of love. The more contemporary description, **sexually transmitted infection (STI)** or **sexually transmitted disease (STD),** reflects the mode of transmission of these diseases more accurately. Use of the term sexually transmitted infections may be preferred in some cases because it recognizes the fact that many of the sexually related conditions are asymptomatic and do not lead to symptoms of disease, yet they are still transmissible. STIs and STDs account for an estimated 4% of infections worldwide, with approximately 19 million new cases occurring in the United States each year. The most recent available statistics (2013) for the estimated incidence of common sexually related infections and diseases are provided in **table 13.5.**

The microbes of STI/STDs enter the skin or mucosa of the penis, external genitalia, vagina, cervix, and urethra. Some can penetrate an unbroken surface; others require a cut or abrasion. Once-predominant STDs such as syphilis and gonorrhea have been surpassed by a growing list led by genital warts (HPV), chlamydia, and trichomoniasis. Evolving sexual practices have increased the incidence of STI/STDs that were once uncommon, and diseases that were not originally considered sexually-acquired are now so classified.[5] Other common sexually transmitted agents include HIV, herpes simplex virus, *Candida albicans* (a yeast), and hepatitis B virus.

Not all urogenital infections are transmitted sexually. Some of these infections are caused by displaced organisms (as when normal flora from the gastrointestinal tract cause urinary tract infections) or by opportunistic overgrowth of normal microbiota ("yeast infections").

Quick Search

For more information, search the internet for "STD Symptoms" video. Watch the "STD Symptoms" video on YouTube.

5. Amebic dysentery, scabies, salmonellosis, and *Strongyloides* worms are examples.

TABLE 13.5	Estimated Case Numbers of Most Common Sexually Transmitted Infections/Diseases in the United States*
STI/STD	Estimated Number of New Cases per Year in the United States
Human papillomavirus	14,100,000
Chlamydiosis	2,860,000
Trichomoniasis	1,090,000
Gonorrhea	820,000
Herpes simplex	776,000
Syphilis	55,400
New HIV infections	41,400
Hepatitis B	19,000

*Data from CDC, 2013, based on reported statistics and clinical data.

Pathogens That Infect During Pregnancy and Birth

The placenta is an exchange organ formed by maternal and fetal tissues that separate the blood of the developing fetus from that of the mother yet permit diffusion of dissolved nutrients and gases to the fetus. The placenta is ordinarily an effective barrier against microorganisms in the maternal circulation. However, a few microbes, such as the syphilis spirochete, can cross the placenta, enter the umbilical vein, and spread by the fetal circulation into the fetal tissues (**figure 13.9**).

Other infections, such as herpes simplex, occur perinatally when the child is contaminated by the birth canal. The common infections of fetus and neonate are grouped together in a unified cluster known by the acronym **STORCH** that medical personnel must monitor. STORCH stands for **s**yphilis, **t**oxoplasmosis, **o**ther

diseases (hepatitis B, AIDS, and chlamydia), **r**ubella, **c**ytomegalovirus, and **h**erpes simplex virus. The most serious complications of STORCH infections are spontaneous abortion, congenital abnormalities, brain damage, prematurity, and stillbirths.

The Requirement for an Infectious Dose

Another factor crucial to the course of an infection is the quantity of microbes that enters the portal of entry. For most agents, infection will proceed only if a minimum number, called the **infectious dose (ID)**, is present. This number has been determined experimentally for many microbes. In general, microorganisms with smaller infectious doses have greater virulence. **Table 13.6** presents

TABLE 13.6	Estimated Infectious Doses of Selected Pathogens*	
Agent of	Infectious Dose Estimate	Primary Route of Infection
Measles	1 virus	Respiratory
Q fever	1–10 cells	Respiratory
Tularemia	10–50 cells	Various
Smallpox	10–100 viruses	Respiratory
Brucellosis	10–100 cells	Various
Viral encephalitis	10–100 viruses	Mosquito bite
Plague	100–500 cells	Flea bite
Gonorrhea	1,000 cells	Sexual contact
Anthrax	8,000–50,000 spores	Respiratory, cutaneous
Typhoid	10,000 cells	Ingestion
Cholera	100,000,000 cells	Ingestion

*Several of these agents are considered potential bioterror pathogens.

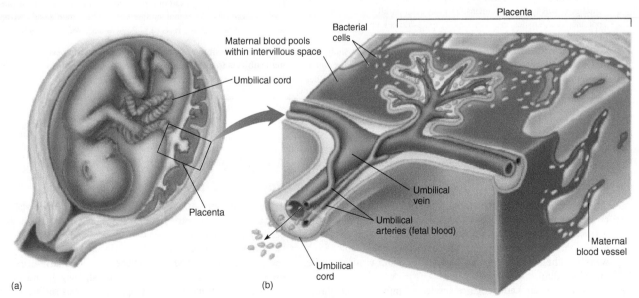

Figure 13.9 Transplacental infection of the fetus. (a) Fetus in the womb. (b) In a closer view, microbes are shown penetrating the maternal blood vessels and entering the blood pool of the placenta. They then invade the fetal circulation by way of the umbilical vein.

13.2 MAKING CONNECTIONS

Human Guinea Pigs

These days, human beings are not used as subjects for determining the effects of infectious disease, but in earlier times they were. The tradition of human experimentation dates well back into the eighteenth century, with the subject frequently the experimenter himself. In some studies, mycologists inoculated their own skin and even that of family members with scrapings from fungal lesions to demonstrate that the disease was transmissible. In the early days of parasitology, it was not uncommon for a brave researcher to swallow worm eggs in order to study the course of his infection and the life cycle of the worm.

In a sort of reverse test, a German colleague of Koch's named Max von Petenkofer believed so strongly that cholera was *not* caused by a bacterium that he and his assistant swallowed cultures of *Vibrio cholerae*. Fortunately for them, they acquired only a mild form of the disease. Many self-experimenters have not been so fortunate.

One of the most famous cases is that of Jesse Lazear, a Cuban physician who worked with Walter Reed on the etiology of yellow fever in 1900. Dr. Lazear was convinced that mosquitoes were directly involved in the spread of yellow fever; and by way of proof, he allowed himself and two volunteers to be bitten by mosquitoes infected with the blood of yellow fever patients. Although all three became ill as a result of this exposure, Dr. Lazear's sacrifice was the ultimate one: he died of yellow fever.

A remarkable, more recent use of human guinea pigs occurred from 1954 to 1973, when the U.S. government staged 153 separate tests using biological warfare agents. The scientists in charge of so-called "Operation Whitecoat" wanted to determine the infectivity of certain agents and how readily they could be acquired through airborne or other means. A group of about 2,000 courageous volunteers agreed to be exposed to some highly virulent pathogens, including the agents of Q fever, tularemia, and leishmaniasis. None of the deadliest pathogens (anthrax, plague, smallpox) was tested on humans. The test subjects all shared some important characteristics: they were young, male draftees, and they belonged to the Seventh Day Adventist religion.

What made them uniquely suited to this highly secret study was their status as conscientious objectors—opposed to service as combat soldiers on religious grounds. Many of them were assigned to other

A specially constructed chamber with vents for exposing test subjects to pathogens

military positions of a medical or clerical type. One of the expectations was that they would consent to be subjects for experiments. The tests, run by the biological warfare program at Ft. Detrick, Maryland, involved direct exposure to airborne pathogens released inside special chambers or, in some cases, breathing aerosols of pure cultures released into the air. Frequently monkeys and actual guinea pigs were exposed simultaneously as a way to track the same infectious agent in animals for comparison.

A number of important discoveries were made. The infectious doses of several pathogens were determined by these studies, as was the effect of particle size. Other tests helped determine the effectiveness of vaccines. It is quite extraordinary that none of the men experienced long-term diseases as a result of these studies, given the high risks involved. It is very unlikely that this sort of testing would be sanctioned in the present era, but there is no doubt that the sacrifices of these men greatly advanced our understanding of the risks of biological warfare.

Give some possible reasons that epidemiologists needed to use human subjects to test for the effects of pathogens. *Answer available at http://www.mhhe.com/talaro9*

examples of dose sizes for a number of pathogens, ranging from small to large infectious doses. In addition, agents that must pass through the stomach (cholera, typhoid) require a higher ID due to their being exposed to the stomach acid. If the number of microbes entering a portal is below an infectious dose, infection and disease will generally not result. But if the quantity is far in excess of the ID, the onset of disease can be extremely rapid. Even weakly pathogenic species can be rendered more virulent with a large inoculum.

Much of our knowledge of modes of infection and infectious dose has come from human and animal experimentation (**13.2 Making Connections**).

Attaching to the Host: Phase Two

How Pathogens Attach

Adhesion is a process by which microbes gain a more stable foothold at the portal of entry. Because adhesion is dependent on binding between specific molecules on both the host and pathogen, a particular pathogen is limited to only those cells (and organisms) to which it can bind. Once attached, the pathogen is poised advantageously to invade the body compartments. Bacterial, fungal, and protozoal pathogens attach most often by appendages and surface structures such as fimbriae (pili), flagella, and adhesive slimes or capsules; viruses attach by means of specialized receptors (**figure 13.10**). In

addition, parasitic worms are mechanically fastened to the portal of entry by suckers, hooks, and barbs. Adhesion methods of various microbes and the diseases they cause are shown in **table 13.7.** Firm attachment to host tissues is almost always a prerequisite for causing

disease because the body has so many mechanisms for flushing microbes and foreign materials from its tissues.

Invading the Host and Becoming Established: Phase Three

Microbes have numerous properties that improve their invasiveness, that is, their capacity to evade host defenses and enter into deeper tissues where they will grow and become established. These properties all contribute to virulence and thus are considered some type of **virulence factor.** These same factors determine the degree of tissue damage that occurs and hence the severity of the disease. The effects of a pathogen's virulence factors on tissues vary greatly. Cold viruses, for example, invade and multiply but cause relatively little damage to their host. At the other end of the spectrum, pathogens such as the tetanus bacillus or rabies virus can severely damage or even kill their host.

Most of the common virulence factors fall into one or more of three categories: antiphagocytic effects, exoenzymes, and toxins. **Figure 13.11** illustrates the workings of some of these factors.

Antiphagocytic Factors

Microbes are likely to encounter resistance from host defenses when first entering the portal of entry. The initial response comes from white blood cells called **phagocytes.** These cells can ordinarily engulf pathogens and destroy them by means of enzymes and antimicrobial chemicals (see chapter 14).

Antiphagocytic factors are a type of virulence factor used by some pathogens to avoid phagocytes or to circumvent some part of the phagocytic process (**figure 13.11c**). The most aggressive strategy involves bacteria that kill phagocytes outright. Species of both *Streptococcus* and *Staphylococcus* produce **leukocidins,** substances that are toxic to white blood cells. Some microorganisms secrete an extracellular surface layer (slime or capsule) that makes it physically difficult for the phagocyte to engulf them. *Streptococcus pneumoniae, Salmonella typhi, Neisseria meningitidis,* and *Cryptococcus neoformans* are notable examples. Some bacteria are well adapted to survival inside phagocytes after ingestion. For instance, pathogenic species of *Legionella, Mycobacterium,* and many rickettsias are readily engulfed but are capable of avoiding further destruction. This survival inside phagocytes has special significance because it provides a place for the microbes to hide, grow, and be spread throughout the body.

Figure 13.10 Mechanisms of adhesion by pathogens. (a) Fimbriae, minute bristlelike appendages. **(b)** Adherent extracellular capsules made of slime or other sticky substances. **(c)** Viral envelope spikes. See table 13.7 for specific examples.

TABLE 13.7	Adhesion Properties of Microbes	
Microbe	**Disease**	**Adhesion Mechanism**
Neisseria gonorrhoeae	Gonorrhea	Fimbriae attach to genital epithelium.
Escherichia coli	Diarrhea	Well-developed fimbriae
Shigella and *Salmonella*	Gastroenteritis	Fimbriae attach to intestinal epithelium.
Vibrio cholerae	Cholera	Glycocalyx anchors to intestinal epithelium.
Treponema	Syphilis	Tapered hook embeds in host cell.
Mycoplasma	Pneumonia	Specialized tip fuses to lung epithelium.
Pseudomonas aeruginosa	Lung infections	Fimbriae and slime layer stick to host cells.
Streptococcus mutans	Dental caries	Dextran slime layer glues cocci to tooth surface.
Influenza virus	Influenza	Viral spikes dock to respiratory receptors.
Poliovirus	Polio	Capsid attaches to receptors on target cells.
HIV	AIDS	Viral spikes adhere to white blood cell receptors.
Giardia lamblia	Giardiasis	Suction disc on underside attaches to intestinal surface.
Trypanosoma	Trypanosomiasis	Flagellum assists in penetration of host cell.

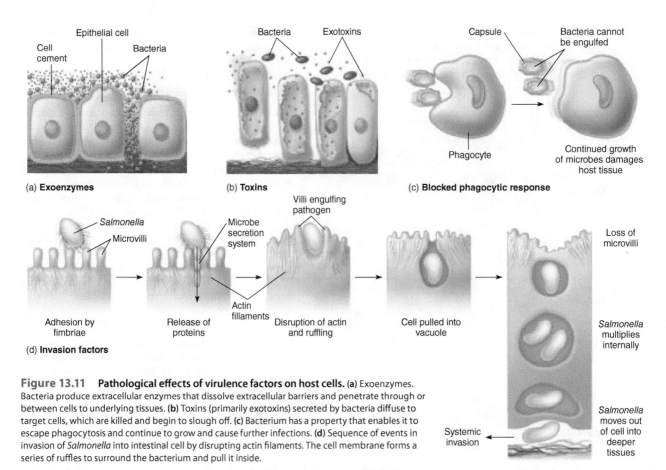

(a) **Exoenzymes**

(b) **Toxins**

(c) **Blocked phagocytic response**

(d) **Invasion factors**

Figure 13.11 **Pathological effects of virulence factors on host cells.** **(a)** Exoenzymes. Bacteria produce extracellular enzymes that dissolve extracellular barriers and penetrate through or between cells to underlying tissues. **(b)** Toxins (primarily exotoxins) secreted by bacteria diffuse to target cells, which are killed and begin to slough off. **(c)** Bacterium has a property that enables it to escape phagocytosis and continue to grow and cause further infections. **(d)** Sequence of events in invasion of *Salmonella* into intestinal cell by disrupting actin filaments. The cell membrane forms a series of ruffles to surround the bacterium and pull it inside.

Getting Inside Host Cells Certain pathogens have developed a secretion system for inserting specialized virulence proteins directly into their host cells **(figure 13.11d).** In the case of *Salmonella* and *E. coli,* the virulence proteins disrupt the actin cytoskeleton of an intestinal cell and force the cell surface to form ruffles that pull the pathogens into the cell interior. Once inside, they multiply within vacuoles and, in time, use the cell as a passageway to break out into the underlying layers of tissues. Other pathogens (*Listeria* and *Shigella*) collect actin filaments and use them as motility organelles to move about in the cells.

Extracellular Enzymes

Many pathogenic bacteria, fungi, protozoa, and worms secrete **exoenzymes** that disrupt the structure of tissues. Other enzymes dissolve the host's defense barriers and promote the spread of microbes to deeper regions of the body. A few examples include:

1. mucinase, which digests the protective coating on mucous membranes and is a factor in amoebic dysentery;
2. keratinase, which digests the principal component of skin and hair, and is secreted by fungi that cause ringworm;
3. collagenase, which digests the principal fiber of connective tissue and is an invasive factor of *Clostridium* species and some parasitic worms; and

4. hyaluronidase, which digests hyaluronic acid, the ground substance that cements animal cells together. This enzyme is an important virulence factor in staphylococci, clostridia, streptococci, and pneumococci **(figure 13.11a).**

Some enzymes react with components of the blood. Coagulase, an enzyme produced by pathogenic staphylococci, causes clotting of blood or plasma. By contrast, the bacterial kinases (streptokinase, staphylokinase) stimulate the pathway that breaks down fibrin clots and expedite the invasion of damaged tissues. In fact, one form of streptokinase (Streptase) is marketed as a therapy to help dissolve blood clots in patients with problems with thrombi and emboli.[6]

Bacterial Toxins: Poisonous Products

A **toxin** is a specific chemical product of microbes, plants, and some animals that has poisonous effects on other organisms. **Toxigenicity,** the power to produce toxins, is a genetically controlled characteristic of many bacterial species and is responsible for the adverse effects of a variety of diseases generally called **toxinoses.** Toxinoses in which the toxin is spread by the blood from the site of infection are called **toxemias** (tetanus and diphtheria, for example), whereas those caused by ingestion of toxins are **intoxications** (botulism). A

6. These conditions are intravascular blood clots that can cause circulatory obstructions.

toxin is named according to its specific target of action: neurotoxins act on the nervous system; enterotoxins act on the intestine; hemotoxins lyse red blood cells; and nephrotoxins damage the kidneys.

A more traditional scheme classifies bacterial toxins according to their origins **(figure 13.12).** A toxin molecule secreted by a living bacterial cell into the infected tissues is an **exotoxin.** A toxin that is not secreted but is released only after the cell is damaged or lysed is an **endotoxin.** Other important differences between the two groups are summarized in **table 13.8.**

Exotoxins are proteins with a strong specificity for a target cell and extremely powerful, sometimes deadly, effects. They generally affect cells by damaging the cell membrane and initiating lysis or by disrupting intracellular function **(figure 13.11b). Hemolysins*** are a class of bacterial exotoxin that disrupts the cell membrane of red blood cells (and some other cells, too). This damage causes the red blood cells to **hemolyze**—to burst and release hemoglobin pigment. Hemolysins that increase pathogenicity include the streptolysins of *Streptococcus pyogenes* and the alpha (α) and beta (β) toxins of *Staphylococcus aureus.* When colonies of bacteria growing on blood agar produce hemolysin, distinct zones appear around the colony. The pattern of hemolysis is often used to identify bacteria and determine their degree of pathogenicity.

The exotoxins of diphtheria, tetanus, and botulism, among others, attach to a particular target cell, become internalized, and interrupt an essential cell pathway. The consequences of cell disruption depend upon the target.

One type of exotoxin is specified as an **A-B toxin (figure 13.13).** A-B toxins are so named because they consist of two parts, an A (active) component and a B (binding) component. The B component binds to a specific receptor molecule on the surface of the host cell. The next step is for the A component to be moved across the host cell membrane. The A components of most A-B toxins interfere with the production of a normal cell protein. Loss of that protein's function then damages a specific target cell or tissue.

Examples include a toxin of *Clostridium tetani* that blocks the action of certain spinal neurons; the toxin of *Clostridium botulinum* that interferes with transmission of nerve-muscle stimuli; pertussis toxin that inactivates the respiratory cilia; and cholera toxin that provokes profuse salt and water loss from intestinal cells. Review the Case Study in chapter 8, which deals with some charactersistics of botulinum toxin. More pathological effects of exotoxins are covered in later chapters on specific organisms (see figures 19.9 and 21.14).

Unlike exotoxins, which contain many specific examples, there is just a single type of endotoxin. It is chemically a substance called lipopolysaccharide (LPS), which is part of the outer membrane of gram-negative cell envelopes. When gram-negative bacteria cause infections, some of them eventually lyse and release these LPS molecules into the infection site or into the circulation. Endotoxin differs from exotoxins in having a variety of systemic effects on tissues and organs. Depending upon the amounts present, endotoxin can cause

(a) Target organs are damaged; heart, muscles, blood cells, intestinal tract show dysfunctions.

(b) General physiological effects— fever, malaise, aches, shock

Figure 13.12 **The origins and effects of circulating exotoxins and endotoxin. (a)** Exotoxins, given off by live cells, have highly specific targets and physiological effects. **(b)** Endotoxin, given off when the cell wall of gram-negative bacteria disintegrates, has more generalized physiological effects.

TABLE 13.8	Differential Characteristics of Bacterial Exotoxins and Endotoxin	
Characteristic	**Exotoxins**	**Endotoxin**
Toxicity	Toxic in tiny amounts	Toxic in higher doses
Effects on the Body	Specific to a cell type (blood, liver, nerve)	Systemic: fever, inflammation, weakness, shock
Chemical Composition	Small proteins	Lipopolysaccharide of cell wall
Heat Denaturation at 60°C	Unstable	Stable
Toxoid Formation	Can be converted to toxoid*	Cannot be converted to toxoid
Immune Response	Stimulate antitoxins**	Does not stimulate antitoxins
Fever Stimulation	Usually not	Yes
Manner of Release	Secreted from live cell	Released from cell wall during lysis
Typical Sources	A few gram-positive and gram-negative	All gram-negative bacteria
Examples of Diseases	Tetanus, diphtheria, cholera, anthrax	Meningitis, endotoxic shock, salmonellosis

*A toxoid is an inactivated toxin used in vaccines.

**An antitoxin is an antibody that reacts specifically with a toxin.

* *hemolysins* (hee-mahl'-uh-sinz) Gt. *hemo,* blood, and *lysin,* to split.

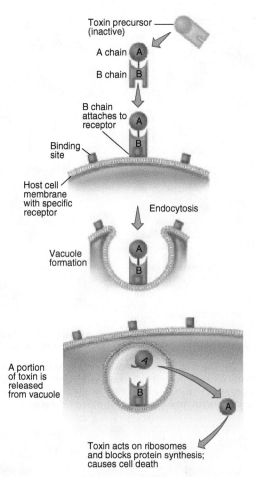

Figure 13.13 The actions of A-B toxin of *Corynebacterium diphtheriae*. The B part attaches to a specific receptor on the cell membrane, and the toxin is engulfed into a vacuole. The A and B parts separate and the A portion is released into the cytoplasm where it blocks the synthesis of a protein required for normal cell function. This toxin is highly destructive of cells, especially those of the heart and nervous system.

fever, inflammation, hemorrhage, and diarrhea. Blood infection by gram-negative bacteria such as *Salmonella, Shigella, Neisseria meningitidis,* and *Escherichia coli* is particularly dangerous in that it can lead to fatal endotoxic shock (see chapter 20).

Effects of Infection on Organs and Body Systems

In addition to the adverse effects of enzymes, toxins, and other factors, multiplication by a pathogen frequently weakens host tissues. Pathogens can obstruct tubular structures such as blood vessels, lymphatic channels, fallopian tubes, and bile ducts. Accumulated damage can lead to cell and tissue death, a condition called **necrosis.** Although viruses do not produce toxins or destructive enzymes, they destroy cells by multiplying in and lysing them. Many of the cytopathic effects of viral infection arise from the impaired metabolism and death of cells (see chapter 6).

The direct effects of virulence factors such as enzymes and toxins can cause significant harm to cells, tissues, and organs. It is important to note that many microbial diseases are actually the result of indirect damage, or the host's excessive or inappropriate response to a microorganism. This means that pathogenicity is not a trait inherent in microorganisms alone but is really a consequence of the interplay between microbe and host. The capsule of *Streptococcus pneumoniae* is a good example. Its presence prevents the bacterium from being cleared from the lungs by phagocytic cells, leading to a powerful inflammatory response by white blood cells and a continuous influx of fluids into the lung spaces—a condition we know as pneumonia.

Of course, it is easier to study and characterize the microbes that cause direct damage through toxins or enzymes. For this reason, these true pathogens were the first to be fully understood as the science of microbiology progressed. But in the last 15 to 20 years, microbiologists have come to appreciate exactly how important the relationship between microbe and host is, and this has greatly expanded our understanding of infectious diseases.

✓ *Check Your Progress* SECTION 13.2

8. Explain several ways that true pathogens differ from opportunistic pathogens.
9. Distinguish between pathogenicity and virulence.
10. Explain the concept of portal of entry and list the major portals of entry with examples of infections.
11. Differentiate between exogenous and endogenous infections.
12. What factors possibly affect the size of the infectious dose?
13. Describe several components of pathogens that are involved in microbial adhesion.
14. Define virulence factors and give examples of them in gram-positive and gram-negative bacteria, viruses, and parasites.
15. Discuss the effects of several virulence factors that act on white blood cells.
16. Define *toxigenicity* and summarize the main features of exotoxins and endotoxins.
17. Which body cells or tissues are affected by hemolysins, leukocidins, hyaluronidase, kinases, tetanus toxin, pertussis toxin, and enterotoxin?

13.3 The Outcomes of Infection and Disease

🗣 Expected Learning Outcomes

14. Describe the clinical stages of infection.
15. Use key terms to describe different patterns of infection.
16. Use correct terminology to explain the manifestations of infections and inflammation.
17. Discuss the major portals of exit and how they influence the end stages of infection and disease.

The Stages of Clinical Infections

As the body of the host responds to the invasive and toxigenic activities of a pathogen, it passes through four distinct phases of infection and disease: the incubation period, the prodromal stage, the period of invasion, and the convalescent period **(figure 13.14).**

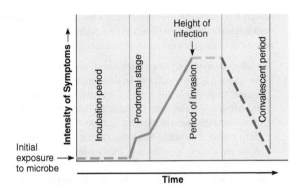

Figure 13.14 Stages in the course of infection and disease. Dashed lines represent periods with a variable length.

The **incubation period** is the time from initial contact with the infectious agent (at the portal of entry) to the appearance of the first symptoms. During the incubation period, the agent is multiplying at the portal of entry but has not yet caused enough damage to elicit symptoms. Although this period is relatively well defined and predictable for each microorganism, it does vary according to host resistance, degree of virulence, and distance between the target organ and the portal of entry (the farther apart, the longer the incubation period). Overall, an incubation period can range from several hours in pneumonic plague to several years in leprosy. The majority of infections, however, have incubation periods ranging between 2 and 30 days.

The earliest notable symptoms of infection appear as a vague feeling of discomfort, such as head and muscle aches, fatigue, upset stomach, and general malaise. This short period (1–2 days) is known as the **prodromal stage.** The infectious agent next enters a **period of invasion,** during which it multiplies at high levels, exhibits its greatest toxicity, and becomes well established in its target tissue. This period is often marked by fever and other prominent and more specific signs and symptoms, which can include cough, rashes, diarrhea, loss of muscle control, swelling, jaundice, discharge of exudates, or severe pain, depending on the particular infection. The length of this period is extremely variable.

As the patient begins to respond to the infection, the symptoms decline—sometimes dramatically, other times slowly. During the recovery that follows, called the **convalescent period,** the patient's strength and health gradually return as the immune response begins to clear the infectious agent and restore normal function to damaged tissues. In the event that the patient does not recover and dies, the infection is considered *terminal.*

The transmissibility of the microbe during these four stages must be considered on an individual basis. A few agents are released mostly during incubation (measles, for example); many are released during the invasive period (*Shigella*); and others can be transmitted during all of these periods (hepatitis B).

Patterns of Infection

Patterns of infection are many and varied. In the simplest situation, a **localized infection,** the microbe enters the body and remains confined to a specific tissue (**figure 13.15a**). Examples of localized infections are boils, fungal skin infections, and warts.

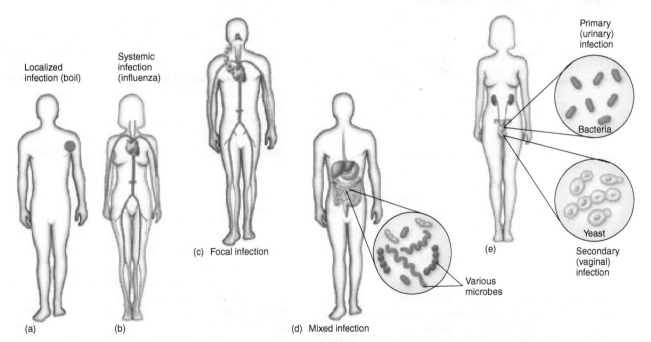

Figure 13.15 The occurrence of infections with regard to location and sequence. (a) A localized infection, in which the pathogen is restricted to one specific site. **(b)** Systemic infection, in which the pathogen spreads through circulation to many sites. **(c)** A focal infection occurs initially as a local infection, but circumstances cause the microbe to be carried to other sites systemically. **(d)** A mixed infection, in which the same site is infected with several microbes at the same time. **(e)** In a primary-secondary infection, an initial infection is complicated by a second one in the same or a different location and caused by a different microbe.

Many infectious agents do not remain localized but spread from the initial site of entry to other tissues. In fact, spreading is necessary for pathogens such as rabies and hepatitis A virus, whose target tissue is some distance from the site of entry. The rabies virus travels from a bite wound along nerve tracts to its target in the brain, and the hepatitis A virus moves from the intestine to the liver via the circulatory system. When an infection spreads to several sites and tissue fluids, usually in the bloodstream, it is called a **systemic infection (figure 13.15***b***).** Examples of systemic infections are viral diseases (measles, rubella, chickenpox, and AIDS); bacterial diseases (brucellosis, anthrax, typhoid fever, and syphilis); and fungal diseases (histoplasmosis and cryptococcosis). Infectious agents can also travel to their targets by means of nerves (as in rabies) or cerebrospinal fluid (as in meningitis).

A **focal infection** is said to exist when the infectious agent breaks loose from a local infection and is seeded or *disseminated* into other tissues **(figure 13.15***c***).** This pattern is exhibited by tuberculosis or by streptococcal pharyngitis, which gives rise to scarlet fever. In the condition called **toxemia,**[7] the infection itself remains localized at the portal of entry, but the toxins produced by the pathogens are carried by the blood to the actual target tissue. In this way, the target of the bacterial cells can be different from the target of their toxin.

An infection is not always caused by a single microbe. In a **mixed infection,** several agents establish themselves simultaneously at the infection site **(figure 13.15***d***).** In some mixed or synergistic infections, the microbes cooperate in breaking down a tissue. In other mixed infections, one microbe creates an environment that enables another microbe to invade. Gas gangrene, wound infections, dental caries, and human bite infections tend to be mixed. These are sometimes called **polymicrobial** diseases and may be the result of biofilm formation at the site of infection.

Some diseases are described according to a sequence of related infections. When an initial, or **primary, infection** is complicated by another infection caused by a different microbe, this subsequent infection is termed a **secondary infection (figure 13.15***e***).** This pattern often occurs in a child whose chickenpox (primary infection) become infected with *Staphylococcus aureus* (secondary infection). Another significant combination is seen in elderly patients who develop secondary pneumonia as a complication of influenza. The secondary infection need not be in the same site as the primary infection, and it usually indicates altered host defenses.

Infections that come on rapidly, with severe but short-lived effects, are called **acute infections.** Infections that progress and persist over a long period of time are **chronic infections.** A Guide to the Terminology of Infection and Disease illustrates other common words used to describe infectious diseases.

A Guide to the Terminology of Infection and Disease

Words in medicine have great power and economy. A single technical term can often replace a whole phrase or sentence, thereby saving time and space in patient charting. The beginning student may feel overwhelmed by what seems like a mountain of new words. However, having a grasp of a few root words and a fair amount of anatomy can help you learn many of these words and even deduce the meaning of unfamiliar ones. Some examples of medical shorthand follow.

The suffix *-itis* means an inflammation and, when affixed to the end of an anatomical term, indicates an inflammatory condition in that location. Thus, meningitis is an inflammation of the meninges surrounding the brain; encephalitis is an inflammation of the brain itself; hepatitis involves the liver; gastroenteritis, the intestine; and otitis media, the middle ear. Although not all inflammatory conditions are caused by infections, many infectious diseases inflame their target organs.

The suffix *-emia* is derived from the Greek word *haeima,* meaning blood. When added to a word, it means "associated with the blood." Thus, septicemia means sepsis (infection) of the blood; bacteremia, bacteria in the blood; viremia, viruses in the blood; and fungemia, fungi in the blood. It is also applicable to specific conditions such as toxemia, gonococcemia, and spirochetemia.

The suffix *-osis* means "a disease or morbid process." It is frequently added to the names of pathogens to indicate the disease they cause: for example, listeriosis, histoplasmosis, toxoplasmosis, shigellosis, salmonellosis, and borreliosis. A variation of this suffix is *-iasis,* as in trichomoniasis and candidiasis.

The suffix *-oma* comes from the Greek word *onkomas* (swelling) and means tumor. Although the root is often used to describe cancers (sarcoma, melanoma), it is also applied in some infectious diseases that cause masses or swellings (tuberculoma, leproma).

Signs and Symptoms: Warning Signals of Disease

When an infection causes pathologic changes leading to disease, it is often accompanied by a variety of signs and symptoms. A **sign** is any objective evidence of disease as noted by an observer; a **symptom** is the subjective evidence of disease as sensed by the patient. Signs tend to be more precise than symptoms and are often measured. Both can be the result of the same underlying cause. For example, an infection of the brain may present with the sign of bacteria in the spinal fluid and symptom of headache. Or a streptococcal infection may produce a sore throat (symptom) and inflamed pharynx (sign). Disease indicators that can be sensed and observed can qualify as either a sign or a symptom depending upon how they are reported. When a disease can be identified or described by a defined collection of signs and symptoms, it is termed a **syndrome.** Signs and symptoms with considerable importance in diagnosing infectious diseases are shown in **table 13.9.**

Signs and Symptoms of Inflammation

The earliest symptoms of disease result from the activation of the body defense process called **inflammation.*** The inflammatory response includes cells and chemicals that respond nonspecifically to disruptions in the tissue. This subject is discussed in greater detail in chapter 14, but as noted earlier, many signs and symptoms of infection are caused by the mobilization of this system. Some common symptoms of inflammation include redness, pain, soreness, and

7. Not to be confused with toxemia of pregnancy, which is a metabolic disturbance and not an infection.

* *inflammation* (in-flam-aye´-shun) L. *inflammation,* to set on fire.

| TABLE 13.9 | Common Signs and Symptoms of Infectious Diseases | |
|---|---|
| **Signs** | **Symptoms** |
| Fever | Chills |
| Septicemia | Pain, irritation |
| Microbes in tissue fluids | Nausea |
| Abnormal chest sounds | Malaise, fatigue |
| Skin eruptions | Chest tightness |
| Leukocytosis | Itching |
| Leukopenia | Headache |
| Swollen lymph nodes | Weakness |
| Abscesses | Abdominal cramps |
| Tachycardia (increased heart rate) | Anorexia (lack of appetite) |
| Antibodies in serum | Sore throat |

swelling. Signs of inflammation include **edema,** * the accumulation of fluid in an afflicted tissue; **granulomas** and **abscesses,** walled-off collections of inflammatory cells and microbes in the tissues; and **lymphadenitis,** swollen lymph nodes.

Rashes and other skin eruptions are common symptoms and signs in many diseases, and because they tend to mimic each other, it can be difficult to differentiate among diseases on this basis alone. The general term for the site of infection or disease is **lesion.** * Skin lesions can be restricted to the epidermis and its glands and follicles, or they can extend into the dermis and subcutaneous regions. The lesions of some infections undergo characteristic changes in appearance and location during the course of disease and thus fit more than one category.

Signs of Infection in the Blood

Changes in the number of circulating white blood cells, as determined by special counts, are considered to be signs of possible infection. **Leukocytosis** * is an increase in the level of white blood cells, whereas **leukopenia** * is a decrease. Other signs of infection revolve around the occurrence of a microbe or its products in the blood. The clinical term for blood infection, **septicemia,** refers to a general state in which microorganisms are multiplying in the blood and are present in large numbers. When small numbers of bacteria or viruses are found in the blood, the correct terminology is **bacteremia** or **viremia,** which means that these microbes are present in the blood but are not necessarily multiplying.

During infection, a normal host will invariably show signs of an immune response in the form of antibodies in the serum or some type of sensitivity to the microbe. This fact is the basis for several serological tests used in diagnosing infectious diseases such as HIV infection or syphilis. Such specific immune reactions indicate the body's attempt to develop specific immunities against pathogens. We concentrate on this role of the host defenses in chapters 14 and 15.

Infections That Go Unnoticed

It is rather common for an infection to produce no noticeable symptoms, even though the microbe is active in the host tissue. In these cases the person does not show overt indications of his infection. Infections of this nature are known as **asymptomatic, subclinical,** or *inapparent* because the patient experiences no symptoms usually associated with disease and does not seek medical attention. However, it is important to note that most infections are attended by some sort of detectable sign. In section 13.4, we further address the significance of subclinical infections in the transmission of infectious agents.

The Portal of Exit: Vacating the Host

Earlier, we introduced the idea that a parasite is considered *unsuccessful* if it does not have a provision for leaving its host and moving to other susceptible hosts. With few exceptions, pathogens depart by a specific avenue called the **portal of exit** (**figure 13.16**). In most cases, the pathogen is shed or released from the body through secretion, excretion, discharge, or sloughed tissue. The usually very high number of infectious agents in these materials increases both virulence and the likelihood that the pathogen will reach other hosts. In many cases, the portal of exit is the same as the portal of entry, but a few pathogens use a different route. As we see in the next section, the portal of exit concerns epidemiologists because it greatly influences the dissemination of infection in a population.

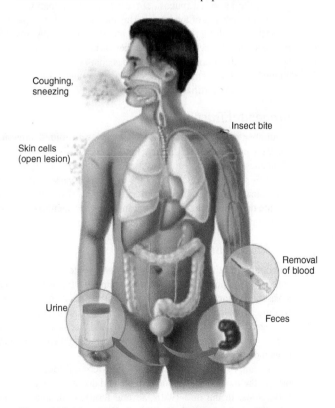

Coughing, sneezing

Insect bite

Skin cells (open lesion)

Removal of blood

Urine

Feces

Figure 13.16 Major portals of exit of infectious diseases.
Pathogens are released from the body through secretion, excretion, or discharge.

* *edema* (uh-dee′-muh) Gr. *oidema,* swelling.
* *lesion* (lee′-zhun) L. *laesio,* to hurt.
* *leukocytosis* (loo″-koh′-sy-toh′-sis) From *leukocyte,* a white blood cell, and the suffix *-osis.*
* *leukopenia* (loo″-koh′-pee′-nee-uh) From *leukocyte* and *penia,* a loss or lack of.

Respiratory and Salivary Portals

Mucus, sputum, nasal drainage, and other moist secretions are the fluids of escape for the pathogens that infect the lower or upper respiratory tract. The most effective means of releasing these secretions are coughing and sneezing (see figure 13.19), although they can also be released during talking and laughing. Tiny particles of liquid released into the air form aerosols or droplets that can spread the infectious agent to other people. The agents of tuberculosis, influenza, measles, and chickenpox most often leave the host through airborne droplets. Droplets of saliva are the exit route for several viruses, including those of mumps, rabies, and infectious mononucleosis.

Epithelial Cells

The outer layer of the skin and scalp are constantly being shed into the environment. A large proportion of household dust is actually composed of skin cells. A single person can shed several billion skin cells a day, and some persons, called shedders, disseminate massive numbers of bacteria into their immediate surroundings. Skin lesions and their exudates can serve as portals of exit in warts, fungal infections, boils, herpes simplex, smallpox, and syphilis.

Fecal Exit

Feces are a very common portal of exit. Some intestinal pathogens grow in the intestinal mucosa and create an inflammation that increases the motility of the bowel. This increased motility speeds up peristalsis, resulting in diarrhea; and the more fluid stool provides a rapid exit for the pathogen. A number of helminth worms release cysts and eggs through the feces. Feces containing pathogens are a public health problem when allowed to contaminate drinking water or when used to fertilize crops.

Urogenital Tract

A number of agents involved in sexually transmitted infections leave the host in vaginal discharge or semen. This is also the source of neonatal infections such as herpes simplex, *Chlamydia,* and *Candida albicans,* which infect the infant as it passes through the birth canal. Less commonly, certain pathogens that infect the kidney are discharged in the urine: for instance, the agents of leptospirosis, typhoid fever, tuberculosis, and schistosomiasis.

Removal of Blood or Bleeding

Although the blood does not have a direct route to the outside, it can serve as a portal of exit when it is removed or released through a vascular puncture made by natural or artificial means. Blood-feeding animals such as ticks and fleas are common transmitters of pathogens. Human immunodeficiency and hepatitis viruses are transmitted by shared needles or through small abrasions in a mucous membrane during sexual intercourse.

Because many microbes can be transferred through blood donation, the monitoring of both donors and donated blood has to be scrupulous. In the mid-1980s, several thousand people suffering from hemophilia were infected with HIV as a result of receiving clotting factors contaminated with the virus. The current risk for transfusion-transmitted infections is about one case in 10 million

transfusions. One factor that increases risk is the presence of emerging disease agents in the blood supply that have not yet been detected. This has already happened with West Nile virus and Chagas disease.

The Persistence of Microbes and Pathologic Conditions

The apparent recovery of the host does not always mean that the microbe has been completely removed or destroyed by the host defenses. After the initial symptoms in certain chronic infectious diseases, the infectious agent retreats into a state called **persistence** or **latency.** In some cases of latency, the microbe can periodically become active and produce a recurrent disease. The viral agents of herpes simplex, herpes zoster, hepatitis B, AIDS, and Epstein-Barr can persist in the host for long periods. The agents of syphilis, typhoid fever, tuberculosis, and malaria also enter into latent stages. The person harboring a persistent infectious agent may or may not shed it during the latent stage. If it is shed, such persons are chronic carriers who serve as sources of infection for the rest of the population.

Some diseases leave **sequelae*** in the form of long-term or permanent damage to tissues or organs. For example, meningitis can result in deafness, a strep throat can lead to rheumatic heart disease, Lyme disease can cause arthritis, and polio can produce paralysis.

 Check Your Progress SECTION 13.3

18. Explain what is happening during each stage of infection. Compare and contrast: systemic versus local infections; primary versus secondary infections; infection versus intoxication.

19. Discuss the distinguishing features of signs and symptoms, using examples.

20. Name some examples of infections and their portals of exit.

21. Using terminology from the guide, give definitions for *urethritis, endotoxemia, chlamydiosis,* and *lymphoma.*

13.4 Epidemiology: The Study of Disease in Populations

 Expected Learning Outcomes

18. Define *epidemiology,* and summarize the major goals of its studies.

19. Relate the significant factors involved in the transmission of infectious diseases.

20. Explain the concept of carriers and describe several types.

21. Use examples to distinguish between the types of vectors, and discuss the importance of zoonoses.

22. Differentiate between communicable and noncommunicable infectious diseases.

23. Characterize the patterns of transmission for communicable diseases.

* *sequelae* (su-kwee'-lee) L. *sequi,* to follow.

So far, our discussion has revolved primarily around the impact of an infectious disease in individuals. Let us now turn our attention to the effects of diseases on the community—the realm of **epidemiology.*** By definition, this term involves the study of the frequency and distribution of disease and other health-related factors in defined human populations. It involves many disciplines—not only microbiology but also anatomy, physiology, immunology, medicine, psychology, sociology, ecology, and statistics—and it considers many diseases other than infectious ones, including heart disease, cancer, drug addiction, and mental illness.

The epidemiologist is a medical sleuth who collects clues on the causative agent, pathology, and sources and modes of transmission and tracks the numbers and distribution of cases of disease in the community. In fulfilling these demands, the epidemiologist asks who, when, where, how, why, and what about diseases. The outcome of these studies helps public health departments develop prevention and treatment programs and establish a basis for predictions.

Origins and Transmission Patterns of Infectious Microbes

Reservoirs: Where Pathogens Persist

One of the important concerns of epidemiology is discovering where the pathogens originate and how they are transmitted. As we saw in the Case Study, these aspects are intensely scrutinized from the very first signs of an outbreak.

For an infectious agent to continue to exist and be spread, it must have a permanent place to reside. The **reservoir** is the primary habitat in the natural world from which a pathogen originates. Often it is a human or animal carrier, although soil, water, and plants are also reservoirs. The reservoir can be distinguished from the infection **source,** which is the individual or object from which an infection is actually acquired. In diseases such as syphilis, the reservoir and the source are the same (the human body). In the case of hepatitis A, the reservoir (a human carrier) is usually different from the source of infection (contaminated food).

Living Reservoirs

Many pathogens continue to exist and spread because they are harbored by members of a host population. Persons or animals with frank symptomatic infection are obvious sources of infection, but a **carrier** is, by definition, an individual who *inconspicuously* shelters a pathogen and spreads it to others without any notice. Although human carriers are occasionally detected through routine screening (blood tests, cultures) and other epidemiological devices, they are unfortunately very difficult to discover and control. As long as a pathogenic reservoir is maintained by the carrier state, the disease will continue to exist in that population, and the potential for epidemics will be a constant threat. The duration of the carrier state can be short or long term, and the carrier may or may not have experienced disease due to the microbe.

Several situations can produce the carrier state. **Asymptomatic** (apparently healthy) **carriers** are infected, but as previously

indicated, they show no symptoms **(figure 13.17a).** A few asymptomatic infections (gonorrhea and genital warts, for instance) can carry out their entire course without overt manifestations. **Figure 13.17b** demonstrates three types of carriers who show no indications of infection at the time they transmit the pathogen. *Incubation carriers* spread the infectious agent during the incubation period. For example, patients with HIV infection can harbor and spread the virus for months and years before their first symptoms appear. Recuperating patients without symptoms are considered *convalescent carriers* when they continue to shed viable microbes and convey the infection to others. Diphtheria patients, for example, spread the microbe for up to 30 days after the disease has subsided.

An individual who shelters the infectious agent for a long period after recovery is a *chronic carrier.* Patients who have recovered from tuberculosis, hepatitis, and herpes infections frequently carry the agent chronically. About one in 20 victims of typhoid fever continues to harbor *Salmonella typhi* in the gallbladder for several years and sometimes for life. The most infamous of these was "Typhoid Mary," a cook who spread the infection to hundreds of victims in the early 1900s.

The **passive carrier** state is of great concern during patient care (see a later section on nosocomial infections). Medical and dental personnel who must constantly handle materials that are heavily contaminated with patient secretions and blood risk picking up pathogens mechanically and accidently transferring them to other patients **(figure 13.17c).** Proper hand washing, handling of contaminated materials, and aseptic techniques greatly reduce this likelihood.

Animals as Reservoirs and Sources Up to now, we have lumped animals with humans in discussing living reservoirs or carriers, but animals deserve special consideration as vectors of infections. The word **vector** is used by epidemiologists to indicate a live animal that transmits an infectious agent from one host to another. (The term is sometimes misused to include any object that spreads disease.) The majority of vectors are arthropods such as fleas, mosquitoes, flies, and ticks, although larger animals can also spread infection; for example, mammals (rabies), birds (ornithosis), or lower vertebrates (salmonellosis).

By tradition, vectors are placed into one of two categories, depending upon the animal's relationship with the microbe. A **biological vector** actively participates in a pathogen's life cycle, serving as a site in which it can multiply or complete its life cycle. A biological vector communicates the infectious agent to the human host by biting, aerosol formation, or touch. In the case of biting vectors, the animal can inject infected saliva into the blood (mosquito), defecate around the bite wound (flea), or regurgitate blood into the wound (tsetse fly).

Mosquito

Mechanical vectors are not necessary to the life cycle of an infectious agent and merely transport it without being infected. The external body parts of these animals become contaminated when they come into physical contact with a source of pathogens. The agent is subsequently transferred to humans indirectly by an intermediate such as food or,

Housefly

412 **Chapter 13** Microbe-Human Interactions

Figure 13.17 Involvement of carriers in transmission of infectious agents. (a) An asymptomatic carrier is infected without symptoms. **(b)** Incubation, convalescent, and chronic carriers can transmit the infection either before or after the period of symptoms. **(c)** A passive carrier is contaminated but not infected and spreads the pathogen through physical contact.

occasionally, by direct contact (as in certain eye infections). Houseflies are notorious mechanical vectors. They feed on decaying garbage and feces, and while they are feeding, their feet and mouthparts easily become contaminated. They also regurgitate juices onto food to soften and digest it. Flies spread more than 20 bacterial, viral, protozoan, and worm infections. Other nonbiting flies transmit tropical ulcers, yaws, and trachoma. Cockroaches, which have similar unsavory habits, play a role in the mechanical transmission of fecal pathogens, as well as contributing to allergy attacks in asthmatic children.

Many vectors and animal reservoirs spread their own infections to humans. An infection indigenous to animals but naturally transmissible to humans is a **zoonosis.*** In these types of infections, the human is essentially a dead-end host and does not contribute to the natural persistence of the microbe. Some zoonotic infections (rabies, for instance) can have multihost involvement, and others can have very complex cycles in the wild (plague). Zoonotic spread

of disease is promoted by close associations of humans with animals, and people in animal-oriented or outdoor professions are at greatest risk. At least 150 zoonoses exist worldwide; the most common ones are listed in **table 13.10.** Zoonoses make up a full 70% of all new emerging diseases worldwide. It is worth noting that zoonotic infections are impossible to completely eradicate without also eradicating the animal reservoirs. Attempts have been made to eradicate mosquitoes and certain rodents. During the H1N1 flu epidemic of 2009, thousands of pigs were slaughtered in the wrongful attempt to control its spread.

One technique that can provide an early warning signal for the occurrence of certain mosquito-borne zoonoses has been the use of *sentinel animals.* These are usually domestic animals (most often chickens or horses) that can serve as hosts for diseases such as West Nile fever, various viral encephalitides, and malaria. Sentinel animals are placed at various sites throughout the community, and their blood is monitored periodically for antibodies to the infectious agents that would indicate a recent infection by means of a mosquito bite. The presence of infected animals provides useful data on

* *zoonosis* (zoh″-uh-noh′-sis) Gr. *zoion,* animal, and *nosos,* disease.

TABLE 13.10	Common Zoonotic Infections	
Disease/Agent	**Primary Animal Reservoirs**	**Mode of Infection**
Viruses		
Rabies	All mammals	Bite; aerosol
Yellow fever	Wild birds, mammals, mosquitoes	Mosquito bite
Viral fevers	Wild mammals	Various mosquitoes
Hantavirus	Rodents	Airborne wastes
Influenza	Chickens, swine	Airborne secretions
West Nile virus	Wild birds, mosquitoes	Mosquito bite
Bacteria		
Rocky Mountain spotted fever	Dogs, ticks	Tick bite
Psittacosis	Birds	Airborne secretions
Leptospirosis	Domestic animals	Animal wastes (urine)
Anthrax	Domestic animals	Airborne spores, cutaneous contact
Brucellosis	Cattle, sheep, pigs	Air- and food-borne
Plague	Rodents, fleas	Flea bite; aerosol
Salmonellosis	Variety of mammals, birds, and rodents	Food-borne
Tularemia	Rodents, birds, arthropods	Tick bite, airborne
Miscellaneous		
Ringworm	Domestic mammals	Cutaneous contact
Toxoplasmosis	Cats, rodents, birds	Food-borne, contact
Trypanosomiasis	Domestic and wild mammals	Tsetse fly; reduviid bug
Trichinosis	Swine, bears	Ingestion of cysts
Tapeworm	Cattle, swine, fish	Ingestion of eggs
Scabies	Domestic animals	Cutaneous contact

the potential for human exposure, and it also helps establish the epidemiological pattern of the zoonosis, including where it may have spread.

Nonliving Reservoirs

Clearly, microorganisms have adapted to nearly every habitat in the biosphere. They thrive in soil and water and often find their way into the air. Although most of these microbes are saprobic and cause little harm and considerable benefit to humans, some are opportunists and a few are regular pathogens. Because human hosts are in regular contact with these environmental sources, acquisition of pathogens from natural habitats is of diagnostic and epidemiological importance.

Soil harbors the vegetative forms of bacteria, protozoa, helminths, and fungi, as well as their resistant or developmental stages such as spores, cysts, ova, and larvae. Bacterial pathogens include the anthrax bacillus and species of *Clostridium* that are responsible for gas gangrene, botulism, and tetanus. Pathogenic fungi in the genera *Coccidioides* and *Blastomyces* are spread by spores in the

soil and dust. The invasive stages of the hookworm *Necator* occur in the soil. Natural bodies of water carry fewer nutrients than soil does but still support pathogenic species such as *Legionella, Cryptosporidium,* and *Giardia.*

The Acquisition and Transmission of Infectious Agents

Infectious diseases can be categorized on the basis of how they are acquired. A disease is **communicable** when an infected host can transmit the infectious agent to another host and establish infection in that host. Although this terminology is standard, one must realize that it is not the disease that is communicated but the microbe. Also be aware that the word *infectious* is sometimes used interchangeably with the word *communicable,* but this is not precise usage. The transmission of the agent can be direct or indirect, and the ease with which the disease is transmitted varies considerably from one agent to another. If the agent is highly communicable, especially through direct contact, the disease is **contagious.** Influenza and measles move readily from host to host and thus are contagious, whereas leprosy is only weakly communicable. Because they can be spread through the population, communicable diseases are our main focus in the following sections.

In contrast, a **noncommunicable** infectious disease does *not* arise through transmission of the infectious agent from host to host. The infection and disease are acquired through some other, special circumstance. Noncommunicable infections occur primarily when a compromised person is invaded by his or her own microflora (as with certain pneumonias, for example) or when an individual has accidental contact with a facultative parasite that exists in a nonliving reservoir such as soil. Some examples are certain mycoses, acquired through inhalation of fungal spores, and tetanus, in which *Clostridium tetani* spores from a soiled object enter a cut or wound. Persons thus infected do not become a source of infection.

Patterns of Transmission in Communicable Diseases

The routes or patterns of disease transmission are many and varied. The spread of diseases is by direct or indirect contact with animate or inanimate objects and can be horizontal or vertical. The term *horizontal* means the disease is spread through a population from one infected individual to another; *vertical* signifies transmission from parent to offspring via the ovum, sperm, placenta, or milk. The extreme complexity of transmission patterns among microorganisms makes it very difficult to generalize. However, for easier organization, we divide microorganisms into two major groups, as shown in **figure 13.18:** transmission by direct routes or transmission by indirect routes, in which some sort of vehicle is involved.

Modes of Direct Transmission For microbes to be directly transferred, some type of contact must occur between the skin or mucous membranes of the infected person and those of the infectee. It may help to think of this route as the portal of exit meeting the portal of entry without the involvement of an intermediate object or substance. Included in this category are fine droplets sprayed directly upon a person during sneezing or coughing (as distinguished from droplet nuclei that are transmitted some distance by air). Most

General Bacteriology - Vol. 1

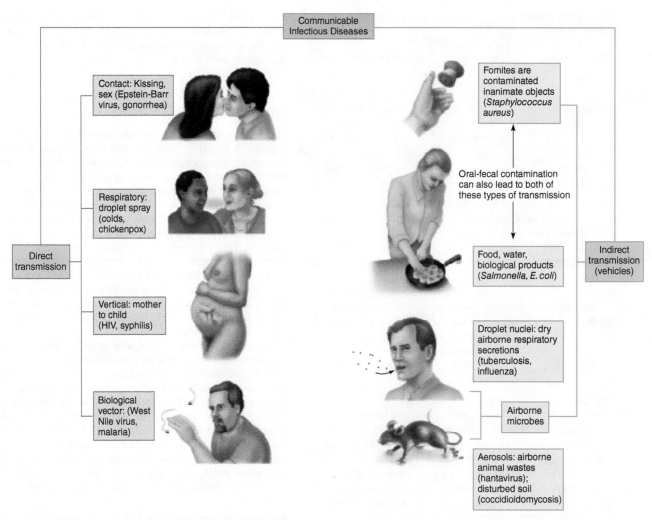

Figure 13.18 Summary of how communicable infectious diseases are acquired.

sexually transmitted diseases are spread directly. In addition, infections that result from kissing or bites by biological vectors are direct. Most obligate parasites are far too sensitive to survive for long outside the host and can be transmitted only through direct contact. Diseases transmitted vertically from mother to baby fit in this contact category also.

Routes of Indirect Transmission For microbes to be indirectly transmitted, the infectious agent must pass from an infected host to an intermediate conveyor and from there to another host. This form of communication is especially pronounced when the infected individuals contaminate inanimate objects, food, or air through their activities. The transmitter of the infectious agent can be either openly infected or a carrier.

Indirect Spread by Vehicles: Contaminated Materials The term **vehicle** specifies any inanimate material commonly used by humans that can transmit infectious agents. A **common vehicle** or source is a single material that serves as the source of infection for many individuals. Some specific types of vehicles are food, water, various biological products (such as blood, serum, and tissue), and fomites.

A **fomite** is an inanimate object that harbors and transmits pathogens. The list of possible fomites is as long as your imagination allows. Probably highest on the list would be objects commonly in contact with the public such as doorknobs, telephones, push buttons, and faucet handles that are readily contaminated by touching. Shared bed linens, handkerchiefs, toilet seats, toys, eating utensils, clothing, personal articles, and syringes are other examples. Although paper money is impregnated with a disinfectant to inhibit microbes, pathogens are still isolated from bills as well as coins.

Outbreaks of food poisoning often result from the role of food as a common

Quick Search
Learn about the effects of climate at "Infectious Diseases— Changing Planet" on YouTube.

vehicle. The source of the agent can be soil, the handler, or a mechanical vector. Because milk provides a rich growth medium for microbes, it is a significant means of transmitting pathogens from diseased animals, infected milk handlers, and environmental sources of contamination. The agents of brucellosis, tuberculosis, Q fever, salmonellosis, and listeriosis are transmitted by contaminated milk. Water that has been contaminated by feces or urine can carry *Salmonella, Vibrio* (cholera), viruses (hepatitis A, polio), and pathogenic protozoans (*Giardia, Cryptosporidium*).

In the type of transmission termed the **oral-fecal route,** a fecal carrier contaminates food during handling, and an unsuspecting person ingests it. Hepatitis A, amebic dysentery, shigellosis, and typhoid fever are often transmitted this way. Oral-fecal transmission can also involve contaminated materials such as toys and diapers. It is really a special category of indirect transmission, which specifies that the vehicle became contaminated through contact with fecal material and that it found its way to someone's mouth.

Indirect Spread by Vehicles: Air as a Vehicle Unlike soil and water, outdoor air cannot provide nutritional support for microbial growth and is less likely to transmit airborne pathogens. On the other hand, indoor air (especially in a closed space) can serve as an important medium for the suspension and dispersal of certain respiratory pathogens via droplet nuclei and aerosols.

Droplet nuclei are dried microscopic residues created when microscopic pellets of mucus and saliva are ejected from the mouth and nose. They are generated forcefully in an unstifled sneeze or cough (**figure 13.19**) or mildly during other vocalizations. Although the larger beads of moisture settle rapidly, smaller particles evaporate and remain suspended for longer periods. Droplet nuclei are implicated in the spread of hardier pathogens such as the tubercle bacillus and the influenza virus.

Figure 13.19 The explosiveness of a sneeze. Special photography dramatically captures droplet formation in an unstifled sneeze. Even the merest attempt to cover a sneeze with one's hand will reduce this effect considerably. When such droplets dry and remain suspended in air, they are droplet nuclei.

Aerosols are suspensions of fine dust or moisture particles in the air that contain live pathogens. Q fever is spread by dust from animal quarters, and psittacosis by aerosols from infected birds. Outbreaks of coccidioidomycosis (a lung infection) often occur in areas where soil is disturbed by wind or digging, releasing clouds of dust bearing the spores of *Coccidioides.*

 Check Your Progress SECTION 13.4

22. Explain the differences between communicable and noncommunicable infectious diseases, and between contact and indirect modes of transmission.
23. Distinguish between reservoirs and sources, using examples.
24. What are the primary differences between mechanical and biological vectors.
25. Define zoonosis and describe the difficulties in controlling zoonotic infections.
26. Explain what it means to be a carrier of infectious disease, and describe four ways that humans can be carriers.
27. What is epidemiologically and medically important about carriers in the population?

13.5 The Work of Epidemiologists: Investigation and Surveillance

 Expected Learning Outcomes

24. Explain the primary methods of tracking infections and diseases in a population.
25. Differentiate among the patterns of disease outbreaks according to frequency, number, and location.
26. Summarize the steps in Koch's postulates, and explain their importance to microbiologists.
27. Discuss nosocomial infections and the ways they impact the clinical environment.
28. Explain what is meant by universal precautions, and discuss how they are implemented.

Epidemiologists are concerned with all of the factors covered earlier in this chapter: virulence, portals of entry and exit, and the course of disease. But they are also interested in **surveillance;** that is, collecting, analyzing, and reporting data on the rates of occurrence, mortality, morbidity, and transmission of infections. Surveillance involves keeping data for a large number of diseases observed in the medical setting and reported to public health authorities. By law, certain **reportable,** or **notifiable, diseases** must be reported to authorities; others are reported on a voluntary basis.

A well-developed network of individuals and agencies at the local, district, state, national, and international levels keeps track of infectious diseases. Physicians and hospitals must report all notifiable diseases that are brought to their attention. Case reporting can focus on a single individual or collectively on group data.

Local public health agencies first receive the case data and determine how they will be handled. In most cases, health officers

investigate the history and movements of patients to trace their prior contacts and to control the further spread of the infection as soon as possible through drug therapy, immunization, and education. In sexually transmitted diseases, patients are asked to name their partners so that these persons can be notified, examined, and treated. It is very important to maintain the confidentiality of the persons in these reports. The principal government agency responsible for keeping track of infectious diseases nationwide is the Centers for Disease Control and Prevention (CDC) in Atlanta, Georgia, which is a part of the United States Public Health Service. The CDC publishes a weekly notice of diseases (the *Morbidity and Mortality Weekly Report*) that provides weekly and cumulative summaries of the case rates and deaths for about 50 notifiable and 65 reportable diseases, highlights important and unusual diseases, and presents data concerning disease occurrence in the major regions of the United States. This notice is available to anyone at http://www.cdc.gov/mmwr/. Ultimately, the CDC shares its statistics on disease with the World Health Organization (WHO) for worldwide tabulation and control.

Epidemiological Statistics: Frequency of Cases

The **prevalence** of a disease is the accumulated total of existing cases with respect to the entire population. It is usually reported as the percentage of the population having a particular disease and provides an indicator of how commonly a disease occurs in a population. Disease **incidence** measures the number of new cases over a certain time period, as compared with the general healthy population. This statistic, also called the case, or morbidity, rate, indicates both the rate and the risk of infection at the time of reporting. The equations used to figure these rates follow:

$$\text{Prevalence} = \frac{\text{Total number of cases in population}}{\text{Total number of persons in population}} \times 100 = \%$$

$$\text{Incidence} = \frac{\text{Number of new cases}}{\text{Total number of susceptible persons}} \quad \text{(Usually reported per 100,000 persons)}$$

As an example, let us use a classroom of 50 students exposed to a new strain of influenza. Before exposure, the prevalence and incidence in this population are both zero (0/50). If in one week, 5 out of the 50 people contract the disease, the prevalence is 5/50 = 10%, and the incidence is 1 in 10 (10 is used instead of 100,000 due to smaller population). If within a month 25 more people acquire the flu, the prevalence becomes 30/50 or 60%, and the incidence (the number of new infections) is 25/50, or 5 in 10.

Using reported cases of AIDS as a real-life example, the most recent statistics show the cumulative total of cases (prevalence) between 1981 and 2011 of 1,200,000 cases, or 0.39% of the population. The incidence of 50,007 cases for 2011 averages out to 19.1 cases per 100,000 people.

The changes in incidence and prevalence are usually followed over a seasonal, yearly, and long-term basis and are helpful in predicting trends (**figure 13.20**). Statistics of concern to the

(a)

(b)

(c)
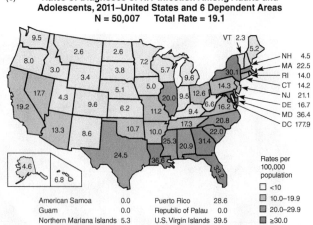

Note. Data include persons with a diagnosis of HIV infection, regardless of stage of disease at diagnosis.

Figure 13.20 Samples of epidemiological data as analyzed by the CDC. (a) A graph that shows the reported incidence of pertussis according to age group traced for 22 years. **(b)** A graph that compares the case rate of TB according to age and race/ethnicity for a single year. **(c)** A map that tracks new cases of HIV infection for a single year. All data are from the CDC.

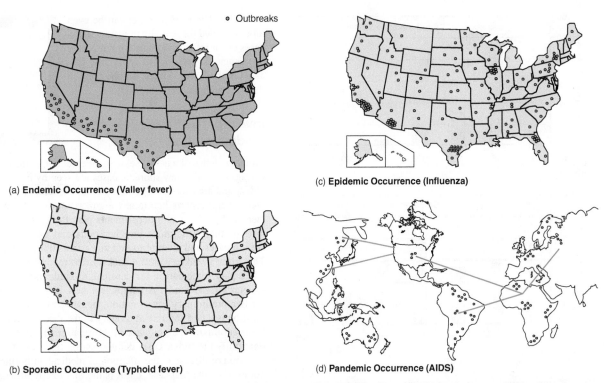

Figure 13.21 Patterns of infectious disease occurrence. (a) In endemic occurrence, cases are concentrated in one area at a relatively stable rate. **(b)** In sporadic occurrence, a few cases occur randomly over a wide area. **(c)** An epidemic is an increased number of cases that often appear in geographic clusters. The clusters may be local, as in the case of a restaurant-related food-borne epidemic, or nationwide, as is the case with influenza. **(d)** Pandemic occurrence means that an epidemic ranges over more than one continent.

epidemiologist are the rates of disease with regard to sex, race, or geographic region. Also of importance is the **mortality rate,** which measures the total number of deaths in a population due to a certain disease. Over the past century, the overall death rate from infectious diseases has dropped, although the **morbidity*** rate, or the number of persons afflicted with infectious diseases, has remained relatively high.

Monitoring statistics also makes it possible to define the frequency of a disease in the population. An infectious disease that exhibits a relatively steady frequency over a long time period in a particular geographic locale is **endemic (figure 13.21a).** Often, the reason for endemicity is the presence of a reservoir in that location. For example, Lyme disease is endemic to certain areas of the United States where the tick vector is found. A certain number of new cases are expected in these areas every year. When a disease is **sporadic,** occasional cases are reported at irregular intervals in random locales **(figure 13.21b).** Tetanus and typhoid fever are reported sporadically in the United States (fewer than 500 cases a year).

When statistics indicate that the number of new cases of an endemic or sporadic disease is increasing beyond what is expected

for that population, the pattern is described as an **epidemic (figure 13.21c).** An epidemic exists when an increasing trend is observed in a particular population. The time period is not defined. It can range from hours in food poisoning to years in STDs, or STIs, such as gonorrhea or syphilis.

The term **outbreak** is often used interchangeably with *epidemic,* but an outbreak is usually on a smaller scale in a limited area. In this chapter's Case Study, the cases started as outbreaks, but as time went on, the numbers of cases and regions affected rose to the level of an epidemic. There is no exact percentage of increase required before an outbreak can qualify as an epidemic. Several diseases are at epidemic levels in the United States, most recent examples being chlamydia and pertussis.

One useful way to analyze data from outbreaks is to graph the number of cases over time in an epicurve format **(Figures 13. A, B, C).** The pattern of epidemics will ordinarily follow one of three patterns: (1) a **point-source epidemic,** which indicates that the infectious agent came from a single source more or less simultaneously (see Case Study, page 218); (2) a **common-source epidemic,** in which all cases came from exposure to the same source that continued to infect others over a period of time; and (3) a **propagated epidemic,** which shows a sustained increase over time, indicating that it is being communicated from person to person.

* *morbidity* (mor-bih′-dih-tee) L. *morbidis,* sick. A condition of being diseased.

13A.

13B.

13C.

Quick Search
Find out about the "10 Worst Epidemics" in recorded history, courtesy of the Discovery Channel.

2 million. The iceberg effect can be even more lopsided for sexually transmitted diseases or for infections that are not reported to agencies. For a list of reportable diseases in the United States, see the table in the back end papers of this book.

Investigative Strategies of the Epidemiologist

Initial evidence of a new disease or an epidemic in the community is fragmentary. A few sporadic cases are seen by health care providers and are eventually reported to authorities. However, it can take several reports before any alarm is registered. Epidemiologists and public health departments play the part of medical detectives that must piece together odds and ends of data from similar cases and attempt to find any connections they may have. This often involves working backward to reconstruct factors that could play some part in the outbreak or epidemic, similar to this chapter's Case Study. A completely new disease requires even greater preliminary investigation, because the infectious agent must be isolated and linked directly to the disease (**13.3 Making Connections**). An early piece of information that drives an investigation is the **index case,** defined as the first case to bring the infection or disease to the attention of medical authorities. It may not even be the first case, but it is the first one reported. Most of the time, it will be followed by other cases, and the ensuing statistics will help fine tune the investigation. An example of an index case was the first case of hepatitis C discovered in the Las Vegas outbreak (Case Study, page 321).

All factors possibly impinging on the disease are scrutinized. Investigators search for *clusters* of cases indicating spread between persons or a public (common) source or vehicle. They also look at possible contact with animals, contaminated food, water, and public facilities and at human interrelationships or changes in community structure. Out of this maze of case information, the investigators hope to recognize a pattern that indicates the source of infection so that they can quickly move to control it.

Hospital Epidemiology and Nosocomial Infections

Infectious diseases that are acquired or develop during a hospital stay are known as **nosocomial* infections.** This concept seems incongruous at first thought, because a hospital is regarded as a place to get treatment for a disease, not a place to acquire a disease. Yet it is not uncommon for a surgical patient's incision to become infected or a burn patient to develop a case of pneumonia in the clinical setting. The rate of nosocomial infections can be as low as 0.1% or as high as 20% of all admitted patients, depending on the clinical setting. The average rate is about 5%. In light of the number of admissions, this adds up to 2 million to 4 million cases a year, which result in nearly 99,000 deaths. Nosocomial infections cost

The spread of an epidemic across continents is a **pandemic,** as exemplified by AIDS and influenza (**figure 13.21d**). See Case Study, page 157, for an example of pandemic spread.

One important epidemiological truism might be called the "iceberg effect," which refers to the fact that only a small portion of an iceberg is visible above the surface of the ocean, with a much more massive part lingering unseen below the surface. Regardless of case reporting and public health screening, a large number of cases of infection in the community go undiagnosed and unreported. In the instance of salmonellosis, approximately 40,000 cases are reported each year. Epidemiologists estimate that the actual number is more likely somewhere between 1 million and

* *nosocomial* (nohz"-oh-koh'-mee-al) Gr. *nosos*, disease, and *komeion*, to take care of. Also known as hospital acquired infections.

13.3 MAKING CONNECTIONS

Koch's Postulates: Solving the Puzzle of New Diseases

An essential aim in the study of infection and disease is determining the precise **etiologic**, or causative, **agent.** In our modern technological age, we take for granted that a certain infection is caused by a certain microbe, but such has not always been the case. More than 130 years ago, Robert Koch realized that in order to support the germ theory of disease, he would have to develop a standard for determining causation that would stand the test of scientific scrutiny. Out of his experimental observations on the transmission of anthrax in cows came a series of proofs, called **Koch's postulates,** that established the principal criteria for etiologic studies. A summary of these postulates is as follows:

1. find evidence of a particular microbe in every case of a disease,
2. isolate that microbe from an infected subject and cultivate it artificially in the laboratory,
3. inoculate a susceptible healthy subject with the laboratory isolate and observe the same resultant disease, and
4. reisolate the agent from this subject.

Valid application of Koch's postulates involves several critical details. Each culture must be pure, observed microscopically, and identified by means of characteristic tests; the first and second isolate must be identical; and the pathologic effects, signs, and symptoms of the disease in the first and second subject must be the same. Once established, these postulates were rapidly put to the test. Within a short time, they had helped determine the causative agents of tuberculosis, diphtheria, and plague. Today, most infectious diseases have been directly linked to a known agent.

Many infectious agents such as viruses and obligately parasitic bacteria can be difficult to culture or cannot be cultured. For these pathogens, the postulates have been modified to take this into account. It is now considered significant to repeatedly observe the infectious agent in tissue samples taken from people with the same disease. A good case in point is Whipple disease, a chronic intestinal infection that for many years could not be tied to a known causative agent. Finally, medical researchers had sufficient evidence of a bacterium being consistently present in infected tissues to give an identity to the mystery pathogen, *Tropheryma whipplei*. Modern sequencing techniques to analyze unculturable microbes and their genes have added a new type of evidence for fulfilling the postulates.

Koch's original postulates—or a modified version—continue to play an essential role in modern epidemiology. Nearly every year, new viral diseases arise or old ones spread out of their usual range. Notable examples include dengue fever, influenza, SARS, and West Nile fever. Viral diseases require some modifications to the postulates. These include that the virus must be cultivated in cell culture, it must be filterable through bacteriological filters, and it must cause a detectable specific immune response.

Explain how we can be so certain that HIV causes AIDS even though there is no animal model for it. *Answer available at http://www.mhhe.com/talaro9*

① Specimen from patient ill with infection of unknown etiology is carried through an isolation procedure.

② A pure culture of the suspected agent is made.

Full microscopic and biological characterization

③ Inoculation of test animal

Observe animal for disease characteristics

Specimen taken

④ Pure culture and identification procedures

The microbe in the initial and second isolations and the disease in the patient and experimental animal must match for the postulates to be satisfied.

time and money as well as suffering. By one estimate, they amount to 8 million additional days of hospitalization a year and an increased cost of $5 billion to $10 billion.

So many factors unique to the hospital environment are tied to nosocomial infections that a certain number of infections are virtu-

ally unavoidable. After all, the hospital both attracts and creates compromised patients, and it serves as a collection point for pathogens. Some patients become infected when surgical procedures or lowered defenses permit resident microbes to invade their bodies. Other patients acquire infections directly or indirectly

from fomites, medical equipment, other patients, medical personnel, visitors, air, and water.

The health care process itself increases the likelihood that infectious agents will be transferred from one patient to another. Treatments using reusable instruments such as respirators and endoscopes constitute a possible source of infectious agents. Indwelling devices such as catheters, prosthetic heart valves, grafts, drainage tubes, and tracheostomy tubes form a ready portal of entry and habitat for infectious agents. Because such high numbers of the hospital population receive antimicrobial drugs during their stay, drug-resistant microbes are selected for at a much greater rate than is the case outside the hospital.

The most common nosocomial infections involve the urinary tract, the respiratory tract, surgical incisions, and the blood (sepsis) **(figure 13.22)**. Gram-negative intestinal flora (*Escherichia coli, Klebsiella, Pseudomonas*) are cultured in more than half of patients with nosocomial infections. Gram-positive bacteria (staphylococci and streptococci) and yeasts make up most of the remainder. True pathogens such as *Mycobacterium tuberculosis, Salmonella,* hepatitis B, and influenza virus can be transmitted in the clinical setting as well.

The potential seriousness and impact of nosocomial infections have required hospitals to develop committees that monitor infectious outbreaks and develop guidelines for infection control and aseptic procedures.

Medical asepsis includes practices that lower the microbial load in patients, caregivers, and the hospital environment. These practices include proper hand washing, disinfection, and sanitization, as well as patient isolation. **Table 13.11** summarizes guidelines for the major types of isolation. The goal of these procedures is to limit the spread of infectious agents from person to person. An even higher level of stringency is seen with *surgical asepsis,* which involves all of the strategies listed previously plus ensuring that all surgical procedures are

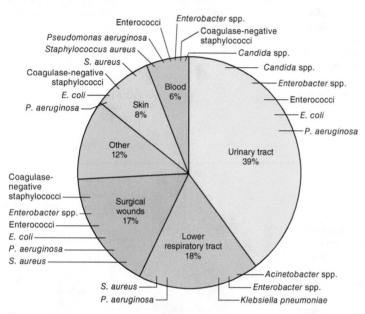

Figure 13.22 Nosocomial Infections. Relative frequency by body site. These data are from the National Nosocomial Infections Surveillance, which is conducted by the Centers for Disease Control and Prevention.

TABLE 13.11	Levels of Isolation Used in Clinical Settings	
Type of Isolation*	**Protective Measures****	**To Prevent Spread of**
Enteric Precautions	Gowns and gloves must be worn by all persons having direct contact with patient; masks are not required; special precautions are taken for disposing of feces and urine.	Diarrheal diseases; *Shigella, Salmonella, E. coli, and Clostridium difficile*; cholera; hepatitis A; rotavirus; and giardiasis
Respiratory Precautions	Private room with closed door is necessary; gowns and gloves are not required; masks are usually indicated; items contaminated with secretions must be disinfected.	Tuberculosis, measles, mumps, meningitis, pertussis, rubella, chickenpox
Drainage and Secretion Precautions	Gowns and gloves are required; masks are not needed; contaminated instruments and dressings require special precautions.	Staphylococcal and streptococcal infections; gas gangrene; herpes zoster; burn infections
Strict Isolation	Private room with closed door is required; gowns, masks, and gloves must be worn; contaminated items must be wrapped and decontaminated.	Mostly highly virulent or contagious microbes; includes tuberculosis, some types of pneumonia, extensive skin and burn infections, herpes simplex and zoster
Reverse Isolation (Also Called Protective Isolation)	Same guidelines as for strict isolation are required; room may be ventilated by laminar airflow filtered through a high-efficiency particulate (HEPA) filter that removes airborne pathogens; infected persons must be barred.	Used to protect patients extremely immunocompromised by cancer therapy, surgery, genetic defects, burns, prematurity, or AIDS and therefore vulnerable to opportunistic pathogens

*Precautions are based upon the primary portal of entry and communicability of the pathogen.

**In all cases, visitors to the patient's room must report to the nurses' station before entering the room; all visitors and personnel must wash their hands upon entering and leaving the room.

conducted under sterile conditions. This includes sterilization of surgical instruments, dressings, sponges and the like, as well as clothing personnel in sterile garments and scrupulously disinfecting the room surfaces and air.

Hospitals generally employ an *infection control officer* who not only implements proper practices and procedures throughout the hospital but also is charged with tracking potential outbreaks, identifying breaches in asepsis, and training other health care workers in aseptic technique. Among those most in need of this training are nurses and other caregivers whose work, by its very nature, exposes them to needlesticks, infectious secretions, blood, and physical contact with the patient. The same practices that interrupt the routes of infection in the patient can also protect the health care worker. It is for this reason that most hospitals have adopted universal precautions that recognize that all secretions from all persons in the clinical setting are potentially infectious and that transmission can occur in either direction.

Universal Blood and Body Fluid Precautions

Medical and dental settings require stringent measures to prevent the spread of nosocomial infections from patient to patient, from patient to worker, and from worker to patient. But even with precautions, the rate of such infections is rather high. An established body of evidence indicates that more than one-third of nosocomial infections could be prevented by consistent and rigorous infection control methods.

Previously, control guidelines were disease-specific, and clearly identified infections were managed with particular restrictions and techniques. With this arrangement, personnel tended to handle materials labeled *infectious* with much greater care than those that were not so labeled. The AIDS epidemic spurred a reexamination of that policy. Because of the potential for undiagnosed HIV-infected patients, the CDC laid down more-stringent guidelines for handling patients and body substances. These guidelines have been termed **universal precautions (UPs),** because they are based on the assumption that all patient specimens could harbor infectious agents and so must be treated with the same degree of care. They also include body substance isolation (BSI) techniques to be used in known cases of infection.

It is worth mentioning that these precautions are designed to protect all individuals in the clinical setting—patients, workers, and the public alike. In general, they include techniques designed to prevent contact with pathogens and contamination and, if prevention is not possible, to take purposeful measures to decontaminate potentially infectious materials. See **Appendix B** for a more detailed list of UPs.

✅ *Check Your Progress* SECTION 13.5

28. Outline the science of epidemiology and the work of an epidemiologist.
29. What types of information do epidemiologists require to differentiate between the incidence and prevalence of infectious diseases?
30. Distinguish between point-source, common-source, and propagated epidemics, and explain what is meant by an index case.

31. List the main features of Koch's postulates and explain why it is so difficult to prove them for some diseases.
32. Nosocomial infections can arise from what general sources?
33. Outline the major agents involved in nosocomial infections and indicate whether they are true pathogens or opportunists.

 CASE STUDY Part 2

Salmonellosis is the second most common food infection, with over 40,000 reported cases every year, but this number is considered only the tip of the iceberg. The CDC estimates an additional 1 million to 2 million cases go unreported. *Salmonella* Typhimurium, the most common serotype implicated in human disease, inhabits the large intestine of a variety of birds, rodents, cattle, and some reptiles. Outbreaks occur on a regular basis and are usually associated with foods such as beef, eggs, chicken, and produce.

The team of CDC investigators went to the plant in Georgia to observe the production facilities and to carry out traceback studies. They wished to determine how the peanut butter was originally contaminated with *Salmonella* and to what extent vectors were involved. Workers said that cockroaches regularly fell into the dry roasted peanuts and they saw rat droppings in the processing area. The team also found that the roof was a collecting place for hundreds of birds and holes in the roof allowed contaminated rainwater to drip into the plant. Even though the peanuts had been roasted at about 90°C (190°F) for 30 minutes, which is considered long enough to kill most pathogens, they were not heated again, and contamination could occur during later stages of processing and packaging. *Salmonella* are relatively hardy bacteria, and although they would not grow in the low-moisture peanut butter, they could remain alive for several months, even years. How the large infectious dose of 100,000 cells could have developed under these circumstances is still a mystery, but it is obvious that the processed peanuts must have harbored high levels of the pathogen.

In 2012, the federal government brought a criminal lawsuit against the four owners of Peanut Corp. They were indicted on 76 charges of conspiracy, fraud, and introduction of adulterated food. Their company had already gone bankrupt in 2009 and was no longer in the peanut business.

- What terms would you use to describe the roles of cockroaches, rats, and birds in transmission?
- What pathologic effect does *Salmonella* have on the intestinal tract?

To conclude this Case Study, go to Perspectives on the Connect website. For more information on this Case Study, go to http://www.cdc.gov/salmonella/typhimurium/update.html.

Chapter Summary with Key Terms

13.1 We Are Not Alone

 A. The human body is in contact with microbes that are constantly present in the environment. Microbes are classified as either part of the normal residents of the body or as **pathogens,** depending on whether or not their colonization of the body results in infection.

 B. *Resident Microbiota: The Human as Habitat*

 1. **Normal resident microbiota** consist of a huge and varied population of microbes that reside permanently on all surfaces of the body exposed to the environment.

 2. Colonization begins just prior to birth and continues throughout life. Variations in normal residents occur in response to changes in an individual's age, diet, hygiene, and health.

 3. Normal residents often provide some benefit to the host but are also capable of causing disease, especially when the immune system of the host is compromised or when they invade a normally sterile area of the body.

 4. An important benefit provided by microbiota is **microbial antagonism.**

 C. *Indigenous Microbiota of Specific Regions*
Resident microbes include bacteria, fungi, and protozoa. They occupy the skin, mouth, gastrointestinal tract, large intestine, respiratory tract, and genitourinary tract.

13.2 Major Factors in the Development of an Infection

 A. **Pathogenicity** is the ability of microorganisms to cause infection and disease; **virulence** refers to the degree to which a microbe can invade and damage host tissues.

 1. **True pathogens** are able to cause disease in a normal healthy host with intact immune defenses.

 2. **Opportunistic pathogens** can cause disease only in persons whose host defenses are compromised by *predisposing conditions.*

 B. *Becoming Established: Phase One—Portals of Entry*

 1. Microbes typically enter the body through a specific **portal of entry.** Portals of entry are generally the same as those areas of the body that harbor microflora.

 2. The minimum number of microbes needed to produce an infection is termed the **infectious dose,** and these pathogens may be classified as **exogenous** or **endogenous,** based on their source.

 C. *Attaching to the Host: Phase Two*
Microbes attach to the host cell, a process known as **adhesion,** by means of fimbriae, capsules, or receptors.

 D. *Invading the Host and Becoming Established: Phase Three*
Microbes that persist in the human host have developed mechanisms of disabling early defensive strategies.

 E. *How Virulence Factors Contribute to Tissue Damage and Disease*
Virulence factors are structures or properties of a microbe that lead to pathologic effects on the host. While some virulence factors are those that enable entry or adhesion, many virulence factors lead directly to damage. These fall in three categories: enzymes, toxins, and the inhibition or destruction of phagocytes.

 1. **Exoenzymes** digest epithelial tissues and permit **invasion** of pathogens.

 2. **Toxigenicity** refers to a microbe's capacity to produce **toxins** at the site of multiplication. Toxins are divided into **endotoxins** and **exotoxins,** and diseases caused by toxins are classified as **intoxications, toxemias,** or **toxinoses.**

13.3 The Outcomes of Infection and Disease

 A. **Infectious diseases** follow a typical pattern consisting of an **incubation period, prodromal stage, period of invasion,** and **convalescent period.** Each stage is marked by symptoms of a specific intensity.

 B. Infections are classified by

 1. whether they remain localized at the site of inoculation (**localized infection, systemic infection, focal infection);**

 2. the number of microbes involved in an infection, and the order in which they infect the body (**mixed infection, primary infection, secondary infection);** and

 3. the persistence of the infection (**acute infection, chronic infection,** subacute infection).

 C. **Signs** of infection refer to *objective* evidence of infection, and **symptoms** refer to *subjective* evidence. A **syndrome** is a disease that manifests as a predictable complex of symptoms.

 D. After the initial infection, pathogens may remain in the body in a **latent** state and may later cause recurrent infections. Long-term damages to host cells are referred to as **sequelae.**

 E. Microbes are released from the body through a specific **portal of exit** that allows them access to another host.

13.4 Epidemiology: The Study of Disease in Populations

Origins and Transmission Patterns of Infectious Microbes

 A. The **reservoir** of a microbe refers to its natural habitat; a pathogen's **source** refers to the immediate origin of an infectious agent.

 B. **Carriers** are individuals who inconspicuously shelter a pathogen and spread it to others. Carriers are divided into **asymptomatic carriers,** incubation carriers, convalescent carriers, chronic carriers, and **passive carriers.**

 C. **Vectors** refer to animals that transmit pathogens.

 1. **Biological vectors** are animals that are involved in the life cycle of the pathogen they transmit; **mechanical vectors** transmit pathogens without being involved in the life cycle.

 2. **Zoonoses** are diseases that can be transmitted to humans but are normally found in animal populations.

 D. Agents of disease are either **communicable** or **noncommunicable,** with highly communicable diseases referred to as **contagious.**

 1. Direct transmission of a disease occurs when a portal of exit meets a portal of entrance.

 2. Indirect transmission occurs when an intermediary such as a **vehicle, fomite,** or **droplet nuclei** connects portals of entrance and exit.

13.5 The Work of Epidemiologists: Investigation and Surveillance

 A. Epidemiologists are involved in the surveillance of reportable and notifiable diseases in populations.

B. Infectious diseases are tabulated with regard to their **prevalence** and **incidence.**

C. Populations are analyzed with regard to **morbidity, mortality,** age, sex, and geographic region.

D. Disease patterns are described as being **endemic, sporadic, epidemic,** or **pandemic** based on the frequency of their occurrence in a population.

E. Epidemiologists look for **index cases** and changes in the occurrence of diseases such as clusters of new cases. They compile evidence and **trace back** to the original source or reservoir.

F. **Nosocomial** infections are infectious diseases acquired in a hospital setting. Special vigilance is required to reduce their occurrence.

Level I. Knowledge and Comprehension

These questions require a working knowledge of the concepts in the chapter and the ability to recall and understand the information you have studied.

Multiple-Choice Questions

Select the correct answer from the answers provided. For questions with blanks, choose the combination of answers that most accurately completes the statement.

1. The best descriptive term for the resident microbes is
 a. commensals b. parasites c. pathogens d. contaminants

2. Resident microbiota is commonly found in the
 a. liver b. kidney c. salivary glands d. urethra

3. Normal resident microbes are absent from the
 a. pharynx b. lungs c. intestine d. hair follicles

4. Virulence factors include
 a. toxins b. enzymes c. capsules d. all of these

5. The specific action of hemolysins is to
 a. damage white blood cells c. damage red blood cells
 b. cause fever d. cause leukocytosis

6. The _____ is the time that lapses between encounter with a pathogen and the first symptoms.
 a. prodrome c. period of convalescence
 b. period of invasion d. period of incubation

7. A short period early in a disease that manifests with general malaise and achiness is the
 a. period of incubation c. sequela
 b. prodrome d. period of invasion

8. The presence of a few bacteria in the blood is termed
 a. septicemia c. bacteremia
 b. toxemia d. a secondary infection

9. A _____ infection is acquired in a hospital.
 a. subclinical b. focal c. nosocomial d. zoonosis

10. A/an _____ is a passive animal transporter of pathogens.
 a. zoonosis c. mechanical vector
 b. biological vector d. asymptomatic carrier

11. An example of a noncommunicable infection is
 a. measles b. leprosy c. tuberculosis d. tetanus

12. A general term that refers to an increased white blood cell count is
 a. leukopenia c. leukocytosis
 b. inflammation d. leukemia

13. The occurrence of Lyme disease mainly in areas where certain species of ticks live would define it as a/an _____ disease.
 a. epidemic b. pandemic c. endemic d. sporadic

14. A positive antibody test for HIV would be a _____ of infection.
 a. sign b. symptom c. syndrome d. sequela

15. Which of the following would *not* be a portal of entry?
 a. the meninges c. skin
 b. the placenta d. small intestine

16. Which of the following is *not* a condition of Koch's postulates?
 a. isolate the causative agent of a disease
 b. cultivate the microbe in a lab
 c. inoculate a test animal to observe the disease
 d. test the effects of a pathogen on humans

Case Study Review

1. This outbreak would be considered an epidemic because:
 a. it happened over a wide geographic region
 b. of a rise in the number of cases over a short time
 c. it was transmitted by vectors
 d. it occurred in all age groups

2. Which of these is the most accurate description of the relationship between rats and *Salmonella?*
 a. Rats carry *Salmonella* on their feet and fur.
 b. Rats pick up *Salmonella* from infected cockroaches.

 c. Rats harbor *Salmonella* as intestinal microbiota.
 d. *Salmonella* lives in the soil around rat nests.

3. Using the Case Study, page 388, as an example, explain the difference between a source and a reservoir; list the signs and symptoms in the Case Study.

424 **Chapter 13** Microbe-Human Interactions

Writing Challenge

For each question, compose a one- or two-paragraph answer that includes the factual information needed to completely address the question. Check Your Progress questions can also be used for writing-challenge exercises.

1. What are the important clinical implications of positive blood or cerebrospinal fluid?

2. What is the expected result if a compromised person is exposed to a true pathogen?

3. Explain how endotoxin gets into the bloodstream of a patient with endotoxic shock.

4. Give a brief description of how the A-B type of toxin works.

5. For each portal of entry, give a vehicle that carries the pathogen and the course it must travel to invade the tissues.

6. What are some important considerations about the portal of exit?

7. What does it mean for salmonellosis to have an iceberg effect?

8. a. Outline the five types of clinical isolation.
 b. Describe the work of an infection control officer.

9. Complete the table.

	Exotoxins	Endotoxins
Chemical makeup		
General source		
Degree of toxicity		
Effects on cells		
Symptoms in disease		
Examples		

Concept Mapping

An Introduction to Concept Mapping found at http://www.mhhe.com/talaro9 provides guidance for working with concept maps.

1. Supply your own linking words or phrases in this concept map, and provide the missing concepts in the empty boxes.

2. Use 6 to 10 bolded words of your choice from the Chapter Summary to create a concept map. Finish it by providing linking words.

Level II. Application, Analysis, Evaluation, and Synthesis

These problems go beyond just restating facts and require higher levels of understanding and an ability to interpret, problem solve, transfer knowledge to new situations, create models, and predict outcomes.

Critical thinking is the ability to reason and solve problems using facts and concepts. These questions can be approached from a number of angles, and in most cases, they do not have a single correct answer.

1. a. Discuss the relationship between the vaginal residents and the colonization of the newborn.
 b. Can you think of some medical consequences of this relationship?
 c. How could normal microbial residents cause some infections to be more severe and other infections to be less severe?

2. If the following patient specimens produced positive cultures when inoculated and grown on appropriate media, indicate whether this result indicates a disease state and why or why not:

Urine from urethra	Liver biopsy	Blood
Lung biopsy	Throat	Urine from bladder
Saliva	Cerebrospinal fluid	Semen

3. Use the following formula to explain the relationships among the several factors and what happens when they change:

$$\frac{\text{Infection}}{\text{(infectious disease)}} = \frac{\text{No. of organisms} \times \text{Virulence}}{\text{Host resistance}}$$

4. Assume that you have been given the job of developing a colony of germ-free chickens.
 a. What will be the main steps in this process?
 b. What possible experiments can you do with these animals?

5. a. Use the following statistics to make simple maps and graphs of the following three diseases. Determine which show endemic, sporadic, or epidemic patterns. Explain how you can determine each type.

	Cases	
United States Region	**2011**	**2012**
Pertussis		
East Coast	3,213	8,162
Midwest	6,162	15,845
South	3,089	2,445
West	6,255	11,864
Total cases	18,719	41,880
Coccidioidomycosis		
East Coast	13	12
Midwest	186	174
South	8	10
West	22,432	16,749
Total cases	22,634	16,939
Dengue fever		
East Coast	75	97
Midwest	34	48
South	132	149
West	31	63
Total cases	251	357

 b. Explain what would have to occur for these diseases to have a pandemic distribution.

6. Describe each of the following infections using correct technical terminology. (Descriptions may fit more than one category.) Use terms such as *primary, secondary, nosocomial, STD, mixed, latent, toxemia, chronic, zoonotic, asymptomatic, local, systemic, -itis, -emia.*

 Caused by needlestick in dental office

 Pneumocystis pneumonia in AIDS patient

 Bubonic plague from rat flea bite

 Diphtheria

 Undiagnosed chlamydiosis

 Acute necrotizing gingivitis

 Syphilis of long duration

 Large numbers of gram-negative rods in the blood

 A boil on the back of the neck

 An inflammation of the meninges

7. a. Suggest several reasons why urinary tract, respiratory tract, and surgical infections are the most common nosocomial infections.
 b. Name several measures that health care providers must exercise at all times to prevent or reduce nosocomial infections.

8. Summarize the epidemiological findings in the three graphs in figure 13.20.

426 **Chapter 13** Microbe-Human Interactions

1. Using **figure 13.11** as a guide, explain the processes occurring between *Salmonella* (pink) and the surface of a host cell (yellow) on both left and right sides of the photo.

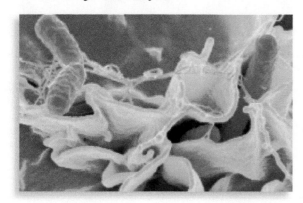

2. Observe this graph from the Case Study outbreak and compare it to the graph patterns on page 418. Explain what type of epidemic it is and the features it displays that are typical for that pattern.

Infections with the Outbreak Strain of *Salmonella* Typhimurium, by Date of Illness Onset
(n=696 for whom information was reported as of April 20, 9pm EDT)

*Some illness onset dates have been estimated from other reported information

CHAPTER **14** An Introduction to Host Defenses
and Innate Immunities

Lymphocytes

Macrophages

The conidial head of *Aspergillus fumigatus,* a pathogenic mold that grows well in human tissues and organs

Section through a granuloma reveals a central compact mass of macrophages surrounded by a collar of lymphocytes

CASE STUDY Part 1 When Phagocytes Fail

The 5-year-old boy's medical history included several episodes of **bacterial pneumonia** starting at 7 months of age that cleared up with antibiotic therapy. At some point, his parents began to notice a troubling new set of symptoms and signs. He complained of **constant pain** in his **wrist** and **jawbone,** and the **tissues** overlying these bones were **swollen** and **inflamed.** They took him to the hospital, where he was admitted for lab tests. The results revealed no abnormalities, and the standard tests for infectious agents came out negative. When an X ray detected small spots in the bones of his wrist and jaw, a biopsy was performed that uncovered **granuloma-like lesions** and signs of **osteomyelitis.** Because of his history of recurrent infections, he was checked for **immune function,** but his B- and T-cell activities were normal. Based on the assumption that he had an infection of **unknown etiology,** he was placed on a **broad range of therapy** consisting of antibacterial, antifungal, and antiviral medications and went home as soon as his condition improved.

After 8 months, he returned to the hospital in a state of severe distress and was readmitted. This time, he coughed, had difficulty in breathing, and complained of chest and abdominal pain. He was immediately given antibiotics and **scanned** by **computerized tomography** (CT), which revealed a **mass in the liver** that extended into the ribcage. Physicians drew a sample of fluid from the liver and sent

> "Systemic aspergillosis is one of the most common infections in children and adults with defective phagocytes."

it for testing. From the liver sample, technicians isolated a pure culture with greenish-gray, wooly colonies typical of the mold *Aspergillus fumigatus.* Microscopic preparations yielded branched, septate hyphae with **brushlike conidial heads** typical of this fungus.

It now became clear that the child had a serious **systemic fungal infection** that was likely responsible for his earlier episode as well. This finding required a different regimen using a powerful **intravenous antifungal drug,** amphotericin B, backed up with interferon and rifampin. He responded well to the medications and was able to return home.

After considering the nature of these new infections, his doctors began to search for an unknown **loss of host defenses** that could account for the child's recurring **opportunistic infections.** They were aware, for instance, that systemic **aspergillosis** is one of the most common infections in children and adults with **defective phagocytes.**

▶ *What physiological activities account for the inflammation and swelling?*

▶ *What is osteomyelitis, and what are some of its causes?*

To continue the Case Study, go to page 451.

14.1 Overview of Host Defense Mechanisms

 Expected Learning Outcomes

1. Summarize the characteristics of basic host defenses.
2. Differentiate between the three lines of defense, describing examples of each.
3. Explain the nature of the different types of innate, nonspecific defenses.

The survival of the host depends upon an elaborate network of defenses that keep harmful microbes and other foreign materials from entering the body and causing damage. Should they penetrate, additional host defenses are immediately summoned to prevent them from becoming established in tissues. Defenses involve barriers, cells, and chemicals, and they range from nonspecific to specific and from inborn or innate to acquired. This chapter introduces the main lines of defense intrinsic to all humans. Topics included in this survey are the anatomical and physiological systems that detect, recognize, and destroy foreign substances and the major activities that account for an individual's nonspecific resistance to infection and disease.

In chapter 13, we explored the human-microbe relationship, with emphasis on the role of microorganisms in disease. In this chapter, we examine the other side of the relationship—that of the host defending itself against microorganisms. As previously stated, in light of the unrelenting contact and colonization of humans, it is something of a miracle that we are not constantly infected and diseased. Our ability to overcome this continual assault on our bodies is the result of a fascinating, highly complex system.

To protect the body against pathogens, the immune system relies on an overlapping network of **host defenses** that operate on several levels. These include **innate, natural defenses** present at birth that provide nonspecific resistance to infection and **adaptive immunities** that are specific and must be acquired. These levels of protection are sometimes divided into categories called the *first, second,* and *third lines of defense* (**table 14.1**).

The *first line of defense* includes any barrier that blocks invasion at the portal of entry. This mostly nonspecific line of defense limits access to the internal tissues of the body. However, it is not considered a true immune response because it does not involve recognition of a specific foreign substance and is very general in its actions.

The *second line of defense* is a more internalized system of protective cells and fluids, which includes inflammation and phagocytosis. It acts rapidly at both the local and systemic levels once the first line of defense has been circumvented, and in most reactions, it is also nonspecific.

The highly specific *third line of defense* is adaptive and acquired on an individual basis as each foreign substance is encountered by white blood cells called lymphocytes. Responses directed toward each different microbe produce unique protective substances and memory cells that can come into play if that microbe is encountered again. Details of how this third line of defense provides long-term immunity is discussed in chapter 15, whereas this chapter focuses on the first and second lines of defense.

The various levels of defense do not operate in a completely separate fashion; most defenses overlap and are even redundant in some of their effects. This cooperative reaction targets invading microbes on several different fronts simultaneously, making their survival unlikely. To present the interactive nature of host defenses, we start with basic concepts that will build a foundation for understanding the more complex reactions of the immune system to come later.

Barriers at the Portal of Entry: An Inborn First Line of Defense

A number of defenses are a normal part of the body's anatomy and physiology. These inborn, nonspecific defenses can be divided into physical, chemical, and genetic barriers that impede the entry of not only microbes but any foreign agent, whether living or not (**figure 14.1**).

Physical or Anatomical Barriers at the Body's Surface

The skin and mucous membranes of the respiratory and digestive tracts have several built-in defenses. The outermost layer (stratum corneum) of the skin is composed of epithelial cells that have become compacted, cemented together, and impregnated with an insoluble protein, keratin. The result is a thick, tough layer that is highly impervious and waterproof. Few pathogens can penetrate this unbroken barrier, especially in regions such as the soles of the feet or the palms of the hands, where the stratum corneum is much thicker than on other parts of the body. Other cutaneous barriers include hair follicles and skin glands. The hair shaft is periodically extruded, and the

TABLE 14.1	General Features of Host Defenses			
Line of Defense	Innate/ Acquired	Specific or Nonspecific	Development of Immunologic Memory	Examples
First	Innate	Nonspecific	No	Physical barriers: skin, tears, coughing, sneezing Chemical barriers: low pH, lysozyme, digestive enzymes Genetic barriers: resistance inherent in genetic makeup of host (pathogen cannot invade)
Second	Innate	Mostly nonspecific	No	Phagocytosis, inflammation, fever, interferon, complement
Third	Acquired	Specific	Yes	T lymphocytes, B lymphocytes, antibodies

Sebaceous glands (fatty acids)

Tears (lysozyme)

Mucus

Saliva (lysozyme, lactoferrin, peroxidase)

Intact skin

Cilia

Wax

Low pH

Normal microbiota

Mucus

Sweat

Stomach acid

Normal microbiota

Intestinal enzymes

Mucus

Paneth cells

Defecation

Urination

Figure 14.1 Defenses. Some nonspecific defense barriers that help prevent entry of microorganisms into the host's tissues.

follicle cells are **desquamated,*** or shed. The flushing effect of sweat glands also helps remove microbes.

The mucocutaneous membranes of the digestive, urinary, and respiratory tracts and of the eye are moist and permeable. Despite the normal wear and tear upon these epithelia, damaged cells are rapidly replaced. The mucous coat on the free surface of some membranes impedes the entry and attachment of bacteria. Blinking and tear production (lacrimation) flush the eye's surface with tears and rid it of irritants. The constant flow of saliva helps carry microbes into the harsh conditions of the stomach. Vomiting and defecation also evacuate noxious substances or microorganisms from the body.

The respiratory tract is constantly guarded from infection by elaborate and highly effective adaptations.

* *desquamated* (des'-kwuh-mayt) L. *desquamo*, to scale off. The casting off of epidermal scales.

Nasal hair traps larger particles. Rhinitis, the inflammation of the nasal mucosal surface marked by the copious flow of mucus and fluids, which occurs in allergy and colds, exerts a flushing action. In the respiratory tree (primarily the trachea and bronchi), a ciliated epithelium (called the ciliary escalator) conveys foreign particles entrapped in mucus toward the pharynx to be removed **(figure 14.2).** Irritation of the nasal passage reflexively initiates a sneeze, which expels a large volume of air at high velocity. Similarly, the acute sensitivity of the bronchi, trachea, and larynx to foreign matter triggers coughing, which ejects irritants.

The genitourinary tract derives partial protection from the continuous trickle of urine through the ureters and from periodic bladder emptying that flushes the urethra.

The composition of microbiota and its protective effect were discussed in chapter 13. Even though the normal microbial residents do not constitute a physical or anatomical barrier, their presence can block the access of pathogens to epithelial surfaces and can create an unfavorable environment for pathogens by competing for limited nutrients or by altering the local pH. Some bacterial residents of the large intestine secrete bacteriocins, which can inhibit or kill other bacteria.

Nonspecific Chemical Defenses

The skin and mucous membranes offer a variety of chemical defenses. Sebaceous secretions exert an antimicrobial effect, and specialized glands such as the meibomian glands of the eyelids lubricate the conjunctiva with an antimicrobial secretion. Other defenses in tears and saliva include **lysozyme** and **defensins.** Lysozyme is an enzyme that hydrolyzes the peptidoglycan in the cell wall of bacteria. Defensins are peptides produced by various cells and tissues that damage cell membranes and lyse bacteria and fungi. Skin cells produce a defensin called dermicidin which helps eliminate bacteria, and paneth cells in the intestine secrete defensins that act on several types of infectious agents. The high lactic acid and electrolyte concentrations of sweat and the skin's acidic pH and fatty acid content are also inhibitory to many microbes.

Internally, the hydrochloric acid content of the stomach renders protection against many pathogens that are swallowed. The

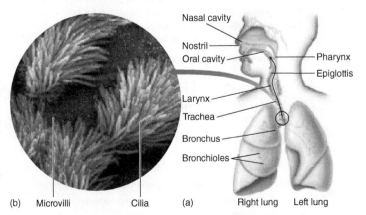

Nasal cavity

Nostril

Oral cavity

Pharynx

Epiglottis

Larynx

Trachea

Bronchus

Bronchioles

Right lung Left lung

(b) Microvilli Cilia (a)

Figure 14.2 The ciliary defense of the respiratory tree. (a) The epithelial lining of the trachea and bronchi contains a brush border of cilia to entrap and propel particles upward toward the pharynx. **(b)** Detail of trachea (5,000×) features tufts of cilia and microvilli on the surface of cells.

intestine's digestive juices and bile are also potentially destructive to microbes. Even semen contains an antimicrobial chemical that inhibits bacteria, and the vagina has a protective acidic pH maintained by lactobacilli that are part of the microbiota.

Genetic Resistance to Infection

In certain cases, the genetic makeup of an individual is different enough to ensure protection from infection by some pathogens. One explanation for this phenomenon is that some pathogens have such great specificity for one host species that they are incapable of infecting other species. Another way of putting it is: "Humans can't acquire distemper from cats, and cats can't get mumps from humans." This specificity is particularly true of viruses, which can invade only by attaching to a specific host receptor. But it does not hold true for zoonotic infectious agents that attack a broad spectrum of animals. Genetic differences in susceptibility can also exist within members of one species. Humans carrying a gene or genes for sickle-cell anemia are resistant to malaria. Genetic differences also exist in susceptibility to tuberculosis, leprosy, and certain systemic fungal infections.

The vital contribution of barriers is clearly demonstrated in people who have lost them or never had them. Patients with severe skin damage due to burns are extremely susceptible to infections; those with blockages in the salivary glands, tear ducts, intestine, and urinary tract are also at greater risk for infection. But as important as it is, the first line of defense alone cannot provide adequate protection. Because many pathogens find a way to circumvent the barriers by using their virulence factors (discussed in chapter 13), a whole new set of defenses—inflammation, phagocytosis, specific immune responses—is ready to react to them.

 Check Your Progress SECTION 14.1

1. Explain the functions of the three lines of defense and indicate which are the most essential to survival.

2. What is the difference between nonspecific host defenses and immune responses?

3. Differentiate innate and acquired immunity. What are the general characteristics of each? Discuss the advantages of having multiple defenses (innate and acquired) against the same microbe.

4. Give four innate immune responses present in the body, and explain how each type functions to combat infection.

14.2 Structure and Function of the Organs of Defense and Immunity

 Expected Learning Outcomes

4. Describe the primary functions and organs of the immune system.

5. Describe several features of the recognition system of host defenses.

6. Characterize pattern recognition receptors and pathogen-associated molecular patterns.

7. Describe the microscopic anatomy of body compartments and how they interconnect.

8. Outline the anatomy and functions of the reticuloendothelial system.

9. Outline the origin and composition of the blood, and characterize the types of blood cells and their functions.

10. Explain the behavior of white blood cells with regard to the blood circulation and tissues.

11. Describe the characteristics and functions of the lymphatic system.

Immunology encompasses the study of all features of the body's second and third lines of defense. Although this chapter is concerned primarily with infectious microbes, be aware that immunology is central to the study of fields as diverse as cancer and allergy. In chapters 15, 16, and 17, you will see that many of the most powerful applications of immunology have been developed for use in health care, laboratory, or commercial settings.

The primary functions of a healthy functioning immune system can be summarized as

1. surveillance of organs, tissues, and other compartments;
2. recognition and differentiation of normal components of the body and foreign material such as pathogens; and
3. attack and destruction of foreign invaders.

Because infectious agents could potentially enter through any number of portals, the cells of the immune system constantly move about the body, surveying the tissues for potential pathogens **(figure 14.3)**. This process is carried out primarily by **white blood cells (WBCs)** or **leukocytes** which have an innate capacity to recognize and differentiate any foreign material in the body, such as invading bacterial cells. Such foreign matter is often called **nonself.** Normal cells of the body, called **self,** are monitored and recognized and are usually not attacked by the immune system. The ability to differentiate nonself and thus spare self from attack is central to the effectiveness of the immune system. In chapter 16, we will see how autoimmune diseases can arise when this system goes awry. While foreign cells must be recognized as a potential threat and dealt with appropriately, normal cells must not come under attack by the immune defenses. Exceptions to this would be "abnormal" or damaged self such as cancer cells.

How Do White Blood Cells Carry Out Recognition and Surveillance?

White blood cells are motile, migratory cells that move about the tissues and body compartments in search of any foreign matter that may have gotten through the first line of defense. Even though each type of blood cell has a particular role to play in defense, most of them have some capacity to locate and interact with foreign matter (figure 14.3). They display special molecules on their membranes known as **pattern recognition receptors (PRRs),** which are like "feelers" for sensing pathogens. There are several different types of PRRs involved in this recognition, including kinases, lectins, and mannose-type molecules. The best-understood PRRs are the **toll-like receptors (TLRs),** which reside within the membranes of early responders such as phagocytes.

Although PRRs and TLRs do not respond to a specific microbe, they can immediately recognize and interact with molecules on the surface of many pathogens called **pathogen-associated molecular patterns,** or **PAMPs.** PAMPs are molecules shared by many microorganisms that act like "red flags" for the white blood cells

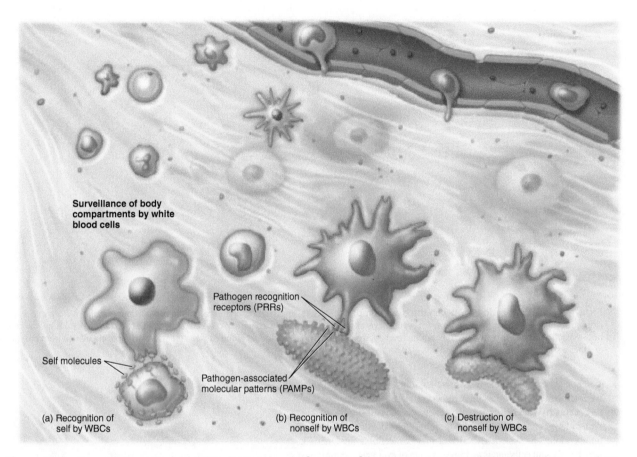

Surveillance of body
compartments by white
blood cells

Pathogen recognition
receptors (PRRs)

Self molecules

Pathogen-associated
molecular patterns (PAMPs)

(a) Recognition of
self by WBCs

(b) Recognition of
nonself by WBCs

(c) Destruction of
nonself by WBCs

Figure 14.3 To search, to recognize, and to eliminate are the functions of the immune system. White blood cells (WBCs) as seen in this view are equipped with a highly developed sense of "touch." **(a, b)** As they sort through the tissues, they "feel" the surrounding environment by means of their pathogen recognition receptors, which distinguish what is foreign or nonself. **(c)** When nonself molecules (PAMPs) are detected, WBCs mount a reaction to eliminate the microbes that carry them. Self molecules do not trigger these reactions. PAMPs are pathogen-associated molecular patterns that many pathogens display.

involved in innate immunity. The detection of PAMPs on pathogens by PRRs and TLRs provides an early alert of invasion and triggers reactions that help to control pathogens before they can invade further. Examples of PAMPs include peptidoglycan, lipoteichoic acid, and lipopolysaccharide from bacterial cell walls, double-stranded RNA found in some viruses, zymosan from fungal cell walls, and bacterial flagellin. We will return to this topic again in section 14.4 on phagocytes.

Because these components are shared among many pathogens and not specific to a single cell type, only a small number of TLRs are needed to recognize a very wide variety of microbes. It is important to emphasize that this type of recognition is not specific or selective for a single type of microbe, making it a type of nonspecific, innate immunity that should not be confused with the specific acquired immunity from the third line of defense.

Compartments and Connections of the Immune System

It will soon become clear in this and subsequent chapters that, unlike many body systems, the immune "system" does not exist in a single, well-defined site. Instead, it encompasses a large, complex, and diffuse network of cells and fluids that penetrate into every organ and tissue. It is this very arrangement that promotes the surveillance and recognition processes that help screen the body for harmful substances.

The body is partitioned into several fluid-filled spaces called the intracellular, extracellular, lymphatic, cerebrospinal, and circulatory compartments. Although these compartments are physically separated, they have numerous connections. Their structure and position permit extensive interchange and communication **(figure 14.4).** The most extensive body compartments that participate in immune function are

1. the **reticuloendothelial*** system (RES),
2. the spaces surrounding tissue cells that contain **extracellular fluid (ECF),**
3. the **bloodstream,** and
4. the **lymphatic system.**

* *reticuloendothelial* (reh-tik"-yoo-loh-en"-doh-thee′-lee-al) L. *reticulum,* a small net, and *endothelium,* lining of the blood vessel.

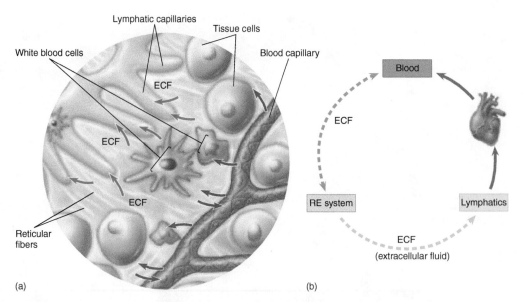

Figure 14.4 **Connections between the body compartments. (a)** The meeting of the major fluid compartments at the microscopic level. The close proximity of these compartments at the cellular level allows for continuous exchange of cells, fluids, and molecules (arrows). **(b)** Schematic view of how main fluid compartments form a continuous cyclic system of exchange. Positioning of the compartments favors rapid circulation from one site to another, either through direct (→) or indirect (---→) connections.

For effective immune responsiveness, the activities in one fluid compartment must be conveyed to other compartments. Let us see how this occurs by viewing tissue at the microscopic level **(figure 14.4a)**. At this level, clusters of tissue cells are in direct contact with the reticuloendothelial system (RES) and the extracellular fluid (ECF), which bathes all cells and is an important site of exchange for nutrients and gases. Other compartments (vessels) that penetrate at this level are blood and lymphatic capillaries. This close association allows cells and chemicals that originate in the RES and ECF to seep or migrate into the blood and lymphatics; any products of a lymphatic reaction can be transmitted directly into the blood through the connection between these two systems; and certain cells and chemicals originating in the blood can move through the vessel walls into the extracellular spaces and migrate into the lymphatic system **(figure 14.4b)**.

The flow of events among these systems depends on where an infectious agent or foreign substance first intrudes. A typical progression might begin in the extracellular spaces and RES, move to the lymphatic circulation, and ultimately end up in the bloodstream. Regardless of which compartment is first exposed, an immune reaction in any one of them will eventually be communicated to the others at the microscopic level. An obvious benefit of such an integrated system is that no cell of the body is far removed from competent protection, no matter how isolated. Let us take a closer look at each of these compartments separately.

Immune Functions of the Reticuloendothelial System

The tissues of the body are permeated by a network of connective tissue fibers, or a reticulum, which originates in the cellular basal lamina, interconnects nearby cells, and meshes with the massive connective tissue network surrounding all organs. This network, or reticuloendothelial system **(figure 14.5)**, is intrinsic to immune

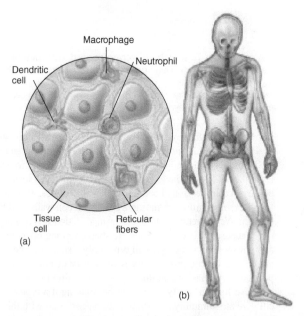

Figure 14.5 **The reticuloendothelial system occurs as a continuous connective tissue framework throughout the body.** **(a)** This system begins at the microscopic level with a fibrous support network (reticular fibers) enmeshing each cell. This web connects one cell to another within a tissue or organ and provides a niche for phagocytic white blood cells, which can crawl within and between tissues. **(b)** The degrees of shading in the body indicate variations in phagocyte concentration (darker = greater).

function because it provides a passageway within and between tissues and organs. It also is heavily endowed with white blood cells of the **mononuclear phagocyte system.** This system is waiting to attack passing foreign intruders as they arrive in the skin, lungs, liver, lymph nodes, spleen, and bone marrow. The RES serves an additional role in carrying extracellular fluid throughout its network.

Origin, Composition, and Functions of the Blood

The circulatory system consists of the circulatory system proper, which includes the heart, arteries, veins, and capillaries that circulate the blood, and the lymphatic system, which includes lymphatic vessels and lymphatic organs (lymph nodes) that circulate lymph. As you will see, these two circulations parallel, interconnect with, and complement one another.

The substance that courses through the arteries, veins, and capillaries is **whole blood,** a liquid connective tissue consisting of **blood cells** (formed elements) suspended in **plasma.** One can visualize these two components with the naked eye when a tube of unclotted blood is allowed to sit or is spun in a centrifuge. The cells' density causes them to settle into an opaque layer at the bottom of the tube, leaving the plasma, a clear, yellowish fluid, on top **(figure 14.6). Serum** is essentially the same as plasma, except it is the clear fluid from clotted blood so it lacks the clotting proteins that plasma contains. Serum is often used in immune testing and therapy (chapter 15).

Fundamental Characteristics of Plasma Plasma contains hundreds of different chemicals produced by the liver, white blood cells, endocrine glands, and nervous system and absorbed from the digestive tract. The main component of this fluid is water (92%), and the remainder consists of proteins such as albumin and globulins (including antibodies); other immunochemicals; fibrinogen and other clotting factors; hormones; nutrients; ions; dissolved gases (O_2 and CO_2); and waste products (urea). These substances support

the normal physiological functions of nutrition, development, protection, homeostasis, and immunity. We return to the subject of plasma and its function in immune interactions later in this chapter.

A Survey of Blood Cells The production of blood cells, known as **hemopoiesis,** or **hematopoiesis,** * begins early in embryonic development in the yolk sac (an embryonic membrane). Later, it is taken over by the liver and lymphatic organs, and it is finally assumed entirely and permanently by the red bone marrow. Although much of a newborn's red marrow is devoted to hematopoietic function, the active marrow sites gradually recede, and by the age of 4 years, only the ribs, sternum, pelvic girdle, flat bones of the skull and spinal column, and proximal portions of the humerus and femur are devoted to blood cell production.

The relatively short life of blood cells demands a rapid turnover that is continuous throughout a human life span. The primary precursor of new blood cells is a pool of undifferentiated cells called pluripotential **stem cells**[1] maintained in the marrow. During development, these stem cells proliferate and *differentiate*— meaning that immature or unspecialized cells develop the specialized form and function of mature cells. The primary lines of cells that arise from this process produce red blood cells (RBCs), white blood cells (WBCs, or leukocytes), and platelets (thrombocytes). The white blood cell lines are programmed to develop into several secondary lines of cells during the final process of differentiation **(figure 14.7).** These committed lines of WBCs are largely responsible for immune function.

The **leukocytes*** are traditionally evaluated by their reactions with a hematologic stain that contains a mixture of dyes and can differentiate cells by color and morphology. When this stain is used on blood smears and evaluated using the light microscope, the leukocytes appear either with or without noticeable colored granules in the cytoplasm and, on that basis, are divided into two groups: **granulocytes** and **agranulocytes.** Greater magnification reveals that even the agranulocytes have tiny granules in their cytoplasm, so some hematologists also use the appearance of the nucleus to distinguish them. Granulocytes have a lobed nucleus, and agranulocytes have an unlobed, rounded nucleus. Note both of these characteristics in circulating leukocytes shown in figure 14.7.

Quick Search
To learn more, search the internet for the videos "How White Blood Cells Are Formed" and "How White Blood Cells Work."

Granulocytes The types of granular leukocytes present in the bloodstream are neutrophils, eosinophils, and basophils. All three are known for prominent cytoplasmic granules that stain with some combination of acidic dye (eosin) or basic dye (methylene blue). Although these granules are useful diagnostically, they also function in numerous physiological events. Refer to figure 14.7 to view the cell types described.

(a) **Unclotted Whole Blood** (b) **Clotted Whole Blood**

Plasma
Buffy coat
Red blood cells
Serum
Clot

Figure 14.6 **The macroscopic composition of whole blood.**
(a) When uncoagulated blood sits in a tube, it stratifies into a clear layer of plasma, a thin layer of off-white material called the buffy coat (which contains the white blood cells), and a layer of red blood cells in the bottom. **(b)** Serum is the clear fluid that separates from clotted blood. Clotting causes the cells to clump in the bottom of the tube in a single mass.

* *hematopoiesis* (hem″-mat-o-poy-ee′-sis) Gr. *haima,* blood, and *poiesis,* a making.

1. Pluripotential stem cells can develop into several different types of blood cells; unipotential cells have already committed to a specific line of development.

* *leukocyte* (loo′-koh-syte) Gr. *leukos,* white, and *kytos,* cell. The whiteness of unstained WBCs is best seen in the white layer, or buffy coat, of sedimented blood.

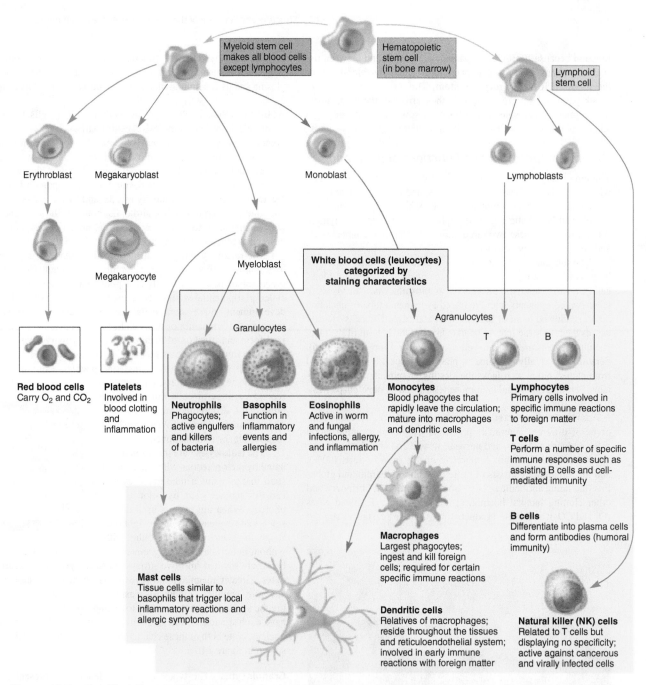

Figure 14.7 Simplified diagram of blood cell and platelet development. The details of several intermediate steps have been omitted. Undifferentiated stem cells in the red marrow give rise to several different cell lines that become increasingly specialized until mature cells are released into circulation. The yellow area indicates mature leukocytes (white blood cells). Photomicrographs of major circulating leukocytes are featured on the next page.

Neutrophils* are distinguished from other leukocytes by their conspicuous lobed nuclei and by their fine, pale lavender granules. In cells newly released from the bone marrow, the nuclei are horseshoe-shaped, but as they age, they form multiple lobes (up to five). These cells, also called polymorphonuclear neutrophils (PMNs), make up 55% to 90% of the circulating leukocytes—about 25 billion cells in the circulation at any given moment. The main work of the neutrophils is in phagocytosis. Their high numbers in both the blood and tissues suggest a constant challenge from

Neutrophil

* *neutrophil* (noo′-troh-fil) L. *neuter,* neither, and Gr. *philos,* to love. The granules are neutral and do not react markedly with either acidic or basic dyes. In clinical reports, they are often called "polys" or PMNs for short.

resident microbiota and environmental sources. Most of the cytoplasmic granules carry digestive enzymes and other chemicals that degrade the phagocytosed materials (see the discussion of phagocytosis in section 14.4). The average neutrophil lives only about 2 days, spending much of this time in the tissues and only about 4 to 10 hours in circulation.

Eosinophils* are readily distinguished in a stain preparation by their larger, orange to red (eosinophilic) granules and bilobed nucleus. They are much more numerous in the bone marrow and the spleen than in the circulation, contributing only 1% to 3% of the total WBC count. The role of the eosinophil in the immune system is not fully defined, although

Eosinophil

several functions have been suggested. Their granules contain peroxidase, lysozyme, and other digestive enzymes, as well as toxic proteins and inflammatory chemicals.

The main protective action of eosinophils is their ability to attack and destroy large eukaryotic pathogens. They are also involved in inflammation and allergic reactions. Among their most important targets are the larval forms of worm parasites that cause ascariasis, filariasis, and schistosomiasis. The binding of eosinophils to the larval surface and the release of toxic compounds into their cells causes disintegration of the larvae. Eosinophils are among the earliest cells to accumulate near sites of inflammation and allergic reactions, where they attract other leukocytes and release chemical mediators.

Basophils* are characterized by palestained, constricted nuclei and very prominent dark blue to black granules. They are the scarcest type of leukocyte, making up less than 0.5% of the total circulating WBCs in a normal individual. Basophils share some morphological and functional similarities with widely distributed tissue cells

Basophil

called **mast* cells.** Although these two cell types were once regarded as identical, mast cells are nonmotile elements bound to connective tissue around blood vessels, nerves, and epithelia, and basophils are motile elements. Both cell types originate from the same bone marrow stem cell line.

Basophils parallel eosinophils in many of their actions, because they also contain granules with potent chemical mediators. These mediators act on other cells and tissues of the body. For example, they may attract white blood cells toward the site of an infection or cause blood vessels to dilate in response to an injury. Mast cells are first line defenders against the local invasion of pathogens; they recruit other inflammatory cells; and they are directly responsible for the release of histamine and other allergic stimulants during immediate allergies (see chapter 16).

Agranulocytes Agranular leukocytes have globular, nonlobed nuclei and lack prominent cytoplasmic granules when viewed with

the light microscope. The two general types are monocytes and lymphocytes. Refer to figure 14.7 for the descriptions that follow.

Although lymphocytes are the cornerstone of the third line of defense, which is the subject of chapter 15, their origin and morphology are described here so their relationship to the other blood components is clear. **Lymphocytes** are the second most common WBC in the blood, comprising 20% to 35% of the total circulating leukocytes. The fact that their overall number throughout the body is among the highest of all cells indicates how important

Lymphocytes

they are to immunity. One estimate suggests that about one-tenth of all adult body cells are lymphocytes, exceeded only by erythrocytes and fibroblasts.

In a stained blood smear, most lymphocytes are small, spherical cells with a uniformly dark, rounded nucleus surrounded by a thin fringe of clear cytoplasm, although in tissues, they can become much larger and can even mimic monocytes in appearance. Lymphocytes exist as two functional types—the **B lymphocytes (B cells,** for short), and the thymus-derived, or **T lymphocytes (T cells,** for short). In humans, B cells mature in special bone marrow sites. T cells mature in the thymus gland. Both populations of cells are transported by the bloodstream and lymph and move about freely between lymphoid organs and connective tissue.

Lymphocytes are the key cells of the third line of defense and the specific immune response. When stimulated by foreign substances (antigens), lymphocytes are transformed into activated cells that neutralize and destroy those foreign substances. B cells contribute to **humoral immunity,** defined as protective molecules carried in the fluids of the body. Activated B cells form specialized **plasma cells,** which produce **antibodies.*** Antibodies are protein molecules that interlock with foreign cells or molecules and participate in their destruction. Activated T cells engage in a spectrum of immune functions characterized as **cell-mediated immunity** in which T cells modulate immune functions and kill foreign cells. The action of both classes of lymphocytes account for the specificity and memory typical of immunity. Lymphocytes are so important to the defense of the body that most of chapter 15 is devoted to their reactions.

Monocytes* are generally the largest of all white blood cells and the third most common in the circulation (3% to 7%). As they mature, the nucleus becomes oval- or kidney-shaped—indented on one side, off center, and often contorted with fine wrinkles. The cytoplasm holds many fine vacuoles containing digestive enzymes. Monocytes are discharged by the bone marrow into the bloodstream,

Monocyte

where they live as phagocytes for a few days. Later, they leave the circulation to undergo final differentiation into **macrophages.***

* *eosinophil* (ee″-oh-sin′-oh-fil) Gr. *eos,* dawn, rosy, and *philos,* to love. Eosin is a red, acidic dye attracted to the granules.
* *basophil* (bay′-soh-fil) Gr. *basis,* foundation. The granules attract to basic dyes.
* *mast* From Ger. *mast,* food. Early cytologists thought these cells were filled with food vacuoles.

* *antibody* (an′-tih-bahd″-ee) Gr. *anti,* against, and O. E., *bodig,* body.
* *monocyte* (mon′-oh-syte) From *mono,* one, and *cytos,* cell.
* *macrophage* (mak′-roh-fayj) Gr. *macro,* large, and *phagein,* to eat. They are the "large eaters" of the tissues.

Macrophages are among the most versatile and important of cells. In general, they are responsible for

1. many types of specific and nonspecific phagocytic and killing functions (they assume the job of cellular housekeepers, "mopping up the messes" created by infection and inflammation);
2. processing foreign molecules and presenting them to lymphocytes; and
3. secreting biologically active compounds that assist, mediate, attract, and inhibit immune cells and reactions.

We touch upon these functions in several ensuing sections.

Another product of the monocyte cell line is **dendritic cells,** named for their long, thin cell processes. Immature dendritic cells move from the blood to the RES and lymphatic tissues, where they trap pathogens. Ingestion of bacteria and viruses stimulates dendritic cells to migrate to lymph nodes and the spleen to participate in reactions with lymphocytes.

Erythrocyte and Platelet Lines These elements stay in the circulatory system proper. Their development is also shown in figure 14.7.

Erythrocytes develop from stem cells in the bone marrow and lose their nucleus just prior to entering the circulation. The resultant red blood cells are simple, biconcave sacs of hemoglobin that transport oxygen and carbon dioxide to and from the tissues. These are the most numerous of circulating blood cells, appearing in stains as small pink circles. Red blood cells do not ordinarily have immune functions, though they can be the target of immune reactions.

Platelets are formed elements in circulating blood that are *not* whole cells. They are formed by the disintegration of a large, multinucleate cell, the megakaryocyte. In stains, platelets are blue-gray with fine red granules and are readily distinguished from cells by their small size. Platelets function primarily in hemostasis (plugging broken blood vessels to stop bleeding) and in releasing chemicals that act in blood clotting and inflammation. Some of the major characteristics of leukocytes are summarized in **table 14.2.**

Components and Functions of the Lymphatic System

The lymphatic part of the circulatory system is a compartmentalized network of vessels, cells, and specialized accessory organs **(figure 14.8).** It begins in the farthest reaches of the tissues as tiny capillaries that transport a special fluid (lymph) through an increasingly larger system of vessels and filters (lymph nodes). It eventually connects to major vessels that drain back into the regular circulatory system. Some major functions of the **lymphatic** or **lymphoid system** relating to immune defenses are:

1. to provide an auxiliary route for the return of extracellular fluid to the circulatory system proper;
2. to act as a "drain-off" system for the inflammatory response; and
3. to render surveillance, recognition, and protection against foreign materials through a system of lymphocytes, phagocytes, and antibodies.

Lymphatic Fluid **Lymph** is a plasmalike liquid carried by the lymphatic circulation. It is formed when certain blood components move out of the blood vessels into the extracellular spaces and diffuse or migrate into the lymphatic capillaries. Because of this, the composition of lymph parallels that of plasma in many ways. It is made up of water, dissolved salts, and 2% to 5% protein (especially antibodies and albumin). Like blood, it also transports numerous

TABLE 14.2	Characteristics of Leukocytes			
Cell Type	Prevalence in Circulation	Primary Function	Features	Appearance*
Neutrophils	55%–90% of white blood cells	General phagocytosis	Life span of 2 days, with only 4–10 hours spent in the circulation	Multilobed nuclei; small purple granules containing digestive enzymes
Eosinophils	1%–3% of white blood cells	Destruction of parasitic worms; mediators of allergy	Found in much higher numbers in the spleen and bone marrow	Bilobed nucleus with large orange granules containing toxic proteins, inflammatory mediators, and digestive enzymes
Basophils	0.5% of white blood cells	Active in allergy, inflammation, parasitic infections	Cytoplasmic granules contain histamines, prostaglandins, and other chemical mediators of the allergic response.	Pale-staining, constricted nuclei with dark blue to black granules
Monocytes	3%–7% of white blood cells	Phagocytosis, followed by final differentiation into macrophages and dendritic cells	Monocytes also secrete several chemicals that moderate the functions of the immune system.	Largest WBC; nuclei large, ovoid, and often indented—no cytoplasmic granules visible using a light microscope
Lymphocytes	20%–35% of white blood cells	Specific (acquired) immunity	Two types of lymphocytes exist. T cells are responsible for cell-mediated immunity, whereas B cells are responsible for humoral immunity.	Small spherical cells with uniformly-staining dark, round nuclei

*See examples in figure 14.7.

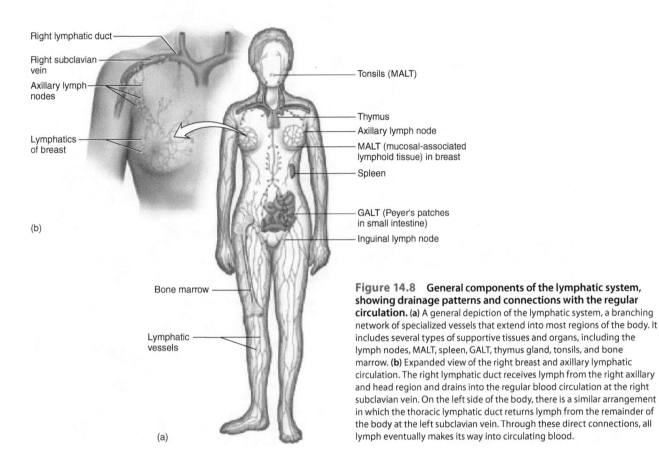

Right lymphatic duct

Right subclavian vein

Axillary lymph nodes

Lymphatics of breast

(b)

Tonsils (MALT)

Thymus

Axillary lymph node

MALT (mucosal-associated lymphoid tissue) in breast

Spleen

GALT (Peyer's patches in small intestine)

Inguinal lymph node

Bone marrow

Lymphatic vessels

(a)

Figure 14.8 General components of the lymphatic system, showing drainage patterns and connections with the regular circulation. (a) A general depiction of the lymphatic system, a branching network of specialized vessels that extend into most regions of the body. It includes several types of supportive tissues and organs, including the lymph nodes, MALT, spleen, GALT, thymus gland, tonsils, and bone marrow. **(b)** Expanded view of the right breast and axillary lymphatic circulation. The right lymphatic duct receives lymph from the right axillary and head region and drains into the regular blood circulation at the right subclavian vein. On the left side of the body, there is a similar arrangement in which the thoracic lymphatic duct returns lymph from the remainder of the body at the left subclavian vein. Through these direct connections, all lymph eventually makes its way into circulating blood.

white blood cells (especially lymphocytes) and miscellaneous materials such as fats, cellular debris, and infectious agents that have gained access to the tissue spaces. Unlike blood, red blood cells are not normally found in lymph.

Lymphatic Vessels The system of vessels that transports lymph is constructed along the lines of blood vessels **(figure 14.9).** The tiniest vessels, **lymphatic capillaries,** accompany the blood capillaries. The lymphatic capillaries permeate all parts of the body except the central nervous system and certain organs such as bone, placenta, and thymus. Their thin walls have a single layer of epithelial cells similar to blood capillaries, with loose junctions that allow free entry of ECF that collects from the circulatory system (see figure 14.4). Lymphatic vessels are found in particularly high numbers in the hands, feet, and around the areolae of the breast.

Two important differences between the bloodstream and the lymphatic system should be mentioned **(figure 14.10).** First, given that one of the main functions of the lymphatic system is returning lymph to the circulation, lymph flows only in one direction, moving from the extremities toward the heart. Eventually, it will be returned to the bloodstream through the thoracic duct and the right lymphatic duct near the base of the neck (see figure 14.8). The second difference concerns how lymph travels through the vessels of the lymphatic system. While blood is transported through the body by means of a dedicated pump (the heart), lymph is moved only through

the contraction of skeletal muscles that surround the lymphatic ducts. This dependence on muscle movement helps to explain the swelling of the hands and feet that sometimes occurs during the night (when muscles are inactive) yet goes away soon after waking.

The parasitic infection filariasis presents a dramatic example of what happens when the lymphatic drainage is blocked by an infectious agent (see figure 23.25). Filarial worms from the infection become caught in the lymph nodes and channels of the extremities and plug them up. This prevents lymph from flowing into the accessory ducts and back to the circulation. The buildup of lymph massively distorts limbs and other body parts such as the scrotum.

Lymphoid Organs Lymphatic organs and tissues with immune functions can be classified as primary and secondary, as summarized here:

Primary organs
 Thymus gland
 Bone marrow

Secondary organs and tissues
 Lymph nodes
 Spleen
 MALT—mucosal-associated lymphoid tissue
 SALT—skin-associated lymphoid tissue
 GALT—gut-associated lymphoid tissue (Peyer's patches)

(a) The finest level of lymphatic circulation begins with blind capillaries (green) that pick up foreign matter from the surrounding tissues and transport it in lymph away from the extremities via a system of small ducts.

(b) The ducts carry lymph into a circuit of larger ducts that ultimately flow into clusters of filtering organs, the lymph nodes.

(c) A section through a lymph node reveals the afferent ducts draining lymph into sinuses that house several types of white blood cells. Here, foreign material is filtered out and processed by lymphocytes, macrophages, and dendritic cells.

(d) and (e) Lymph continues to trickle from the lymph nodes via efferent ducts into a system of larger drainage vessels, which ultimately connect with large veins near the heart. In this way, cells and products of immunity continually enter the regular circulation.

Lymphatic capillary
Tissue cells
Capillary bed
Venule
Lymph duct
Arteriole
a
b
At cellular level of anatomy
Afferent lymphatic ducts
Section of lymph node
Parafollicle region
Medulla
Cortical follicles
At regional level of anatomy
Lymph node
Efferent lymphatic duct
c
Main lymphatic duct
Lymphatic duct
Lymphatic duct
Lymphatic duct
d
Major transport vessels
e
Blood circulation
Veins that feed into heart

Figure 14.9 Scheme of circulation in the lymphatic vessels and lymph nodes.

The **primary lymphoid organs** include the thymus and bone marrow, because they are a source of immune cells and a "nursery" for developing white blood cells. They are the sites of origin and maturation of lymphocytes—white blood cells with specific immune function. They subsequently release these cells to populate the secondary lymphatic sites.

Secondary lymphoid organs such as the spleen and lymph nodes are circulatory-based locations where encounters with microbes and immune responses often take place. Associated lymphoid tissues are collections of cells widely dispersed throughout body tissues such as the skin and mucous membranes, ready to react with any locally entering infectious agents.

Figure 14.10 Comparison of the circulation patterns of the regular circulatory and lymphatic systems. The movement of lymphatic flow is in one direction (green) from lymphatic capillaries to collecting vessels and ducts to large lymphatic trunks to subclavian veins to the heart. The flow of blood on the other hand, is cyclic, with blood continuously flowing through arteries to capillaries to veins to the heart and back around. With this combined system the lymphatics can collect excess tissue fluid and return it to the bloodstream. The two systems can also participate together in surveillance of the tissues for foreign invaders. Note: The lymphatic flow (green) is shown on only one side to keep the comparison uncluttered.

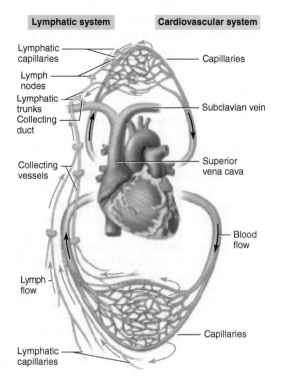

Lymphatic system | Cardiovascular system
Lymphatic capillaries
Lymph nodes
Lymphatic trunks
Collecting duct
Collecting vessels
Lymph flow
Lymphatic capillaries
Capillaries
Subclavian vein
Superior vena cava
Blood flow
Capillaries

Figure 14.11 The thymus gland. Immediately after birth, the thymus is a large organ that nearly fills the region over the midline of the upper thoracic region. In the adult, however, it is proportionately smaller (to compare, see figure 14.8a). Section shows the main anatomical regions of the thymus. Immature T cells enter through the cortex and migrate into the medulla as they mature.

The Thymus Gland The **thymus** originates in the embryo as two lobes in the pharyngeal region that fuse into a triangular structure. It is located in the thoracic cavity near the tip of the sternum. The size of the thymus is greatest proportionately at birth **(figure 14.11),** and it continues to exhibit high rates of activity and growth until puberty, after which it begins to shrink gradually through adulthood.

Children born without a complete thymus (DiGeorge syndrome, see chapter 16) or who have had their thymus surgically removed are severely immunodeficient and fail to thrive. Adults have developed enough mature T cells that removal of the thymus or reduction in its function has milder effects. Do not confuse the thymus with the thyroid gland, which is located in the cervical region near the larynx and has an entirely different function.

Lymph Nodes Lymph nodes are small, encapsulated, bean-shaped organs stationed, usually in clusters, along lymphatic channels and large blood vessels of the thoracic and abdominal cavities (see figure 14.8). Major aggregations of nodes occur in the loose connective tissue of the armpit (axillary nodes), groin (inguinal nodes), and neck (cervical nodes). Both the location and architecture of these nodes clearly specialize them for filtering out materials that have entered the lymph and providing appropriate cells and niches for immune reactions.

Spleen The spleen is a lymphoid organ in the upper portion of the abdominal cavity nestled below the diaphragm and left of the stomach. It is somewhat similar to a lymph node except that it serves as a filter for blood instead of lymph. While the spleen's primary function is to remove worn-out red blood cells from circulation, its most important immunologic function centers on the filtering of pathogens from the blood and their subsequent phagocytosis by resident macrophages. Although adults whose spleens have been surgically removed can live a relatively normal life, asplenic children are severely immunocompromised.

Associated Lymphoid Tissue Embedded throughout systems lined with mucous membranes are discrete bundles of lymphocytes and other white blood cells termed the **mucosal-associated lymphoid tissue** or **MALT.** The positioning of this widespread system provides a local, rapid mechanism for responding to the constant influx of microbes entering via the gastrointestinal, respiratory, urinary, and other portals of entry. The pharynx houses a prominent source of MALT in the form of tonsils. The breasts of pregnant and lactating women also become temporary sites of lymphoid tissues that add protective antibodies to breast milk (see colostrum, 15.3 Making Connections).

The intestinal tract houses the best-developed collection of lymphoid tissue, called **gut-associated lymphoid tissue,** or **GALT.** Examples of GALT include the appendix, and **Peyer's patches,** compact aggregations of lymphocytes in the ileum of the small intestine. GALT provides immune functions against intestinal pathogens and is a significant source of some types of antibodies. Other, less well-organized collections of secondary lymphoid tissue include *skin-associated lymphoid tissue* and *bronchial-associated lymphoid tissue.*

Check Your Progress SECTION 14.2

5. Describe the main elements of the process through which the immune system distinguishes self from foreign cells and particles.

6. How is surveillance of the tissues carried out and what is responsible for it?

7. What does the term *nonself* mean in reference to the immune system?

8. What are the main components of the reticuloendothelial system, and why is it also called the mononuclear phagocyte system?

9. How does the RES communicate with tissues and the vascular system?

10. Explain the functions of stem cells and summarize the stages of hematopoiesis.

11. Differentiate between granulocytes and agranulocytes.

12. Describe the main types of granulocytes and agranulocytes, their functions, and their incidence in the circulation.

13. Give the principal function of lymphocytes, and differentiate between the two lymphocyte types and between humoral and cell-mediated immunity.

14. What is lymph, and how is it formed?

15. Differentiate between primary and secondary lymphoid organs.

16. Outline the functions of the lymphatic system and describe the actions of associated lymphatic tissues such as MALT and GALT.

14.3 Second Line Defenses: Inflammation

 Expected Learning Outcomes

12. Describe the main events in the inflammatory reaction, and explain what is occurring in each.

13. Summarize the functions of cytokines, chemokines, and other inflammatory mediators.

14. Describe the mechanism behind fever, and explain its beneficial and harmful effects.

Now that we have introduced the principal anatomical and physiological framework of the immune system, we address some mechanisms that play important roles in host defenses: (1) inflammation, (2) phagocytosis, (3) interferon, and (4) complement. Because of the generalized nature of these defenses, they are primarily nonspecific in their effects, but they also support and interact with the specific immune responses described in chapter 15.

The Inflammatory Response: A Complex Concert of Reactions to Injury

At its most general level, **inflammation** is a reaction to any traumatic event in the tissues that restores homeostasis: It is a normal and necessary process that helps to clear away cellular debris. Most of us manifest inflammation in some way every day. It appears in the flare of a cut, the blistering of a burn, the painful lesion of an infection, and the symptoms of allergy, but sometimes it goes unnoticed.

> **Quick Search**
> To learn more about this process search for videos on "Acute Inflammation."

It is readily identifiable by a classic series of signs and symptoms characterized succinctly by four Latin terms: *rubor, calor, tumor,* and *dolor.* Rubor (redness) is caused by increased circulation and vasodilation in the injured tissues; calor (warmth) is the heat given off by the increased flow of blood; tumor (swelling) is caused by increased extracelluar fluid accumulating in the tissues; and dolor (pain) is caused by the stimulation of nerve endings from the pressure of swelling or by chemical mediators (**figure 14.12**). A fifth symptom, *loss of function,* is sometimes added for a complete picture of effects that can accompany inflammation. Although these manifestations are often unpleasant, they serve an important warning that injury has taken place and set in motion responses that can save the body from further injury.

Factors that can elicit an inflammatory response include trauma from infection (the primary emphasis here), tissue injury or death, and specific immune reactions. Although the details of inflammation are very complex, its chief functions can be summarized as follows:

1. to mobilize and attract immune components to the site of the injury,
2. to set in motion mechanisms to repair tissue damage and localize and clear away harmful substances, and
3. to destroy and block microbes from further invasion (**figure 14.13**).

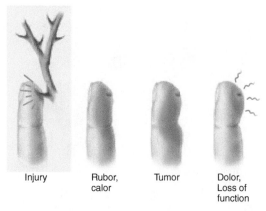

| Injury | Rubor, calor | Tumor | Dolor, Loss of function |

Figure 14.12 The response to injury. This classic series summarizes the reactions of the tissues to an assault. Each of the events is an indicator of one of the mechanisms of inflammation described in this chapter.

The inflammatory response is a powerful defensive reaction, a means for the body to maintain stability and restore itself after an injury. But when it is chronic, it has the potential to actually *cause* tissue injury, destruction, and disease (**Clinical Connections** page 441).

The Stages of Inflammation

The process leading to inflammation is a dynamic sequence of events that can be acute—lasting from a few minutes or hours—to chronic—lasting for days, weeks, or years. Once the initial injury has occurred, a chain reaction takes place at the site of damaged tissue, summoning beneficial cells and fluids into the injured area. As an example, we look at an injury at the microscopic level and observe the flow of major events (figure 14.13).

Vascular Changes: Early Inflammatory Events

Following an injury, some of the earliest changes occur in the vasculature (arterioles, capillaries, venules) in the vicinity of the damaged tissue. These changes are controlled by nervous stimulation, **chemical mediators,** and **cytokines*** released by blood cells, tissue cells, and platelets in the injured area. Some mediators are *vasoactive;* that is, they affect the endothelial cells and smooth muscle cells of blood vessels. Others are **chemotactic factors,** also called **chemokines,** that affect white blood cells. Inflammatory mediators cause fever, stimulate lymphocytes, prevent infection spread, and cause allergic symptoms (**14.1 Making Connections** and **figure 14.14**). Although the constriction of arterioles is stimulated first, it lasts for only a few seconds or minutes. Once a clot has formed to prevent blood loss, it is followed in quick succession by the opposite reaction, **vasodilation.** The overall effect of vasodilation is to increase the flow of blood into the area, which facilitates the influx of immune components and also causes redness and warmth (rubor and calor).

* *cytokine* (sy'-toh-kyne) Gr. *cytos,* cell, and *kemein,* to move. A protein or polypeptide produced by WBCs that regulates host defenses.

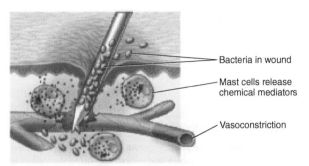

(a) **Injury/Immediate Reactions:** Blood vessels narrow (vasoconstriction); blood clots; and mast cells release chemokines and cytokines into injured area.

- Bacteria in wound
- Mast cells release chemical mediators
- Vasoconstriction

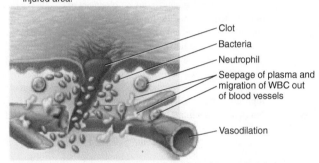

(b) **Vascular Reactions:** Nearby blood vessels dilate; increased blood flow; increased vascular permeability; increased leakage of fluid forms exudate.

- Clot
- Bacteria
- Neutrophil
- Seepage of plasma and migration of WBC out of blood vessels
- Vasodilation

(c) **Edema and Pus Formation:** Collection of fluid; edema/swelling; infiltration by neutrophils and formation of pus.

- Scab
- Neutrophils
- Pus
- Fibrous exudate

(d) **Resolution/Scar Formation:** Macrophages, lymphocytes, and fibroblasts migrate in; initiate immune response and repair of injury; scar and loss of normal tissue.

- Scar
- Lymphocytes
- Fibroblast
- Macrophage

☐ Rubor/calor of inflammation ☐ Edema (tumor) and dolor ☐ Repaired or damaged tissue

Process Figure 14.13 **The major events in inflammation.**

CLINICAL CONNECTIONS

The Down Side of Inflammation

Not every aspect of inflammation is protective or results in the proficient resolution of tissue damage. As one looks over a list of diseases, it is rather striking how many of them are due in part or even completely to an overreactive or dysfunctional inflammatory response.

Some *-itis* reactions mentioned in chapter 13 are a case in point. Inflammatory exudates that build up in the brain in African trypanosomiasis, cryptococcosis, and other brain infections can be so injurious to the nervous system that impairment is permanent. Frequently, an inflammatory reaction leads to an abscess, a swollen mass of neutrophils and dead, liquefied tissue that can harbor live pathogens in the center. Abscesses are a prominent feature of staphylococcal, amebic, and enteric infections.

Other pathologic manifestations of chronic diseases—for example, the tubercles of tuberculosis, the lesions of late syphilis, the disfiguring nodules of leprosy, and the cutaneous ulcers of leishmaniasis—are due to an aberrant tissue response called *granuloma formation* (see Case Study figure, page 427). Granulomas develop not only in response to microbes but also to inanimate foreign bodies that are difficult to break down. This condition is initiated when neutrophils and macrophages ineffectively and incompletely phagocytose the pathogens or materials involved in an inflammatory reaction. This failure to manage the debris of inflammation is sometimes referred to as "frustrated phagocytosis." Macrophages respond by storing ingested materials in vacuoles and becoming inactive. Over a given time period, macrophages fuse into giant, inactive multinucleate cells called foreign body giant cells. These sites are further infiltrated with lymphocytes. The resultant collections make the tissue appear granular—hence, the name. A granuloma can exist in the tissue for months, years, or even a lifetime. This chapter's Case Study provides a striking example of massive proliferation of failed phagocytes.

One common cytokine, tumor necrosis factor (TNF), is a potent inflammatory mediator. It regulates a wide variety of initial immune activities such as phagocytosis, and it is a powerful pyrogen. Unfortunately, the overproduction of TNF is also involved in a number of diseases such as septic shock, psoriasis, asthma, and autoimmunity. Several drugs (adalimumab [Humira] and etanercept [Enbrel], for example) have been developed as therapy to counteract the damaging effects of TNF.

Medical science is rapidly searching for additional applications based on new information about inflammatory mediators. One highly promising area appears to be the use of chemokine inhibitors that could reduce chemotaxis and the massive, destructive influx of leukocytes. Such therapy could ultimately be used for certain cancers, hardening of arteries, and Alzheimer disease.

Explain how inflammatory mediators stimulate tissue injury and disease. *Answer available at http://www.mhhe.com/talaro9*

14.1 MAKING CONNECTIONS

The Dynamics of Inflammatory Mediators

Just as the nervous system is coordinated by a complex communications network, so too is the immune system. Hundreds of small, active molecules are constantly being secreted to regulate, stimulate, suppress, and otherwise control the many aspects of cell development, inflammation, and immunity. These substances are the products of several types of cells, including monocytes, macrophages, lymphocytes, fibroblasts, mast cells, platelets, and endothelial cells of blood vessels. Their effects may be local or systemic, short term or long lasting, nonspecific or specific, protective or pathologic.

The field of cytokines has become so increasingly complex that we can include here only an overview of the major groups of important cytokines and other mediators. The major functional types can be categorized into

1. cytokines that mediate nonspecific immune reactions such as inflammation and phagocytosis,
2. cytokines that regulate the growth and activation of lymphocytes,
3. cytokines that activate immune reactions during inflammation,
4. hematopoiesis factors for white blood cells,
5. vasoactive mediators, and
6. miscellaneous inflammatory mediators.

Nonspecific Mediators of Inflammation and Immunity

- *Tumor necrosis factor* (*TNF*), a substance from macrophages, lymphocytes, and other cells. It increases chemotaxis and phagocytosis and stimulates other cells to secrete inflammatory cytokines. It also serves as an endogenous pyrogen and stimulates blood coagulation. Unfortunately it is has the potential to cause damage to tissues when produced in excess.
- *Interferon alpha and interferon beta*, produced by leukocytes and fibroblasts, inhibit virus replication and cell division and increase the action of certain lymphocytes that kill other cells.
- *Interleukin* is a term that refers to a group of small peptides originally isolated from leukocytes. There are currently more than 36 known interleukins. We now know that other cells besides leukocytes can synthesize them and that they have a variety of biological activities.
 - *Interleukin-1* (*IL-1*), a product of macrophages and epithelial cells. It has many of the same biological activities as TNF, such as inducing fever and activating certain white blood cells.
 - *Interleukin-6*, secreted by macrophages, lymphocytes, and fibroblasts. Its primary effects are to stimulate the growth of B cells and to increase the synthesis of liver proteins.
- *Various chemokines.* By definition, chemokines are cytokines that stimulate the movement and migration of white blood cells (chemotactic factors). Included among these are complement $C5_a$, interleukin-8, and platelet-activating factor.

Cytokines That Regulate Lymphocyte Growth and Activation

- *Interleukin-2,* the primary growth factor from T cells. Interestingly, it acts on the same cells that secrete it. It stimulates mitosis and secretion of other cytokines. In B cells, it is a growth factor and stimulus for antibody synthesis.
- *Interleukin-4,* a stimulus for the development of B cells and production of allergy antibodies. It inhibits macrophage actions.
- *Granulocyte colony-stimulating factor* (*G-CSF*), produced by T cells, macrophages, and neutrophils. It stimulates the activation and differentiation of neutrophils.
- *Macrophage colony-stimulating factor* (*M-CSF*), produced by a variety of cells. M-CSF promotes the growth and development of macrophages from undifferentiated precursor cells.
- *Interferon gamma,* a T-cell-derived mediator whose primary function is to activate macrophages. It also promotes the differentiation of T and B cells, activates neutrophils, and stimulates diapedesis.

Vasoactive Mediators

- *Histamine,* a vasoactive mediator produced by mast cells and basophils. It causes vasodilation, increased vascular permeability, and mucus production. It functions primarily in inflammation and allergy.
- *Serotonin,* a mediator produced by platelets and intestinal cells. It causes smooth muscle contraction, inhibits gastric secretion, and acts as a neurotransmitter.
- *Bradykinin,* a vasoactive amine from the blood or tissues. It stimulates smooth muscle contraction and increases vascular permeability, mucus production, and pain. It is particularly active in allergic reactions.

Miscellaneous Inflammatory Mediators

- *Prostaglandins,* produced by most body cells; complex chemical mediators that can have opposing effects (for example, dilation or constriction of blood vessels) and are powerful stimulants of inflammation and pain.
- *Leukotrienes* stimulate the contraction of smooth muscle and enhance vascular permeability. They are implicated in the more severe manifestations of immediate allergies (constriction of airways).
- *Platelet-activating factor,* a substance released from basophils, causes the aggregation of platelets and the release of other chemical mediators during immediate allergic reactions.

Which inflammatory mediators would be involved in rubor? In tumor? In dolor? In calor? *Answers available at http://www.mhhe.com/talaro9*

Edema: Leakage of Vascular Fluid into Tissues

Postcapillary venules, small veins that drain blood from the capillary beds, are important in several aspects of inflammation. When they constrict, this causes a slowing of circulation and a pooling of extracellular fluid at the site. Some vasoactive substances cause the endothelial cells in the walls of these venules to separate and form gaps through which blood-borne components exude into the extracellular spaces. Capillaries also become leaky under the influence of cytokines. The fluid part that escapes into the tissues is called the *exudate.* Accumulation of this fluid gives rise to local swelling and hardness known as **edema.** The edematous exudate contains varying amounts of plasma proteins, such as globulins, albumin, the clotting protein fibrinogen, blood cells, and cellular debris. Depending upon its content, the exudate may be clear (called *serous*),

Figure 14.14 **Major chemical mediators of the inflammatory response and their effects.** See 14.1 Making Connections for more information on the effects of mediators.

or it may contain red blood cells or **pus.** Pus is composed mainly of white blood cells, microbes, and the debris generated by phagocytosis. In some types of edema, the fibrinogen is converted to fibrin threads that enmesh the injury site (see figure 14.13c). Within an hour, multitudes of neutrophils responding chemotactically to special signaling molecules converge on the injured site.

Unique Dynamic Characteristics of White Blood Cells In order for WBCs to leave the blood vessels and enter the tissues, they adhere to the inner walls of the smaller blood vessels such as capillaries and venules. From this position, they are poised to migrate out of the blood into the tissue spaces by a process called **diapedesis.***

Diapedesis, also known as transmigration, is aided by several related characteristics of WBCs. For example, they are actively motile and readily change shape. Their migration is assisted by the nature of the endothelial cells lining venules. Venules contain complex adhesive receptors that develop increased "stickiness" under the influence of inflammatory mediators. This causes WBCs to adhere or marginate at the endothelial cells. From this location, they can readily crawl into the extracellular spaces (**figure 14.15**).

Another factor in the migratory habits of these WBCs is **chemotaxis,*** defined as the tendency of cells to migrate in response to a specific chemical stimulus released at a site of injury or infection. Through this means, cells swarm from many compartments to the site of infection and remain there to perform general functions such as phagocytosis, repair, and specific immune reactions. These basic properties are absolutely essential for the sort of intercommunication and deployment of cells required for most immune reactions.

The Benefits of Edema and Chemotaxis Both the formation of edematous exudate and the infiltration of neutrophils are physiologically beneficial activities. The influx of fluid dilutes toxic substances, and the fibrin clot can effectively trap microbes and prevent their further spread. The neutrophils that aggregate in the inflamed site are immediately involved in phagocytosing and destroying microbes, dead tissues, and particulate matter (by mechanisms discussed in section 14.4 on phagocytosis). In some types of inflammation, accumulated phagocytes contribute to pus. Certain bacteria (streptococci, staphylococci, gonococci, and meningococci) are

* *diapedesis* (dye″-ah-puh-dee′-sis) Gr. *dia,* through, and *pedan,* to leap.

* *chemotaxis* (kee-moh-tak′-sis) NL. *chemo,* chemical, and *taxis,* arrangement.

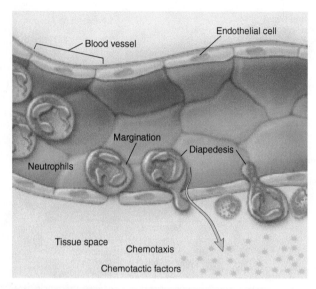

Figure 14.15 **Diapedesis and chemotaxis of leukocytes.** Cross section of a venule depicts white blood cells squeezing themselves between spaces in the vessel wall through diapedesis. This process also indicates how the pool of leukocytes adheres to the endothelial wall. From this site, they are poised to migrate out of the vessel into the tissue space and respond to chemotactic factors released during various inflammatory reactions.

especially powerful attractants for neutrophils and are thus termed **pyogenic**, or pus-forming, bacteria.

Late Reactions of Inflammation Sometimes a mild inflammation can be resolved by edema and phagocytosis. Inflammatory reactions that last more than a few days attract a collection of monocytes, lymphocytes, and macrophages to the reaction site. Clearance of pus, cellular debris, dead neutrophils, and damaged tissue is performed by macrophages, the only cells that can engulf and dispose of such large masses. At the same time, specific immune reactions of acquired immunity are brought into play. B lymphocytes react with foreign molecules and cells by producing specific antimicrobial proteins (antibodies), and T lymphocytes kill intruders directly. Late in the process, the tissue is completely repaired, if possible, or replaced by connective tissue in the form of a scar (see figure 14.13*d*). If the inflammation cannot be relieved or resolved in this way, it can become chronic and create a long-term pathologic condition (see Making Connections 14.1).

Fever: An Adjunct to Inflammation

An important systemic component of inflammation is fever, defined as an abnormally elevated body temperature. Although fever is a nearly universal symptom of infection, it is also associated with certain allergies, cancers, and other organic illnesses. Fevers whose causes are unknown are called fevers of unknown origin, or FUO.

The body temperature is normally maintained by a control center in the hypothalamus region of the brain. This thermostat regulates the body's heat production and heat loss and sets the core temperature at around 37°C (98.6°F), with slight fluctuations (1°F) during a daily cycle. Fever is initiated when a circulating substance called

CLINICAL CONNECTIONS

Some Facts About Fever

Fever is such a prevalent reaction that it is a prominent symptom of hundreds of diseases. For millenia, people believed fever was part of an innate protective response. Hippocrates offered the idea that it was the body's attempt to burn off a noxious agent. Sir Thomas Sydenham wrote over 400 years ago: "Why, fever itself is Nature's instrument!" So widely held was the view that fever could be therapeutic that pyretotherapy (treating disease by inducing an intermittent fever) was once used to treat syphilis, gonorrhea, leishmaniasis (a protozoan infection), and cancer. This attitude fell out of favor when drugs for relieving fever (aspirin) first came into use in the early 1900s, and an adverse view of fever began to dominate.

Changing Views of Fever

In recent times, the medical community has returned to the original concept of fever as more healthful than harmful. Experiments with vertebrates indicate that fever is a universal reaction, even in cold-blooded animals such as lizards and fish. A study with febrile (feverish) mice and frogs indicated that fever increases the rate of antibody synthesis. Work with tissue cultures showed that increased temperatures stimulate the activities of T cells and increase the effectiveness of interferon. Artificially infected rabbits and pigs allowed to remain febrile survive at a higher rate than those given suppressant drugs. Fever appears to enhance phagocytosis of staphylococci by neutrophils in guinea pigs and humans.

Hot and Cold: Why Do Chills Accompany Fever?

Fever almost never occurs as a single response; it is usually accompanied by chills. What causes this oddity—that a person flushed with fever periodically feels cold and trembles uncontrollably? The explanation lies in the natural physiological interaction between the thermostat in the hypothalamus and the temperature of the blood. For example, if the thermostat has been set (by pyrogen) at 102°F but the blood temperature is 99°F, the muscles are stimulated to contract involuntarily (shivering) as a means of producing heat. In addition, the vessels in the skin constrict, creating a sensation of cold, and the piloerector muscles in the skin cause goose bumps to form.

Explain the physiological mechanism for feeling cold during a fever.
Answer available at http://www.mhhe.com/talaro9

pyrogen* resets the hypothalamic thermostat to a higher setting. This change signals the musculature to increase heat production and peripheral arterioles to decrease heat loss through vasoconstriction (**Clinical Connections,** above). Fevers range in severity from low-grade (37.7°C to 38.3°C, or 100°F to 101°F) to moderate (38.8°C to 39.4°C, or 102°F to 103°F) to high (40.0°C to 41.1°C, or 104°F to 106°F). Pyrogens are described as *exogenous* (coming from outside the body) or *endogenous* (originating internally). Exogenous pyrogens are products of infectious agents such as viruses, bacteria,

** pyrogen* (py'-roh-jen) Gr. *pyr,* fire, and *gennan,* produce. Same origin as *funeral pyre* and *pyromaniac.*

protozoans, and fungi. One well-characterized exogenous pyrogen is endotoxin, the lipopolysaccharide found in the cell walls of gram-negative bacteria. Blood, blood products, vaccines, or injectable solutions can also contain exogenous pyrogens. Endogenous pyrogens are liberated by monocytes, neutrophils, and macrophages during the process of phagocytosis and appear to be a natural part of the immune response. Two potent pyrogens released by macrophages are interleukin-1 (IL-1) and tumor necrosis factor (TNF).

Benefits of Fever The association of fever with infection strongly suggests that it serves a beneficial role, a view still being debated but gaining acceptance. Aside from its practical and medical importance as a sign of a physiological disruption, increased body temperature has additional benefits:

- Fever inhibits multiplication of temperature-sensitive microorganisms such as the poliovirus, cold viruses, herpes zoster virus, systemic and subcutaneous fungal pathogens, *Mycobacterium* species, and the syphilis spirochete.
- Fever impedes the nutrition of bacteria by reducing the availability of iron. It has been demonstrated that during fever, the macrophages stop releasing their iron stores, which could retard several enzymatic reactions needed for bacterial growth.
- Fever increases metabolism and stimulates immune reactions and naturally protective physiological processes. It speeds up hematopoiesis, phagocytosis, and specific immune reactions.

Treatment of Fever With this revised perspective on fever, whether to suppress it or not can be a difficult decision. Some advocates feel that a slight to moderate fever in an otherwise healthy person should be allowed to run its course in light of its potential benefits and minimal side effects. All medical experts do agree that high and prolonged fevers or fevers in children or patients with cardiovascular disease, seizures, and respiratory ailments are risky and must be treated immediately with fever-suppressant drugs. The classic therapy for fever is an antipyretic drug such as aspirin or acetaminophen (Tylenol) that lowers the setting of the hypothalamic center and restores normal temperature. Any physical technique that increases heat loss (tepid baths, for example) can also help reduce the core temperature.

 Check Your Progress SECTION 14.3

17. Describe the major events in the inflammatory response, including the stimuli, physiological reactions, and signs and symptoms.
18. Of rubor, calor, dolor, and tumor, which are signs and which are symptoms?
19. What actions of the inflammatory and immune defenses account for swollen lymph nodes and leukocytosis?
20. What is pus, and what does it indicate?
21. In what ways can edema be beneficial and in what ways is it harmful?
22. Describe the physiological events leading to fever and review the ways that fever is naturally beneficial.
23. Explain the processes of diapedesis and chemotaxis, and show how they interrelate.
24. Briefly account for the origins and actions of the major types of inflammatory mediators and cytokines.

14.4 Second Line Defenses: Phagocytosis, Interferon, and Complement

 Expected Learning Outcomes

15. Define *phagocytosis* and identify which cells serve this function.
16. Indicate the major stages of phagocytosis, and describe what is happening at each stage.
17. Explain how phagocytes kill pathogens.
18. Describe the origin of interferon, and explain its role in controlling viruses and other immune functions.
19. Characterize the complement system, its origins, and basic functions.

Phagocytosis: Partner to Inflammation and Immunity

By any standard, a phagocyte represents an impressive piece of living machinery, meandering through the tissues to seek, capture, and destroy a target. The general activities of phagocytes are:

1. to survey the tissue compartments and discover microbes, particulate matter (dust, carbon particles, antigen-antibody complexes), and injured or dead cells;
2. to ingest and eliminate these materials; and
3. to extract immunogenic information (antigens) from foreign matter.

Major Categories of Phagocytes

It is generally accepted that all cells have some capacity to engulf materials, but professional phagocytes do it for a living. The three main types of phagocytes are neutrophils, monocytes, and macrophages.

Neutrophils and Eosinophils As previously stated, neutrophils are general-purpose phagocytes that react early in the inflammatory response to bacteria and other foreign materials and to damaged tissue. A common sign of bacterial infection is a high neutrophil count in the blood (neutrophilia), and neutrophils are also a primary component of pus. Eosinophils are attracted to sites of parasitic infections and antigen-antibody reactions, though they play only a minor phagocytic role.

Extended Functions of Neutrophils Neutrophils are truly one of the "workhorses" of innate immunity. In addition to their phagocytic functions, they also have a distinct system for capturing pathogens called *neutrophil extracellular traps*, or NETS. Neutrophils are programmed to die after they have gone through their regular engulfment and killing of bacteria and other pathogens. But their death does not end their protective actions. Dying neutrophils throw out a fibrous matrix composed of DNA, enzymes, histones, and other cell contents that continue to stop invading microbes even after the cells are completely lysed. This NET works at several levels to trap bacteria and fungi, degrade their virulence factors, kill them with microbicidal chemicals, and, to top it off, immobilize microbes and prevent them from spreading.

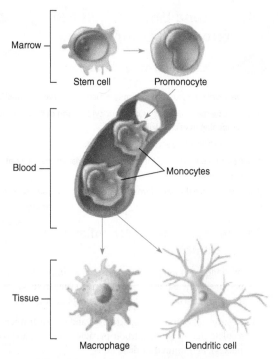

Marrow

Stem cell Promonocyte

Blood

Monocytes

Tissue

Macrophage Dendritic cell

Figure 14.16 The developmental stages of monocytes and macrophages. The cells progress through maturational stages in the bone marrow and peripheral blood. Once in the tissues, a macrophage can remain nomadic or take up residence in a specific organ.

Macrophages: Large-Tissue Phagocytes After emigrating out of the bloodstream into the tissues, monocytes are transformed by various inflammatory mediators into macrophages. This process is marked by an increase in size and by enhanced development of lysosomes and other organelles **(figure 14.16).** At one time, macrophages were classified as either fixed (adherent to tissue) or wandering, but this terminology can be misleading. All macrophages retain the capacity to move about. Whether they reside in a specific organ or wander depends upon their stage of development and the immune stimuli they receive. Specialized macrophages called *histiocytes* migrate to a certain tissue and remain there during their life span. Examples are alveolar (lung) macrophages; Kupffer cells in the liver; Langerhans cells in the skin; and macrophages in the spleen, lymph nodes, bone marrow, kidney, bone, and brain. Other macrophages do not reside permanently in a particular tissue and drift nomadically throughout the RES. Not only are macrophages dynamic scavengers, but they also process foreign substances and prepare them for reactions with certain lymphocytes (see chapter 15).

Mechanisms of Phagocytic Recognition, Engulfment, and Killing

The term **phagocytosis** literally means "eating cell process." But phagocytosis is more than just the physical act of engulfment, because phagocytes also actively attack and dismantle foreign cells with a wide array of antimicrobial substances. Phagocytosis can

occur as an isolated event performed by a lone phagocytic cell responding to a minor irritant in its area or as part of the orchestrated events of inflammation described in section 14.3. The events in phagocytosis include chemotaxis, ingestion, phagolysosome formation, destruction, and elimination **(figure 14.17).**

Quick Search For more information on this subject search the internet for "Bacterial Phagocytosis by Neutrophils."

Chemotaxis, Binding, and Ingestion Phagocytes migrate into a region of inflammation with a deliberate sense of direction, attracted by a gradient of stimulant products from the pathogen and host tissue at the site of injury.

Once a phagocyte encounters the pathogen, it uses its toll-like receptors (TLRs, discussed in section 14.2) to make contact with the pathogen (figure 14.17). Recall that TLRs are receptors that recognize and bind the pathogen-associated molecular pattern (PAMP) receptors of various microbes. There are about 10 different TLRs in the membranes of phagocytes. The exposed end of a receptor hooks on to a PAMP and immediately dimerizes or joins with a second TLR to encase the molecule **(figure 14.18).** This relays a signal into the nucleus that stimulates the intracellular phagocytic processes and the release of chemical mediators.

On the scene of an inflammatory reaction, phagocytes often trap cells or debris against the fibrous network of connective tissue or the wall of blood and lymphatic vessels. Once the phagocyte has "caught" its prey, it extends pseudopods that enclose the cells or particles in a pocket and internalize them in a vacuole called a *phagosome.*

Phagolysosome Formation and Killing In a short time, **lysosomes** migrate to the scene of the phagosome and fuse with it to form a **phagolysosome.** Other granules containing antimicrobial chemicals are released into the phagolysosome, forming a potent brew designed to poison and then dismantle the ingested material (see figure 14.17). The destructiveness of phagocytosis is evident by the death of bacteria within 30 minutes after contacting this battery of antimicrobial substances.

Destruction and Elimination Systems Destructive chemicals await the microbes in the phagolysosome. The oxygen-dependent system, known as the **respiratory burst,** or oxidative burst elaborates products of oxygen metabolism called **reactive oxygen intermediates (ROI).** Myeloperoxidase, an enzyme found in granulocytes, forms halogen ions (OCl^-) that are strong oxidizing agents. Other products of oxygen metabolism such as hydrogen peroxide, the superoxide anion (O_2^-), activated or singlet oxygen ($^1O^-$), and the hydroxyl free radical (HO) separately and together have formidable killing power. This series of reactive oxygen products delivers a "knockout" punch necessary to kill aerobic pathogens such as fungi and many bacteria (see this chapter's Case Study). Other chemicals that come into play are lactic acid, lysozyme, and *nitric oxide* (NO), a powerful mediator that kills bacteria and inhibits viral replication. Cationic proteins that injure bacterial cell membranes and a number of proteolytic and other hydrolytic enzymes complete the job. The bits of undigestible debris are

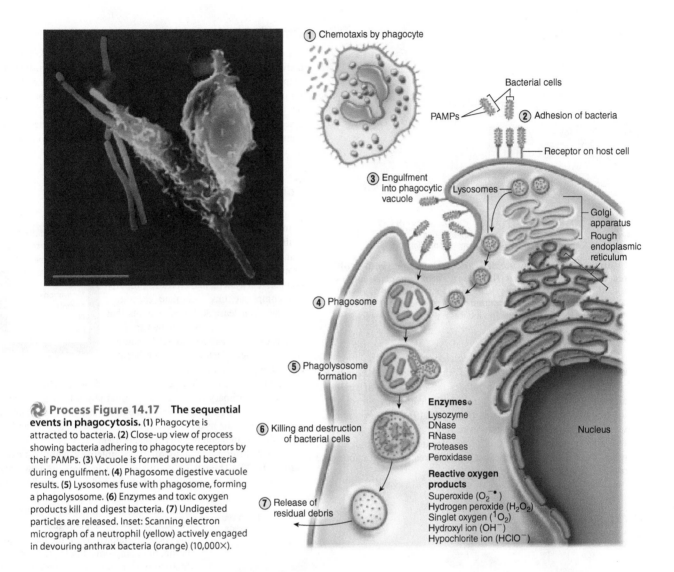

Process Figure 14.17 The sequential events in phagocytosis. (1) Phagocyte is attracted to bacteria. **(2)** Close-up view of process showing bacteria adhering to phagocyte receptors by their PAMPs. **(3)** Vacuole is formed around bacteria during engulfment. **(4)** Phagosome digestive vacuole results. **(5)** Lysosomes fuse with phagosome, forming a phagolysosome. **(6)** Enzymes and toxic oxygen products kill and digest bacteria. **(7)** Undigested particles are released. Inset: Scanning electron micrograph of a neutrophil (yellow) actively engaged in devouring anthrax bacteria (orange) (10,000×).

Figure labels:
1. Chemotaxis by phagocyte
2. Adhesion of bacteria — Bacterial cells — PAMPs — Receptor on host cell
3. Engulfment into phagocytic vacuole — Lysosomes — Golgi apparatus — Rough endoplasmic reticulum
4. Phagosome
5. Phagolysosome formation
6. Killing and destruction of bacterial cells
7. Release of residual debris

Nucleus

Enzymes
Lysozyme
DNase
RNase
Proteases
Peroxidase

Reactive oxygen products
Superoxide ($O_2^{-\bullet}$)
Hydrogen peroxide (H_2O_2)
Singlet oxygen (1O_2)
Hydroxyl ion (OH^-)
Hypochlorite ion ($HClO^-$)

released from the macrophage by exocytosis. As we shall see in chapter 15, macrophages and dendritic cells combine phagocytosis with further processing of microbial antigens required for specific immune responses with lymphocytes.

Interferon: Antiviral Cytokines and Immune Stimulants

Interferon (IFN) was described in chapter 12 as a small protein produced naturally by certain white blood and tissue cells. It is used in therapy against certain viral infections and cancer and can be used as an immune enhancer, as we saw in this chapter's Case Study. Although the interferon system was originally thought to be directed exclusively against viruses, it is now known to be involved also in defenses against other microbes and in immune regulation and intercommunication. Three major types are *interferon alpha,* a product of lymphocytes and macrophages; *interferon beta,* a prod-

uct of fibroblasts and epithelial cells; and *interferon gamma,* a product of T cells. See 14.1 Making Connections for a summary of interferon actions.

All three classes of interferon are produced in response to viruses, RNA, immune products, and various antigens. Their biological activities are extensive. In all cases, they bind to cell surfaces and induce changes in genetic expression, but the exact results vary. In addition to antiviral effects discussed in the next section, all three IFNs can inhibit the expression of cancer genes and have tumor suppressor effects. Interferon alpha and IFN beta stimulate phagocytes, and IFN gamma is an immune regulator of macrophages and T and B cells.

Characteristics of Antiviral Interferon

When a virus binds to the receptors on a host cell, a signal is sent to the nucleus that directs the cell to synthesize interferon. After transcribing and translating the interferon gene, newly synthesized

Figure 14.18 Phagocyte detection and signaling with toll-like receptors. Toll-like receptors (TLRs) span the membrane of phagocytes and other cells of the immune system. When a molecule such as a PAMP on a particular pathogen is recognized by this receptor, the TLRs merge and bind the foreign molecule. This induces production of chemicals and triggers engulfment.

interferon molecules are rapidly secreted by the cell into the extracellular space, where they bind to other host cells. The binding of interferon to a second cell induces the production of another class of proteins that inhibit viral multiplication by preventing the translation of viral proteins (**figure 14.19**). Interferon is not virus-specific, so its synthesis in response to one type of virus will also protect against other types. Because this protein is an inhibitor of viruses, it has been a valuable treatment for a number of viral infections.

Other Roles of Interferon

Interferons are also important immune regulatory cytokines that activate or instruct the development of white blood cells. For example, interferon alpha produced by T lymphocytes activates a subset of cells called natural killer (NK) cells. In addition, one type of interferon beta plays a role in the maturation of B and T lymphocytes and in inflammation. Interferon gamma inhibits cancer cells, stimulates B lymphocytes, activates macrophages, and enhances the effectiveness of phagocytosis.

Complement: A Versatile Backup System

Among its many overlapping functions, the immune system has another complex and multiple-duty system called **complement** that, like inflammation and phagocytosis, is brought into play at several levels. The complement system, named for its property of "complementing" immune reactions, consists of at least 30 blood proteins that work in concert to destroy a wide variety of bacteria, viruses, and parasites. The sources of complement factors are liver hepatocytes, lymphocytes, and monocytes.

> **Quick Search**
> For a dynamic look at the complement system, look up "Activation of Complement" at McGraw-Hill Higher Ed.

Complement functions as a *positive feedback loop* or *cascade reaction*. Its primary action is a sequential physiological response like that of blood clotting, in which the first substance in a chemical series activates the next substance, which activates the next, and so on, until a desired end product is reached.

Three different versions of the complement pathways exist (**figure 14.20**). Their main distinguishing features are how they are activated, major participating factors, and specificity. The end stages of all three converge at the same point and yield a similar end result, that is, destruction of a pathogen. Because the focus of damage is on the cell membrane, the complement defense is not effective on microbes such as gram-positive bacteria and fungi whose outer walls block access to the membrane. The *classical pathway* is the most specific, activated mainly by the presence of antibody bound to microorganisms. In the nonspecific *lectin pathway*, a host serum protein or lectin binds a sugar called mannan present in the walls of fungi and other microbes. (Proteins that bind carbohydrates are called lectins.) The *alternative pathway* is initiated by complement proteins binding to certain surface molecules of microbes. Note that because the complement numbers (C1 to C9) are based on the order of their discovery, some factors are not activated in numerical order.

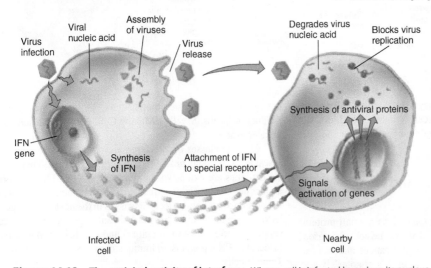

Figure 14.19 The antiviral activity of interferon. When a cell is infected by a virus, its nucleus is triggered to transcribe and translate the interferon (IFN) gene. Interferon diffuses out of the cell and binds to IFN receptors on nearby uninfected cells, where it induces production of proteins that eliminate viral genes and block viral replication. Note that the original cell is not protected by IFN and that IFN does not prevent viruses from invading the protected cells.

(a) **Initiation**

Classical Pathway	MB-Lectin Pathway	Alternative Pathway
Complement-fixing antibodies have rapid, specific effects	Mannose-binding lectin (MBL) binds mannose on pathogen surfaces. Nonspecific for bacteria and viruses	Molecules on surfaces of bacteria, fungi, viruses, and parasites. Nonspecific
C1q, C1r, C1s, Factors C4, C2, C3	MBL, MASP-1, MASP-2, Factors C4, C2, C3	Factors B, D and, C3

C3 convertase converts the C3 molecule to an activator of the cascade — C3$_b$.

C3 convertase enzyme

Gram-negative bacterial cell

C5

C3

C5$_b$ C3$_b$

C3$_a$ C5$_a$

(b) **Cascade and Amplification.** C5 factor is acted on by C3$_b$, which converts it to C5$_b$. C5$_b$ becomes bound to the membrane and serves as the starting molecule for the chain of events that assemble the complex in (c) and (d).

C8 C9

C6 C5$_b$

C7

Two products of the cascade reaction — C3$_a$ and C5$_a$ — have additional inflammatory functions. Both molecules stimulate mast cell degranulation, enhance chemotaxis of white blood cells, and act as inflammatory mediators.

(c) **Polymerization.** C5$_b$ is a reactive site for the final assembly of an attack complex. In series, C6, C7, and C8 aggregate with C5$_b$ and become integrated into the membrane. They form a substrate upon which the final component, C9, can bind. Up to 15 of these C9 units ring the central core of the final membrane attack complex (MAC).

Completed MAC Lysis

(d) **Membrane Attack.** Insertion of MACs produces hundreds of tiny holes in the cell membrane. This can cause lysis and death of eukaryotic cells and many gram-negative bacteria.

Lysis of bacterial cell

Process Figure 14.20 Overview of the complement pathways. (a) All three pathways have different triggers and starting points, but they all converge at the same place, C3 convertase. This enzyme begins the series of reactions **(b,c,d)** that give rise to the membrane attack complex characteristic of the complement "machinery." The final result is the formation of tiny openings in the cell membrane and the destruction of the target pathogen.

Overall Stages in the Complement Cascade

In general, the complement cascade goes through four stages: initiation, amplification and cascade, polymerization, and membrane attack. The starting reaction requires some type of initiator molecule such as antibodies, lectins, or microbial surface receptors **(figure 14.20a)**, depending on the pathway. The presence of this initiator on the pathogen's membrane propels the chain of actions involving complement chemicals C1 through C4, with each step serving a dual purpose. We are omitting the fine details of the amplification part of the complement system, but the end result is a molecule, **C3,** that is a key factor in subsequent polymerization of the remaining complement factors in the membrane of the target cell. C3 is acted on by a convertase enzyme that splits it into factors $C3_a$ and $C3_b$. $C3_b$ forms the recognition site and anchor for the final series of reactions to come **(figure 14.20b)**. $C3_b$ by itself provides an additional defense, called opsonization, to coat the surface of some bacterial cells and make them easier to phagocytose. This is similar to some actions of antibodies described in chapter 15.

$C3_b$ moves the cascade reaction forward by splitting factor C5 into $C5_a$ and $C5_b$. One of these molecules—$C5_b$—is key to finishing up polymerization of the remaining complement factors described next. You will notice that the two cleavage products—$C3_a$ and $C5_a$—have functions of their own. Both of them contribute to a variety of inflammatory and phagocytic actions.

The final events in the complement series involve the interactions of $C5_b$, C6, C7, and C8 that give rise to an anchoring complex within the membrane **(figure 14.20c)**. This is followed by the insertion of several C9 molecules in the pattern of a ring-shaped formation termed the **membrane attack complex or MAC (figure 14.20d).** The MAC is the primary destructive force of the complement system. It effectively perforates and lyses the membranes of gram-negative bacteria, fungi, parasitic protozoans, and enveloped viruses. Except for the classical pathway, these reactions are nonspecific and can be active against a wide spectrum of microbes.

An Outline of Major Host Defenses

At this point, it should be apparent that the body's defenses often work in both parallel and redundant ways to fight pathogens. The result is a constant onslaught of defenses functioning at many levels. This can be illustrated by **figure 14.21,** organized by the three lines of defense that started out our discussion and that lead us naturally into chapter 15.

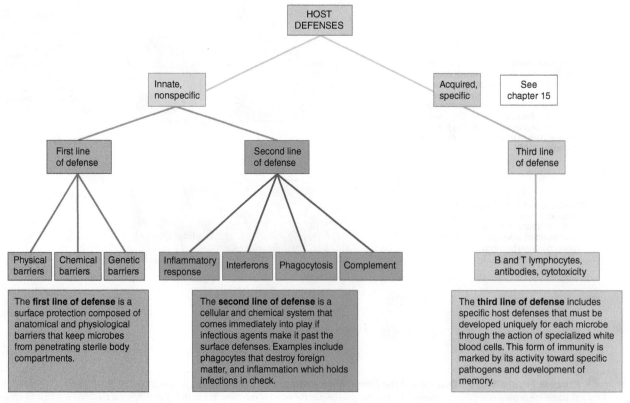

Figure 14.21 Flowchart summarizing the major components of the host defenses. Defenses are classified into one of two general categories: (1) innate and nonspecific or (2) acquired and specific. These can be further subdivided into the first, second, and third lines of defense, each being characterized by a different level and type of protection. The third line of defense is the most complex and is responsible for specific immunity. It is covered in greater detail in chapter 15.

Check Your Progress SECTION 14.4

25. Describe the events that give rise to macrophages.
26. What types of macrophages are there, and what are their principal functions?
27. Outline the major phases of phagocytosis.
28. Briefly describe the three major types of interferon, their sources, and their biological effects.
29. Describe the mechanism by which interferon acts as an antiviral compound.
30. Describe the general complement reaction in terms of a feedback system or cascade.
31. What are some factors that trigger the complement cascade?
32. Using figure 14.21 as a guide, give examples for each category shaded brown, purple, and gold.

CASE STUDY Part 2

The boy's physicians examined his white blood cells using the nitroblue tetrazolium test, which monitors the effectiveness of phagocyte activity, and the neutrophil cytochrome assay, which can measure activities associated with the metabolism of oxygen. Both tests indicated a low rate of phagocyte responsiveness, which is highly diagnostic of a genetic disease known as chronic granulomatous disease (CGD).

About one in 200,000 children in the United States are diagnosed yearly with chronic granulomatous disease (CGD); of these, around 90% are males. CGD is somewhat complex in its inheritance, but there are essentially two forms. The X-linked type occurs as a defective gene on the X chromosome and is

more severe. Over half of all cases are X-linked. The autosomal defect is located on a different chromosome and tends to be milder. In both types, the genetic codes carry errors that prevent phagocytes from producing certain key metabolic enzymes.

The neutrophils and macrophages of CGD patients can carry out the usual phagocytic activities such as amoeboid motion, chemotaxis, engulfment, and digestion of microbes in phagocytic vesicles, but they are unable to actively kill certain types of aerobic pathogens. They lack the enzymes to synthesize the battery of reactive oxygen intermediates (ROIs)—superoxide ion, hydrogen peroxide, and hydroxyl radical—that are essential to kill these microbes. As a result, the ineffective phagocytes harbor live microbes that can break away and continue their infectious path. In time, these phagocytes shut down, die, and build up in the infected tissue in masses (granulomas).

This case is a striking example of how important every element of immunity can be. Although the components do overlap in some of their effects, each one carries out some essential function that cannot be totally duplicated. CGD individuals have a mostly intact immune response, but they lack a complete phagocyte defense that comes into play early in the infection process. Phagocytes (neutrophils, monocytes, and macrophages) are most active against bacteria and eukaryotic pathogens, but they also are important participants in many other immune reactions.

- What elements of host defenses and immunity would remain intact in a child with CGD?
- What is a granuloma, and what factors in CGD cause it?

To conclude this Case Study, go to Perspectives on the Connect website.

For additional information on this disease, go to http://emedicine.medscape.com/article/1116022-print.
Other immune disorders are covered in chapter 16.

Chapter Summary with Key Terms

14.1 Overview of Host Defense Mechanisms

The *first line of defense* is an inborn, nonspecific system composed of anatomical, chemical, and genetic barriers that block microbes at the portal of entry. The *second line of defense* is also inborn and nonspecific and includes protective cells and fluids in tissues, and the *third line of defense* is acquired and specific and is dependent on the function of T and B cells.

14.2 Structure and Function of the Organs of Defense and Immunity

A. **Immunology** is the study of **immunity,** which refers to the development of resistance to infectious agents by white blood cells (WBCs). WBCs conduct surveillance of the body, recognizing and differentiating **nonself** (foreign) cells by means of molecules or **pattern recognition receptors (PRRs)** in their membranes. PRRs recognize a number of indicators carried on foreign cells called **pathogen-associated molecular patterns (PAMPs).** Under normal conditions, **self** cells are left alone but nonself cells are destroyed by the concerted efforts of several types of immune reactions.

B. For purposes of immunologic study, the body is divided into three compartments: the blood, lymphatics, and the

reticuloendothelial system. A fourth component, the extracellular fluid, surrounds the first three and allows constant communication between all areas of the body.

C. **Circulatory System: Blood and Lymphatics**

1. **Whole blood** consists of **blood cells** (formed by **hematopoiesis** in the bone marrow) dispersed in **plasma. Stem cells** in the bone marrow differentiate to produce white blood cells (**leukocytes**), red blood cells (**erythrocytes**), and megakaryocytes, which give rise to **platelets.**

2. Leukocytes are the primary mediators of immune function and can be divided into **granulocytes** (**neutrophils, eosinophils,** and **basophils**) and **agranulocytes** (**monocytes** and **lymphocytes**) based on their appearance. Monocytes later differentiate to become **macrophages.** Lymphocytes are divided into **B cells,** which produce **antibodies** as part of **humoral immunity,** and **T cells,** which participate in **cell-mediated immunity.** Leukocytes display both **chemotaxis** and **diapedesis** in response to chemical mediators of the immune system.

D. *Lymphatic System*
1. The **lymphatic system** parallels the circulatory system and transports lymph while also playing host to cells of the immune system. Lymphoid organs and tissues include **lymph nodes,** the spleen, and the **thymus,** as well as areas of less well-organized immune tissues such as **GALT** and **MALT.**

14.3 Second Line Defenses: Inflammation
A. The inflammatory response is a complex reaction to tissue injury marked by *redness, heat, swelling,* and *pain.*
1. Blood vessels narrow and then dilate in response to **chemical mediators, cytokines,** and **chemokines.**
2. **Edema** swells tissues, helping prevent the spread of infection.
3. WBCs, microbes, debris, and fluid collect to form **pus.**
4. Pyrogens may induce fever.

14.4 Second Line Defenses: Phagocytosis, Interferon, and Complement
A. Phagocytosis: Partner to Inflammation
1. Macrophages and neutrophils engage in **phagocytosis,** engulfing microbes in a phagosome. Uniting the phagosome with a **lysosome** results in destruction of the phagosome contents.
2. Phagocytes use a type of PRRs called **toll-like receptors (TLRs)** to recognize and adhere to foreign markers on microbes such as PAMPs.
B. **Interferon (IFN)** is a family of proteins produced by leukocytes and fibroblasts that inhibit the reproduction of viruses by degrading viral RNA or blocking the synthesis of viral proteins.
C. **Complement** is a complex defense system that results, by way of a cascade mechanism, in the formation of a membrane attack complex that kills cells by creating holes in their membranes.

Level I. Knowledge and Comprehension

These questions require a working knowledge of the concepts in the chapter and the ability to recall and understand the information you have studied.

? Multiple-Choice Questions

Select the correct answer from the answers provided. For questions with blanks, choose the combination of answers that most accurately completes the statement.

1. An example/examples of a nonspecific chemical barrier to infection is/are
 a. unbroken skin
 b. lysozyme in saliva
 c. cilia in respiratory tract
 d. all of these

2. Which nonspecific host defense is associated with the trachea?
 a. lacrimation
 b. ciliary lining
 c. desquamation
 d. lactic acid

3. Which of the following blood cells function primarily as phagocytes?
 a. eosinophils
 b. basophils
 c. lymphocytes
 d. neutrophils

4. Which of the following is *not* a lymphoid tissue?
 a. spleen
 b. thyroid gland
 c. lymph node
 d. GALT

5. What is included in GALT?
 a. thymus
 b. Peyer's patches
 c. tonsils
 d. breast lymph nodes

6. A signaling molecule from microbes recognized by phagocytes is
 a. pyrogen
 b. PAMP
 c. complement
 d. lectin

7. Monocytes are _____ leukocytes that develop into _____.
 a. granular, phagocytes
 b. agranular, mast cells
 c. agranular, macrophages
 d. granular, T cells

8. Which of the following inflammatory signs specifies pain?
 a. tumor
 b. dolor
 c. calor
 d. rubor

9. Toll-like receptors are proteins on _____.
 a. phagocytes that recognize foreign molecules
 b. viruses that stimulate immune reactions
 c. skin cells that provide barriers to infection
 d. lymphocytes that damage parasitic worms

10. An example of an inflammatory mediator that stimulates vasodilation is
 a. histamine
 b. collagen
 c. complement $C5_a$
 d. interferon

11. _____ is an example of an inflammatory mediator that stimulates chemotaxis.
 a. Endotoxin
 b. Serotonin
 c. A fibrin clot
 d. Interleukin-2

12. An example of an exogenous pyrogen is
 a. interleukin-1
 b. complement
 c. interferon
 d. endotoxin

13. _____ interferon, produced by T lymphocytes, activates cells called _____ and is involved in destroying viruses.
 a. Gamma, fibroblasts
 b. Beta, lymphocytes
 c. Alpha, natural killer cells
 d. Beta, fibroblasts

14. In what process is tumor necrosis factor (TNF) *not* involved?
 a. chemotaxis of phagocytes
 b. fever
 c. the inflammatory response
 d. the classic complement pathway

15. Which of the following substances is *not* produced by phagocytes to destroy engulfed microorganisms?
 a. hydroxyl radical
 b. superoxide anion
 c. hydrogen peroxide
 d. bradykinin

16. Which of the following is the end product of the complement system?
 a. properdin
 b. cascade reaction
 c. membrane attack complex
 d. complement factor C9

Case Study Review

1. What are signs of chronic granulomatous disease?
 a. unresolved inflammation
 b. opportunistic fungal infections
 c. low levels of white blood cells
 d. recurrent infections
 e. a, b, and c
 f. a, b, and d

2. What feature of CGD phagocytes is defective?
 a. the ability to engulf pathogens
 b. production of toxic forms of oxygen
 c. mechanisms to eliminate viruses
 d. chemotaxis

3. Explain why children with CGD would be more prone to infections from fungi and bacteria than from viruses.

Writing Challenge

For each question, compose a one- or two-paragraph answer that includes the factual information needed to completely address the question. Check Your Progress questions can also be used for writing-challenge exercises.

1. a. Use the lines on the figure to describe the major components of the first line of defense.
 b. What effects do these defenses have on microbes?

2. a. Describe the initial response system that is found in the primary responders to foreign matter.

3. Explain what PRRs and TLRs are and the nature of their interaction with PAMPs.

4. Make a simple drawing of the functions of toll-like receptors.

5. Describe the mechanisms by which leukocytes migrate from the bloodstream into an area of infection. What chemical factors are they reacting to?

6. Prepare a simplified outline of the cell lines of hematopoiesis.

7. Discuss the multiple, overlapping functions of the immune system. Which tissues and organs are involved in the immune response, and how does each function?

8. In what ways is a phagocyte a tiny container of disinfectants?

9. Briefly outline what leads to the result shown in the adjacent figure. Give the name and actions of this structure.

10. Macrophages perform the final job of removing tissue debris and other products of infection. Indicate some of the possible effects when these scavengers cannot successfully complete the work of phagocytosis.

Concept Mapping

An Introduction to Concept Mapping found at http://www.mhhe.com/talaro9 provides guidance for working with concept maps.

1. Construct your own concept map using the following words as the *concepts*. Supply the linking words between each pair of concepts.

 defenses inflammation

 leukocytes antibodies

 lymphocytes neutrophils

 monocytes fever

 macrophages

Level II. Application, Analysis, Evaluation, and Synthesis

These problems go beyond just restating facts and require higher levels of understanding and an ability to interpret, problem solve, transfer knowledge to new situations, create models, and predict outcomes.

Critical Thinking

Critical thinking is the ability to reason and solve problems using facts and concepts. These questions can be approached from a number of angles, and in most cases, they do not have a single correct answer.

1. Suggest some reasons that there is so much redundancy of action and there are so many interacting aspects of immune responses.
2. a. What are some possible elements missing in children born without a functioning lymphocyte system?
 b. What is the most important component extracted in bone marrow transplants?
3. A patient's chart shows an increase in eosinophil levels.
 a. What does this cause you to suspect?
 b. What does it mean if the basophil levels are very high?
 c. What if the neutrophil levels are very high?
4. How can adults continue to function relatively normally after surgery to remove the thymus, tonsils, spleen, or lymph nodes?
5. Explain why the X-linked form of CGD is more common in boys and more severe than autosomal forms of the disease.
6. An obsolete treatment for syphilis involved inducing fever by deliberately infecting patients with the agent of relapsing fever. An experimental AIDS treatment involved infecting patients with malaria to induce high fevers. Can you provide some possible explanations behind these peculiar forms of treatment?

7. Patients with a history of tuberculosis often show scars and other lesions in the lungs and experience recurrent infection. Account for these effects on the basis of the inflammatory response.
8. *Shigella, Mycobacterium,* and numerous other pathogens have developed mechanisms that prevent them from being killed by phagocytes.
 a. Suggest two or three factors that help them avoid destruction by the powerful antiseptics in macrophages.
 b. Suggest the potential implications that these infected macrophages can have on the development of disease.
9. Account for the several inflammatory symptoms that occur in the injection site when one has been vaccinated against influenza and tetanus.
10. a. Knowing that fever is potentially both harmful and beneficial, what are some possible guidelines for deciding whether to suppress it or not?
 b. What is the specific target of fever-suppressing drugs?

Visual Challenge

1. Each numbered figure 1–4 represents a cell that provides an immune defense. Each lettered figure A–D shows a pathogenic microbe. Name the type of defense and match it with its primary target microbe and effects.

 (2) Page 435
 (3) Page 435
 (4) Page 435

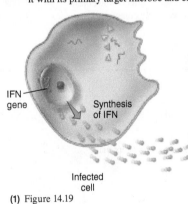
IFN gene — Synthesis of IFN
Infected cell
(1) Figure 14.19

 A Figure 18.8
 B Figure 23.21 inset
 C Table 25.1
 D Opener, Chapter 14

LEARNSMART **connect** |MICROBIOLOGY www.mcgrawhillconnect.com
Enhance your study of this chapter with study tools and practice tests. Also ask your instructor about the resources available through ConnectPlus, including the media-rich eBook, interactive learning tools, and animations.